WHERE
TO
FISH
1988–1989

81st EDITION

EDITED BY
D. A. ORTON

THOMAS HARMSWORTH PUBLISHING

81st Edition published 1988 by
Thomas Harmsworth Publishing
13 Nicosia Road
London SW18 3RN

British Cataloguing in Publication Data
Where to fish. 1988–1989
1. Fishing—Great Britain—Directories
799.1'025'41   SH605
ISBN 0-948807-07-5

Printed and bound in Great Britain at
The Bath Press, Avon

NOW YOU KNOW WHERE TO FISH
READ THESE TITLES FOR TIPS ON HOW!

CONTENTS

Abbreviations: The following abbreviations are used throughout the book: S, salmon; T, trout; MT, migratory trout, NT, non-migratory trout; C, char; FF or FW, freshwater (ie coarse fish); RD, River Division (or its equivalent); s, season; m, month (Water Authority list only); f, fortnight; w, week; d, day; t, ticket, ns, nearest railway station. In the lists of fishing stations the abbreviation m means mile or miles, except when it is used in conjunction with t, ie, mt, when it means monthly ticket. Likewise, st means season ticket, wt weekly ticket, dt daily ticket, and so on.

Brian Leadbetter on his way to becoming World Champion.

This customary review of the angling scene was faced in our 1986/87 edition with a picture of Tony Pawson displaying the handsome trophy he had won in the 1984 World Flyfishing Championship. This time we show Brian Leadbetter who won the 1987 event, fished this time in England — for the the first time — on two reservoirs, Rutland and Grafham, on a small stillwater fishery, Avington, and on the River Test, the hallowed chalk stream which is the nursery of our fly fishing philosophy, and in large measure the whole world's, too.

Not only did an Englishman win the individual trophy in 1987; England won the team event too, with Australia, New Zealand and Wales following in 2nd, 3rd and 4th places. Nor was the margin of victory a narrow one. These events are won on a points system: those scored by the teams just named, in aggregate, amounted to 45% of the total scored by all twenty contending teams.

This triumph chimes nicely with the mood of a year which saw our whole sport climbing towards the crest of a wave; its adversaries in retreat and self-confidence renewed by an expensive programme of motivational research carried out by the fishing tackle trade with results which proclaimed in a most positive way that we anglers are thought of as highly as ever by our fellow-countrymen and women, even if not all of them wish to join us rod in hand at the waterside on the strength of that regard!

That, after a bad press suffered over swans accidentally poisoned by lost or discarded fishing leads, came as good news indeed, but the next was better still. Another threatening cloud had been hanging over us. Inspired, no doubt, by the best of good intentions, the pre-election government had announced plans for a total privatisation of the water industry, right down to the issue of permits to fish or take a stroll round a reservoir's perimeter track.

Discussion had been minimal; the bit seemed to be jammed between the horse's teeth; disaster loomed. Fishing depends first and foremost on a supply of natural water in a state fit for fish and their food-organisms to thrive in. The 19th Century record of privately owned water supply and sewage disposal undertakings had been an abysmal one: even with these services in integrated public ownership as they have been for more than ten years the record has been. flawed. Disintegration, though, was clearly no answer, with pollution prevention and fisheries welfare placed in the hands of those with the strongest financial incentives to go on neglecting them.

Now, as we prepare this edition for press, a Green Paper is in circulation, presenting a Government re-think under which a national public body — the National Rivers Authority — is proposed to take responsibility for pollution-monitoring, fisheries, land drainage and virtually all other functions which belong under the environmental umbrella.

The news could hardly be better and at the end of that road we may find, at last, national fishing licences by which, at an appropriate price, we may fish for at least some species anywhere in Britain under cover of the licence already procured to fish the waters near to home. That, however, has yet to be thrashed out in detail and for the time being the licence situation will be as it is reflected in the pages which follow (11-18).

The research mentioned earlier brought to light or confirmed many interesting facts about anglers. One of them was that entry into the sport is almost 100% via existing anglers, in the family or beyond it. We ourselves and no-one else of significance recruit the anglers of the future. So, if we wish our sport to continue to thrive, forming a "market" large enough to be serviced with an attractive choice of well-stocked fisheries and other services, we must not neglect this obligation.

Some of the licence-issuing water authorities and permit-issuing private proprietors have shown practical recognition of this aspect of matters by starting to issue both free or at much reduced charge to the genuine beginner. Have you a friend you might enjoy introducing to the sport? If so, ask about concession terms on licences and permits at the tackle shops and fisheries you patronise. Where you see this sign, such privileges are already in force.

So "Tight lines" for 1988/89, wherever you fish — and "Take a Friend Fishing", as the posters in the tackle shops and the advertisements in the fishing papers are saying.

TAKE A FRIEND FISHING

7

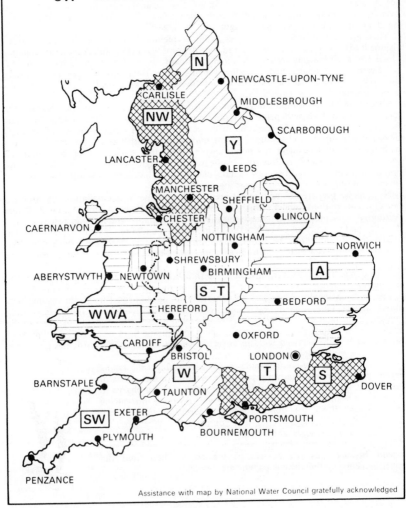

N	Northumbrian Water Authority
NW	North West Water Authority
Y	Yorkshire Water Authority
S-T	Severn-Trent Water Authority
WWA	Welsh Water Authority
A	Anglian Water Authority
T	Thames Water Authority
S	Southern Water Authority
W	Wessex Water Authority
SW	South West Water Authority

Assistance with map by National Water Council gratefully acknowledged

FISHERY AGENTS

ENGLAND

Richard Harris & Stokes, 125 Eign Street, Hereford HR4 0AJ. More than 30m of Wye under management. (0432 54455.) (*advt p 162*)

Hatton Fishing Tackle, St Owen Street, Hereford (272317). Up-to-the-minute information on Wye fishing; applications for advice etc should be accompanied by a stamped/addressed envelope.

John Sale & Partners, 18–20 Glendale Rd, Wooler, Northumberland. (0668 81611.)

Knight Frank & Rutley, 20 Hanover Square, London W1R 0AH. (01-629 81871.)

Rod Box, 52 St George's Street, Winchester, Hants. Day or season lettings on some of finest dry fly, chalk stream fishing. Salmon, sea trout fishing in Scotland, Ireland, Norway, Alaska and Iceland. (0962 61561.) (*advt p 19*)

Savills, 20 Grosvenor Hill, Berkeley Square, London, W1X 0HQ. (01-499 8644.)

Strutt & Parker, 13 Hill Street, Berkeley Square, London, W1X 8DL. (01-629 7282.) Telex: 8955508 STRUTT G)

John D Wood, 23 Berkeley Square, London, W1X 6AL. (01-629 9050.) and: 3 St. Georges House, St. Georges St. Winchester, Hants. (0962 63131.)

WALES

Knight, Frank & Rutley, 14 Broad St, Hereford, HR4 9AL. (0432 273087.)

Woosnam and Tyler, Dolgarreg, North Road, Builth Wells, Powys, LD2 3DD. Salmon fishing on Wye, Usk and tributaries. By the day or week. (0982-553248.)

SCOTLAND

Bell-Ingram, Durn, Isla Rd, Perth PH2 7HF. (0738-21121.) Deveron, Cassley, Dee, etc.

John Dickson & Son (Inc Forrest & Son), 35 The Square, Kelso. (24687.) For Tweed and Teviot (Kelso AA trout fisheries), and Makerstoun, trout only.

Knight, Frank & Rutley, 2 North Charlotte St, Edinburgh EH2 4HR. (031-225 7105.)

Lovat Estate, Beauly, Inverness. (782205.)

Macsport Ltd, P.O. Box 2, Banchory, AB3 3TD Kinecardineshire. (03302 3022/2855.) Advice on travel and sporting holidays. The complete service on sporting lets also.

Mrs J Atkinson, 8 Sinclair Street, Thurso 63291. Halladale and Naver Rivers; trout fishing on lochs in Caithness and Sutherland.

Major Neil Ramsay & Co, Farleyer, Aberfeldy, Perthshire. (Aberfeldy 20540.) For salmon fishing on upper Tay, two beats.

Savills, 46 Charlotte Square, Edinburgh EH2 4QH. (031-226 6961.)

Savills, 12 Clerk Street, Brechin, Angus DD9 6AE. (03562-2187.)

Strutt & Parker, 26 Walker St, Edinburgh EH3 7HR. (031-226 2500.)

Thurso Fisheries Ltd, Thurso East, Thurso, Caithness. (Thurso 63134.) River Thurso.

IRELAND

Battersby & Co, Dublin. (760331.)

Lisney and Son, 24 St Stephen's Green, Dublin 2. (Telex 93942, 615222, 20 lines.)

OVERSEAS TOUR PROMOTERS

G Aitken, 32 Offley Road, Kennington S.W.9 (01-582 7087) OLS.

Pemba Channel Fishing Club, P.O. Box 44, Msambweni via Mombasa, Kenya

Tasmania, Tasmanian Travel Centre, 80 Elizabeth St, Hobart, Tasmania 7000, Australia

BRITISH FISH FARMS

Annandale Trout Farm, Johnstone Bridge, Lockerbie, Dumfriesshire DG11 1HD. (05764 392.)

Belleau Bridge Trout Farm, Alford, Lincs. Brown, brook and rainbow trout for stocking. (Swaby 225.)

Berkshire Trout Farm, Lower Denford, Hungerford, Berkshire. Brown and rainbow trout. (Hungerford 0488 82520.) (*advt p 141*)

Bibury Trout Farm, Bibury, near Cirencester, Gloucestershire. Rainbow and brown trout bred on Coln. (Bibury 215.) (*advt p 143*)

Burwarton Trout Farm, Cleobury North, Bridgnorth, Salop WV16 6RP. Rainbow trout. (074633 601.)

Chirk Fishery Co Ltd, Chirk, Wrexham, Clwyd LL14 5BL. Brown, brook and rainbow trout; ova, fry, yearlings and two-year-olds. (Chirk 0691 772420.)

Exe Valley Fishery Ltd, Exbridge, Dulverton, Somerset. Brown and rainbow trout available. (Dulverton 23328.)

Glenaray Fish Farm, Low Balantyre, Inveraray PA32 8XJ. Brown and rainbow trout. (0499 2233.)

Keld Head Hatchery, High Costa Mill, Pickering, N. Yorks. Owned by Yorkshire Water Authority, Rivers Division, 21 Park Square S., Leeds LS1 2QG. Trout supplied within YWA area or elswhere by arrangement.
Inquiries to 0751 73161.

Hooke Springs Trout Farm, The Mill House, Hooke, Beaminster, Dorset. Brown and rainbow trout. (Beaminster 862553.)

Howietoun Fishery, Sauchieburn, Bannockburn, Stirling. Brown and Ballantine trout. Salmon and Sea Trout—Eggs, Ova, Fry and Smolts. (Bannockburn 0786 812473.)

Loch Leven Fishery, Kinross Estates Office, Kinross. Trout. (Kinross 2256.)

Midland Fishery, Nailsworth, Gloucestershire GL6 0PL. Brown and rainbow trout and ova. (Nailsworth 2053.)

The Solway Fishery, New Abbey, Dumfries. Brown, brook and rainbow trout. (New Abbey 235.)

Stambridge Trout Fisheries, Great Stambridge, near Rochford, Essex. King carp and tench; brown and rainbow trout and goldfish. (Canewdon 274.)

Trent Fish Culture Co Ltd, Mercaston, Brailsford, near Derby DE6 3BL. Brown, Rainbow and American brook trout. Ova, fry, yearlings and two-year-olds to 13 in; larger fish on application. (0335-60318.)

Watermill Trout Farms Ltd, Welton Springs, Louth, Lincs. Brown and rainbow trout. (0507 602524.)

Welham Park Fish Hatcheries Ltd, Malton, Yorkshire. Brown and Loch Leven trout. (Malton 3785.)

Westacre Trout Farm, King's Lynn, Norfolk. Brown and rainbow trout for immediate delivery. (Castleacre 240.)

Whitebrook Fisheries Ltd, Crucorney Trout Farm, nr Abergavenny, Gwent. Rainbow trout of all sizes for sale on farm. (0873 890545.)

Wye Valley Fisheries, Tyn-y-Cwm Mill, Beulah, Llanwrtyd Wells, Powys. Rainbow trout. (Langammarch Wells 244.)

POLLUTION

Anglers are united in deploring pollution. To combat it, urgent action may be called for at any time from any one of us. If numbers of fish are found dead, dying, or seriously distressed, take samples of both fish and water and contact the office of the Director of Scientific Services at the appropriate Regional Water Authority.

FISHING IN ENGLAND and WALES

Regional Water Authorities, Close Seasons, Licence Duties, etc.

THE next edition of Where to Fish is likely to reflect major changes in the arrangements for the licensing of the sport and in the restrictions imposed statutorily on its practice. This will be because the Regional Water Authorities are expected by then to have passed into history as part of an operation to return the water supply industry to where it stood a hundred years ago in the orbit of entrepreneurial capitalism.

For good or for ill: choose your prediction. A matter beyond prediction is whether the great change impending will relieve us for a while from further minor tinkerings with structures in the midst of the big splash, or will merely encourage more of them. It therefore remains as necessary as ever for anglers to make detailed local enquiries regarding the local statutory position respecting licences and seasons before visiting the waterside. The officers given in the various sections which follow under the headings of the RWAs are the authoritative source of information, but tackle shops may be relied upon to keep themselves briefed as changes occur. Where a licence is in force, it is an offence to fish without one. The burden is on the angler to make himself aware of the position wherever he may be fishing. Ignorance is not accepted as an excuse.

Anglers are reminded that the expression 'immature' in relation to salmon means that the fish is less than 12in long; taking immature salmon is prohibited throughout England and Wales. In relation to other fish the expression 'immature' means that the fish is of a length less than that prescribed by bye-law. Unless otherwise stated, it may be assumed that the length is measured from the tip of the snout to the fork of the tail.

The word 'salmon' means all fish of the salmon species. The word 'trout' means all fish of the salmon species commonly known as trout. The expression 'migratory trout' means trout that migrate to and from the sea. The expression 'freshwater (ie coarse) fish' means any fish living in fresh water except salmon, trout, all kinds of fish which migrate to and from tidal water, eels and their fry.

NOTE: *In the following lists, telephone numbers are given to enable anglers to contact officers outside office hours. This facility is included specifically to enable prompt advice to be given in cases of serious pollution. Anglers are asked to use these numbers with discretion and not to disturb officers in their off-duty hours unnecessarily.*

Abbreviations: The following abbreviations are used throughout the book: S, salmon; T, trout; MT, migratory trout, NT, non-migratory trout; C, char; FF or FW, freshwater (ie coarse fish); RD, River Division (or its equivalent); s, season; m, month (Water Authority list only); f, fortnight; w, week; d, day; t, ticket, ns, nearest railway station. In the lists of fishing stations the abbreviation m means mile or miles, except when it is used in conjunction with t, ie, mt, when it means monthly ticket. Likewise, st means season ticket, wt weekly ticket, dt daily ticket, and so on.

SOUTHERN WATER AUTHORITY, Guildbourne House, Worthing, Sussex BN11 1LD.
Regional Fisheries Officer: J R Chandler, BSc, MIBiol, FZS, MIWEM.

Rivers controlled: Medway, Stour, Rother, RM Canal, Adur, Arun, Ouse, Cuckmere, all rivers in Pevensey Levels, Test, Itchen, Hamble, Meon, Beaulieu, Lymington, Fletch, Keyhaven, Eastern Yar, Medina, and the tributaries of all these rivers.

Area offices.

Kent: Capstone Road, Chatham.
Pollution reporting: Medway (0634) 830655

Sussex: Falmer, Brighton.
Pollution reporting: Brighton 606766.

Hampshire: Otterbourne, Winchester.
Pollution reporting: Twyford 714585.

Isle of Wight: St Nicholas, 58 St John's Road, Newport.
Pollution reporting: Newport 526611 or Sandown 2106.

Close Seasons: S 2 October—17 Jan. MT 31 October—1 May. NT 31 October—3 April. FF. 14 March—16 June. All close seasons are "periods between" dates quoted.

Licences: For the whole of the Southern Water Authority area. (No divisional licences issued.) S, MT, T, FF, Eels: s £30, f £10, d £5, T, FF, Eels: s £4, m £2.50, s (jun.) £2.50, FF. Free to OAP and disabled.

Supplementary licences: (one additional rod) s £1.

SOUTH WEST WATER AUTHORITY, Headquarters: Peninsula House, Rydon Lane, Exeter, Devon EX2 7HR. (Tel: 219666.)
Environmental Protection Manager: R Furniss.

Recreation Officer: E S Bray.
Reservoirs controlled: Avon Dam, Darracott, Fernworthy, Kennick, Meldon, Slade, Squabmoor, Tottiford, Trenchford, Venford, Wimbleball, Wistlandpound, Argal, Burrator, College, Colliford, Crowdy, Porth, Siblyback, Stithians, Tamar Lakes.
East Area: Manley House, Kestrel Way, Exeter. (Tel: 76201.)
Environmental Protection Officer: C V M Davies.
Rivers controlled: Avon, Axe, Dart, Erme, Exe, Lyn, Otter, Taw, Teign, Torridge and tributaries.

West Area: Victoria Square, Bodmin, Cornwall. (Tel: 5777.)
Environmental Protection Officer: M E Cominetti.
Rivers controlled: Camel, Fowey, Looe, Lynher, Plym, Tamar, Tavy, Yealm and tributaries.

River Licence Fees: For whole of SWW area.
Salmon and Sea Trout: s £27.80, w £13.90, d £3.50. Concessions: s £13.90, w £7, d £1.80.
Trout: s £6.90, w £3.50, d £1.50. Concession: s £3.50, d £0.80.
Freshwater Fish: s £2.10, w £0.80. Concession: s £1.10.
Persons eligible for Concession Licences are OAPs, Children under 16, students under 18 in full-time education, and Registered Disabled. Children under 10 do not need a licence but in all cases must have permission from the owner of the fishing.
Rod Seasons: Salmon: N.B. As part of the Authority's strategy on salmon cropping, the seasons on some rivers have been changed experimentally. They are indicated by a letter "E". Avon—15 April to 30 November (E). Erme—15 March to 31 October. Axe, Lim, Otter, Sid—15 March to 31 October. Camel—1 April to 15 December. Dart—1 February to 30 September (E). Exe—14 February to 30 September. Fowey, Looe—1 April to 15 December. Tamar, Tavy, Lynher—1 March to 14 October. Plym—1 April to 15 December. Yealm—1 April to 15 December (E). Taw, Torridge—1 March to 30 September. Lyn—1 February to 31 October. Teign—1 February to 30 September (E). **(September 1st—30th: two fish only per angler*.) Migratory trout:** Avon—15 April to 30 September. Erme—15 March to 30 September. Axe, Lim, Otter, Sid—15 April to 31 October. Camel, Gannel, Menalhyl, Valency—1 April to 30 September. Dart—15 March to 30 September. Exe—15 March to 30 September. Fowey, Looe, Seaton, Tresillian—1 April to 30 September. Tamar, Lynher, Plym, Tavy, Yealm—3 March to 30 September. Taw, Torridge, Lyn—15 March to 30 September. Teign, Bovey—15 March to 12 October. **Brown trout:** Camel, Fowey—1 April to 30 September. Other rivers and streams—15 March to 30 September. All other waters—15 March to 12 October. **Rainbow Trout** and **Coarse Fish**—entire region—NO CLOSE SEASON.

* NB. The two fish limit applies only to the River Teign.

WESSEX WATER AUTHORITY, Wessex House, Passage Street, Bristol BS2 0JQ.
Chief Fisheries and Recreations officer: Major T Wills, MBE (Tel: Bristol 290611.)
Principal Assistant: A J R Barber.
Pollution reporting: to the Regional Control Centre: Freephone 9917.

Avon and Dorset Division
Divisional Fisheries and Recreations Officer: Dr D Wilkinson, Wessex Water Authority, Avon and Dorset Division, 2 Nuffied Road, Poole, Dorset. (Tel: 0202 671144.)
Rivers controlled: Hampshire Avon and Stour, Frome, Piddle, Brit and Char. (All rivers entering the sea between Lyme Regis and Christchurch.)
Close seasons: S, Avon and Stour—30 September to 1 February. Frome and Piddle—30 September to 1 March. MT—31 October to 15 April. NT, River Avon and tributaries above Bickton Mill and the tributaries flowing into the River Avon above the Mill Dam, except the part of the River Nadder above the road bridge at Barford St. Martin—15 October to 15 April. All other running waters—15 October to 1 April. Reservoirs, lakes and ponds: 15 October to March 17. FF—14 March to 16 June.
Licences: Details below.

Bristol Avon Division
Divisional Fisheries and Recreations Officer: A Taylor, Wessex Water Authority, Bristol Avon Division, P.O. Box 95, Broad Quay, Bath BA1 2YP. (Tel: 0225 313500.)
Rivers controlled: Bristol Avon and tributaries.
Close seasons: S—30 September to 1 February. MT—31 October to 15 April. NT—15 October to 1 April. FF—14 March to 16 June.
Licences: Details below.

Somerset Division
Divisional Fisheries and Recreations Officer: C B Arden, Wessex Water Authority, Somerset Division, P.O. Box 9, King Square, Bridgwater, Somerset TA6 3EA. (Tel: 0278 457333.)
Rivers controlled: Axe, Brue, Parrett and their tributaries, including Tone, Huntspill, King's Sedgemoor Drain and Bridgwater and Taunton Canal.
Close seasons: S—30 September to 1 February. MT—31 October to 15 April. NT—15 October to 1 April. FF—14 March to 16 June.

Licences: S, MT, NT, FF; s £25. w £4. MT, NT, FF; s £8.20, w £2. FF; s £6.35, w £1.55. Half-price licences for juniors (12–15 yrs incl.) OAP and regd. disabled. These licences are valid anywhere in the Region.

NORTH WEST WATER AUTHORITY, Dawson House, Gt Sankey, Warrington WA5 3LW.
Regional Fisheries Manager: Dr C Harpley NWW, P.O. Box 30, New Town House, Buttermarket Street, Warrington WA1 2QG. Tel: 53999.
Pollution reporting: 8.45 am to 5.00 pm: Warrington 53999. Other times: 061-370 3155.

North District
District Fisheries Officer: C M Newton, Chertsey Hill, London Road, Carlisle CA1 2QX.
Rivers controlled: Esk, Liddel, Lyne, Irthing, Petteril, Wampool, Caldew, Ellen, Derwent, Eamont, Eden, Cocker, Ehen, Irt, Esk, and their tributaries. The lakes Derwentwater, Thirlmere, Ullswater, Haweswater, Bassenthwaite.

Central District
District Fisheries Officer: N C Durie, Beathwaite, Levens, Kendal, Cumbria LA8 8NL.
Rivers controlled: Brathay, Lune, Duddon, Crake, Rawthey, Leven, Kent, Keer, Greta, Wenning, Ribble, Hodder, Wyre, Calder, and their tributaries. The lakes Windermere, Pendlewater, Coniston Water, Esthwaite Water, Grasmere, Rydal Water.

South District
District Fisheries Officer: Dr J B Leeming, New Town House, P.O. Box 30, Buttermarket Street, Warrington WA1 2QG.
Rivers controlled: Yarrow, Douglas, Roch, Irwell, Alt, Tame, Etherow, Mersey, Goyt, Bollin, Dean, Weaver, Dane, Gowey, and their tributaries.

Close seasons: Salmon, 1 November to 31 January, except R. Eden system—15 October to 14 January. **Migratory trout,** 16 October to 30 April, except rivers Annas, Bleng, Esk, Mite, Irt, Calder, Ehen and all tributaries—1 November to 30 April. **Trout,** 1 October to 14 March. **Coarse Fish,** 15 March to 15 June.

Licences: S s £29, part s (from June 1) £22 w £7. MT s £12, w £3, NT s £5, w £1.75. FF. s £4, w £1. Reductions of approx 50% in force on season and part-year licences for junior, OAP and disabled anglers registered as such.

NORTHUMBRIAN WATER AUTHORITY, Northumbria House, Regent Centre, Gosforth, Newcastle-upon-Tyne NE3 3PX.
Chief Fisheries Officer: A S Champion, Legal Directorate and Works at the above address. (Tel: 0912-843151, ext 1410.)
Pollution reporting: To the above.
Rivers controlled: Aln, Coquet, Wansbeck, Blyth, Tyne, Wear, Tees and tributaries, and all other rivers flowing into North Sea between Goswick Sands in the north and White Stones, Boulby Cliff, near Staithes, Yorks, other than the Tweed and its tributaries. **Close seasons:** S—1 November to 31 January. MT—1 November to 2 April. NT—1 October to 21 March. FF—statutory for rivers and streams. Still-waters; no close season. **Licences:** S, MT, NT, FF, £37.50 (OAP, dis, juv, £18.80), f £11.50, dt £5.80. Trout FF and eels £9.50 (OAP, dis, juv, £4.80), f £3.60. Coarse fish and eels £3.60 (OAP, dis, juv, £1.80).

YORKSHIRE WATER AUTHORITY, 21 Park Square South, Leeds LS1 2QG. (Tel: 0532 440191.)
North & East Division: 32-34 Monkgate, York YO3 7RH. (Tel: 0904 642131.)
Southern Division: Castle Market Building, Exchange Street, Sheffield. (Tel: 0742 26421.)
Amenity, Fisheries and Recreation Manager: Dr D J Shillcock, located at Rivers Division, 21 Park Square South, Leeds LS1 2QG. (Tel: 0532 440191.)
Pollution reporting: To appropriate Div. Offices or Fisheries Department at Rivers Div. at above address.
Rivers controlled: Yorkshire Ouse, its tributaries (including Ure, Wharfe, Nidd, Derwent, Swale, Aire, Don and Calder and their tributaries); Yorkshire Esk and tributaries, Hull and tributaries, part of Humber and all tributaries of Humber from Blacktoft to Spurn Point, all rivers entering sea between Spurn Point and White Stones to the west of Staithes near Whitby, and all lakes, canals and reservoirs within Authority's area.
Close seasons: S and MT—1 November to 5 April. NT—1 October to 24 March. FF—28 February to 31 May. Fishing on Esk between Ruswarp Weir and Ruswarp Road Bridge, Whitby, is prohibited. Night Fishing on the Esk is also prohibited. **Licences:** Salmon, trout, freshwater fish and eels including the Esk: s £39.10 (OAP, dis, juv £19.55), w £15.80 (OAP, dis, juv £7.90). d £7.90 (OAP, dis, juv £3.95), S, MT, NT, FF (except S and MT in the Esk and its tributaries and in streams to the North of the Esk) s £4.90 (OAP, dis, juv (£2.45) w £2 (OAP, dis, juv £1). State retirement pensioners, disabled persons and juveniles (children 10–15 years old, inclusive) applying for a concessionary licence may be asked to provide proof that they qualify. Children under ten years of age do not need licences. All season licences expire on 24 March.

ANGLIAN WATER, Ambury Road, Huntingdon PE18 6NZ. (Tel: Huntingdon 0480 56181.)
Estates, Recreation & Conservation Officer: Mr D J Dent
Regional Fisheries Scientist: Dr R S J Linfield, address above.
Licences: (Uniform throughout Authority area.) Salmon, trout, fw fish and eels.
Regional—Standard: Annual licence £7.50, 7 day licence £1.50, Concessionary licence—i.e. Juveniles 12–15 years inclusive, Retired Persons and Registered Disabled Persons £2. **Divisional:** £4.

 Lincoln Division: (Previously Lincs River Division). Anglian Water (Lincoln Division), Waterside House, Waterside North, Lincoln LN2 5HA. (Tel: (0522) 25231.)
Scientist: Dr A J Bates.
Fisheries & Conservation Scientist: Dr T Coles (Tel (0205) 60047).
Pollution reporting: To Scientist.

Rivers controlled: Ancholme, Eau & Witham, The South Forty Foot Drain and the Louth Navigation etc.
Close seasons: Trout enclosed waters—30 October to 31 March incl. Salmon & Trout other than rainbow trout in enclosed waters—29 September to 28/29 February incl. Coarse fish—No close season in enclosed waters—otherwise 15 March to 15 June incl.

Oundle Division: (Previously Welland & Nene River Division). Anglian Water (Oundle Division), North Street, Oundle, Peterborough, Cambs, PE8 4AS. (Tel: Oundle (0832) 73701.)
Scientist: Dr Robert Markall.
Fisheries Scientist: Dr A Ferguson (078086 321).
Recreation & Conservation Officer: Dr D Moore.
Pollution reporting: To Scientist.
Rivers controlled: Welland and tributaries. Nene and tributaries.
Close seasons: Trout enclosed waters—30 October to 31 March incl. Salmon & Trout other than rainbow trout in enclosed waters— 29 September to 28/29 February incl. Coarse Fish—15 March to 15 June incl.

Norwich Division: (Previously Norfolk & Suffolk River Division). Anglian Water (Norwich Div.), Yare House, 62/64 Thorpe Road, Norwich, NR1 1SA. (Tel: Norwich (0603) 615161.)
Scientist: Dr G Phillips.
Fisheries Scientist: Dr J Wortley.
Recreation & Conservation Officer: Paul Woodcock.
Pollution reporting: To Scientist.
Rivers controlled: Ant, Thurne, Bure, Wensum, Yare, Waveney, Blythe, Alde, Deben, Gipping and the Broads.
Close seasons: Trout enclosed waters— 30 October to 31 March incl. Salmon & Trout other than rainbow trout in enclosed waters—29 September to 28/29 February incl. Coarse Fish—15 March to 15 June incl.

Cambridge Division: (Previously Gt. Ouse River). Anglian Water (Cambridge Division), Gt Ouse House, Clarendon Road, Cambridge, CB2 2BL. (Tel: Cambridge (0223) 61561.)
Scientist: R Price.
Fisheries Scientist: P Noble.
Recreation & Conservation Officer: Dr C Spray.
Pollution reporting: To Scientist.
Rivers controlled: Heacham, Ingol, Babingley, Gt. Ouse, Tove, Ouzel, Ivel, Old Bedford River/New Bedford River, Old West River, Lark, Little Ouse, Wissey, The Relief Channel, Cut Off Channel, Nar, Middle & South Level Drains.
Close seasons: Trout enclosed waters—30 October to 31 March incl. Salmon & Trout other than rainbow trout in enclosed waters—29 Sept to 28/29 February incl. Coarse Fish—15 March to 15 June.

Colchester Division: Anglian Water (Colchester Division), 33 Sheepen Road, Colchester, CO3 3LB. (Tel: (0206) 763344.)
Scientist: M Pearson.
Fisheries Scientist: Dr R Burrough.
Recreation & Conservation Officer: T Pearson.
Pollution reporting: To Scientist.
Rivers controlled: Stour, Colne, Blackwater, Chelmer, Crouch and the Mar Dyke.
Close seasons: Trout enclosed waters— 30 October to 31 March incl. Salmon & Trout other than rainbow trout in enclosed waters— 29 September to 28/29 February incl. Coarse Fish—15 March to 15 June incl.

SEVERN-TRENT WATER AUTHORITY, Abelson House, 2297 Coventry Road, Sheldon, Birmingham B26 3PR.
Regional Manager, Leisure Services: M L Parry. (Tel: 021-743 4222.)

Severn Area
Fisheries and Amenity Officer: A S Churchward, Severn-Trent Water Authority, Portland Road, Malvern, Worcs. WR14 2TA. (Tel: 0684 892511.)
Pollution reports: To this address and other tel nos given on licence.
Rivers controlled: Severn, Warwickshire Avon, Teme, and all other tributary streams in the

Severn south of Bridgnorth as well as canals and pools. The Authority also owns or rents water on the Avon and Severn (details on licence), Draycote Reservoir.
Fisheries and Amenity Officer: Dr J V Woollard, Severn-Trent Water, Shelton, Shrewsbury SY3 8BJ. (Tel: 0743 231666.)
Rivers controlled: Severn and tributaries north of Bridgnorth, Teme above Leintwardine, Vyrnwy, Tanet, Banwy, Tern, Roden, Mease, Perry. Clywedog Reservoir.
Close seasons: S—30 September to 2 February. NT (excluding rainbow trout)—16 October to 17 March in lakes and reservoirs. 1 October to 17 March in other waters (all dates inclusive). Rainbow trout—no close season.

Trent Area
Fisheries and Amenity Officer: R G Templeton, Severn-Trent Water, Trentside Offices, Scarington Road, West Bridgford, Nottingham NG2 5FA. (Tel: 0602 608161.)
Pollution reports: To this address and other tel nos given on licence.
Rivers controlled: Trent, part Soar, Tame and their tributaries, all other waters in the area.
Fisheries and Amenity Officer: G D Nicholds, Severn-Trent Water, Northern Division, Raynesway, Derby DE3 7JA. (Tel: 0332 661481.)
Rivers controlled: Trent west of Swarkestone, Derbyshire Derwent, Dove, Manifold, Churnet, Derbyshire Wye and their tributaries. Ladybower Reservoir.
Close seasons: Brown trout—16 October to 17 March. Rainbow trout: in Rivers Derwent and Amber, and their tributaries, upstream of their confluence except between Blackwell Mill and Cressbrook Mill and above Ashford on Derbyshire Wye. On these fisheries, from 14 November to 15 May. No close season in any other waters in S-TWA area.

Licences: Whole area: T and FF, s £4.50, 28-day £1.80, s OAP 90p.
Severn Catchment. S, s £32.65, d £6.55. OAP etc s £6.55.

THAMES WATER AUTHORITY, Nugent House, Vastern Road, Reading, RG1 8DB. (Tel: Reading 59377.)
Amenity and Recreation Manager: Dr B D Hughes, Thames Water Authority, Nugent House, Vastern Road, Reading. (Tel: 593391.) For general enquiries, ring Reading 593538.
Senior Fishery Officers:
Upper Thames: David Jenkins, Denton House, Iffley Turn, Oxford, OX4 4HJ. Tel: Oxford 778921. River Thames (source to Benson Lock); Rivers Churn, Coln, Windrush, Evenlode, Cherwell, Ray, Cole, Ock, Thame, Wye and Oxford Canal; Reservoirs: Farmoor, Wroughton.
Mid Thames: Dr A J Butterworth, Ladymead, Bypass Road, Guildford, Surrey. Tel: Guildford 577655. River Thames (Benson Lock to Teddington); Rivers Kennet, Lambourn, Loddon, Blackwater, Wey and Basingstoke Canal; Reservoirs: Thames Valley Reservoirs.
Thames East: J Reeves, Aspen House, The Grange, Crossbrook Street, Waltham Cross, Herts, EN8 8LX. Tel: Waltham Cross 23611. Rivers Lee, Stort, Roding and tributaries, Colne, Misbourne, Gade and Ver; Reservoirs: Lee Valley Reservoirs.
Metropolitan: S Colclough, Rivers House, Crossness Sewage Treatment Works, Abbey Wood, London, SE2 9AQ. Tel: 01-310 5500. River Thames (Teddington to Yantlet), Rivers Darent, Cray and Mole; Reservoirs: London reservoirs (south of Thames).

River Pollution, Fish Mortality and Disease: Reports by Members of the Public: Dial 100 and ask for FREEFONE 3266. This number covers the whole of the Thames Water catchment 24 hours a day, 7 days a week. It is a freefone system and persons making a call will incur no charge.

Seasons: Salmon and Trout (excluding rainbow trout): 1 April to 30 September; enclosed waters: 1 April to 29 October. Rainbow trout: 1 April to 30 September (does not apply to enclosed waters). Freshwater fish: 16 June to 14 March.

Rod licences: Annual £7.50; 15 day £2; OAP, disabled and juvenile (12–15 years) £2. Licence for second rod £2. Annual licences run from 1 April each year to 31 March in the year following.

OPEN SEASONS

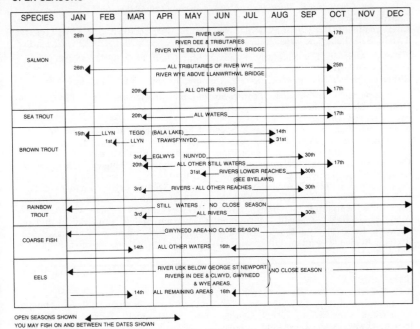

OPEN SEASONS SHOWN
YOU MAY FISH ON AND BETWEEN THE DATES SHOWN

WELSH WATER AUTHORITY, Cambrian Way, Brecon, Powys LD3 7HP.
(Supplanting all former Welsh River Authorities and the Wye River Authority.)
Principal Fisheries Officer: W J Ayton.

LICENCES

1. Salmon and migratory trout
Every angler fishing for salmon or sea trout must possess a licence which is now universal, and entitles the holder to fish throughout the Authority's area.

Categories of licence are season, fortnight and day. There are concessions for juveniles and OAPs for the season category only.

Fortnightly licences cover a period of 336 consecutive hours and replace the former weekly licence. A day licence is valid for 24 consecutive hours. s £26.80, (Concession) s £17.95, f £12.50, d £4.

A licence for salmon/sea trout also covers non-migratory trout, freshwater fish and eels.

2. Non-Migratory Trout
These licences cover the entire WWA area, including rivers, lakes and ponds, etc. There are three categories, season, fortnight and day, but juvenile and OAP concessions are allowed only on season categories. s £7.65, (Concession) s £5.20, f £1.85, d £1.50.

A licence for non-migratory trout also covers freshwater fish and eels.

3. Coarse Fish and Eels
These licences cover the entire WWA area. There are three categories of licence, season, fortnight and day, but juvenile and OAP concessions apply only to the season category. s £4.60, (Concession) s £3.00.

In all cases a juvenile is defined as someone under 17 years of age and an OAP is a person in receipt of a state retirement pension at the time of issue of the licence.

Special junior licence, for all species of fish, periods and areas, available to children under 10 years of age, at a cost of 70p.

DIVISIONS OF THE AUTHORITY
Dee and Clwyd Area: Shire Hall, Mold, Clwyd. (Tel: (0352) 58551.)
Fisheries Officer: B P Hodgson.
Rivers controlled: Dee (Welsh) Clwyd, Elwy, Alwen, Alyn, Ceiriog, Ceirw, Lliw, Tryweryn, Twrch, Bala Lake and their feeders.

Gower Area: 86 The Kingsway, Swansea, Mid Glam. (Tel: (0792) 468000.)
Fisheries Officer: J Lambert.
Rivers controlled: Neath, Afon, Kenfig, Ogmore, Ewenny, Tawe and Loughor.

Gwynedd Area: Penrhos Road, Penrhosgarnedd, Bangor, Gwynedd. (Tel: (0248) 351144.)
District Fisheries Officer: M F Harcup.
Area Fisheries Officer: R C Cresswell.
Rivers controlled: Waters in an area bounded by watersheds of rivers (including their tributaries and all lakes) running into the sea between the eastern boundary of the Division's area at Old Gwyrch, Denbighshire, and the southern extremity at Upper Borth, Cardiganshire. The principal rivers are: Dulas, Conway, Lledr, Llugwy (with Lakes Elsi, Crafnant, Cowlyd, Eigiau, Conway, Melynllyn, Dulyn), Aber, Ogwen (with Lakes Anafon, Ogwen, Idwal, Ffynnon, Loer), all waters in Anglesey, Seiont, Gwyrfai, Llyfni (with Lakes Padarn, Cwellyn, Gader, Nantlle), Erch, Soch, Rhydhir, Afon Wen, Dwyfawr, Dwyfach (with Lake Cwmystradllyn), Glaslyn, Dwyryd, Prysor (with Lakes Dinas, Gwynant, Llagi Adar, Trawsfynydd, Gamallt, Morwynion, Cwmorthin), Glyn, Eisingrug (with Lakes Techwyn Isaf, Techwyn Uchaf), Artro, Mawddach, Eden, Wnion (with Lakes Cwm Bychan, Bodlyn, Gwernan, Gregennen), Dysynny, Dovey, Dulas, Twymyn (with Lake Tal-y-Llyn).

Taff and Usk Areas: South East Division Office, Pentwyn Road, Nelson, Treharris. (Tel: (0445) 450577.)
Area Fisheries Officer: Dr G Mawle.
Rivers controlled: Ely, Taff, Rhymney, Usk and tributaries, including Cilienni, Honddu, Yscir, Bran, Cray, Senni, Tarrell, Cynrig, Crawnon, Rhiangoll, Gwryne-fawr, Grwyne-fechan, Olway, Afon, Lwyd and Sirhowy..

West Wales Area: Hawthorne Rise, Haverfordwest, Dyfed. (Tel: (0437) 4581.)
District Fisheries Officer: A G Harvey.
Area Fisheries Officer: D C Gardner.
Rivers controlled: Towy, Teifi, Taf, Eastern and Western Cleddau, Gwaun, Nevern, Aeron, Clarach, Rheidol, Ystwyth, Tawe (Swansea), Wyre, Llwchwr, Amman, Gwendraeth Fach, Gwendraeth Fawr, and the tributaries of these rivers.

Wye Area: St Nicholas House, St Nicholas Street, Hereford HR4 0BB. (Tel: (0432) 575411).
Fisheries Officer: P G Hilder.
Rivers controlled: Wye and all rivers and brooks of the Wye watershed including Monnow, Trothy, Lugg, Arrow, Ithon and Irfon.

Check before you go

While every effort has been made to ensure that the information given in "Where to Fish" is correct, the position is continually changing and anglers are urged, in their own interests, to make preliminary inquiries before travelling to selected venues. This is especially important with reference to prices quoted. Inevitably, the rate of inflation is affecting stability in this quarter. Anglers' attention is also drawn to the fact that the hotels mentioned under the various fishing stations do not necessarily have water of their own. Any amendments or further data for inclusion in subsequent editions, and any criticism, will be welcome.

Fishing to Let

on

THE SOUTH'S PREMIER TROUT STREAMS. HAMPSHIRE'S ITCHEN AND TEST, WILTSHIRE'S NADDER TO NAME BUT A FEW OF THE EXCITING OPPORTUNITIES

from

THE ROD BOX

For personal consultation, telephone Winchester, England, 0962 61561 and ask for our Fishing to Let office.

You can also write to us at Rod Box Fishing to Let 52 St Georges Street, Winchester, Hampshire, England.

Book early to ensure that we can offer you the fishing you require.

TELEPHONE (0962) 61561 FOR IMMEDIATE ATTENTION

According to recent research, 50% of all anglers in Britain are in the age-group 12-24. This one, aged 11, falls just outside it but confirms another point made, that virtually all anglers start young. James Sugg has started to make his mark while young, too. In September 1986, while fishing in a Salmon & Trout Association event at Latimer Park, near Chesham, he won not only the prize awarded to the "Junior Fisherman of the Day" but also the trophy for the heaviest fish caught that day by all contenders, the 4 lb. rainbow trout he is shown with in the picture. *Photo: Patrick Mackreth, Chilterns Branch, Salmon & Trout Assn.*

ENGLISH FISHING STATIONS

MAIN catchments are given in alphabetical order, fishing stations listed in mouth to source order, first main river, then tributaries. Where national borders are crossed—e.g. Wye and Border Esk—allocation has been arbitrary. Some small streams have been grouped in counties rather than catchments.

Water Authority rod licences are now required almost everywhere in England and Wales for all freshwater fishing. Details appear on pages 11-18. A list of fishing clubs appears at the end of each national section. "Free fishing" means only that a riparian owner is reputed to allow fishing without making a charge. It does not imply a right and such information should be checked locally before an attempt to fish is made. All charges shown are exclusive of VAT unless otherwise stated. Reduced charges to juniors, the disabled, pensioners, and in some instances to ladies, are now quite commonplace. In many instances, they are specified. Where they are not, they may nevertheless be in force. If in doubt, ask when booking.

ADUR

(For close seasons, licences, etc, see Southern Water Authority, p 11-12)

Rises SW of Horsham and flows into the English Channel at Shoreham. A coarse-fish river of no great reputation, but occasionally provides good sport.

Shoreham (Sussex). Bass, codling, flats, eels, mullet from harbour and shore.

Bramber and **Steyning** (Sussex). Bream, roach, chub, dace, pike and carp. Pulborough AS has 3m from Beeding Bridge upstream to Streatham Bridge. On tidal water, low water best. Dt available from House of Pipes, Bramber, £1.50.

Henfield (Sussex). Roach, bream, perch, chub, dace (mullet good Sept). Henfield AS and Comrades AC have fishing rights on about 8m. No dt. Apply hon sec Henfield AS for annual membership. Lake at Bolney; brook fishing at Beeding.

Shermanbury Place. Coarse fishing lakes stocked with carp, tench, roach, rudd, trout and eels in vicinity also $\frac{1}{2}$m of river. St, dt. Phone Dorking 883621 for details.

ALDE

(For licences, etc, see Anglian Water Authority, p 14-15)

A small Suffolk stream, rising near Saxmundham and flowing into the North Sea at Orford Haven, $6\frac{1}{2}$m NE of Felixstowe. Coarse fish

Aldeburgh (Suffolk). Bass, codling, flat-fish, etc, can be taken in estuary from jetty and boat; cod and whiting from beach; October and November best months. Hotels: Brudenell, White Lion, Wentworth, East Suffolk *(see also Suffolk, Sea Fishing Stations).*

Snape (Suffolk). River tidal. Roach, dace, eels below sluice. Fishing free.

Saxmundham (Suffolk). Saxmundham Brook, 2m W; roach, etc; fishing free. Good local beach fishing. Tackleist: Saxmundham Angling Centre, Market Place, tel: 0728 3443: licences; details of local lake fishing for carp, tench, rudd and pike. Hotels: White Hart, Bell.

ALN

(For close seasons, etc, see Northumbrian Water Authority, p 14)

Short Northumberland river, flowing into North Sea at Alnmouth. Trout and sea trout, occasional salmon; runs improving as pollution reduced.

Alnwick (Northumberland). Aln AA water (owned by the Duke of Northumberland) includes most reaches between Denwick Bridge and Alnmouth Bridge (4 to 5m). Portion running through grounds at Lesbury House private. Visitors' (excl Sundays) st £15, mt £12, wt £8, dt £2.50 (concession-rates for jun) from Murraysport, Narrowgate, Alnwick, and R L Jobson, Tower Showrooms during business hours. Coquet and Till within easy reach. Hotels: White Swan and Hotspur, Alnwick; Schooner, Alnmouth.

ANCHOLME

(For close seasons, etc, see Anglian Water Authority, p 14-15)

This river, in South Humberside and Lincolnshire, with its tributaries drains about 240 square miles of country. Falls into the Humber at **South Ferriby**, where there is a sluice and tidal lock. The lower part is embanked for about 19 miles and is owned by Anglian Water. The fishing rights are leased to Scunthorpe and District Angling Association. Temporary membership day permits are available from their bailiffs on the bankside or local tackle shops. Match bookings to Mrs T Mouncey, Sluice Road, South Ferriby, Barton on Humber. The river is abundantly stocked with coarse fish, especially roach and bream. Winter shoals found mainly at **Brigg** and **Snitterby** — **Brandy Wharf** areas. Fishing accesses: South Ferriby Sluice, 4m from **Barton on Humber: Saxby Bridge,** 6m from Barton on Humber: **Broughton, Castlethorpe, Cadney** and **Hibaldstow Bridges** near Brigg through which town river passes; Brandy Wharf, Snitterby, **Bishop Bridge**, 6m from **Market Rasen**. At Barton on Humber are **Barton Broads** (10 acres), owner Mr Murray, Barton on Humber 32237, **Westfield Lakes** (18 acres), owner Westfield Lakes Hotel, Barton on Humber 32313; **Pasture House Fishery,** 20 acres, Mrs K Smith, Barton on Humber 635119; North Lincolnshire Sailing Club (59 acres), bailiff Mr W Haddock, Queens Avenue, Barton on Humber.

ARUN

(For close seasons, etc, see Southern Water Authority, p 11-12)

Rises on NW border of Sussex, flows past Horsham and enters English Channel at Littlehampton. Noted coarse-fish river, largely controlled by clubs. Some sea trout; May to October.

Littlehampton (Sussex). See under *Sea Fishing Stations*. HQ of Littlehampton and Dist AC is at Arun View Hotel, right by river. Lower reaches now leased by Sussex RD and Permits required— free from the Authority.

Arundel (Sussex). River tidal and mainly mud-bottomed. Roach and dace run large; bream, perch, pike, chub and occasional sea trout. Bass and mullet taken in fair numbers June, July, August between Ford and Arundel Bridge. Leger best method when tide running; trotting down successful in slack water. Association of Sussex Angling Societies has from Arundel Bridge to South Stoke Bridge, both banks, and Burpham backwater; also 5m on **R Rother,** and lake. Dt (£1.25) from Black Rabbit Inn, Castle Service Station; George & Dragon Inn (Burpham) and tackle shops. Hotels: Norfolk, Bridge, Black Rabbit.

Chalk Springs Fishery, Park Bottom, Arundel (BN1 0AA). Three lakes, five acres, stocked with brown and rainbow trout of 2 lb and above. Dt £15. Part day £8, £9, £11.50. St considered on request. Tel: 0903 883742.

Amberley (Sussex). Bream, roach, dace, perch, pike, occasional sea trout. Worthing Piscatorial Society, Rother AC and Bognor Freshwater AC have stretches on the Arun at **Greatham** and **Bury Ferry.** The Central Association of London and Provincial Angling Clubs hold both banks downstream of Houghton Bridge to Stoke Bridge. This area to Stopham involved in Sussex RD improvement scheme.

Pulborough (Sussex). Pike, bream, roach, chub, dace, sea trout (May 1–Oct 29, sport improving). Central Association of London and Provincial ACs leases 3m to Stopham (mainly north bank) and stretch on south bank from railway bridge downstream: dt from bailiffs. River above Greatham Manor *(see Amberley).* Pulborough and District AS has fishing on the tidal Arun from Pulborough to Greatham, 1m on **Rother,** 3m on **Adur.** St £15, con, from sec G Marshall, 31 Cleve Way, Billinghurst. Dt £1.50, Adur only, from House of Pipes, Bramber. At **Wisborough Green** Crawley AS has water; Dt available.

Fishing Clubs

When you appoint a new secretary, do not forget to give us details of the change. Write to Thomas Harmsworth Publishing, 13 Nicosia Road, London SW18 3RN. Thank you!

Tributaries of the Arun

WESTERN ROTHER:
Petworth (Sussex). Pike, perch, roach, dace, chub, few trout and sea trout. Mostly preserved by Leconfield Estate, which grants permits only to estate workers. Hants and Sussex AA has $5\frac{1}{2}$m in all; limited dt from Rapley's Garage, Coultershaw. Portsmouth and Dist. AS has $3\frac{1}{2}$m of **Chichester Canal; Burton Park Lake** and **Costrong Farm Res.** jointly with Hants and Sussex AA. St £21 (joining fee £10), wt £10, dt £2.50; carp, tench, pike, roach, rudd and trout. Hants and Sussex AA has stretch downstream from Coultershaw Mill to Shopham Bridge, and 1m (N bank only) from Shopham Bridge. Then both banks for 1m from Fittleworth Bridge. St £21 + £10 joining fee, dt £2.50, from sec. St £150 for two stocked stretches totalling about $4\frac{1}{2}$m, both banks, from King & Chasemore (estate agents), Petworth. Both stretches stocked mainly with brown trout. **Burton Mill Pond** holds good pike, perch, roach, rudd, carp, tench. **Duncton Mill,** 9 acres, trout; st, tel: 0798 42294. Hotel: Angel.
Selham (Sussex). Pitshill Fly Fishing Waters: $1\frac{1}{2}$m double bank downstream from Lods Bridge; also $\frac{1}{2}$m of tributary. St £150; contact King & Chasemore, Lombard Street, Petworth. Tel: 0798 42011. Rotherbridge Fly Fishing Assc have 3m downstream of Pitshill beat; agents, King & Chasemore. Both these beats are stocked with b and r trout.
Midhurst (Sussex). Rother AC has river and three lakes; coarse fish incl bream, tench, carp and grayling. £6 entrance, annual sub £10. Juniors £2.50 and £2. Dt £1.25 from Rice Bros, West Street, The Rother Inn, Lutener Rd., and The News Shop, North Street, Midhurst, for part of river only. Membership Secretary D Merritt, 17 Sandrock, June Lane, Midhurst.
Chithurst (Sussex). Petersfield & Dist AC is affiliated to the Hants and Sussex Anglers Alliance who have fishing on the Arun, **Rother,** and eleven stillwaters. Fishing is predominately coarse with all species available. Coombe Pond, Rake, has tench to 4lb. Joining fee £10, st £19, dt £3. Dt £1.75 adult, £1 junior are available for Heath lake (with carp to 27lb), Petersfield, from local tackle shop. Enquiries to hon sec. Tel: 0730 66793.

AVON (Bristol)

(For close seasons, licences, etc, see Wessex Water Authority, p 13)

Coarse fishing now excellent in places. Large chub, barbel, pike, bream, good roach and dace. Trout in weir pools, including exceptional specimens occasionally, and in some tributaries.

Bristol. On Avon and Frome and in Somerset. Much of Avon and tributaries controlled by Bristol and District Amalgamated Anglers (referred to later as Bristol Amalgamated), a merger of 11 clubs which makes all their waters available on one subscription, though each club retains its identity. Members have choice of more than 100m of fishing. Cards (concessions for ladies, juniors and pensioners) are available from tackleists in the main Avon centres or hon sec. Dt available. Full membership £10, ladies and juniors £3, OAP and dis, £2. Veterans free. Full members only may fish at **Tockenham Lake.** Tel: 0272-672977. Bristol Amal is among clubs affiliated to Bristol & West of England Federation, which itself has good water on Avon, **Kennet and Avon Canal, Frome** and **Ham Green Lake.** Good sport with trout on Blagdon Lake, Chew Valley and Barrow Reservoirs *(see Somerset streams, lakes and reservoirs).* Among coarse fishing lakes in area are **Bowood** (2m W of Calne, dt at waterside); **Longleat** apply P Bundy, Bailiff, Parkhill Cottage, Longleat, Warminster (Tel. 215082); St £25, dt £2. **Bitterwell Lake** (N of Bristol) common, mirror and crucian carp, tench, bream, roach, rudd and perch. Dt on bank, £1, from Mrs Scully, The Chalet, Bitterwell Lake, Coalpit Heath, Bristol BS17 2UF. **Henleaze Lake** (north of Bristol, dt June–Sep from R W Steel, 63 Hill View, Henleaze, Bristol). Tackleists: Geo Gibbs Ltd, 3/4 Perry Road; S Veals, 61 Old Market Street; Scotts, 42 Soundwell Road; Staple Hill; S Shipp, Staple Hill;

Sheppard's, 46 Bond Street; J B Sports, 31a Sandy Park Road, Brislington; Sportsfair, The Horsefair; Brachers, 68 Bedminster Parade; Ken Davis, 410 Wells Road; Sportsmans, 14 St Michael's Hill; Newmans, 331 Church Road; Bryants, 107 Coldharbour Rd, Redland.

Keynsham (Avon). Mainly roach and dace. Keynsham AA has water extending to Chewton, at Compton Dando and Woolland (trout) *(see tributary Chew)*. St £4 (jun £1.75), dt at discretion of committee members. Special facilities for young anglers. Bristol & West of England Federation has water here. Bristol Amal has six stretches of river here and one at **Wilsbridge** *(see Bristol)*. Free fishing from towpath below Hanham Weir.

Saltford (Avon). Bristol Amal has stretch at Avon Farm and one field at Swineford. Bathampton AA has $2\frac{1}{2}$m; most coarse fish, including carp and tench, few large trout. Tickets from bailiffs, local tackleists and hon sec. Tackleist in Saltford: J D Roberts, 18 High St.

Bath (Avon). Coarse fish; barbel present from here to Limpley Stoke; few large trout. Some free fishing. Bristol Amal and Bath AA have water at Kensington Meadows and from Bathampton to city weirs. Good trout fishing in tributary streams, all preserved. **Kennet and Avon Canal** to Limpley Stoke aqueduct preserved by Bathampton AA. Cam, Midford, Wellow and By (Box) Brooks all within easy reach (trout) and Woodborough Lake. Knowle AA has **Emborough Pond**, Ston Easton; carp, tench, roach, perch, pike; dt from keeper. Tackleists: I M Crudgington, 37 Broad Street; (information and tickets for Bath AA and Bathampton AA waters).

Batheaston (Avon). Bathampton AA has $\frac{1}{2}$m; coarse fish, large trout; tickets from hon sec, bailiffs, tackleists. Bristol Amal has two fields here.

Bathampton (Avon). All-round fishing. Bristol Amal, Bath AA and Bathampton AA have water; dt from S Veals & Sons, 61 Old Market Street, Bristol, Bathampton AA also has water at **Kelston** ($3\frac{1}{2}$m), **Newbridge, Saltford** and **Fox's Wood**, and on **Kennet and Avon Canal, Hunstrete** and **Woodborough Lakes** (good carp, tench), **Wellow** and **Box Brooks**, some ponds near Bridgwater. St £10, (jun £2.50) dt £1 for some waters, from hon

sec. and local tackleists.

Claverton (Avon). Bathampton AA has 2m; very good chub, few trout. Bath AA also has water.

Warleigh (Avon). Bathampton AA has four meadows here: (as Claverton above). Bath AA has five meadows.

Limpley Stoke (Wilts). Good all-round fishing; large carp, with tench, chub, roach, bream and trout; fly-fishing on **River Frome**, Freshford to Farleigh Hungerford, and **Midford Brook** from Avon to Midford village; stocked with trout every year; preserved by Avon and Tributaries AA; visitors accompanied by member only. Bathampton AA holds **Kennet and Avon Canal** from Limpley Stoke to confluence with Avon at Bath ($5\frac{1}{2}$m); dt from hon sec, tackleists and bailiffs. Bath AA controls 3m from Limpley Stoke down to Kensington; coarse fish and trout; tickets from hon sec, two stretches. Bristol Amal has water on the Avon, trout and coarse fishing *(see Bristol)*.

Midford (Avon). **Midford Brook**; trout only; preserved and stocked by the Avon and Tributaries AA. Dt to members' friends only.

Freshford (Avon). Bristol Amal has water on Avon here; dt issued for former Golden Carp AA water. **Frome:** trout, coarse fish, stocked and preserved by Avon and Tributaries AA (annual sub £60); from Avon up to Farleigh Hungerford (about 7m). Frome has mayfly hatch. Limited dt for members' friends. Association also has part of Avon, Freshford to Avoncliffe, fly only water on **Midford, Wellow** and **Cam Brooks**, and ponds.

Bradford-on-Avon (Wilts). Coarse fish, including pike, few trout. **Kennet and Avon Canal**; coarse fish. Some miles of Avon and canal preserved by Bradford-on-Avon and Dist AA. Dt from hon sec or tackleists Wests, Roundstone Street; Roses, Fore Street; Smith and Ford, Fore St (all Trowbridge) and Smith and Ford, The Shambles, Bradford-on-Avon.

Melksham (Wilts). Coarse fish, few trout. Roughly 2m up and 1m downstream from river bridge rented by Bristol Amal, which has taken over Melksham AA preserves following merger. Assn also has water at **Beanacre**. St £6 from hon sec or tackleists. RD licences from hon sec and Avon Angling & Sports Centre (tackleist), 13 Bath Road. Lavington AC has water on **Semington Brook** at Lavington Mill and Baldham Mill.

Lacock (Wilts). Bristol AA, Chippenham AC and Calne AC all have water here. Tickets from Coles, Market Place, Chippenham. Dt on site for **Silverlands Lake**. Carp and tench. Isis AC has water at **Pewsham**; apply hon sec for permit details. *(For details of Bristol Amal membership, see under Bristol).*

Chippenham (Wilts). Chub, barbel, bream, perch, roach. Chippenham AA has water; st £6.50, wt £3, dt £1.50 from tackleists. Bristol Amal has about $1\frac{1}{2}$m between here and Lacock. Isis AC has water on Avon and **Marden**; members only. RD licences, tackle and bait from Coles, Market Place, Robs Tackle, Tackle Box.

Christian Malford (Wilts). Several fields controlled by Bristol Amal here, and at

Sutton Benger Isis AC has 4m including 2 weirs and backwater; further water near **Seagry Mill**. Somerfords FA has water upstream from Seagry to Kingsmead Mill (part of it, from Dauntsey road bridge, is trout water) and 2m above Kingsmead Mill on left bank and 1m on right bank. Good chub and perch. Assn also has water on **Frome**. Dt for trout and coarse fishing issued. Golden Valley FC has water at Seagry.

Malmesbury (Wilts). Bristol Amalgamated has acquired further extensive stretch to add to five fields already held; members only; trout and coarse fish. RD licences from Sports and Leisure, 36 High Street.

Lower Moor Fishery, Oaksey, Malmesbury, Wiltshire SN1 69TW. Forty-five acres of trout fishing on three lakes. Two confined to nymph and dry fly. Dt £11 or £6.50. Junior £5.50 (4 and 2 fish limits). Licences available at fishery.

Tributaries of the Avon (Bristol)

FROME (Bristol). Rises near Chipping Sodbury and joins Avon estuary near Bristol. Coarse fishing mostly, but upper reaches restocked with trout.

Frampton Cotterell (Glos). Coarse fish. Most of lower Frome controlled by Bristol Amal *(see Avon).*

Yate (Glos). Frome Vale AC has water from Moorend Weir to viaduct. Dodington Park Lake, 6m; carp, perch; preserved. Badminton Park Lake, 8m; carp; preserved by the Duke of Beaufort; apply Estate Office, Badminton, Glos.

CHEW: Trout and coarse fish.

Keynsham (Avon). Bristol Amal has two fields. Keynsham AA has fishing *(see Avon).*

Malmesbury (Wilts). Five fields right bank downstream held by Bristol Amal. Bristol Amal also has long stretch of Woodbridge Brook.

Chewton Keynsham (Avon). Water held by Bristol Amal; no dt. Keynsham AA also has water; dt issued for fly and coarse fishing. Stretch in Keynsham Park free to licence holders.

Compton Dando (Avon). Mainly trout, grayling and dace. Keynsham AA has water here from above Woollard Weir some way downstream; no dt. Bristol Amal has water between here and Burnett; dt from hon sec, Golden Carp AA.

Pensford (Avon). Trout and coarse fish. Preserved by Knowle AA, tickets from Rising Sun Inn *(see Stanton Drew).* Lakes: **Hunstrete Park Lake**; carp, tench, bream, roach, perch; Bathampton AA; members only.

Stanton Drew, Chew Magna, Chew Stoke (Avon). Trout dominant; some roach and dace; preserved, major portion by Knowle (Bristol) AA; wt (from hon sec only), and dt. Trout licences necessary. Average $\frac{3}{4}$lb; brown and rainbow—occasional big fish. No spinning. Dt from local inns and Bristol tackleists from June 15 to Sept 30 (Mon–Fri only). Stretches of 2m at Compton Dando and $\frac{1}{2}$m at Chew Magna held by Bristol amal; trout; bait or fly. **Emborough Pond**; carp, tench, roach, perch; dt (limited) from bailiff. *(For Chew reservoirs see Somerset (lakes and streams)).*

BOYD BROOK: Trout, coarse fish, Bristol Amal has water at **Doynton** (Glos); dt issued (see Lacock). Golden Valley FC has stretch above and below **Bitton.**

CAM BROOK: Trout, Avon and tributaries AA has water (members' friends only). Bath AA has stretch at **Dunkerton** (Som). Bristol Amal has water at **Midford**; dt issued.

BY (BOX) BROOK: Trout, coarse fish. Bathampton AA has water at **Shockerwick** (Som) and **Box** (Wilts); st £10, dt

£1. By Brook Fly FC and Two Mills Flyfishers have water for members. Manor House Hotel, **Castle Combe**, has $\frac{1}{2}$m of good trout fishing in grounds.

WELLOW BROOK: Trout. Bath AA and Bathampton AA have stretches; fly only; members only.

SEMINGTON BROOK: Trout, coarse fish. Lavington AC has Worton Brook. St £15 and st £3. Concessions for juniors. Members only. Tel: 0380 830425. Baldham Mill fishery now rented by St George's AC, Trowbridge. For **Erlestoke Lake,** Bulkington; D Hampton, Longwater, Lower Road, Erlestoke, Devizes, Wilts.

FROME: Coarse fish, trout.

Frome (Som). Frome and Dist AA has several miles between Marston and Beckington. Regular matches. Information from R Lee, tel: Frome 61433. Dt trout fishing on private lake near Maiden Bradley from tackleist, The Sports Shop, 5 Westway, Frome (Tel: 62712).

Wolverton (Avon). Trout, coarse fish. Bristol Amal no longer holds the fishery here.

MARDEN: Coarse fish, trout.

Calne (Wilts). Trout, grayling, pike, perch, roach, dace, bream; 6m held by Calne AA; St, wt, dt. Isis AC has stretch at Newleaze Farm; members only. Above Calne is strictly preserved dry fly water. **Bowood Lake**, large pike (to 26lb), perch, carp, tench, roach; Details from Bowood Estate, who issue st. North end of lake private. *Note: access to lake only through Pillars Lodge entrance on Calne-Melksham road.*

Peaceful co-existence. Angler and ducks demonstrate it at Damerham. *Photograph by John Tarlton.*

AVON (Hampshire)

(For close seasons, licences, etc, see Wessex Water Authority, p 13)

In years gone by the most famous mixed fishery in England. Roach, chub, dace, barbel and pike all bred prolifically and grew exceptionally large, especially in the lower reaches. There was a good sea trout run and while salmon did not enter the river in large numbers, the average size was exceptional. In its upper reaches, the Avon is a typical chalk stream, populated by free-rising trout and grayling. A decline in the coarse fishing which set in thirty years ago has been the subject of investigation and there are now signs that remedial measures in hand have begun to restore the river to its former status.

Christchurch (Dorset). Avon and Stour. Excellent sea and coarse fishing in Christchurch Harbour. Bass, mullet, flounders and (higher up) dace, roach, bream and eels. Fishing permits for this water and the Royalty Fishery on the Avon (excluding Parlour and Bridge Pool) can be obtained from Davis Tackle Shop, 75 Bargates, Christchurch (Tel: 485169). June 16 to Mar 14 inclusive. The price structure ranges between £20 per day for salmon fishing and £4 for coarse fishing. Davis will supply brochure on receipt of request and SAE. Pike fishing permitted Nov 1–Mar 14 at no extra charge (no spinning). This fishery was once the most famous in England for large coarse fish, noted specially for large barbel. Parlour and Bridge Pool permits from Fishery Manager: advance bookings only. Advance bookings only on following waters: Top Weir Compound; C/S/MT, £22 rod/day; C/MT, £16. Parlour Pool; C/S/MT, £25; C/MT, £18. Bridge Pool; S/MT, £65 2 rods; MT £60 2 rods. All prices include VAT. S & MT tickets for Parlour and Bridge Pool issued only until Sept 30; the "MT only" tickets solely in the month of October. Limit 2 salmon per day, except Parlour, one per day. Permits for fishings on Stour and in Christchurch Harbour also obtainable from Davis Tackle Shop *(see also Stour (Dorset))*. For other salmon and sea trout fishing apply early in writing to the Royalty Fishery Manager, West Hants Water Co, Mill Road, Christchurch. *(Note: brochure on Royalty Fishing available from fishery manager or Davis.)* Good sea fishing at Mudeford; boats available *(see Sea fishing stations)*. Tackleists: G K Pepler, Davis Fishing Tackle Shop, 75 Bargates (open from 7.45 am, Sundays incl); Hales Tackle, 258 Barrack Road. Hotels: Shortwood House, Magdalen Lane; King's Arms; Avonmouth; Fisherman's Haunt; Sea Witch; Pines; Belvedere.

Winkton (Dorset). Davis Fishing Tackle, 75 Bargates, Christchurch now sole agents for coarse fishing on this fishery. Season is July 1 to Jan 31; good roach, chub, perch, pike; also dace, barbel, tench. Dt £2.50. Salmon fishing is all preserved. Hotel: Plaish House.

Ringwood (Hants). Ringwood & Dist AA has fishing on rivers as follows: **Avon;** Breamore, $1\frac{1}{2}$m (barbel, chub), Fordingbridge (trout), Ibsley, 2m (S and specimen coarse fish), side streams at Ibsley, Ringwood, 2m (coarse fish), East Mills, $1\frac{1}{2}$m (coarse fish), Fordingbridge Park, $\frac{1}{4}$m (coarse fish); **Stour;** Twelve stretches totalling more than 12m (coarse fish); **Test;** over 2m at Broadlands Est. (members only); also nine still waters totalling over 120 acres. See also "Moors" entry. St £26 + £4 entry; Junior £12; OAP, dis, ladies £13. Dt for much of the water from tackle shops. N Ward, Avon Dairy Farm, The Bridges, Ringwood, issue dt on behalf of riparian owners, £1, also wt and st. Salmon fishing at **Somerley** let by st. Apply Water Bailiff, Alan Jones, 1 Ellingham Cottages, Ellingham. Tel: 0425 471188. Dt £2.50 from Ringwood Tackle for $\frac{3}{4}$m both banks above Ringwood; $1\frac{1}{4}$m E. bank below. Tackleists: Ringwood Tackle, 5 The Bridges, West Street, Ringwood. Tel: 04254 5155; Hales Tackle; Davis, Christchurch. Hotels: Crown, Star Inn, Fish Inn, Nag's Head, White Hart.

Fordingbridge (Hants). Trout, grayling, perch, pike and roach. Salisbury AC has good water at **Burgate** and **Hale.** Dt for Burgate water from Burgate Manor Farm *(see Salisbury)*. Albany Hotel has short river frontage (licences obtainable). Fordingbridge AC has water on Avon and **Stour;** members only. Few dt for Bickton Estate water from river bailiff, 2 New Cottages, **Bickton;** St (trout streams) £300, st (coarse) £35, st (salmon) £60, dt (trout streams) £12. No RD licence needed as block licence purchased. Tackle shop on premises. Two excellent stillwater trout fisheries in the vicinity. **Damerham** and **Lapsley's Fishery** (ex Allens Farm). Hotels: Royal Arms; George Inn; Victoria House, Sandleheath; Compasses Inn.

Breamore (Hants). Bat and Ball Hotel has 2m of salmon, trout and coarse fishing on dt basis. From £2.50. Phone Beamore 252. Accommodation.

Downton (Wilts). Trout, roach, grayling, dace. Hotel: Bull.

Salisbury (Wilts). Avon, Wylye and Bourne; trout, grayling, coarse fish; preserved. Salisbury and Dist AC has water on Avon, **Bristol Avon, Wylye, Nadder**, lakes and pits, including **Shearwater Lake**, on **Longleat Estate**, Warminster, St (restricted) £12; excellent trout, grayling, roach, etc. Dt for some waters from I Rae, The Boathouse, Castle St, Salisbury and Burgate Manor Farm, Fordingbridge. Dt for good coarse fishing (incl carp) on **Steeple Langford Lakes** from bailiff. London AA has Britford Fishery; $1\frac{1}{2}$m SE; excellent

coarse fishing, good sport with trout, some salmon (trout of $6\frac{1}{2}$lb and salmon of 31lb taken recently). Members only; no dt. Fishing on short stretch of Avon at Fisherton Recreation Ground for small charge; apply Town Clerk, Salisbury City Council. Humberts, 8 Rollestone Street, may know of annual rods to let. For Longford and Trafalgar Estates apply T Williams, Keeper's House, Charlton, nr Salisbury. Hotels: County, White Hart and Red Lion. Tackleists: John Eadie, 20 Catherine Street. (RD licences.)

Netheravon (Wilts). Trout, grayling; strictly preserved. The 6m from **Enford** to **Bulford** is The Services Dry Fly FA (Salisbury Plain) water; members only. Brown trout average $1-1\frac{1}{2}$lb, annual bag 1,200–1,300, many grayling. Best time: mid-May to mid-June and mid-Sept to mid-Oct. Assn also has five ponds stocked with trout. Dt for members' private guests only. Enquiries to Brigadier C A Landale. Tel: 0980 33371 x2771.

AVON (Hampshire) tributaries

BOURNE: Enters near Salisbury. Trout, grayling, coarse fish. Fishing stations: **Porton** and **Salisbury** (Wilts).

EBBLE: Joins Avon below Salisbury; good trout fishing, but mostly private.

WYLYE: Trout, grayling.

Wishford (Wilts). Preserved by Wilton Fly-Fishing Club.

Stapleford (Wilts). Salisbury AC has fishing here; members only.

Codford St Mary and Bapton (Wilts). Privately preserved.

Warminster (Wilts). Warminster AC has water on Wylye, and coarse fishing on lakes and ponds; members only (membership restricted to rural area). **Longleat** Estate owns just over 2m of upper river. Excellent coarse fishing in three lakes in Longleat Park, carp included. Tickets are

issued by Bailiff, Parkhill Cottage, Longleat Estate. St £25, dt £2. Salisbury and Dist. AC has **Shearwater Lake** on this estate. The Sutton Veny Estate, Pound Barton (Tel Warminster 40682), lets rods, part rods and quarter-rods on $3\frac{1}{4}$m of Wylye. Not less than £360 per season. Enquiries to Estate Office for precise terms.

Heytesbury (Wilts). Privately preserved.

NADDER: Tributary of Wylye. Trout, grayling, roach, dace. Mostly preserved by landowners. Fishing stations: **Wilton, Tisbury**. Tisbury AC has about 4m; dt and wt from Arundell Arms, Beckford Arms and hon sec; exchanges with Warminster and Salisbury clubs. Club also has lake at Old Wardens Castle; carp, tench, etc. For stretch near **Salisbury** Salisbury AC issue dt for trout and coarse fishing.

POLLUTION

Anglers are united in deploring pollution. To combat it, urgent action may be called for at any time from any one of us. If numbers of fish are found dead, dying, or seriously distressed, take samples of both fish and water and contact the office of the Director of Scientific Services at the appropriate Regional Water Authority.

AXE

(For close seasons, licences, etc, see SW Water Authority, p 12)

Rises in Dorset and flows south to the English Channel at Seaton. Trout, sea trout and salmon. Fishing difficult to come by, but one or two hotels can provide facilities.

Seaton (Devon). Trout, salmon. Some sea trout fishing available on ticket from Abbeygate Farm, near Axminster, and from Ackermans; Dt. Axe estuary fishable (for bass, mullet, flounders, etc), on ticket from harbour Filling Station. Tackle and WA licences: F Ackerman & Co Ltd, Fore Street *(see Sea Fishing Stations)*. Hotel: Pole Arms. R and b trout fishing available at **Colyton,** dt £3; Mrs E Pady, Higher Cownhayne Farm, Colyton, tel: 0297 52267.

Axminster (Devon). Axe, Yarty; trout and salmon. Trouting good especially in April and May. Taunton Fly Fishing C has beats on the Axe at Chard, Tytherleigh, Musbury. George Hotel has $4\frac{1}{2}$m

available, 3 rods for hotel guests. Dt £5, hotel guests only. Other hotels: Western, Shute Arms, and Bear Inn, Colyton (trout tickets; fish on small side).

Crewkerne (Som). Axe (3m off); trout. Parret (1m off); trout, roach, dace. Stoke-sub-Hamdon AA has trout fishing on **Parret**; members only. Yeovil AA has trout and coarse fishing on **Yeo** and tributaries; st £3, dt £1 from hon sec and Yeovil tackleists That Tackle Shop. Trout fishing **Sutton Bingham Reservoir,** near Yeovil *(see Somerset (lakes and streams))*. Tackleists: That Tackle Shop, 29 Princes Street, Sports, and Doneys, Bond St; all Yeovil.

BLACKWATER

(For close seasons, licences, etc, see Anglian Water Authority, p 14–15)

Rises in NW of county, flows by Braintree to Maldon and empties into North Sea through large estuary. Generous restocking following pollution in 1976 producing improved results. Coarse fish include pike, chub, rudd and some carp.

Maldon (Essex). Maldon AS has two fisheries on main river, seven on the canal and four on stillwater: Railway Pond, Totham Pit and Totham Grove Res. St £16, with concession for ladies, OAP and young anglers. No dt. Stretch from Langford to Beeleigh; Ilford PS; no tickets. Permits for Beeleigh Lock to Heybridge Basin Lock from bailiffs on bank; Leisure sport **Chigborough** gravel pits at **Drapers Farm.** Coarse fish, good eels, flounders. St £12. Phone Chertsey 64872. Tackleists: Last Sports, High Street. Hotels: Swan, White Hart, King's Head.

Chigboro' Fisheries, Malden, Essex CM9 7RE. Sixteen acre lake with brown and rainbow trout of average weight 2 lbs. St from £135. Dt £13.50 (4 fish), or £8.50 (2 fish), from bailiff on water or office. Tel: 0621 57368. Braxted Water trout fishery is also under this management.

Witham (Essex). Blackwater and **Brain.** Coarse fish. Kelvedon and Dist AA has $7\frac{1}{2}$m from here to **Braintree**; members only. **Witham Lake,** $5\frac{1}{2}$ acres; **Bovingdon Mere, Hatfield Peverel;** 4 acre lake coarse fishery, Colchester APS waters.

Kelvedon (Essex). Kelvedon and Dist AA has various stretches as well as water on Suffolk **Stour, Rivenhall Lake**, nr Witham, a reservoir near Tiptree and gravel pits. St and dt from M Murton, 189 High Street, Kelvedon. Tench, crucian carp, rudd, roach. Club organises sea-fishing boat trips. Maldon AS has water here and at **Feering** and **Braxted**; members only *(see Witham, Coggeshall and Maldon)*.

Coggeshall (Essex). Coarse fish. Kelvedon and Dist AA has water here; members only *(see Witham and Kelvedon)*.

Braintree (Essex). Braintree and Bocking AS owns most of water on main river, both banks, from Shalford to Bradwell Village and on **Pant.** Well stocked with roach, perch, rudd, dace, and chub. St £15, juv £5, OAP £3 from local tackleist *(see below)* and hon sec. *For Gosfield and Sparrows Lakes see Essex (streams and lakes).* Tackle: The Right Angle Tackle Shop, 18 New Street. Hotels: Horne, White Horse, Nag's Head.

CHELMER AND CAN: Coarse fish; **Chelmsford** (Essex). River stocked with roach, dace bream, tench, carp, pike, perch. Above Chelmsford waters are private, but most of those below are controlled by Chelmsford AA: Dt available for towpath £1.50 from bailiff on bank. Dt £1.50 for **Heybridge Canal** from Beeleigh to Hall Bridge from bailiff on bank. Free fishing in rivers & lake in town centre. Clubs: Chelmsford AA, (15m of river, 9 lakes, st £16, concessions for ladies, OAP, jun). Marconi AS,

Christy AA and Maldon AS. Leisure sport gravel pit at **Boreham**. St £14 + £2 key deposit. Phone Chertsey 64872 for details. Tackleists: Brians Sport & Tackle, 50b, Moulsham Street. Edwards Tackle, 7, Broomfield Road. Ronnie Crowe, Maldon Road, Gt. Baddow. Hotels: County, South Lodge.

Hartford End. TWA has trout fishery here; dt (strictly limited) from Amenity and Fisheries Manager.

BLYTH (Northumberland)

(For close seasons, etc, see Northumbrian Water Authority, p 14)

Rises near Throckington and flows 20m to North Sea at Blyth. Trout and grayling, with coarse fish (especially roach) in lower reaches.

Bedlington (Northumberland). Brown trout and grayling (both average about 9in) with roach in lower reaches. Seaton Burn and Bedlington and Blagdon

Angling Associations have water; some dt (Mon–Fri only) for holiday visitors outside 50m radius for lower reaches from hon secs, £2.

BLYTHE (Suffolk)

(For close seasons, licences, etc, see Anglian Water Authority, p 14-15)

Short Suffolk river, about 20m long, rising in lakes in Heveningham Hall Park (pike, roach and rudd; tickets when Hall open), 4m SW from Halesworth. W and dt for coarse fishing in Henham Dairy Ponds. R **Wang** and trout fishery at Peasenhall. Fishing in river negligible until below Holton, where there is good roach fishing to Blyford. Immediately downstream river is tidal to **Wenhaston** *(see under Sea Fishing Stations)*. Several hotels.

BRUE

(For close seasons, licences, etc, see Wessex Water Authority, p 13)

Rises in Mendips and flows to Bristol Channel at Burnham. Coarse fish, except in higher reaches, where there are trout. River has reputation for carp; grayling introduced recently. Fishes well from September onwards as a rule.

Highbridge (Som). Roach, bream, etc. North Somerset AA has some of best waters. St, wt, dt. Best Sept onwards. Club also has Apex Pit, between Highbridge and Burnham, and Newtown Pond, Highbridge (carp to 20lb). Bristol and District AA now has 3m from Highbridge and ½m at Basonbridge. Tickets and licences from hon sec or tackleists: P Thyer, Church Street. Also from Information Bureau, Victoria Street, Burnham-on-Sea. Further information from hon sec. Huntspill River is 2m; Bridgwater AA water *(see Bridgwater– Parret)* Bristol Amalgamated has

water at **East Huntspill, Burtle, Tealham Moor, Westhay** and **Lydford-on-Fosse**. £8 *(see Bristol)*. Hotels: Highbridge; The George (clubs accommodated).

Bason Bridge (Som). Area around milk factory noted for carp; fish run up to 16lb or so. Also roach, chub, tench, perch and pike. Bristol Amal holds extensive stretches here *(see under Bristol Avon)* and Highbridge AA also has water.

Mark (Som). Carp, pike, perch, roach, chub, tench. N Somerset AA has 2½m on river and 3 to 4m on North Drain; dt and wt from hon sec *(see also Axe-*

Somerset streams). Highbridge AA also has water on North Drain. Inn: Pack Horse.

Edington (Som). Roach, bream, carp, perch, pike; free.

Glastonbury (Som). Roach, bream, chub, etc, in lower stretches of River Brue. Glaston Manor, Bristol Amal and N

Somerset AA clubs have water. Dt from hon secs. Trout from **Baltonsborough** to **West Lydford**. Fishing extends from White House, Westhay, to Fosseway Bridge, West Lydford (trout av $\frac{1}{2}$lb). No dt. Weekly tickets only from D Smith, 6 Barn Close, Street. Tackleist: G Miller, 22 Benedict St (club permits).

BUDE RIVER AND CANAL

(For close seasons, licences, etc, see South West Water Authority, p 12)

Two branches of River Neet from Week St Mary and Stratton (latter often referred to as the Strat) converge at Hele Bridge, flow into the Bude Canal and out again towards Bude. Neet has small brown trout in good seasons. Bude Canal has $1\frac{1}{4}$ miles of wider than average canal with good banks and full variety of coarse fish. Visitors should apply to Willow Valley Camping park, Dye House, Bush, Bude, for Neet upstream of Stratton or to M J Proudfoot, Whales Borough Farmhouse, Marhamchurch, for Hele Bridges system.

Bude (Cornwall). Bass from beaches, breakwater and rocks; bass and mullet in estuary of Bude River. Details from hon sec Bude & Dist SAC, or Bude Stratton Town Council, The Castle. Bude Angling Association has fishing on a total of $6\frac{1}{2}$m of banks of **Tamar** and **Claw** from near Bude to half way to Launceston. Wild brown trout plus some dace in downstream beats. Membership £5, st £5, mt £5, wt £3, dt £1; from Ray Beare

Sports, Belle Vue, Bude, or the DIY Centre, The Square, Holsworthy, Devon. Membership enquiries (with 50p if map req.) to hon sec., Bude AA. **Tamar Lake** and **Crowdy** (trout reservoir) controlled by SW Water Auth *(see Cornwall lakes, etc)*. **Bude Canal** (roach, dace, rudd, perch, carp and tench) leased by Bude Canal AA; wt £5, dt £1 from Tourist Information Centre, Bude. Hotel: Globe, The Strand, Bude.

BURE

(See Norfolk and Suffolk Broads, p 84)

CAMEL

(For close seasons, licences, etc, see South West Water Authority, p 12)

A spate river, rising on the moors near Davidstow, flowing about 30m to enter the Atlantic between Pentire and Steppar Points. Salmon, sea trout and small brown trout. Salmon enter from April; grilse from June, with the main runs in October, November and December. Sea trout from June to August. Best brown trout fishing in tributaries Allen, De Lank, Lanivet and Ruthern and in the topmost reaches of the main river. Rainfall influences salmon fishing to an exceptional extent.

Wadebridge (Cornwall). Trout, sea trout, salmon; good bass fishing in tidal reaches, with bass and pollack in estuary. Large stretches held by Wadebridge and Dist AA (at Pencarrow, Grogley, Nanstallon, Wenford, Key Bridge, $4\frac{1}{2}$m total), Bodmin and Dist AA and riparian owners. Membership of Wadebridge & Dist. AA is via a short waiting list. £14

p.a. + £6 joining fee. Dt for visitors £3 and £4 according to date, wt £15 or £25, from sec, or Appleton & Cragg, 1 Egloshayle Road. Fowey within reach, with tickets for both Liskeard and Lostwithiel AC waters. Of Camel tributaries, Allen now provides fair sea trout sport in lower reaches— permission from landowners—and Ruthern holds trout, sea trout and some salmon, while bass may be taken from Amble. Tackleist: Lenaghan's, 27 Molesworth Street (licences). Hotels: Molesworth Arms, Bridge-on-Wool, Swan and Lanarth Hotel and Country Club, St Kew. *(For sea fishing see Padstow).*

Bodmin (Cornwall). A few miles from the Camel and Fowey, where Bodmin AA issues permits (ten per day) on some of the best water including the De Lank. Salmon and sea-trout fishing for disabled

anglers provided at St. Breward. Details from hon sec St £18 + £5 entrance (for adults only), wt £10, dt £4 (except between Nov 1 and Dec 15, when dt charge is £8). St, wt and dt from hon sec or Bodmin Trading Co, Church Square. Concessions for juv and OAP. Hotels: Westberry, Dunmere caravan site phone Bodmin 2032. Free maps and SWWA licences also available from hon sec R Burrows, 26 Meadow Place, Bodmin, on receipt of sae. Telephone 5513 (after 5pm).

CHESHIRE (Lakes/Reservoirs)

BOLESWORTH LAKE, Tattenhall, Chester. Now let on a long lease by Bolesworth Estate Co, Tattenhall. No details disclosed.

BOSLEY RESERVOIR. Fishing station: **Bosley.** Roach (good), bream, pike, perch, carp, few trout. Dt from J Arnold (bailiff), Lakeside Estate, Harington Arms, Bosley.

CAPESTHORNE POOLS. Fishing station: **Siddington.** Park and Garden pools controlled by Stoke-on-Trent AS. Large carp, tench, bream, roach, rudd and pike. Dt for Park pool £2.80 from A Bradley, East Lodge Capesthorne (Tel: Chelford 861584). Stock pond carp and tench. Dt £2.50, ½ day £1.25. Top pool now fished privately. No tickets.

DOVE MERE, SAND MERE, WOODLANDS LAKE. Allostock, Knutsford. Prince Albert AS waters, heavily stocked, including large carp. St £30; waiting list.

GREAT BUDWORTH MERE. Nr. Northwich, 50-acre lake holding good bream, pike, etc. Northwich AA; tickets from hon sec. St £10, wt £3. **Pickmere** and **Petty Pool** are assn waters nearby; members only for south bank of Pickmere; permission from farmers elsewhere.

LAKE REDESMERE. Fishing station: **Siddington.** Excellent roach and pike, with bream, carp, tench and some trout. Stoke-on-Trent AA water.

LANGLEY BOTTOMS and LAMALOAD RESERVOIRS. Nr **Macclesfield.** Good

fly fishing for trout. Prince Albert AS. Limited dt from Match-Tac or Barrows Tackle, Macclesfield.

LEADBEATERS RESERVOIR, Macclesfield. Trout and coarse fish. Macclesfield Prince Albert AS water.

MANCHESTER RESERVOIRS: Tintwistle (A628). Trout, perch. **Vale House:** fly fishing, for trout. **Bottoms:** bait fishing. **Cote Lodge** (Glossop): bait fishing. These NWWA reservoirs are now leased to various clubs. Enquiries to Fisheries Section, New Town House, Buttermarket St, Warrington, tel: 53999.

MILL LODGE, BOLLINGTON. 3 acres. Large carp. Prince Albert AS.

OULTON MILL POOL. Fishing station: **Tarporley.** Well stocked with good carp, bream, tench and pike. Dt from Mill Office.

ROMAN LAKES. Fishing station: **Marple.** Roach, perch, carp (up to 20lb) and brown trout. Dt from Lakeside Café.

ROSSMERE LAKE. 6 acres. Fishing station: Wilmslow. Heavily stocked. 80 match pegs. Prince Albert AS.

TABLEY MERE. Fishing station: **Plumley.** Coarse fish, especially carp, tench and perch. Estate Office, Tabley, Knutsford, Cheshire. Information from Lymm AC, who now lease mere and moat. Sec S Griffiths, 18 Manor Rd, Lymm. Tel: Lymm 2763.

THORNEYCROFT HALL LAKES, Gawsworth. Prince Albert AS water. Carp, tench, roach, pike.

Keep the banks clean

Several clubs have stopped issuing tickets to visitors because of the state of the banks after they have left. Spend a few moments clearing up.

COLNE (Essex)

(For close seasons, licences, etc, see Anglian Water Authority, p 14–15)

Rises in north of county and flows to North Sea via Colchester. Improving as coarse fishery.

Colchester (Essex). Colchester APS controls 2½m, roach, chub, perch, pike, bream, dace; no tickets. The society has also **Layer Pits** (6m S; pike, perch, bream, roach, rudd, tench, carp) (members only, restricted to 30m radius). Society also has water on **Stour**, Hatfield Peverell Lakes, Witham Lake and Thorpe Pit. St £18 + £8 entry. Concessions to jun, OAP, disabled. Colchester Piscatorial Society has water on Langham Ponds, Stour and Colne; members only. Belmain AS has water on Stour at Little Horkesley; members only. Birch Hall Lake fished by Kelvedon AA, who now also fish ½m of Colne. *(See also*

Essex streams, lakes and reservoirs.)
Tackleists: Radcliffe, High Street; Wass, Long Wyre Street; Home & Sports Ltd, St Botolph Street. Hotels: George, Red Lion.
Halstead (Essex). Coarse fish, including tench. **Gosfield Hall Lake** (45 acres), well stocked carp, with perch, roach, tench, pike, rudd; dt £2. Also **Sparrows Pond**, Gosfield; coarse fish including carp and tench; Halstead & Hedingham AC members only (st £10) has several miles of Pant, stretch of Colne, from Yeldham to Halstead, 2 reservoirs and pits. Tackleist: E McDowell, High Street. *(See Essex, streams and lakes.)*

COQUET

(For close seasons, etc, see Northumbrian Water Authority, p 14)

Rises in Cheviots and enters North Sea near Warkworth. Salmon, sea trout and trout. Usually a late river. Sport with salmon and sea trout affected by abstraction at Warkworth, but trout fishing still very good. Facilities for visitors restricted.

Warkworth (Northumberland). Trout, sea trout; salmon from Feb onwards to late summer and autumn. Duke of Northumberland leases large part of his water to Northumbrian Anglers' Federation. St £25 salmon, £20 trout; ft £20. Concessions for OAP. Applications to Head Bailiff, Thirston Mill, Felton, Northumberland or tackle dealers.

Acklington (Northumberland). Trout, sea trout and salmon. Northumbrian AF water on Coquet and tributary, Thirston Burn *(see also Felton)*. St (S) £12.50 (T) £6.50, (extra permit £12.50 required for tidal stretch).

Felton (Northumberland). Salmon, sea trout (spring and autumn), trout. Northumbrian A Fedn; permits from Post Office *(see Warkworth)*.

Weldon Bridge (Northumberland). Nearest station: Morpeth, 9½m. Trout (sea trout and salmon, late summer and autumn). Hotel: Anglers' Arms (RD licences).

Rothbury (Northumberland). A late salmon run and excellent sea trout fishing in June and Oct. Brown trout, including fish to 3lb. Northumbrian AF has 4m of Coquet *(see Warkworth)*. Whitton Farm House Hotel, managed by a keen game fisher, offers 2½m to guests. Best months—trout, May, June and Sept; av wt ½lb but fish up to 1¾lb. Salmon and sea-trout, June and Sept/Oct. RD licences at Hotel. Other hotels: Queen's Head and Newcastle. Tackleists: J R Soulsby & Sons, from whom licences and Federation permits can be had.

Holystone (Northumberland). Salmon (late). trout; mostly private. Holystone Burn, trout; Grasslees Burn, trout. Inn: Salmon, where pariculars can be had.

Harbottle (Northumberland). Good trout and some late salmon fishing on Coquet and Alwin. Upper Coquetdale AC has extensive parts of upper river; members only.

CORNWALL (streams, lakes, etc)

(For close seasons, licences, etc, see South West Water Authority, p 12)

The six reservoirs mentioned below are all South West Water Authority waters. Fishing on all of them is by dt from self-service units on site.

ARGAL and COLLEGE RESERVOIRS. (3m W of Falmouth.) **Argal:** 65 acres, fly only for rainbow trout, largest $6\frac{3}{4}$ lb. Season: April 1–Oct 31 incl. Dt £6, evening £4, 5 fish limit, concessions for OAP etc. Boats £5.50 per day, £4 $\frac{1}{2}$ day, bookable in advance. **College:** 38 acres, coarse fishing. St £36, dt £2; 12-month season: all fish to be returned.

STITHIANS RESERVOIR. (3m S of Redruth.) 247 acres. Brown and rainbow trout; fly, spinning, bait fishing zoned. Season Mar 15–Oct 12. St £24, dt £2. 4 fish limit. No boats. Permits from Golden Lion, Menherion.

PORTH RESERVOIR. (4m E of Newquay.) 40 acres, bream, rudd, tench and carp. Season April 1–Oct 31. Dt £2, concessions for OAP etc. Self-service ticket unit.

CROWDY RESERVOIR. (2m E of Camelford.) 115 acres. Brown and rainbow trout; fly, spinning and bait fishing zoned. Season April 15–Oct 12. St £24, dt £2. 4 fish limit. Self-service ticket unit at dam car-park.

SIBLYBACK LAKE. (5m N of Liskeard.) 140 acres. Fly only for stocked rainbow trout. Season April 1–Oct 31. Dt £6 (evenings £4); 5 fish limit; boats £5.50 per day, £4 per $\frac{1}{2}$ day. Self-service ticket unit in car park. Light refreshments available. A public picnic site overlooks the reservoir. Tackleists: A B Harvey, Market Strand; Berks, Arwenack Street, both Falmouth. J Bray, Market Street, Penryn; Central Sports, 2 Crantock Street, Newquay. Botterel & Son, Fore Street, Liskeard. Hotels: Golden Lion, Menherion; Crellow House Hotel, Stithians; Pencubitt Hotel, Liskeard. Details of Falmouth hotels from Town Information Bureau.

COLLIFORD LAKE. (Nr. Liskeard; 900 acres.) Fly fishing for naturally-bred brown trout. St £48, dt £4 (5 fish), concessions for jun, OAP. No boats.

BREAM. Fishing station: **Par.** Heavily polluted, but tributary **Redmoor River** has good head of trout. Sand-eels at Par sands, mackerel from the bay, pollack by Gribben Head and near harbour, and bass between harbour and Shorthorne Beach. Boats for hire at Par and Polkerris. Hotels: Royal, Par; Carlyon Bay, St Austell.

CONSTANTINE BROOK. Fishing station; **Constantine,** ns Penryn WR, 6m. Trout; free on permission of farmers. Constantine joins estuary of **Helford River** (few trout, permission of farmers). Sea fishing off Helford Mouth *(see Falmouth).* Ashton, near **Helston, Wheal Grey Pool;** stocked coarse fishery with large carp. **Boscathnoe Reservoir,** Heamore, near Penzance; stocked coarse fishery. Both Marazion AC waters. Contact hon sec.

DRIFT RESERVOIR. Near **Penzance** (3m) sixty-five acres in quiet valley. Brown and rainbow trout (fly only). St £40, wt £10 and dt £3.50 (half price junior) from Chyandour Estate Office, Penzance (Penzance 3021) or Mr Terry Shorland, Driftways, Drift Dam, Penzance (0736 63869). Also near Penzance are 3 carp pools at **Tindeen Fishery,** dt £1.50, tel: Germoe 3486; **St Buryan Lake** carp pool, tel: St Buryan 220.

GWITHIAN BROOK. Fishing station: **Camborne.** Brook fishes well for trout, especially from Roseworthy down to Red River, but fish run small ($\frac{1}{2}$-pounder would be a good one). Very good beach and rock fishing in area. Club: Camborne AA. Tackleists: The County Angler, Cross Street; Camborne Fishing Centre, 71 Trelowarren Street. Hotels: Golden Lion, Regal, Tyack's.

HAYLE. Fishing stations: **Relubbus, Hayle Causeway** and **Gwinear.** Trout and sea trout; rapidly improving. Good beach fishing near Hayle, and estuary fishing very good, particularly for bass, mullet and flats; plenty of natural bait. Enquiries, Hayle Angling & Trophy Centre, 5 Penpol Terrace.

LOOE. Fishing station: **Liskeard.** Looe River, 1m runs to Sand place and Looe town. Here West Looe River, 8m long, joins on right bank. Good trout fishing; sea trout in July. Liskeard and Dist AC has water on West Looe, East Looe and Inny *(see Lynher below).* St, wt and dt £2. **Shillamill Lakes,** 3 lakes, 6m NW of Looe on B3359. Carp, tench, r trout. J Facey, tel: 0503 20271. Hotels: Ship,

Boscarn. Good sea fishing *(see separate entry)*. *(See also Sea Fishing Stations.)*
LYNHER. Fishing stations: **Liskeard, Callington,** ns Saltash. Lynher holds trout, salmon and peal. Trout run small; pounders now rare. Many stretches owned by Liskeard and District AC (Bathpool to Pillaton Mill). Salmon and peal run right up. Permits for all Liskeard AC water (which includes fisheries on **Fowey, Camel, Seaton** and **Looe, Inny** and **Lynher** Rivers; 30m in all). T from hon sec and tackleists (see below). At Sportsman's Arms, Notter Bridge, Saltash, permits for a small portion can be obtained at a small fee. Siblyback Lake is near. SWWA have carp pool at **Crafthole,** near Saltash; carp, tench; Royal Albert Bridge AC have 2 acre coarse fishing lake at **St Germans.** Hotel: Webb's, Liskeard. Tackleists: Godfreys Stores, Barn Street, Liskeard.
MENALHYL. Newquay. Brown trout. Contact sec, Mawgan AC.
PETHERICK WATER. Fishing station: **Padstow.** Small trout, RD licences from Radford's, Duke St, Padstow (also tackle and bait). Boats available for estuary fishing, which can be excellent for bass, plaice, turbot, ray. Hotels: Dinas, Metropole.
RETALLACK WATERS. St Columb. 7 lakes, 4000 yds coarse fishing; carp, roach, rudd, tench, eels and r and b trout. Dt £2, OAP juv 50%. J M Bazely, tel: St Columb 880052.
ST ALLEN RIVER. Fishing Station: **Truro.** St Allen and Kenwyn Rivers at Truro; Tresillian River (3m from Truro on St Austell road); Kennel or Parranarworthal River (5m from Truro); free on farmer's permission; trout six to the pound; a few sea trout run into **Lower Tresillian** River. Good reservoir trout and coarse fishing at **Argal** and **College,** Penryn; and **Stithians,** Nr Redruth; at

Perranporth, 4 acre carp lake. Contact M Rooth, tel: 0872 572388. Hotel: Royal, Lemon St *(see also Sea Fishing Stations).*
ST AUSTELL RIVER. Fishing station: **St Austell.** Salmon fishing until Dec 15 in Rivers Camel and Fowey. Good sport with bass in bay; boats for hire at Charlestown and Mevagissey. Roche AC has rights in disused china clay pits; trout, coarse fish; wt and dt. Inquiries to tackleists. Hotels: White Hart, Rashleigh Arms at Charlestown; Carylon Bay and Cliff Head at Carlyon Bay.
SEATON RIVER. Fishing station: **Menheniot.** Seaton rises N of Liskeard, runs 1m E of the town and to the sea in 9m. Good trout stream, though bushed over. Fishing by permission from landowners, although Liskeard and Dist AC has considerable stretch. St £20, wt £9, dt £2 on all waters.
TAMAR LAKE (LOWER). Fishing station: **Kilkhampton** (Bude 5m). 40 acres. Coarse fishing for carp, tench, rudd, bream and dace. A South West Water Authority water. St £24, dt (from self-service unit at reservoir) £2. No boats. Tackleists: Weys of Bude, Queen Street.
TAMAR LAKE (UPPER). 81 acres. Rainbow trout: fly only. Season Apr 1–Oct 31. SWWA water. Dt (from self-service unit at reservoir dam) £6, evenings £4. 5 fish limit. Concessions for OAP etc. Boats £5.50 per day, £4 per $\frac{1}{2}$ day. Boat for disabled. Tackle for hire, but not on Thursdays and Fridays. Picnic area and refreshment kiosk. Tackleist: Fishing Tackle Shop, 13 Lower Lux Street.
TIDDY. Fishing station: **St Germans.** Sea trout to Tideford, trout elsewhere; free on permission of farmers. Accommodation at Blue Cap Hotel.
VALENCY. Fishing station: **Boscastle.** Valency is 4m long; holds small trout and few sea trout. Hotels: Wellington, in Boscastle (RD licences); Eliot Arms, Tregadillet 15m. Sea fishing good for bass, mackerel, pollack, etc.

CUCKMERE

(For close seasons, licences, etc, see Southern Water Authority, p 11–12)

Formed by two tributaries, which join at Hellingly, and enters sea at Cuckmere Haven, west of Beachy Head. Mainly coarse fish, river closely preserved where any good.

Alfriston (Sussex). St £15 (OAP, juv £7), for both banks from Berwick to Alfriston from the Compleat Angler FC, or any

Eastbourne tackle shop. Dt £1 for enclosed waters for visitors. Below Alfriston Lock the river is salt and tidal, being open to mouth at Cuckmere Haven. In summer grey mullet are plentiful near Exceat Bridge (Eastbourne –Seaford road); also bass and occasionally sea trout. Cuckmere is tidal to $\frac{1}{2}$m upstream from Alfriston.

Berwick (Sussex). Water held by Compleat Angler FC *(see Alfriston)*.

Hailsham (Sussex). Cuckmere 2m. Hailsham AA has several stretches containing roach, perch, pike, bream and tench.

At Hempstead Farm, dace, chub and bream may be taken. Some trout at Broad Farm, **Hellingly**. Hailsham AA also has water on **Pevensey Haven, Wallers Haven** and **Chilley Stream** *(see Pevensey Levels)*, Abbots Lake ($3\frac{1}{2}$ acres) **Arlington**, Hackhurst Lake, Lower Dicker, St £15, ft £4, dt £1.50, from Hailsham AA hon sec or local tackle dealers.

CUMBRIA (lakes)

(See English Lake District, p 46)

CUMBRIA (streams)

(For close seasons, licences, etc, see NW Water Authority, p 13–14, unless otherwise stated)

ANNAS. Fishing station: **Bootle**. Small trout; good sea trout and salmon; late. Millom AA has fishing. Also water on **Esk, Lickle, Irt** and **Lazy**. St £40 from hon sec Millom & Dist AA. RD licences from D Scott, Post Office, Bootle; Silecroft Post Office and Wadesons, Market Square, Millom. Accommodation at Close Cottage.

BLACK BECK. Fishing station: **Green Road.** This stream rises on Thwaites Fell, and in $7\frac{1}{2}$m reaches Duddon Estuary. Millom AA has water; permission also from riparian owners. (Lancashire RD.)

CALDER. Empties into Irish Sea some 150 yards from mouth of Ehen. Salmon, sea trout, brown trout. Sea trout run large; 10lb and more. Best June onwards; salmon July–Oct. Brown trout sport improving.

Calderbridge (Cumbria). Calder AA owns Calder Abbey Estate waters and the whole of the Lord Egremont Estate water on the upper reaches of the Calder and **Wormgill**. Approx 5m in all. Visitor's st £20, local juv £10 (includes fishing on **Ennerdale Water).** Twenty only issued pa; apply to hon sec Calder AA. *(For tackleist see Egremont.)*

EHEN. Outflow of Ennerdale Water. Flows into Irish Sea on west coast of Cumberland. Salmon, sea trout (June to Oct) and brown trout. At **Egremont** the local anglers' assn has about 8m of good salmon and sea trout fishing; st £20, wt £10; May 1–Oct 31; apply hon sec or tackleist. Hotels: Black Beck, Egremont

and Sea Cote (St Bees); Scawfell, Seascale. Good fishing in upper reaches held by Wath Brow and Ennerdale AA; st and wt. Tackleist: W Holmes, Main Street, Egremont. *(For Ennerdale Water see English Lake District, Cumbria.)*

ELLEN. Rises on Great Lingy Hill and flows into the Solway Firth at Maryport. Salmon and sea trout runs increasing; best late July onwards. Good brown trout fishing (Mar–June best).

Maryport (Cumbria). Trout; sea trout, salmon. Local club: Ellen AA, which has water. Tickets and licences (st, dt) from R Thompson (tackleist), 127 Crosby Street (information on river and sea fishing; boats) and Scott's, Aspatria. Hotels: Golden Lion; Waverley.

Aspatria (Cumbria). Trout; sea trout, and salmon from early Sept. Club: Aspatria AC; permits £13.50 to £3 from R & J Holt, The Colour Shop. Hotels: Grapes, Sun.

ESK. Rises near Scawfell and flows into Irish Sea near Ravenglass. Good runs of salmon, sea trout, July onwards.

Ravenglass (Cumbria). Salmon, sea trout. Rivers Mite and Irt here join Esk estuary *(see also Irt)*. Ravenglass; Millom AA has 620 yds south bank on Esk. St £40. Outward Bound School, Eskdale Green, has brown and rainbow trout fishing in private tarn (also perch). Limited to specific days. Enquiries to Bursar (Eskdale 281). May and June are best for trout; June, July, Aug for sea trout; Sept, Oct for salmon. *(See also Eskdale.)*

A nice bag of fine winter grayling taken on trotted redworm. These were caught from a small tributary of the Derbyshire Derwent, but grayling are found in fast-flowing clean rivers in most parts of Gt. Britain S. of the Scottish Highlands. *Photo: Bruno Broughton, who also caught the fish.*

Hotel: Pennington Arms where licences are sold and help given in arranging fishing locally.

Eskdale (Cumbria); ns Drigg, 5m—Trout; sea trout, salmon; various private owners. Inexpensive fishing on **Wastwater** and **Burnmoor Tarn**. Good sea fishing (especially for bass) within five miles.
IRT. Outflow of Wastwater, joining Esk in tidal water. **Bleng** is main tributary. Good runs of salmon and sea trout July onwards, some heavy fish taken.
Gosforth. Gosforth AC has 3m, mostly both banks; members only.
Holmrook (Cumbria). Salmon, sea trout, brown trout. Lutwidge Arms Hotel has sold its rights to $1\frac{1}{2}$m stretch east of Holmrook to Sporting Tribune. It is advisable to book in advance. Wt £60, dt £10, from Bridge Garage, Holmrook. Tel: 0940 4247. Lutwidge Arms Hotel will give information to anglers. Millom AA holds two stretches, Holme Bridge and Drigg Village; members only *(see River Duddon)*. Tackleist: E W Mitchell & Son. RD licences also from Wadeson's (newsagent), Market Square, Millom.
Netherwastdale (Cumbria). On **Wastwater Lake**; trout, permits *(see English Lake District)*. RWA licence from YHA caravan site, Gosforth. Greendale Tarn and Low Tarn feed Wastwater. Sport is good in May and June.
MITE. Flows south for short course from slopes near Eskdale to join estuary of Irt

and Esk at **Ravenglass**. A late river. Sea trout, good brown trout but small, occasional salmon later on, but few opportunities for visitors.

WAMPOOL. Fishing stations: **Wigton** and **Curthwaite**. Wampool, under the name of Chalk Beck, rises on Broad Moor. Sea trout in lower reaches mostly free. *(For licences see Waver.)*
WAVER. Trout stream, flowing into the Solway Firth. Some water free, but most subject to agreement by farmers and landowners. RWA licence may be obtained from L Saunderson (Ironmongers), King Street, **Wigton**. Waver has run of sea trout and herling, particularly in its lower reaches.
Abbey Town (Cumbria). Crummock Beck; some free, but local knowledge needed.
Wigton (Cumbria). Wiza Beck, Wampool, 2m N. Waver, 2m W. Ellen, 8m SW. Lakes: Moorhouse Tarn, 2m N (private). Tackleist: Saunderson (Ironmongers), King Street. Hotels: Royal Oak and Kildare.

CRUMMOCK BECK (tributary of Waver). Flows into Holm Dub, tributary of Waver. Free, but difficult to fish. *(For licences see Waver.)*
Leegate (Cumbria). Waver, 1m E.

WHICHAM BECK. Fishing station: **Silecroft**. After a course of 6m runs into Haverigg Pool, which joins Duddon estuary at Haverigg (NWWA).

DARENT

(For close seasons, licences, etc, see Southern Water Authority, p 11–12)

Rises by Westerham and enters Thames estuary at Dartford. Small Kentish stream once famous for its trout. Fishing destroyed early in present century by pollution. River was restocked with trout by Kent RA and sport improving.

Dartford (Kent). Dartford and Dist A & PS have pits along river valley which hold coarse fish, including carp and tench. Hotel: Bull.
Otford (Kent). Trout, perch, roach, dace. Darent Valley Trout Fishers have good stretch of water nearly up to Shoreham; strictly private and members only (waiting list). Holmesdale AS has junior water.
Shoreham (Kent). Trout, perch, roach, dace. Now strictly preserved.

Sevenoaks (Kent). River preserved.
Sundridge Lakes, nr Westerham, 5 and 15 acres, stocked with large carp, roach, and limited numbers of pike. St £57.50; inquire Geoffrey Bucknall, Rod & Line Ltd, 70/72 Loampit Vale, Lewisham. **Longford Lake:** private water of Holmesdale AS. Day tickets issued only to members' friends. Bromley (Kent) and Dist AS has Kent Sand Pits, Sevenoaks, and trout water on Darent; members only. *(See also Kent lakes and streams.)*

Tributary of the Darent

CRAY: Coarse fish.
Crayford (Kent). Free fishing at Five Arches. Thameside AS has Cray; bream, roach, perch, rudd, pike; members only. They also have a lake at Northfleet and Shorne Country Park lakes. Coarse fish.

members only; no dt. **Ruxley Pits, Orpington:** coarse fish; Orpington AA has lakes in a Nature Reserve. No dt. Waiting list for membership. Tackleist: Orpington Angling Suppliers, 304 High Street, St Mary Cray.

DART

(For close seasons, licences, etc, see South West Water Authority, p 12)

Rises in centre of Dartmoor and at once divides into two, the East and West Dart. East Dart runs to Postbridge and thence to Dartmeet, where it unites with West Dart, which flows through Two Bridges. The West Dart above Dartmeet and the East Dart above Walla Brook, including tributaries, belong to Duchy of Cornwall. The river has runs of salmon and peal (sea trout). Best months for salmon are April and May in the lower reaches and May to September higher up. For peal July to September are favoured.

Dartmouth (Devon). Sea fishing from boats and rocks; pollack, bass, mackerel, bream, plaice, brill, turbot, dabs, pouting, conger, whiting, wrasse, garfish and shad, mullet in tidal water. Excellent sport at The Skerries; large turbot. Club: Dartmouth & Dist AA. Salmon, peal and trout fishing in Dart on Dart AA water *(see Totnes, Buckfastleigh)* and a trout reservoir. Lake; Slapton Ley; pike, rudd, etc, 8m *(see Devonshire, small streams and lakes)*. Also, **Old Mill,** SWAA carp pool, dt Sportsmans Rendezvous. Tackleists: Sportsman's Rendezvous, 16 Fairfax Place, Sea Haven, Newcomen Road; Bosun's Locker, Bayard's Cove. Hotels: Castle, Raleigh, Manor House, Seven Stars, etc.

Totnes (Devon). Salmon, peal, trout. Dart AA controls most of left bank from just above Totnes to $\frac{1}{2}$m below Buckfastleigh. Tickets with maps of water, from Blake Sports, 73 Fore Street (who also caters for bass and mullet anglers in Totnes tidal reaches). 6-day tickets available from June 1, but only to visitors resident outside Devon. (No Sunday fishing) St (S) £105 (MT) £47.50 (NT) £25. wt (S) £20 (MT) £15 (NT) £10. After June 1, wt (S) £5, (NT) £2. Dt for weir pool, £5. Salmon av 10lb; peal $2\frac{1}{2}$lb in May–June and about 1lb thereafter. 4lb and 5lb peal not rare. School peal run from late June to mid-Aug. Nearly all peal caught after dark in normal conditions; Aug usually best. Fly only for peal and trout (latter run 3 or 4 to lb). *Note UDN has marred sport.* Hotels:

Seymour, Royal Seven Stars and Cott Inn (at Darlington). At Staverton, near Totnes, is the Sea Trout Inn, right by the river. Old Mill, Harberton, has $\frac{1}{2}$m trout fishing on **River Harbourne.**

Buckfastleigh (Devon). Salmon, peal, trout. Dart AA has most of left bank from Austin's Bridge down. *(For ticket conditions and details of fish see under Totnes.)* Tickets and maps of water from The Sports Shop, 36 Fore Street, Buckfastleigh; Blakes Sports Shop, Totnes; also from Percy Hodge Ltd, 104 Queen Street, Newton Abbot. Holne Chase Hotel, near Ashburton, has about 1m right bank upstream from bridge free to residents. Limited st, £75, and dt £8, to non-residents. Fishing on Duchy of Cornwall waters arranged for guests. Fly only. Five holding pools. Permits also from Black Rock Guest House; Bossell Guest House (tuition available); Dart Bridge Farm.

Princetown (Devon). Permits for salmon and trout fishing on main river, **East and West Dart, Wallabrook, Swincombe** and **Cherrybrook** from The Land Steward, Duchy of Cornwall Office, Bowhill, Bradninch, Exeter and most tackleists in S Devon, also the Forest Inn, Hexworthy. Two Bridges Hotel, Princetown, OLW Sports Shop, Buckfastleigh, Yelverton and Princetown Post Office. Salmon best May–Sept. Charges: S and MT, st £45, wt £20, dt £5, T, st £20, mt £4, wt 75p. Accommodation: Tavistock Inn, Poundsgate.

Hexworthy (Devon); ns Tavistock or Newton Abbot. Salmon, sea trout (peal), brown trout. Hotel: Forest Inn; tickets,

d, w or s, at hotel, for Duchy of Cornwall water; good centre for E and W Dart and Cherrybrook.

DEBEN

(For close seasons, licences, etc, see Anglian Water Authority, p 14–15)

Short Suffolk river (about 30 miles long) rising near Debenham and flowing to North Sea near Felixstowe. Coarse fishing.

Woodbridge (Suffolk). Tidal. Roach, pike, tench, perch above town. Club: Woodbridge and Dist AC, who also have Loam Pond, Sutton, and Holton Pit; st £10, dt £1.50, from tackleist or Saxmundham Angling Centre or Anglia

Photographics, Halesworth. Tackleist: Rod & Gun Shop, Church St. Hotels: Bull, Crown.

Wickham Market (Suffolk). Roach, perch, pike. Woodbridge AC water; apply hon sec.

DERWENT (Cumbria)

(For close seasons, licences, etc, see North West Water Authority, p 13–14)

Rises on north side of Scawfell and flows through Borrowdale, Derwentwater and Bassenthwaite Lakes to the Solway Firth at Workington. Salmon and trout practically throughout length. A late river. Best months for salmon, July to October. Trout fishing on some stretches excellent. River also holds pike and perch.

Cockermouth to **Workington** (Cumbria). Salmon, sea trout, brown trout. Trout and salmon fishing may occasionally be permitted on dt. Enquiries to Fishery Manager, Cockermouth Castle. Permit charges under review. Permits for **Cocker** also (limited). Waters through town can be fished on permit from Tourist Information Office by residents and visitors staying locally on weekly basis. Cockermouth AA has water on **Cocker** (members only) but issues dt £5 for **Cogra Moss. Mockerkin Tarn,** stocked with carp. Wt and dt from The Gun Shop, Lorton St. Fishing within reach on Bassenthwaite, Loweswater, Crummock and Buttermere. Other tackleists: D Lothian, main St (information re Cocker fishing) and N H Temple, 9 Station Street, Keswick; both issue licences and permits, and will give information. Workington tackleist: Simpson's Sports, 1 South William Street. Hotels: Trout, Globe, Cockermouth Pheasant, Bassenthwaite Lake, Sun, Bassenthwaite.

Brigham (Cumbria). Trout, sea trout, salmon. Broughton Working Men's AA has about 1m from here to Broughton Cross. Permits to local working men only.

Bassenthwaite (Cumbria). Derwent, 1m N; trout, salmon; private. Lakes: Bassenthwaite; pike, perch. trout, occasional salmon *(see English Lake District—Bassenthwaite)*. Hotels: Swan, Pheasant, Armathwaite Hall.

Keswick (Cumbria). For rivers Derwent and Greta. Salmon, trout (average ¼lb); mid-August onwards for salmon. Permits for Keswick AA water (Threlkeld to Bassenthwaite). Visitors Salmon st £39, wt £28, dt £8. Trout permit includes Derwentwater, wt £5, dt £1 (reductions for juniors all fishing) from Temple Sports, Station Street and Field and Stream, Main Street, Keswick. Tickets issued for Derwent cover **Greta** also. *(See following page.)* Hotels: Hazeldene, Queen's Royal Oak, Lake, George, County King's Arms. The Derwentwater Hotel. Permit charges subject to annual revue.

Borrowdale (Cumbria). Trout, salmon; gin-clear as a rule and best fished after dark. Lakes: Derwentwater; trout, perch, pike; small charge for fishing. Watendlath Tarn 2m S; Blea Tarn, 4m S; trout. Hotels: Scawfell; Borrowdale; Lodore Swiss.

It's never too young to start. The late Frank Swayer gives a six-year-old her first lesson. The scene — a Game Fair. Game Fairs, covering all field sports, do their round of the country year by year. *Photograph: John Tarlton.*

Tributaries of the Derwent (Cumbria)

COCKER: Salmon, sea trout, trout. July to October best for migratory fish. Mostly private, but dt for Cockermouth AA water (and for **Loweswater, Butteremere** and **Crummock Water**) from The Gun Shop, Lorton Street, Cockermouth.

Scalehill (Cumbria). Cockermouth. 7m Cocker: Salmon, sea trout, trout. Private. National Trust lakes: **Crummock Water**; pike, trout, char. **Loweswater**, 2m W; pike, trout. **Buttermere**, 4m (see below). April, May best for trout in Loweswater; June and July in Crummock and Buttermere. St, dt and boats. For **Loweswater** and north end of Crummock and Buttermere. St from Shop, Loweswater. Hotel: Scale Hill.

Cogra Moss. 40 acre trout reservoir 8m S of Cockermouth. Browns and rainbows. St £55 (jun £33), wt £15, dt £5. Season April 1–Sept 30. From The Gun Shop, Lorton Street, D W Lothian, Main Street, Cockermouth; Inglenook Caravan Park, Lamplugh.

Buttermere (Cumbria). National Trust property. Char, trout, pike; tickets, boats, as for Loweswater (above); for Buttermere and south end of Crummock apply Buttermere Stores. Trust permit covers all three lakes.

NEWLANDS BECK: Trout.

Braithwaite (Cumbria); ns Keswick, 2m. Beck; fishable above Braithwaite, ruined by dredging below.

GRETA: Trout (av $\frac{1}{4}$lb); salmon. **Threlkeld** (Cumbria). Keswick AA increased their holdings in 1980 *(tickets, see Keswick)*. Best months for salmon Sept and Oct; mostly spinning and worm fishing. St. John's Beck from Thirlmere is best from lake for $1\frac{1}{2}$m and from Wanthwaite Bridge to New Bridge; between is canalised; trout. Glenderamackin Beck; trout; fishable throughout length, but fish few and far between.

DEVONSHIRE (streams and lakes)

(For close seasons, etc, see SW Water Authority, p 12, unless otherwise stated)*

AVON. Rises on Dartmoor and flows 22m SE, entering English Channel near Thurlestone via long, twisting estuary. Tide flows to Aveton Gifford. Trout (3 or 4lb), sea trout, salmon.

Thurlestone (Devon). Near mouth of Avon estuary. Capital bass fishing off Bantham Sands at mouth.

Aveton Gifford (Devon). About $6\frac{1}{4}$m of left bank and $8\frac{1}{4}$m of right bank, 1m both banks above Gara Bridge, $\frac{1}{2}$m left bank only below Gara Bridge controlled by Avon FA. Sea trout (end of May onwards), some salmon; good dry-fly trout water (3 to the lb). Banks heavily wooded; good wading. Mt £36, wt £18.50, from hon sec, post office at Loddiswell; P O'Neil, 55 Church Street, Kingsbridge and J E Coombes, 19 Stella Road, Preston, Paignton.

Kingsbridge (Devon). Avon, $2\frac{1}{2}$m N at **Loddiswell**; trout, salmon, sea trout. Futher information from hon sec Avon FA *(see also Aveton Gifford)*. Capital bass and pollack in Kingsbridge estuary. Tackleist: Perrott Bros, 26 Fore Street. Hotels: King's Arms; Buttville; Torcross (for Slapton Ley).

Brent (Devon). Salmon, trout, sea trout. Avon FA water below *(see Aveton Gif-*

ford). Mrs J Theobald, Little Aish Riding Stables, South Brent, issues dt for stretch of Aish Woods. Red Brook, 2m N; trout. Black Brook, 2m S; trout. Hotel: Anchor.

AVON DAM (8m NE of Totnes). Brown trout, zoned worm, spinning and fly fishing free to SWWA licence-holders. No boats. Season March 15–Oct 12. Reservoir is about $1\frac{1}{2}$m beyond **Shipley Bridge**, car park available.

BELLBROOK VALLEY TROUT FISHERY, Oakford, Tiverton EX16 9EX. Two small lakes and three large pools, stocked with r trout to 13lb. Dt £7 plus £1.25/lb fish caught. $\frac{1}{2}$ day £4 plus same. Accommodation at fishery farmhouse. Tel: 03985 292. *(Advt below.)*

BURRATOR RESERVOIR, Yelverton. 150 acres. Zoned fly fishing and spinning for brown and rainbow trout. Dt £2, st £24 (concessions for OAP and Jun) from R Timms, Burrator House, Burrator, Yelverton; or D K Sports, 88 Vauxhall Street, Plymouth.

ERME. Rises on Dartmoor and flows 14m S to Bigbury Bay. Trout.

Ivybridge. Fishing now restricted to local young people only.

Bellbrook Valley Trout Fishery

OPEN ALL YEAR! FISH FOR TOP QUALITY RAINBOWS IN OUR IDYLLIC VALLEY FROM 5 SMALL LAKES

THE CREAM OF DEVON'S FISHERIES

First class accommodation provided in 17th century farmhouse. *Details from* **Peter & Margaret Swaby, Bellbrook Farm, Oakford, Tiverton, Devon. Tel: (03985) 292.**

FERNWORTHY RESERVOIR, near **Chagford.** South West Water Authority. 76 acres, b trout; May 1–Oct 12. Dt £7.50 (evenings £4.50). Boat £5.50 (evenings £4). 4 fish limit; concessions to OAP and Jun. Self-service unit by hut on S side of reservoir.

GAMMATON, and **JENNETS RESERVOIRS, Bideford** *(see Bideford).*

MELDON RESERVOIR (3m SE of Okehampton). Brown and rainbow trout. Spinning, bait and fly fishing free to SWWA licence holders. Season March 15–Sept 30.

LYN, near Lynmouth (Devon). Ns **Barnstaple** or **Minehead.** This beautiful river has good run of salmon, July onwards. Also sea trout and brown trout; latter small. Season March 1–Oct 31. For SWWA stretch, 4m between Lynmouth and Brendon, S & MT: st £100, wt £16, dt £5. T: st £12.50, wt £4.20, dt £1, from Mrs Christelow, Combe Park Lodge, Lynton; Williams, Lower Bourne House, High St, Porlock; The Pet Shop, Lynton; Pilesports, Lynmouth. Mrs Lester, Glebe House, Brendon, issues dt for 3m (both banks) of East Lyn. Other contacts for East Lyn fishing are Simpkins, Rockford Inn, Brendon; Rising Sun Hotel, Lynmouth; Doone Valley Riding Stables, Brendon. Tackliests: A J Holman, The Avenue Post Office. Frances Sully, Sports Outfitter, The Parade, Minehead. *(See also Sea Fishing Stations.)*

PLYM. Devon trout stream which enters English Channel at Plymouth. (Cornwall RD.)

Plymouth (Devon). On Plym and Tavy. Trout, sea trout and salmon in Tavy, but Plym now mainly a trout stream. Plymouth and Dist Freshwater AA has short stretch of Plym; two dt per day £3 (Mon-Fri) for Plym Bridge upstream from D K Sports, The Barbican, Plymouth. (Tel: 663483), remainder of river private except for portion above Bickleigh Bridge, controlled by Tavy, Walkham and Plym FC. Club issues tickets (salmon, sea trout, brown trout) for its water *(see Tamar–Tavy).* **Burrator Reservoir** (13m); trout; tickets *(see separate entry).* Sea fishing excellent *(see Sea Fishing Stations and Cornwall, streams, lakes, etc.)*

MEAVY (tributary of the Plym). Fishing stations: **Shaugh** and **Clearbrook.**

OAREWATER, Brendon. Trout, Dt and wt from W Burge, Oaremead.

SID, Sidmouth. Trout. For details, contact SW Water Authority.

SLADE RESERVOIRS, Ilfracombe. In **Upper Slade** and **Lower Slade,** coarse fishing for carp, tench, bream, roach and perch. St £24, £12, £6; dt £2 from Lee Road Post Office, Slade, Ilfracombe.

SLAPTON LEY, ns **Dartmouth,** 7m; Kingsbridge, 8m. Pike, roach, eel and perch. Part of nature reserve, bank fishing prohibited. For boats (£7 per day approx) apply Field Centre, Slapton Village (Kingsbridge 580466). Half-day rates also offered. Life-jackets available, compulsory for anglers under 16 years of age. Excellent sea fishing for bass, turbot, plaice, brill and large whiting. Hotels: The Torcross and (in Slapton) the Tower Inn. Many guest houses.

SQUABMOOR RESERVOIR. Ns E Budleigh. Bait fishing for coarse fish. St £24, dt £2 from Knowle post office and Exmouth Tackle and Sports, 20 The Strand, Exmouth.

STAFFORD MOOR FISHERY, Winkleigh EX19 8RQ. Two lakes of fourteen acres and eight acres; regularly stocked with rainbow trout. A new pond, $1\frac{1}{2}$ acres, to be stocked with fish in excess of 3 lb. Tackle, flies, on sale. Dt £10, £8, £4.50, at fishery. Tel: 08054 360; house, 371/363.

KENNICK and TOTTIFORD RESERVOIRS. (8m NE of Newton Abbot.) 45 and 35 acres. Rainbow trout. Fly only. £6, evenings £4.50. 5 fish limit. Season: April 1–Oct 31. No boats. Tickets from self-service unit on site.

VENFORD RESERVOIR. Ns Hexworthy. Brown, and rainbow trout. Spinning and bubble-float fishing, free to SWWA licence-holders. Season: March 15–Sept 30.

WISTLANDPOUND RESERVOIR, Arlington. Brown trout. Fly only. Apr 1–Oct 31. Dt £7.50, evenings £4.50. Concessions to OAP and Jun, from self-service unit at reservoir.

YEALM. Rises on southern heights of Dartmoor and flows 12m south and west to English Channel, which it enters by a long estuary. Trout, sea trout (about 6–8 lb), occasional late salmon. Fishing private. Good bass and pollack in estuary (Cornwall RD).

Newton Ferrers (Devon). On estuary. One of finest deep-sea fishing stations in south-west. Hotel: River Yealm. *(See sea fishing section.)*

DORSET (streams)

(For close seasons, licences, etc, see Wessex Water Authority, p 13)

BRIT AND ASKER. Fishing station: **Bridport.** Trout. Rivers mostly private or overgrown, but Civil Service Sports Council has stretch of Brit for members only. Also **Radipole Lakes;** dt for latter; coarse fish. Tickets from Weymouth tackleists. Dt for **Osmington Mills Lake** (carp and tench) from tackleist: Lawrie Rathbone (Tel: 0308 23475), Tackle Shop, West Bay, Bridport *(see also Sea Fishing Stations).*

BLAKEWELL FISHERY. 1m E. Barnstaple. Brown and rb. trout av. $1\frac{1}{4}$lb. Dt £10.50, $\frac{1}{2}$ dt £6. 4 fish and 2 fish limits.

CHAR. Fishing station: Charmouth. Char is some 7m long; trout, private, but leave may sometimes be obtained. General sea fishing. Hotels: Coach and Horses, Queen's Arms, Hammons Mead.

CORFE. Rises 1m W of Corfe Castle (ns Wareham, $4\frac{1}{2}$m), and runs into Poole Harbour 5m down. Coarse fishing sometimes available from landowners.

DURHAM (reservoirs)

DERWENT. Edmundbyers. May 1–Oct 14, 1,000 acre trout water run by Sunderland & South Shields Water Co, 29 John Street, Sunderland. Well stocked with 2-year-old brown rainbow trout (av $\frac{3}{4}$lb); fly only. St (from company) £145. Dt £5, obtainable on site. Motor boats £13, rowing boats £6.50. RD licence required. Tel:

Edmundbyers 55250 for boat bookings. Hotel: Lord Crewe Arms. **Note:** *Reservoir also partly in Northumberland.*

SMIDDY SHAW, and WASKERLEY. Good trouting, preserved by North-West Durham AA. Season April 1–Sept 30. No dt. Nearest towns: **Wolsingham, Consett** and **Stanhope.**

EDEN

(For close seasons, licences, etc, see North West Water Authority, p 13–14)

Rises south of Kirkby Stephen and empties into Solway Firth 5m NW of Carlisle. Salmon, sea trout, brown trout. Still some spring fish, but now more a back-end river. Sea trout in lower and middle reaches and tributaries from June onwards. Trouting best in middle and upper reaches, fish run to good average size for north. Chub and grayling in parts.

Carlisle (Cumbria). Salmon in spring and autumn, sea trout and herling in July and August, brown trout fair, some chub and dace. Carlisle AA has 7m on Eden. S, st (limited) £25, wt £12.50, dt £5. T, st £10, wt

£4.50, dt £1. Tickets (and RD licences) from tackleists: Raine, 21 Warwick Road; McHardy's, South Henry Street; Carlisle Angling Centre, 105 Lowther Street. Inquire Mrs Elwes, Warwick Hall,

Warwick-on-Eden, for salmon and trout fishing. Hotels: Crown and Mitre, Central, Hilltop.

Wetheral (Cumbria). Salmon and sea trout preserved for 4m to 5m by the Yorkshire Fly-fishers' Club here and at Great Corby; Cairn Beck, 2m, Irthing, 3m N. Scotby Beck, 2m W at Scotby. Hotel: Crown.

Armathwaite (Cumbria). Salmon, trout, grayling. Croglin Waters, 3m E.

Lazonby (Cumbria). Salmon, trout and grayling. A private shooting and fishing lodge with restricted licence, Bracken Bank Lodge (Tel: 241), has three good stretches on Eden for its guests (salmon and trout) at Great Salkeld, Little Salkeld and Syke Foot, with some fine pools. Trout average $\frac{1}{2}$lb. Also good beck fishing and sport in moorland streams. Good shooting (especially grouse driving) may also be had by guests at Bracken Bank. Details sent on application to the proprietor. R N Burton. St £200, upper river wt (S) £25, (T) £20, Dt (S) £5, (T) £3.50. Lower river, 15 Jan–30 Apr wt £75, dt £17.25 (S), £5.75 (T). Apart from st these charges are for residents, all excluding VAT.

Great Salkeld (Cumbria). Fetherston Arms Hotel, Kirkoswald, has $2\frac{1}{2}$m (Lazonby 284). High Drove Inn has salmon and trout fishing; salmon 75p day, trout 50p.

Langwathby (Cumbria). Salmon, trout; preserved by Yorkshire FFC.

Culgaith (Cumbria). Trout; preserved by Yorkshire FFC from Culgaith to below Langwathby apart from vicinity of Watersmeet. Winderwath, left bank; now Penrith AA from Eden Bridge, Temple Sowerby *(see also Temple Sowerby)*; mt from hon sec. Eller Beck, 1m S Eamont, 4m W Tees, 6m NE. Trout, private. Hotels: Black Swan, Culgaith, King's Arms, Temple Sowerby.

Temple Sowerby (Cumbria). Salmon, trout, grayling; preserved (with some miles of Eamont) by Yorkshire FFC; members only. Penrith AA (with 45m of fishing in all) has $1\frac{1}{4}$m down from Eden Bridge on left bank *(see also Culgaith)*. Wt and st issued at various prices for different stretches. Eller Beck, 1m W. Lyvennet; trout, preserved as Eden. King's Arms Hotel has trout fishing for guests on $1\frac{1}{2}$m of Eden; licences and tickets available at hotel; trout average 1lb.

Kirkby Thore (Cumbria). Salmon, trout and grayling. Penrith AA preserves 2m on main river and Kirkby Thore Beck from road bridge 1m upstream.

Appleby (Cumbria). Eden trout are very free risers, averaging about three to pound with better fish to 3 and even 4lb. Ample accommodation available at Tufton Arms also at White Hart, Glen, Royal Oak, Courtfield, Appleby Manor, Crown and Cushion Inn. Tickets £8 for Upper Appleby fishings from John Pape *(see below)*. Brown trout, fly only. Sedge fishing in evenings good May to August. Grayling provide good winter sport. 14m of Assn water; but membership full, no guest tickets. Licences and local flies from John Pape, Appleby Shoe & Sports Supplies, Market Place.

Kirkby Stephen (Cumbria). Kirkby Stephen and Dist AA has about 20m on main river and becks, fly only. *(See Belah and Scandal tributaries.)* Visitors' st £35 from hon sec. Dt £5 from Robinson, Silver Street (waiting list for membership). Thornaby AA has "Outhgill" ($1\frac{1}{2}$m), White Bracken ($\frac{1}{2}$m) and Stenkrith ($\frac{1}{2}$m) stretches; trout only (3 to lb); members only *(see Thornaby under Tess)*. Hotel: King's Arms. Licences from Newsagent, 46 Market St. Tackleist: H S Robinson.

Tributaries of the Eden

PETTERIL joins Eden at Carlisle. Good trout fishing, but lower half mostly private. Penrith AA has 10m of water on upper reaches.

Plumpton (Cumbria). Trout. Penrith AA preserves from Kettleside Farm to Petteril Bank.

IRTHING. Rises on Grey Fell Common and joins Eden east of Carlisle. Salmon, trout, grayling and few sea trout.

Brampton (Cumbria). Irthing; 1m N; Gelt, 1m S; trout, grayling, chub. Brampton AS preserves; st (£14), wt (£10), dt (£4) and RWA licence from Mrs G Graham, Moat St, Brampton. Trout average $\frac{1}{2}$ to$\frac{3}{4}$lb, early months best. Kingwater, 2m N. Cambeck, $1\frac{1}{2}$m N, Eden 5m W; salmon, trout; preserved. Lakes: Talkin Tarn, 2m SE; pike, perch. Tindale Tarn, 6m SE; pike, perch, trout. Hotels: White

Lion, Scotch Arms, Sand House, Howard Arms. Tackleist: W Warwick, Front Street.

EAMONT flows from Ullswater Lake. A good grayling water. Penrith AA has most of this water. Lake Ullswater good trout fishing; free, but RWA licence required.

Penrith (Cumbria). Eamont, 1m S; salmon, trout. Upper portion (trout only) preserved by Penrith AA (fly only) from Pooley Bridge on left bank to Yanwath Viaduct, and on right bank from Pooley Bridge to Yanwath Wood. Also on **Eden, Lowther** and on becks. £30 wt covers a variety of fishings. Yorkshire Flyfishers preserve left bank of Eamont from Broughton Castle down to Barrack Bank and then on left bank only to below Udford; members only. Other water on Eamont private. Lakes: Ullswater, 5m S; trout; free to licence holders. **Haweswater,** 10m SE; rights in hands of North West Water Authority, and guests at Haweswater Hotel, Mardale, Bampton, near Penrith, may obtain permits at hotel (see Westmorland lakes). Crown & Mitre Hotel, Bampton Grange, has 8m of salmon and trout fishing on Eden and tributaries available to residents. Other hotels: Crown, George, Gloucester Arms, Kings Arms, Edenhall, near Langwathby. Licences from tackleists: S Norris, 21 Victoria Road or C R Sykes, 4 Great Dockray, both Penrith; or Langwathby PO.

Pooley Bridge (Cumbria). Eamont; salmon, trout. Penrith AA water *(see Penrith).* Ullswater; good trout fishing; only RD licence needed; boats available *(see also Patterdale).* Hotels: Sun, Crown.

Patterdale (Cumbria). The becks Goldrill, Grisedale, Deepdale and Hartsop; free. Aira Force below NT property (3m) free. N Hawes and Riggindale Becks, permits N West Water Authority. Blea Tarn and Smallwater, N West Water Authority. **Ullswater.** Trout numerous, average three to pound. Evening rise during May and June yields heavy baskets; six brace of trout in evening quite common. Day fishing also good; and heavier fish begin to move about middle of May. Fishery managed by National Trust. Numerous boats available. Angle Tarn, permits. Greenside Reservoir, Red Tarn, Grisdale Tarn, free. (Kepple Cove Tarn is dry.) Hotels: Ullswater, Patterdale; White Lion, Brotherswater; Glenridding (boats); Royal Dockray, 3m; Old Church, 5m; Brackenrigg, 6m; Rampsbeck, 6m; Howtown, 6m; Sharrow Bay, 6m; Waterfoot.

LOWTHER (tributary of Eamont). Salmon and trout. Abstraction affecting salmon sport—autumn run now very late. Sport with trout remains good (av $\frac{3}{4}$lb). Crown and Mitre Hotel, **Bampton** (via Penrith), has more than 3m fishing for guests (trout and late salmon) including Haweswater Beck; a good centre, only 100 yds from river. Penrith AA holds substantial stretches of good fly water on river; other assn water on Eden, Eamont and Petteril; £5. RD licences from hotel or Penrith tackleists.

LYVENNET. Good trout stream; runs in a few miles below Temple Sowerby. Leave from farmers in some parts. 1m preserved for Yorkshire Flyfishers' Club.

BELAH. Flows from Pennine fells to join Eden 2m below Kirkby Stephen. Lower reaches, from Brough Sowerby, rented by Kirkby Stephen and Dist AA; members only.

SCANDEL BECK, Smardale (Cumbria) and **Crosby Garrett** (Cumbria). Potts or Helmbeck 2m W; Eden 3m NE; trout; preserved. Kirkby Stephen & Dist AA has water on Scandal Beck. *(See Kirkby Stephen under Eden.)*

ENGLISH LAKE DISTRICT

(For close seasons, licences, etc, see North West Water Authority, p 13-14)

BASSENTHWAITE, 5m Cockermouth; 8m Keswick. Long famous for its pike, also perch and some brown trout. Now owned by Lake District National Park Authority, Brockhole, Windermere. Prices and information from Blencathra Centre, Threlkeld, Keswick. Hotels:

Pheasant Inn, Swan, Armathwaite Hall.

BLEA TARN. About 2m above Watendlath Tarn; perch; some trout. Wt £1, dt 25p, from Mrs Myers, Blea Tarn Farmhouse.

BLELHAM TARN (in Lancashire). Ns **Windermere.** Pike, perch, some trout, wt £1.20, dt 30p from National Trust

Warden, Low Wray Campsite.

BROTHERSWATER. ns **Windermere** 10m; Ullswater is $2\frac{3}{4}$m; trout. National Trust property; excellent free fishing; boats available.

BURNMOOR TARN, Boot (2m). Good trout and pike. National Trust; fishing free.

BUTTERMERE. National Trust lake. Char, trout, pike, perch. Permits (wt £5, dt £1) which cover Crummock and Loweswater, too, from Mrs Richardson, Gatesgarth Farm and The Gun Shop, Cockermouth. Hotels: Bridge, Fish. Guest Houses: Trevene, Wood House.

CODALE TARN, 4m from **Grasmere.** Perch, some trout; free. Hotels: *(see Grasmere).*

CONISTON. Trout, char, perch, pike. Free; RD licence needed only for trout and char. Boats from Coniston Power Boat Co, Bridge End Café, and café at boathouse. Tackle and licences from J D Fox, Yewdale Road, and W R Garner, Low House, Coniston. Local club: Coniston AA, which has fishing on tarns and becks. *(See Yew Tree Tarn.)* Hotels: Sun, Black Bull, Crown, Ship Inn.

CRUMMOCKWATER. National Trust lake. Pike, trout, char; salmon and sea trout from Cocker sometimes caught by trolling. Fishes best June and July. Wt £5 and dt £1 (covering also Buttermere and Loweswater) from Mrs Beard, Rannerdale Farm or Gun Shop, Cockermouth. Best periods for Crummock, Buttermere and Loweswater are: Trout, late May and early June (good mayfly hatch); char, July and August (special technique required—trolling 60 to 90 feet down). *(For hotels see Buttermere.)*

DERWENTWATER. Keswick. Trout very good size are best fished for from a boat in mayfly season. Good sized perch and pike, salmon present but rarely taken. Fishing rights leased to Keswick AA. St £12.50, wt £5, dt £1 from Temples, Station Road, Keswick. Boats may be hired from Nicoll End, and Keswick landings. Hotels: too numerous for detailed reference.

DEVOKE WATER near **Ravenglass** (5m E). Moorland tarn offering sport with fair-sized trout. Millom AA holds rights. No tickets.

DRUNKEN DUCK TARNS, Ambleside. Brown trout to $4\frac{1}{2}$lb, rainbow to 6lb. Wt £60, dt £12 (reductions for $\frac{1}{2}$ day and evenings), from Drunken Duck Hotel; early booking necessary. Six rods, incl two for Grizedale AC. Guided days on Windemere May/June; boat, food incl.

EASEDALE TARN, 3m from **Grasmere.** Good perch, few trout. Managed by National Trust, Rothay Holme, Rothay Road, Ambleside LA22 0EJ. Fishing free. *(See Grasmere).*

ELTERWATER, ns **Windermere.** Pike and perch, few trout.

ENNERDALE, ns **Whitehaven.** Trout, char; controlled by Ennerdale Lake Fishery formed by Calder AA, Egremont Anglers, Wath Brow and Ennerdale Anglers; St £2 and wt £1 issued. Enquiries to Mr E Wright, Secretary, 43 Dale View Gardens, Green Dykes, Egremont.

ESTHWAITE WATER (nr **Hawkshead,** Lancashire). ns Windermere, 3m. Good pike, perch and trout (av $\frac{3}{4}$lb). Fishing by permit only (St £85, wt £18, dt £5) from Collins & Butterworth, Post Office, Hawkshead, near Ambleside (also daily boat permits, tackle and licences).

Nearest accommodation is in Hawkshead, Sawrey and Windermere.

FISHER TARN, ns **Kendal,** 3m. Kendal's water supply. Few trout of good average size; privately leased.

GRASMERE, ns **Windermere.** Pike, perch, few trout; free to RWA licence-holders. Boats available. For **Rydal Water** and **River Rothay** apply Windermere, Ambleside and Dist AA, c/o Musgroves Ltd, Lake Rd, Windermere. *(See Lancashire and Westmorland small streams.)* Hotels: Swan, Red Lion, Rothay, Prince of Wales, Dale Lodge, Ben Place (private), Moss Grove (private).

GREAT RUNDALE TARN, ns **Long Marton,** 5m. Seamore Tarn and Little Rundale Tarn are in the vicinity. Small trout.

GRIZEDALE LEA RESERVOIR. Trout; hon sec, Kirkham and Dist FFC issues dt (limited), boat extra; fly only.

HAWESWATER, ns **Penrith** or **Shap.** A good head of wild brown trout, char, gwyniad and perch. Bank fishing, fly only, free to all holders of NWWA licence.

HAYES WATER, ns **Penrith.** Trout (3 to lb) and perch. Penrith AA; members only.

KILLINGTON RESERVOIR, ns **Oxenholme,** 3m. Trout, pike, perch. Leased to Kent AA. St £11, wt £4.50, dt £2 from Kendal tackle shops or Keeper at reservoir. Concession st to jun. Parties should book in advance through Kent AA sec.

KNOTT END TARN: Birkby, Ravenglass. Heavily stocked brown and rb trout to 6 lbs. Dry fly and nymph (barbless hook) only. Ticket 0800–1700 hrs £7. Evenings: £7. Bookings to W Arnold 06577 255.

LOGHRIGG TARN, ns **Windermere.** Pike, perch; wt £1.20, dt 30p, from Tarn Foot Farm.

LOWESWATER. National Trust lake. Pike, perch, trout (av 1½–2lb but hard to catch; fly only up to June 10); Kirkstile Inn, Loweswater. For wt and dt (covering also Buttermere and Crummockwater) apply at Gun Shop, Cockermouth, where RD licences are also obtainable or Scale Hill Hotel, Lorton 232.

MOCKERKIN, near Loweswater. Tarn stocked with carp by Cockermouth AA. Wt and dt from The Gun Shop, Lorton Street, Cockermouth.

RYDAL WATER and **HIGH ARNSIDE TARN,** ns **Windermere.** Pike, perch and fair-sized trout; preserved by Winder-

mere, Ambleside and Dist AA. Tickets from Musgrave's Ltd, Windermere.

SKELSMERGH, ns **Kendal,** 3m. Swarms with small roach and rudd, fishing free; bank treacherous.

SMALLWATER TARN, ns **Penrith.** Water Authority has rights. Trout; difficult of access and often disappointing. (Cumb RD.)

SPRINKLING TARN. Right up Stye Head Pass. Trout. Good on a favourable day until July.

STYE HEAD TARN. Same information as Sprinkling Tarn.

TARN HOWS. Hawkshead. National Trust, but fishing reserved. No permits.

THIRLMERE. Perch, pike, trout. Preserved by N West Water Authority, who issue privilege tickets only to employees.

ULLSWATER, ns **Penrith.** Covers 2,200 acres. Noted trout fishery. Also perch, and gwyniad. Trout average 3 to lb but fish up to 8lb taken. Fishery managed by the National Trust. HQ: 42 Queen Anne's Gate, London SW1H. Hotels: Ullswater, Patterdale, White Lion, Glenridding, Waterfoot, Waternook, Sharrow Bay, Rampsbeck, Brackenrigg, Howtown, Crown, Sun (last two Pooley Bridge). Boats available.

WASTWATER. Trout, char. No tickets at present. Hotels: Lutwidge Arms Hotel, Holmrook, and Bridge Inn, Santon Bridge and Strands. Other tarns: Greendale, High Fell, Scoats: brown trout. *(See also Bassenthwaite and for river fishing to outflow see Irt.)*

WATENDLATH TARN. Keswick 6m. Good pike fishing. Many small trout.

WHINFELL TARN, ns **Kendal,** 5m. Rudd, perch and pike plentiful. Fishing prohibited by owner.

WINDERMERE, ns **Windermere.** Largest lake. 10½m long and nearly 1m wide. Good pike and perch, also eels, char and trout (trout best March–June). Fishing free, apart from RD licence. Big fish taken by trolling. Boats from Bowness Bay. Local club: Windermere, Ambleside & Dist AA, which issues dt and wt for fishing on **Rydal Water, Rivers Rothay, Brathay** and **Troutbeck,** and four tarns *(see Grasmere and Lancashire and Cumbria small streams).* Tackleist: P Musgrave & Sons Ltd, Lake Road. Hotels: Storrs, Old England, Royal, Crown, Belsfield, Hydro; Windermere Hotel (formerly Rigg's) is 1m from lake. Hotels at Ambleside: Lowood, Salutation,

White Lion, Waterhead, Water Edge (facing Windermere Lake).
YEW TREE TARN, near Coniston. Now owned by National Trust and leased to

Coniston and Torver Anglers. Brown and rainbow trout; dt £4 and £2 from Raven, The Gift and Tackle Shop, Yewdale Road, Coniston.

ESK (Border)

(Esk in England is under North West Water Authority; close seasons, licences, etc, see p 13–14. Statutory close times apply to river in Scotland; no licences needed)

Rises in Dumfriesshire and flows into the Solway Firth but is classed as an English river. Upper reaches of Esk and main tributary, Liddle, good for brown trout but rivers are primarily sea trout and salmon waters from Langholm and Newcastleton to the mouth. Heavy run of sea trout and herling from July to September. Salmon in spring and autumn, September and October being best months. Chub and dace in lower reaches provide good sport in winter.

Canonbie (Dumfries and Galloway). Salmon, sea trout, herling, trout; Esk and Liddle Fisheries Association issue permits: St £120, wt £25. No dt *(see Langholm)*. Hotels: Cross Keys, Riverside Inn.

Langholm (Dumfries and Galloway). Salmon, sea trout, herling, trout. Certain stretches of Esk and its tributaries (the Liddle, White Esk, Ewes, Wauchope and Tarras) are under the control of the Esk and Liddle FA. Tickets from Secretary's office, Bank of Scotland, Langholm; J I Wylie, river-watcher, Byreburnfoot, Canonbie; J M White, Market Place; or (for the Liddle) from Mr Ewart, tackleist, Newcastleton. St £96, wt

£20/40 according to season. "All waters" tickets as follows: St £260, wt (to end of May) £50, (from June 1) £100. No dt. (Jun ½ price.) Permits from R J B Hill, Bank of Scotland Buildings, Langholm, Dumfriesshire DG13 0AD. No RWA licence needed. Netherby Estate Offices, Longtown, issue permits for salmon and sea trout fishing at **Netherby.** No Sunday fishing and restricted night fishing. There are also restrictions on spinning and worm fishing. Full particulars from secretaries. Hotels: Crown, Eskdale, or Cross Keys (Canonbie); Langholm Guest House.

Westerkirk (Dumfries and Galloway). Salmon, sea trout, herling, trout.

Tributaries of the Border Esk

LIDDLE: Salmon, sea trout, herling, brown trout.

Newcastleton (Roxburgh). Salmon, sea trout, herling, brown trout. Esk and Liddle Fisheries Association has much water. Tickets (st £84 and wt £20/£40, also visitors st £24) from Messrs Ewart, Fishing Tackle Shop, South Hermitage Street. Hotels: Liddlesdale, Grapes (fishing arranged on Esk, Liddle and other local waters) *(see also Esk–Langholm).*

LYNE: Lyne rises on Bewcastle Fells and joins Esk ½m above Metal Bridge. Salmon, sea trout, herling, trout. Riparian owners sometimes give permission.

SARK: Trout stream about 10m long, forming for a short distance boundary between England and Scotland, and emptying into Solway at Gretna; has run

of sea trout and herling (best July onwards).

Gretna (Dumfries and Galloway). Gretna AA has water *(see under Kirtle Water, below).*

KIRTLE WATER: Stream which empties into the Solway at Kirtlefoot. Sea trout, herling, trout. About 3m from mouth controlled by Gretna AA. Association controls also 5m on Sark; st, wt and dt, (covering sea trout and salmon) from Central Café, Gretna. Humbers Lodge Hotel, Rigg and Kirtleside Farm, Rigg.

Kirtlebridge (Dumfries and Galloway). Sea trout and trout; short free length. Winterhope Burn. Penoben Burn. Annan, 3m SW. Well-stocked reservoir 3m off, **Middlebie Dam,** fishable by permit; trouting very good.

Kirkpatrick (Dumfries and Galloway). Trout.

ESK (Yorkshire)

(For close seasons, licences, etc, see Yorkshire Water Authority, p 14)

Rises on Westerdale Moor and runs into sea at Whitby. Salmon, trout and grayling. This stream, from which salmon had disappeared, was artificially restocked, and now holds good head of fish. Represents most successful effort at artificial restocking with salmon. Good runs of sea trout as a rule; brown trout plentiful but on small side. River largely controlled by Esk Fishery Association.

Whitby (Yorks). Salmon, sea trout, trout, grayling, eels; largely preserved by the Esk FA from Whitby to beyond Glaisdale. Applications for vacancies in association should be addressed to the hon sec. Visitors' tickets available only for water between Ruswarp and Sleights. No maggot fishing is allowed. Fishing from Iburndale Beck down to Ruswarp Dam. St, dt. Salmon, sea trout and brown trout. Tickets from boat-landing at Ruswarp *(see also under Sea Fishing Stations)*.

Ruswarp (Yorks). Salmon, sea trout, trout, grayling, eels; preserved for 2m by Esk Fishery Association. Tickets from Boatyard, Ruswarp.

Sleights (Yorks). Salmon, sea trout, trout, grayling, eels; preserved by Esk Fishery Association. Tickets from Boatyard, Ruswarp.

Goathland (Yorks). Salmon, sea trout, trout, grayling. Murk Esk; trout. Goathland AC water; members only.

Grosmont (Yorks). Trout, salmon; preserved by the Esk FA above to Glaisdale, and below to Whitby.

Egton Bridge (Yorks). Salmon, trout; some water preserved by the Esk FA. Other water ($1\frac{1}{2}$m both banks) owned by Egton Estates Co. Tickets sometimes

issued. Trout fishing in **Randymere Reservoir,** between here and Goathland and **Scaling Dam** (worm and fly). Hotels: Horse Shoe; Wheatsheaf Inn; Station.

Glaisdale (N Yorks). Salmon, sea trout, trout; preserved below by the Esk FA *(see Whitby)*. Hotel: Angler's Rest. Licences from Esk FA bailiff, K Fletcher, 2 Sandsend Cottages, Egton Bridge, Whitby. Dt from Yorkshire Water Authority.

Danby (N Yorks). Salmon, sea trout, brown trout, grayling, preserved by landowners and Danby AC. Danby AC has about 8m of water, also between Castleton and Leaholm; st (limited) £10, dt £1.50 (£3 in Oct), from Duke of Wellington (Danby); Post Offices, Castleton and Danby; John Simpson Gun Shop, Stokesley, N Yorks, and F Farrow, Butcher, 11 Dale End, Danby, (Club bailiff). Restrictions on method according to date. Accommodation, licences, tickets, available at Duke of Wellington.

Castleton (N Yorks). Trout: Danby AC water *(see Danby)*. Hotel: Moorlands.

Westerdale (N Yorks). Trout, grayling. Stokesley AC has about 3m above and below village. Members only.

Tributaries of the Esk (Yorkshire)

MURK ESK: Salmon and trout. Tributaries are: Little Beck, Brocka Beck, Eller Beck. Little Eller Beck. Fishing station:

Grosmont.
COMMONDALE BROOK: Commondale (Yorks). Trout: preserved by the owners.

ESSEX (streams, lakes and reservoirs)

(For close seasons, licences, etc, see Anglian Water Authority, p 14–15)

PIPPS HILL COUNTRY CLUB LAKE, Basildon. 25 acre coarse fishery. Large carp. Dt £3.50 from Bailiff. Pipps Hill Country Club, Cranes Farm Rd, Basildon (Tel: 0268 23456).

ARDLEIGH RESERVOIR, nr Colchester. 130 acre reservoir stocked with brown, (generously) and rainbow trout. 7 acre

winter rainbow fishery available, £10–£12. Season: last Sat in March to Oct 29. Fly only to Sep 30. Full st £255, (modified) £205. Dt £8, evenings £6. Concessions to juniors, free tuition. Boats £6.50 per day, £4.50 $\frac{1}{2}$ day, evenings £3.50. Special boat for dis. 2 rods available on small pond stocked with big fish. £12 per session. AWA licence req. Spinning and bait fishing for trout and coarse fish from Oct 1, dt £8, boat £4.50. Coarse fishing Nov–Jan, dt £4; boats £3. Fishing and fly-tying courses offered. Enq to Fisheries & Est Officer, Ardleigh Reservoir, Nr Colchester, Essex CO7 7PT, with sae. Tel: 0206 230642.

BERWICK PONDS, Rainham. Elm Park and Dist AS has lake and carrier; coarse fish; dt from bailiff.

BIRCH HALL LAKE. Near **Colchester;** coarse fish; Kelvedon AC; club also has Rivenhall Lake, near **Witham,** Silver End Pit, and stretches on Blackwater; all members only.

CONNAUGHT WATERS, Chingford. Roach, bream, carp; free.

COBBLERS MEAD LAKE, Corringham. Excellent coarse fishing; large bream and carp, good tench and roach. Monthly competitions and trophies. Members only, st £15; G Hyde, Box 18, Canvey Island, tel: 0268 683946; or Basildon Angling Centre, 422 Whitmore Way, Basildon.

EPPING FOREST PONDS. Most notable is Wake Valley Pond, near Wake Arms on A11; roach and small carp. Ponds usually free but for Warren Pond at **Chingford** a dt 11p must be obtained from keeper; roach, bream, perch, carp, tench, pike. Ornamental Water: dt £1.50. Perch Pond: £1. Hollow Pond, Eagle Pond, £1. Highams Park Lake and Connaught Water: £1. From bailiff on site. The office of Superintendent of Epping Forest is at The Warren, Loughton. IG10 4RW.

FISHERS GREEN, Waltham Abbey. Pike, tench, bream, roach. A Leisure Sport restricted permit fishery. St £26 + £2 key deposit. Concessions for jun OAP, dis. Applications to LSA, Thorpe Park, Staines Road, Chertsey KT16 8PN. Tel: Chertsey 64872.

GOSFIELD LAKE, Halstead (Essex). 45 acres; well-stocked with carp, perch, roach, tench, pike; boats available. Inquire C W Turp, Gosfield Lake Ltd, Church Road, Gosfield. St £66, 24 hr: £5.50, 12 hr: £2.75, (1 rod). Concessions to jun, obtain from the shop.

HANNINGFIELD RESERVOIR. Near **Chelmsford.** Excellent trout fishery. Regular stocking. Bank and boat fishing. Season: Apr 1–Oct 31. Full Season Ticket: £276; Mon–Fri: £207; Named

week-day: £161; Day tickets at £10 per day. Motor Boats £12 per day, rowing boats £7 per day. Part day and evening boats also available. All prices include VAT. Bag limit 6 fish. Car parks and fishing lodge. Total catch around 50,000, average weight $1^3/_4$lbs. Enquiries telephone Basildon 710101.

HATFIELD FOREST LAKE. Near Hatfield Broad Oak and Bishop's Stortford. National Trust property; good pike and tench, carp and bream; some roach and rudd. St £20-£40 and dt £2. Punts. For tickets apply Lake Warden, The Shell House, Takeley, Bishop's Stortford CM22 6NH (Tel: 0279 870477). Restrictions on use of groundbait.

LAYER PITS. 6m S of **Colchester;** controlled by Colchester APS; coarse fish; members only. Colchester Piscatorial Society has **Langham Ponds;** no tickets.

STAMBRIDGE TROUT FISHERIES, Great Stambridge, Essex, now offers fishing for trout and coarse fish. Tel: 03706 274.

STANFORD-LE-HOPE. Two "Leisure Sport" gravel pits. Carp, roach, tench. St £17, concessions to Jun, OAP, dis. applications to LSA, Thorpe Park, Staines Road, Chertsey KT16 8PN. Tel: Chertsey 64872.

MARDYKE: Fishing stations: **Purfleet** and **Ockendon.** Rises by East Horndon and flows 12m to Thames at Purfleet. Fishing formerly negligible, but Essex RD has restocked and there are some club lengths.

PANT. Bocking. Upper part of R Blackwater *(see Blackwater in main list).*

RODING. Rises near Dunmow and flows 30m south and south-west to enter the Thames in East London. Polluted in lower reaches, but higher up holds coarse fish.

Ongar. Coarse fish; good chub, roach, dace and perch. Practically whole of fishable Roding controlled by clubs, principally Ongar and Dist AS (members only; river and pit), Collier Row AS (st available from hon sec). Essex RD have from Gangbridge to Fyfield Bridge; dt. Fishing showing considerable improvement. Tackleists: Edko Sports, 136 North Street, **Romford;** Morris, Kings Road and Roblin, 114 High Street, both **Brentwood.**

Passingford Bridge. Roach, chub, pike; bream, carp, tench. Barkingside and Dist AS has $1^1/_2$m downstream; bailiff on water. Dt from bailiffs on bank for $^3/_4$m

upstream of bridge. Woodford AS has $1\frac{1}{4}$m north of bridge; members only (st for associates from hon sec), Elm Park AS has water; dt from bailiff. Tackleist: Edko Sports, 136 North Street, **Romford.**
SCRUBBS LAKE, Hadleigh (Essex). Good perch, roach, rudd, etc; dt.
SHOEBURY PARK LAKE, Shoeburyness (Essex). Coarse fish; dt issued.
SOUTH WEALD LAKES. Two lakes near **Brentwood.** Elm Park, Hornchurch and Dist AS water; tench, carp, roach, pike, perch; dt for one lake only from bailiff; other lake, strictly members only.
THE CHASE, Dagenham (Essex). White Hart Anglers' water; gravel pit; roach, bream, tench (excellent), carp (common, mirror and crucian), rudd, pike, perch; no night fishing; hempseed banned; dt from bailiff; RD licences needed. Tackleists: Edko Sports, 136 North Street, Romford; Ridge & Co, 277 Oxlow Lane.

WANSTEAD & WOODFORD LAKES AND PONDS. Eagle Pond, **Snaresbrook** (roach, perch, carp); Knighton Wood Pond, **Woodford; Hollow Pond, Whipps Cross;** all free.

OTHER TICKET WATERS. Stambridge Fisheries Angling Centre, Gt. Stambridge, N **Rochford** (fly fishing for trout; coarse fishing). Priory Lakes, Priory Park, **Southend;** Eastwood Pit, **Rayleigh;** Essex Carp Fishery (crucian carp, bream) at Mollands Lane, **South Ockendon;** Old Hall Lake, **Herongate;** Moor Hall Farm Fishery, **Aveley;** Aveley Lakes (Tel: 0708 868425), trout fishing; **Ongar;** Raphael Park Lake, **Romford; Danbury Park Lakes, near Chelmsford;** Harwood Hall at Corbets Tey, and Parklands Lake, both near **Upminster;** Warren Pond, **Chingford;** carp, bream. Tickets mostly available from bailiffs on site.

(For Walthamstow reservoirs, see p 72–73)

EXE

(For close seasons, licences, etc, see South West Water Authority, p 12)

Rises on Exmoor and runs south through Devon to Exmouth. Salmon and trout, with grayling and coarse fish in lower reaches. At several points on upper reaches trout fishing (moorland) and occasional salmon fishing may be had by hotel guests.

Exeter (Devon). Bream; mirror, king and common carp; dace, gudgeon, pike, perch, roach, rudd, tench and eels. **Exeter Ship** and **Tiverton Grand Western Canals** contain bream, carp, pike, perch, rudd, roach, tench, eels and odd dace. Better part of Exeter canal from Broadwater (lime Kilns) to Turf (where canal enters Exe estuary). Hotels on canal banks: Double Locks, Turf. Exeter & Dist AA (amalgamation of local clubs) has coarse fishing rights on R Exe (ten fishings) on **Culm** and **Creedy,** from City Basin to Double Locks on Exeter Ship Canal, and on ponds at Kingsteignton, Sampford Peveril and Mamhead. St £10. Visitors wt £4, dt £1.50. For fishing on Tiverton Canal contact Estates Surveyor, County Hall, Exeter (tel: 77977) or tackle shops. Tiverton AC has dt available for left bank at Exwick. SWWA has 3m of salmon fishing on lower Exe in Cowley and Countess Wear areas. Dt £2.50, st £33 from Feb 14 to June 15. Apply

Exeter AC, Smythen Street. Tickets for Exeter & Dist AA waters from hon sec or tackleists. 2m W of city, **Haldon Ponds** trout fishery, stocked with rb to 10lb, b to 7lb. Wt £35, dt £6, evening £3. Rods limited pd. Boats. Phone Exeter 32967. One permit a day available for salmon fishing (weekdays only) from Exeter Angling Centre, Smythen Street; P K Angling, Clifton Road; Gun & Sports Shop, Fore Street, Heavitree; Tony Gould, 47 Longbrook Street.

Brampford Speke (Devon). Salmon, trout, dace; preserved. Pynes Water, from here down to Cowley Weir ($2\frac{1}{2}$m) fished by local syndicate. Exeter & Dist AA water towards Stoke Canon *(see Culm).*

Thorverton (Devon). Trout, salmon, dace; private hence up to within $1\frac{1}{2}$m of Bickleigh. Fisherman's Cot has beat *(see Bickleigh).* For dt £2, 4 fish limit, contact T Mortimer, High Banks, Latchmore, tel: 0392 860241.

Silverton (Devon). Trout, salmon, dace, pike, perch; preserved. Exeter & Dist AA has coarse fishing on Culm here *(see Exeter and Culm)*.

Bickleigh (Devon). Trout, salmon. Fisherman's Cot Hotel has $\frac{3}{4}$m both banks adjoining hotel for salmon and/or trout. Reserved for residents.

Tiverton (Devon). Exe, Lowman and Little Dart; trout, salmon. **Tiverton Canal;** pike, perch, roach, tench. Exe perserved for 2m both above and below town (trout and grayling) by Tiverton FFC, fly only. St £5.50 for residents only. Dt £1, $\frac{1}{2}$m above Tiverton; fly only, for visitors. Hotels: Boar's Head and Bark House at Oakford Bridge; Fisherman's Cot, Bickleigh (beat on Exe). At Tiverton Junction is Railway Hotel, where accommodation can be had by anglers fishing **Tiverton Canal;** tickets. Tackleist: Country Sports, 9 William St (permits, licences, etc) *(see Exeter)*.

Dulverton (Som). Salmon, trout, grayling. Usually good run of salmon (May onwards and autumn) to Dulverton and beyond, depending on water conditions. Trout fishing good on Exe and **Barle** (four to lb). Some free fishing available; contact Lance Nicholson *(see below)*.

Grayling less plentiful. Guests at Carnarvon Arms may fish on more than 7m on Exe, Barle and Haddeo; individual beats and gillie. Dt (S) £5.50–£9 (NT) £4. Some free fishing for guests at Lion Hotel. Royal Oak, Winsford, issues permits. Exe Valley Fishery. Two small lakes stocked with browns and rainbows averaging 2lb +. Dt available March–October. Limit: 2 brace. Licences from hotels. Tackleist: Lance Nicholson, High Street (permits, casting tuition).

Exford (Som). Trout. Crown Hotel can arrange fishing on Exe and instruction on stocked trout ponds. Trout fishing also available on Nutscale, Clatworthy and Wimbleball Reservoirs (rainbow and brown) and Badgeworthy Water and Oarewater (both banks) in Doone Valley on Exmoor. Salmon is available in the area, especially in the Lyn.

Winsford (Som). Exe; trout. Royal Oak Inn has 1m of fly fishing on Exe, through village near hotel, plus arrangement with firm J S Sporting who have 5 beats at Bridgetown. Wt £30, dt £5, £5 extra per salmon killed. Tarr Steps Hotel has 3m of salmon and trout fishing, fly only, on the Barle *(advt below)*.

Tributaries of the Exe

CREEDY: Trout, coarse fish.
Cowley Bridge (Exeter). Coarse fish. Exeter and Dist AA has rights *(see Exeter)*.
Crediton (Devon). Trout; preserved by owners. Yeo 3m; trout; leave from farmers. Crediton FFC has about 5m on Creedy and Yeo. Limited wt (Mon–Fri only); fly only. Tackleist: Ladd's Sports. Hotels: Ship, White Hart.

CULM: Trout, coarse fish, few grayling. **Stoke Canon, Rewe and Silverton** (Devon). Dace, roach, perch and occasional grayling. Exeter and Dist AA has water *(see Exeter)*.
Cullompton (Devon). Trout. River mostly preserved. Kentisbere Brook, Ashford Brook, Fulford Water. Licences from Cullompton Gun Shop; Country Sports,

Moorland trout do not commonly run large, but may offer excellent sport. The one coming ashore was taken in the Barle on a summer evening. *Photo: John Tarlton.*

3 Station Rd. Hotels: Railway and Cullompton.

Uffculme. Permits for stretch from here to Five Fords (about $1\frac{1}{2}$m mostly both banks) issued by J E Metters, 4 Groveway, London SW9 0AR, tel: 01-735 4805; st £25, mt £10, wt £5, dt £1.50.

Hemyock (Devon). Trout. Upper Culm FA preserves about 4m both banks. Trout season begins April 1; brown trout, fly only. St £8, mt £4, wt £2, dt £1 from hon sec or Hemyock P.O. No Sunday fishing. Lower water preserved, and no fishing obtainable between Hemyock and Culmstock. Hotel: Railway. Accommodation also at Sanders.

Clayhidon (Devon). Upper Culm FA preserves about 4m in this district *(see Hemyock).* No Sunday fishing. Hotel: Half Moon.

Killerton (Devon). National Trust controls coarse fishing on Killerton Estate; tickets from hon sec, Exonian AA or City of Exeter AA *(see Exeter),* for some water.

BARLE. Runs through beautifully wooded valley and holds salmon (av 7–10lb) and trout (av 8–10 in).

Tarr Steps (Devon). Salmon, trout. Tarr Steps Hotel *(advt p 53)* Hawkridge, has 3m of salmon and trout fishing, fly only, free for guests. Non-guests dt S £10, T £5. Tel: 064385 293.

Withypool (Som). Trout; some salmon. Crown Hotel, Exford, can arrange fishing. Inn: Royal Oak.
Simonsbath (Som). Exmoor Forest Hotel has rights on 8m of Barle, free to hotel guests. Dt S £6, T £2, for non-residents. RWA licences at hotel. Spinning for salmon allowed. Convenient for **Wimbleball Reservoir** *(see Exford).*

FAL

(For close seasons, licences, etc, see South West Water Authority, p 12)

Rises near Roche and flows about 23 miles, due south, past Grampound and Tregony to the English Channel at Falmouth. Fair trouting.

Falmouth (Cornwall). Excellent trout fishing in South Cornwall Water Board reservoirs (Argal and Stithians) *(see Cornwall streams, lakes etc).* Trout in many of the small streams flowing into creeks around Falmouth; free in most on permission of farmers. Coarse fish in stocked pond at Tory Farm, Ponsanooth; permission from farmer. Tackleists: A B Harvey, Market Strand (RD licences; reservoir permits); Berks, Arwenack Street; Cunningham's, 10 Lower Market Street, Penryn. Further information from Falmouth and Penryn AA. *(For sea fishing see Sea Fishing Stations.)*
Tregony (Cornwall), ns **Grampound Road,** 5m. Trout, 2m off runs Polglaze brook, 4m long; trout.

FOWEY

(For close seasons, licences, etc, see South West Water Authority, p 12)

Rises in east Cornwall and enters English Channel by estuary at Fowey. Noted sea-trout river, with salmon and many small brown trout. Restocked annually with salmon fry by SWWA.

Fowey (Cornwall). Trout, sea trout, salmon. Fishing for rod and line above Lostwithiel partly preserved; free below. July–August best time for ST, Sept–Oct for S. St £30.50, dt £3.85, conc. 50% from Gift and Sports Shop. Into east side of harbour, opposite town, flows Pont Brook, 4m long, holding small trout; free. Capital sea fishing *(see Sea Fishing section).* Hotels: Fowey, Rockside, Riverside, Ship, Old Quay House, Greenbank. Tackleists: Gift and Sports Shop, 10 The Esplanade.
Lostwithiel (Cornwall). Salmon, sea trout, brown trout. Good salmon fishing now up to Dec 15. Fly fishing best, but minnow good in coloured water. National Trust **Lanhydrock** fishing; sec, Lanhydrock AA, tel: 0208 4281. Lostwithiel best centre for Fowey. Lostwithiel FA has about 1½m and issues tickets for salmon and trout season licence holders. Fishing extends from just outside town to just above end of Whitmarsh Moor. Season tickets, £8.50, from Bodmin Trading Co, Church Square, Bodmin, tel: 0208 2557, J C Penhaligon, 15 Queen Street, Lostwithiel and R Johnson, The Tackle Box, 11 Trinity Street, St Austell (Juniors £1). Hotels: Royal Talbot, Monmouth, King's Arms, Earl of Chatham, Royal Oak, Globe, Trevone Guest House and Carotel Ltd (flatlets).
Bodmin Road (Cornwall). Trout, sea trout, salmon. Liskeard and Dist AC has 6m water on middle and upper reaches; S, 1 Apr–15 Dec. ST, 1 Apr–30 Sept; tickets available (£10 week, £3 day) from Bodmin Trading Co, Church Square, Bodmin. Hotel: Royal, at Bodmin, where guests can obtain fishing on **Camel.**

POLLUTION

Anglers are united in deploring pollution. To combat it, urgent action may be called for at any time from any one of us. If numbers of fish are found dead, dying, or seriously distressed, take samples of both fish and water and contact the office of the Director of Scientific Services at the appropriate Regional Water Authority.

FROME AND PIDDLE (Dorset)

(For close seasons, licences, etc, see Wessex Water Authority, p 13)

Frome rises in West Dorset and flows into the English Channel at Poole Harbour, near Wareham. Piddle rises in a mill pond 1 mile north of Piddletrenthide and enters Poole Harbour near mouth of Frome near Wareham. Both are chalk streams and closely preserved, but sport may sometimes be had. Some very good sea trout have been caught in the Frome, which also receives a run of heavy salmon. Trout in both rivers plentiful and good. Bass run up to where the river enters Poole Harbour. Piddle carries small stock of heavy salmon.

Wareham (Dorset). On Frome and Piddle; salmon, sea trout, trout, grayling, pike, roach and dace. Salmon and trout preserved, but leave sometimes from owners of waters. Morden Estate Office, Charborough Park, Wareham, sometimes has rods available for entire season (never for day or week) as follows: salmon, Frome and Piddle; trout, Piddle and Bere; River Stour. Avon and Dorset RD lets 14 rods for the season (on the basis of two per day) for fishery on Piddle; salmon, sea trout (details from Div Fisheries and Recreations Officer). Authority also has some free fishing for coarse fish on south bank below South Bridge on landowners' permission for access to banks. RD licence needed. By hiring a boat from Frome Boat Service, Wareham Quay, coarse fishing at Wareham on RD licence. Local society: Wareham and Dist AS, which has stretch of north bank and pond at Creech; members only. Hotels: Red Lion and Black Bear. Tackleist and bait: G Elmes & Son, St John's Hill.

Wool (Dorset). Frome: Salmon, sea trout. Woolbridge Manor (100 yards from river) has $1\frac{1}{4}$m; fly and spinning. Salmon run large, fish over 30lb not rare. Dt £18. RWA licence required. Nr **Puddletown, Pallington Lakes, Tincleton,** two trout, one coarse. Trout dt £10; four fish limit. Coarse fishing £2. Beats on river: £10 per day. At **Tolpuddle, Wessex Fly Fishing,** Lawrences Farm. River, lake, accm and tuition *(advt p 44)*.

Dorchester (Dorset). Frome: trout; preserved for 3m above and $2\frac{1}{2}$m below town by the Dorchester FC of 5 members only (ann sub £130); dry fly only; limited dt £10, from Exhibition Hotel, London Rd. Rest of river strictly preserved by land owners. RWA licences from Mr Atlin, 1 Athelstan Rd, Dorchester. Other society: Dorchester and Dist AS (coarse fishing only) who issue dt for short stretch of **Stour.** Hotels: King's Arms, Antelope. **Flowers Farm Lakes,** Hilfield; trout fishery of 5 lakes, brown and rainbow. Dt £11.50. Dorchester, Dorset DT2 7BA; tel: 03003 351.

GIPPING (Orwell)

(For close seasons, licences, etc, see Anglian Water Authority, p 14–15)

Rises between Stowmarket and Bury St Edmunds, and flows into the North Sea by an estuary near Ipswich. Coarse fish.

Ipswich (Suffolk). Most coarse fish. Gipping APS (Annual mem £17) issues dt £1 for 1m of their water on river and other fishings in gravel pits and on **R Stour.** New 350 acre coarse fish reservoir at Stutton-Holbrook, 5m SE of Ipswich. "**Alton Water**". St £10, dt £1 from tackleists or manager Gipping APS. Leisure sport stretch on river is at **Bramford.** St £10. Details from LSA, Thorpe Park, Chertsey, Surrey; tel:

09328 64872. Good codling, skate, whiting and flounder fishing below town. Tackleists: Viscount Tackle, Clapgate Lane; R Markham, Woodbridge Road East; Breakaway Tackle Dev. Co, Bramford Road; Ipswich Angling Centre, Felixstowe Road; Peachy's Sports, Meredith Road.

Stowmarket (Suffolk). Stowmarket and Dist AA has short stretch of **Rattle;** members only.

GLOUCESTERSHIRE (streams)

BIDEFORD BROOK. Fishing station: **Awre.** Rises in Abbot's Wood and flows 7m to Severn estuary; coarse fish; preserved. **Blackpool Brook** enters at Awre; Forest of Dean AC; members only.

CONE. Fishing station: **Woolaston.** Cone rises by Hewelsfield, and is 5m long. Eels and flounders.

FROME. Rises near Cheltenham and flows into Severn estuary. Coarse fish; a few trout higher up. Fishing stations: **Stonehouse** (Glos), coarse fish, and **Stroud** (Glos), a few trout and coarse fish. Several brooks in vicinity. Stroud AA controls 2m Thames at Lechlade and 1m at Newbridge. Enquire Batemans *(see below)*. Pike and coarse fishing in Stroudwater Canal. Stroud tackleist: Batemans Sports, Kendrick Street, GL5 1AB, tel: 04536 4320, who issue st £6 for local club waters and tickets for small carp lakes.

NAILSWORTH BROOK (tributary of Frome). Fishing stations: **Nailsworth** (Glos) and **Woodchester** (Glos). Brook reported polluted in parts. Lakes: Longfords Lake, pike, carp. Woodchester Park lakes: pike, perch, roach,

tench, brown and rainbow trout; now strictly preserved. **Coombe Lakes,** Wootton-under-Edge. Dt for trout (fly only) and coarse fishing. Boats available. Advance bookings. Tel: 3136. At Nailsworth is The Midland Fishery trout farm *(see list on page 10)*.

HOPE BROOK. Fishing station: **Westbury-on-Severn,** ns Grange Court, $1\frac{1}{2}$m. Hope Brook rises 2m above Longhope, runs thence 5m to Westbury and Severn estuary (1m). Coarse fish, mostly preserved, farmers sometimes give leave. Inn: Red Lion.

LITTLE AVON: Small Gloucestershire stream flowing into Severn estuary. **Berkeley** (Glos). Coarse fish, trout, Waterley Brook. Fishing below Charfield preserved. Close by station rises Billow Brook, which runs thence 3m to estuary. Clubs have water on **Gloucester and Berkeley Canal;** 16m Sharpness to Gloucester.

LYD. Chub, roach, perch. Fishing station: **Lydney.** Lydney AA holds stretch from railway station to Tufts Junction. Club also has **Lydney Lake** (carp, roach and perch). **Lydney Canal** and a dam.

HAMPSHIRE (streams, lakes and canal)

(For close seasons, licences, etc, see Southern Water Authority, p 11–12)

BASINGSTOKE CANAL. Fishing stations: **Basingstoke, Greywell, North Warnborough, Odiham, Winchfield, Crookham, Fleet, Farnborough, Aldershot, Ash Vale, Brookwood, Woking** (Surrey), **Byfleet** (Surrey). Pike, carp, roach, good tench, perch; most of canal let to clubs; fishing from towpath only; boat fishing on flashes; dt from hon secs or New Inn, Odiham. Farnborough AS also has rights on **Whitewater** at **Heckfield, Loddon** at **Winnersh, Wey** at **Frensham** and gravel pits; St £13 from Raisons, tackleists, Park Road, Farnborough for **Willow Park Fisheries.** Ash Vale, three lakes stocked with carp, tench and other coarse fish. Bait and refreshments on site. Dt on site £1 and £1.50, concession for jun. Thirteen "Leisure Sport" gravel pits at **Frimley;** another two at **Ash Vale.** Carp, tench, roach and perch. Large specimens recorded. St £12 and £15 from LSA, Thorpe Park, Chertsey. Tel: 64872.

Tackleists: Cordings, 18 New Market Square, Basingstoke; Raison's, Park Road, Farnborough; Fleet Sports Centre, 182 Fleet Road, Fleet: Hayes, 36 Station Road, Aldershot. **Ewhurst Lake** (6m N); pike, perch, roach; strictly limited st £30; inquire of estate office. **Hollybush Lane Fishery,** Farnborough. 20 acres of water stocked carp, pike and other coarse fish. Dt £1.50 from J & A Newsagents, 201 Lynchford Road, Farnborough, 300 yds from fishery. St £12 & £6 from Fisheries Manager, Lake View, Old Bury Hill, Dorking. Tel: Dorking 883621.

BEAULIEU. The Beaulieu River is approx 14 miles long. Tickets for tidal stretch, Beaulieu to Needs Ore (bass, mullet, flounder) st £20, dt £2. Access from Bailey's Hard and Buckler's Hard. Tickets from Harbour Master, Buckler's Hard (tel: 200) or Resident Land Agent, John Montagu Building, Beaulieu (tel:

0590 612345). Coarse fishing on **Hatchett Pond** and **Cadmans Pool** (Forestry Commission); bream, carp, tench and pike; tickets from Forestry Commission, Queen's House, Lyndhurst SO43 7NH, campsite offices during camping season and local tackle-shops (st £38.20, mt £11.95, wt £5.30, dt £2.30, VAT incl). SWA rod licences are not required for Forestry Com. waters within New Forest. Hotels: Montagu Arms at Beaulieu; Master Builder's Arms at Buckler's Hard.

DAMERHAM TROUT LAKES, Fordingbridge (3m). Six lakes, and river for St holders. R and b trout. Open April 1 until October 31. Advance bookings only. A justly famous fishery. St £480, half £260, dt £17, $\frac{1}{2}$ £10. 20 rods per day. Tel: Rockbourne 446 (07253 446). Hotel: Compasses Inn. Tel: 07253 231.

FLEET POND. Fishing station: **Fleet.** Cove AS water. No tickets. Tackleist: Fleet S C, 182 Fleet Road.

HAMBLE. Sea trout and trout. **Bishop's Waltham.** Fishing mostly private, but leave sometimes obtainable.

LADYWELL LAKES. Alresford, Hants. 3 lakes totalling about $2\frac{1}{2}$ acres and providing 900 yds of fishable bank, stocked with brown and rainbow trout averaging approx 2lbs. One lake brown trout only. Also short length of chalk stream with wild brown trout. St £290, $\frac{1}{2}$ st £150, dt £14, $\frac{1}{2}$ dt £7.50. Enquiries and bookings to Mr and Mrs Ng, 55 West Hill Avenue, Epram, Surrey. Reduction for groups, and special arrangement for day hire of fishery. Bag limits, and restriction to single fly no larger than hook size 8.

LYMINGTON RIVER. Fishing station: **Lymington.** Sea trout (2–11lb), brown trout ($\frac{3}{4}$ to 1lb). Sea trout best June to Sept. Fishing improved by Brockenhurst Manor FFC; private.

MEON. Trout, with sea trout as far as Titchfield Mill. Fishing station: **East Meon;** Hants and Sussex Alliance has water; inquire hon sec. RD licence required. Portsmouth and Dist AS hold some eight coarse fisheries in and around **Portsmouth,** plus river trout fishing on Arun and Rother. Enquiries to hon sec.

SANDLEHEATH. Six lakes and three chalk stream beats at **Rockbourne Trout Fishery, Sandleheath,** Fordingbridge, Hampshire SP6 1QG. Excellent fishing for rainbow trout in lakes and brown trout in streams, fly only, various period terms from dt £16 to 32 visits, 4 free guests, £460. Concessions for Jun. Tuition: tackle hire. Tel: 07253 603 or 09328 63718 for full details.

TWO LAKES, near **Romsey.** Very large trout on dry fly (average over 2lb). St only, £460 incl VAT. Apply Mr Alex Behrendt, Two Lakes, Crampmoor, nr Romsey, Hants.

WAGGONERS' WELLS, near **Hindhead.** Three lakes; one trout, two coarse fishing (National Trust waters). Fly fishing for trout, April 1–Sept 30, st £25, dt £4, restocked annually. Coarse fishing: carp, perch, tench, roach; st £10, dt £1.50, plus 50p each extra rod. Jun. half price. Permits on site. Apply to The Ranger, Summerden North, Waggoners' Wells, Grayshott, near Hindhead, Surrey. (Tel: Liphook 723722.) Hotels: Punchbowl Hotel, Hindhead and Pickard Motor Hotel, Hindhead.

WARBURN. Dace, trout, salmon; preserved; leave sometimes from landowners; joins sea at **Key Haven.**

HERTS AND GREATER LONDON
(reservoirs and lakes)

(See also London Reservoirs, p 71–73)

ALDENHAM (Herts). **Aldenham Country Park Lake.** Property of Herts CC. Coarse fishing, incl. tench, pike, carp. Dt £1.50 (jun 75p) punt £3. From bailiff on site or from Park Manager, Park Office, Dagger Lane, Elstree, Herts WD6 3AT.

SHEPPERTON (Middx). **Ashmere;** three lakes stocked with rainbow trout, one with brown and rainbow. Boats available. Annual membership only.

Apply Mrs K Howman, Ashmere Fisheries, Felix Lane, Shepperton (Tel: 0932 225445). 20 acres of well-stocked coarse fishing lakes at junction of Chertsey Road and Littleton Lane, S of M3. Dt £1 from local tackle shops, Dt and st (£10) from Fishery Manager, Lake View, Old Bury Hill, Dorking. (Dt after 9 am available at Redcote Bungalow, on site.)

STANSTEAD ABBOTS. "Leisure Sport" fisheries consisting of 6 gravel pits, mill stream and part of main river. Season tickets £18. Concessions to jun, OAP, dis. Applications to LSA, Thorpe Park, Staines Road, Chertsey, Surrey. Tel: Chertsey 64872.

TRING (Herts). Four large reservoirs: **Marsworth, Startops End** and **Wilstone** (2m from Tring, $3\frac{1}{2}$m from rly station) main feeders for Grand Union Canal. Fishing at times very good. Fourteen bream over 10lb in 1980, tench to $9\frac{1}{2}$lb,

pike to 26lb. British record catfish, $43\frac{1}{2}$lb, taken at Tring. No Sunday fishing. St £37 (including right to night fish), dt £2, con £1, evening £1. Boats, £10. Tickets obtainable on bank from bailiff, B C Double, Watery Lane, Marsworth or tel: Tring 2379. New British record tench caught here in 1985. The fourth reservoir is a private trout fishery. Applications may be made to go on waiting list. *(Advt below.)* Hotels: Anglers' Retreat, Startops End, Rose & Crown.

HULL

(For close seasons, licences, etc, see Yorkshire Water Authority, p 14)

Tidal river (to Hempholme Lock) is free fishing to anyone holding current RD licence, but hit by pollution. From Beverley first-class sport may be had with roach, dace, pike, chub, bream, etc. Higher up still, on West Beck, there is excellent but strictly preserved trout fishing of chalk-stream character.

Hull (North Humberside). River polluted. Drains giving good coarse fishing. Hull & Dist AA has water on **Derwent** at **Breighton, Wressle** and **Newton;** on the Rye at **Butterwick** and **Swinton;** and on

the **Trent** at **Carlton.** Also the **Brandsburton Ponds** (open all the year) on the Broomfleet and other ponds, $4\frac{1}{2}$m of Market Weighton Canal, 17m from Hull, mixed coarse fishery, match water,

Specimen roach are not caught as freely in rivers these days as they were in years gone by. There are exceptions, though, such as the one in the picture, which came form Hempholme Lock on the R. Hull. *Photo: Bruno Broughton.*

on the **Leven Canal** and the **Barmston Drain.** St £10 and match pegs 25p on a number of waters. Enq to hon sec. Stone Creek and Patrington Haven hold flounders. Other club: Hull Rock AC. Good sea fishing. Tackleist: G W Hutchinson & Co, 27 Anlaby Rd.

Beverley (N Humberside). Tidal River Hull and drains *(for latter see Hull).* River Hull gives good coarse fishing; from Hull Bridge upstream through **Arram, Aike Wilfholme, Baswicke** and **Hempholme** to Frodingham Beck: Yorkshire Water Authority, for enquiries; weedy June to Nov. **Leven Canal** (6m): roach, bream, pike, tench and chub. 1m reserved for fly-only trout fishing. For details of this contact Draper, tel 0482 896879. Coarse fishing stretch Hull & Dist AA water. Dt from Everett's Fishing Tackle, Beverley,

Leven Marina, and 11 The Meadows, Leven. Hotel: Beverley Arms.

Brandesburton (N Humberside). River Hull 3 m W, excellent coarse fishing in gravel pits *(see Hull).*

Wansford (N Humberside). **Driffield Canal.** Restored as trout and grayling fishery by Yorkshire WA, but now taken over by local Fisheries Consultative Association. Tickets from Wansford Post Office. 6m coarse fishing in **Market Weighton Canal** now delegated to local clubs. Dt available. **West Beck** preserved by Golden Hill AS and West Beck PS; members only.

Driffield (N Humberside). Centre for noted Driffield Trout Stream and Driffield Beck; strictly preserved. See below. For **Kellythorpe** trout fishery, Driffield, tel: 0377 42297.

Tributaries of the Hull

FOSTON BECK (or **KELK** or **FRODING-HAM BECK**):

North Frodingham, Foston-on-the-Wolds and Lowthorpe (N Humberside). Rises in Yorkshire Wolds; true chalk stream containing brown trout averaging well over the pound. Preserved from Bracey Bridge to Foston Mill by Foston FC (members only). For $^3/_4$m below Foston

Mill water stocked with trout by Millhouse Beck AC; private.

DRIFFIELD BECK:

Driffield (N Humberside). Provides chalk stream fishing for trout and grayling of high order; strictly preserved. Controlled by Driffield AC, Golden Hill Club and West Beck PS. *(See Driffield on River Hull).*

ISLE OF MAN

The geographical nature of the Isle of Man tends to dictate the type of river, fish and hence fishing one may encounter when angling in the Island. Being a relatively mountainous place, rivers and streams are small, swift flowing and very clear. There are no coarse fish on the Isle of Man but nevertheless excellent sport can be had in the numerous trout streams where the art of approach to the river bank and the gentle and accurate cast of the true angler becomes vital.

There are very few preserved stretches of river in the Island, a well chosen word with the land owner is often all that is required to enable an angler to fish in peace. Approximately a half mile of the River Douglas through the Nunnery Estate is exclusively reserved for the Manx Game FF. Small sections of the rivers Dhoo and Glass can only be fished under permit from the Douglas and District Angling Club—visitors membership £6 (£2 for children), is available from Mr G M Curtis, 22 Sunningdale Drive, Onchan.

Natural baits (worms, bread, cheese) and artificials are allowed on the Island's rivers, ponds and streams but anglers are reminded that only artificials are allowed when reservoir fishing (except Eairy Dam). Further details of all freshwater angling can be obtained from the Freshwater Fishery Inspector, Cornaa, Maughold. Anglers must abide by the regulations wherever they fish. (1) Not to use or carry a gaff or tailer. (2) Not to use a line the diameter of which exceeds 0.033 cm, excepting that a fly line used solely for fly fishing may exceed 0.033 cm diameter, provided the leader exceeds five feet in length and does at no point exceed 0.033 cm in diameter. (0.033 cm diameter is approximately equivalent to 10lb breaking strain). (3) Not use more than one hook on a line unless (a) Pennel or Stewart tackles are being used for bait fishing; (b) a "point with two droppers" is being used for fly fishing only; (c) a spinner is being used for spinning only. (4) Not to use a hook larger than No 6 Redditch scale, unless the hook is comprised in an artificial fly. (5) Return to the water all fish foul hooked. (6) Return to the water unharmed any freshwater fish hooked which is less than 18 cm in length overall. (7) Chest waders prohibited.

The river fishing season commences on the Thursday preceding Good Friday, and finishes on the 30 September for trout and 31 October for salmon. The reservoir season begins on the same date but continues until October 30. A freshwater fishing licence is required to fish any river, pond or reservoir.

Salmon fishing takes place mainly in the Autumn as the Island does not enjoy a spring run of any size. Salmon and sea trout are usually taken during or after spate conditions. There is a bag limit for the rivers of 6 T and 2 S in any one day. Fish are small and rarely if ever exceed 20lb—a more reasonable average would be 5–10lb.

The Board of Agriculture and Fisheries pursues a continual stocking programme of rivers, ponds and reservoirs throughout the spring and early summer, with trout (brown and rainbow) or a takeable size, i.e. in excess of 7" and in the 1lb to 2lb range.

At present there are eight reservoirs open for fishing. They are: (a) The West Baldwin Reservoir (300 mg) is near the centre of the Island. A main road goes past the end of the dam. There is an infrequent bus service to West Baldwin village $1\frac{1}{3}$ miles from the reservoir. (b) Clypse and Kerrowdhoo Reservoirs lie, one beyond the other, about $1\frac{1}{2}$ miles north of Onchan Village. A private road runs, off the road to Grange Farm, to the Attendants house where there is room to park cars. (c) Ballure Reservoir is just south of Ramsey. Access is by a private road branching off the main road to Douglas, on the Douglas side of the MER crossing near the town boundary. (d) Block Eary Reservoir is on a tributary of the Sulby river and lies on the north slopes of Snaefell. Access is by a private road, leaving the Sulby to Tholt-y-Will road about $\frac{3}{4}$ mile from Tholt-y-Will. The private road is too rough for motor cars and they must not be taken on it. (e) Cringle Reservoir is just north of the road from Ronague to Foxdale and is on the south slopes of South Barrule. Cars can be parked on the reservoir land. (f) Sulby Reservoir is close to the A14 Sulby-Snaefell road. (g) Eairy Dam is alongside the A24 Douglas to Foxdale road. It is not a water supply and restrictions on the use of live bait do not apply.

Fishing Licences
Freshwater fishing licences—needed before *any* fishing commences—cost: St (rivers) £12, reservoirs £40. (jun £4 and £13 respectively.) Wt (available to Sep 30) rivers: £3, Reservoirs: £10, (jun £1 and £3 respectively.) Jun: under 16 years of age.

They are available from: I.O.M. Department of Agriculture and Fisheries, Bucks Road, Douglas, from local Commissioners offices in Onchan and Laxey, and from any Post Office.

No licence required for sea fishing, which from pier, rocks or boat is excellent, especially for pollack—locally called "callig"—mackerel, cod and codling, whiting and plaice. Chief bait for ground fish is herring, but lugworm, sand-eels and shellfish also found. Whiffing with white and coloured flies and india-rubber sand-eel for pollack, mackerel and cod is successful. Good centres for most species are Peel, Port Erin, Port St Mary and Ramsey. At Port Erin is sea-fish hatchery and aquarium under control of Liverpool University. Tourist Board, Douglas, issues useful booklet on sea and river fishing. Principal rivers as follows:

COLBY RIVER. Trout. This stream is 4m long; preserved in lower reaches.

DOUGLAS RIVER. Salmon, sea trout, trout. Douglas formed by junction of Dhoo and Glass, half a mile above the town of **Douglas.** Fishing on Glass River and lower part of Dhoo preserved, but free above **Union Mills.** Glass largely rented by Douglas AC; permits and licences from Nods for Rods, Castle Street and Angling Centre, Victoria St.

GLEN MOOR BURN, 3m long. Trout; fishing free, but not very good. Fishing station: **Kirk Michael.**

LAXEY RIVER. Trout; free but poor. This stream is 5m long. 1m above junction with sea at Laxey, Glen River (trout), 3m long, joins on right bank. Fishing station: **Laxey.**

NEB. Trout; mostly free and good; salmon from Aug. Neb (sometimes called Peel River) rises above **Little London** and runs 3m to **Glen Helen** (Hotel: Glen Helen). Here Blaby joins. Neb runs 4m to **St John's.** Here **Foxdale River,** 6m long, joins on left bank. Hence to **Peel** is 3m. 3m S is **Glen Maye River** 4m long; sea

trout below waterfall, trout above.

SANTON BURN. 6m long; trout; mostly preserved, but poor; salmon from Aug. Fishing station: **Santon.**

SILVERBURN. Trout, sea trout; free. This stream rises on the slopes of South Barrule, runs 5m to **Ballasalla,** where Awin Ruy, 4m long, joins on left bank. Silver Burn runs 3m to the sea at **Castletown.** Best sport downstream for about 1m to Castletown.

SULBY. Salmon (from Aug), sea trout; free; good after spates. Sulby rises on western slopes of Snaefell and runs 7m to **Sulby Glen.** Sulby is island's largest river and best for salmon and sea trout; brown trout poor. Five miles S is **Cornaa River,** 5m long, which runs into sea at Port Cornaa, the site of the Fishery Board's hatchery. Good for salmon and sea trout in lower portion (Sept, Oct). Fishing station: **Ramsey.** Excellent sea fishing; bass from beach, plaice and cod from pier. Hotels: Mitre, Prince of Wales.

WYLLIN BURN. 4m long; trout; free; fishing poor. Near **Kirk Michael.**

For further information about sea fishing on the island, see p 191

ISLE OF WIGHT

(For close seasons, licences, etc, see Southern Water Authority, p 11–12)

Freshwater fishing on the Island is better than is generally appreciated. The **Yar** from St Helens, Bembridge, to Alverstone holds fair numbers of roach, dace and rudd, with perch, carp and bream in some stretches. There are put & take stillwater trout fisheries; and reservoirs stocked by the IWFAA with carp and tench also: **Gunville Pond,** Carisbrooke and **Somerton Reservoirs,** Cowes. **Yafford Fish Farm** ponds are near Brighstone. Temporary membership tickets for society waters from tackle dealers. Wt, dt. Southern WA rod licence required, available from following tackleists: G C Young, The Sports Shop, 74 Regent Street, Shanklin; W Bates & Son, 5 Springhill, Ventnor; The Sports & Model Shop, Ryde; David's Food Market, Lane End Court, Bembridge; 'Scotties', Lugley Street, Newport. Light sea fishing, for which freshwater tackle may be employed, available at Whippingham (River Medina), Fishbourne (Wootton Creek) and in Bembridge Harbour; mullet, bass, flatfish, etc. *(For boats, bait, etc, see Sea Fishing Stations).*

A sport for everyone. Pupils from Riddlesworth Hall Prep. School for Girls, Norfolk, learn the art of casting a fly. *Photograph by Richard Mildenhall. Reproduction by courtesy of The Observer.*

ITCHEN

(For close seasons, licences, etc, see Southern Water Authority, p 11–12)

Rises some miles north-west of Petersfield and flows via Winchester into Southampton Water at Southampton. Famous Hampshire chalk stream. Trout fishing excellent, but strictly preserved for most part. Some salmon and sea trout lower down, but also preserved. Principal tributaries are **Alre** and **Candover Brook;** both strictly preserved.

Southampton (Hants). Itchen and Test estuaries. Pout, whiting and eels in Southampton Water; and whiting, bass, grey mullet from the piers and quays. Coarse fishing from public footpath between Woodmill and Mansbridge. Tackleist: Patstone & Cox Ltd, 25 High Street, who can generally give information as to any waters available in district. *(See also Sea Fishing Stations.)*

Eastleigh (Hants). Trout, salmon and grayling; preserved. Here is Bishopstoke FC water, which affords excellent sport. Water holds large trout. Salmon run right up to Brambridge. Some sea trout also come up; private. Small stretch at Bishopstoke and another at Woodmill (tidal) is public fishing.

Bishopstoke (Hants), ns Eastleigh. Salmon, trout and grayling; preserved by Bishopstoke FC and other owners.
Winchester (Hants). Trout above city; trout and grayling below. All fishing on the R Itchen strictly preserved other than water between Durngate Mill and Wharf Mill which runs through city embracing Water Lane and The Weirs. SWA licence required. Obtainable from tackleist The Rod Box, 52 St Georges St *(advt p 19)*, who also offer dry fly fishing on st and dt basis and other rods on celebrated private stretches of the Test and on the Itchen, **Nadder, Anton, Bourne** and

Whitewater, and on lakes. Charges on request. Phone 0962 61561 for details of these and other fishings.
Itchen Abbas (Hants). Trout; preserved by riparian owners. **Avington Trout Fishery,** lakes fed by R Itchen, provide remarkable trout fishing. British rainbow record broken there several times. Detailed information on 1988 plans not available as we go to press. (Tel: Itchen Abbas 312.)
Alresford (Hants). **Candover Brook, Alre,** Itchen; trout; strictly preserved by riparian owners. Grange Lakes, Alresford Pond; coarse fish; preserved.

KENT (lakes and streams)
(For close seasons, licences, etc, see Southern Water Authority, p 11–12)

BAYHAM LAKE nr **Lamberhurst.** 16 acre lake stocked with rb trout, average size large. Boats. Variety of st offerings £100–£300. Dt £15 (5 fish); ½ day £10 (3 fish). For further details phone John Parkman 0892 890276.
BEWL WATER: 770 acre SWA fly-only trout fishery nr. **Lamberhurst.** St (full) £260. (Mon-Fri) £200. Dt £7.50. Evenings, £5.50. Concessions for beginners and jun, with reduced limits. Motor and pulling boats. £11 and £6.50; evenings: £7.50 and £4.50. Season: April 4—Oct 26. Enquiries (in season) 0892 890352 (out of season) 890661.
BROOKLANDS LAKE and HORTON KIRBY LAKES. Fishing station: **Dartford.** Dartford and Dist APS; St £15 (waiting list) dt for lakes £1.50.
CHIDDINGSTONE CASTLE LAKE. Good coarse fishing. No night fishing. Prepaid booking advisable at weekends. Dt £5 from Senior Custodian. Apply Miss M H Eldridge, hon sec. Chiddingstone Castle, near **Edenbridge.** Tel: 0892 870347.
DARENTH, SUTTON-AT-HONE Carp, pike and other coarse fish. St £33 and £19. £2 key deposit (Darenth). Both LSA restricted fisheries.
LARKFIELD LAKES. Carp, pike etc, St £17. Concessions on all for jun, OAP, dis. Applications to LSA, Thorpe Park, Staines Lane, Chertsey, Surrey. Tel: 64872.
HAWKHURST. Small stillwater fishery for rainbow trout. Fish to 3lb. Phone 3457.
LONGFORD LAKE. Fishing station: **Sevenoaks.** Private water of Holmesdale

AS, who also now have junior water Montreal Park Lake; st £17.50, £12 joining fee. Dt £2 for friends of members only, from S Banks, 57 Chevening Rd, Chipstead, Kent. *(See also Darent.)*
LULLINGSTONE LAKE, near **Eynsford.** Trout. Kingfisher APS; no tickets.
MOTE PARK LAKE. Fishing station: **Maidstone** *(see Medway).* Coarse fish (including specimen bream, tench and pike); dt for non-residents £2.50 from Arts and Recreations Office, Old Palace, Mill Street, Maidstone, Kent and local tackle shops. Concession for OAP.
MURSTON PITS. At Murston, 1¼m N of **Sittingbourne,** Sittingbourne AC has three pits; coarse fish; no dt, enquiries to hon sec. Tackleist: Dean's, East Street.
OARE PITS. At Oare, 1½m N of **Faversham,** Faversham AC has large pool containing carp (30lb plus), tench, bream, roach and pike. Also other pits holding coarse fish. St £17 + £17 entrance fee. DT £1.50 from waterside or hon sec.
PETT POOLS. Fishing stations: **Winchelsea,** 2m; **Rye,** 4m. Coarse fish; dt £2.50 (limited) from M Piddington, Market Stores, Pett. St £24 from SWA Fisheries Dept, Capstone Road, Chatham, Kent. Ft £8 and dt from Rye Bay Supermarket, Coast Road, Winchelsea Beach, East Sussex.
ROMNEY MARSH. Much good fishing on marsh, especially in main drains to Rother; best in summer (large bream shoals); water on low side in winter. Clubs with water here are: Ashford and

Dist APS; Cinque Ports AS; Clive Vale AC; Clive Vale reservoirs (carp), Ecclesbourne Reservoir, Hastings, Bexhill and Dist AA (members only); Rye and Dist AS; Tenterden and Dist APS; Linesmen AC (also waters on **Medway, Beult** and **Stour;** details from hon sec).

ROYAL MILITARY CANAL. Summer fishing only; level partially lowered in winter for drainage. Stations: **Hythe and Ashford.** Cinque Ports AS has from Seabrook to West Hythe Dam; carp, bream, chub, roach, rudd, tench, dace, perch, pike; dt and wt from bailiff, from Light Railway Restaurant, J B Walker Ltd, 84 Stade Street, (tel: 0303 66228) (both Hythe) and hon sec. Ashford and Dist A & PS has about 16m from West Hythe Dam to Iden Lock (south bank only from dam to Appledore Bridge) and quarry stocked with large carp. St £10, wt £3.50, dt £1.50, jun 30p. Roach, rudd, chub, tench, perch, carp, bream, dace, pike. Tickets available from inns near canal at West Hythe, Ruckinge, Warehorne, Appledore, and from cottage at canal bridge. Hon sec Ashford and Dist APS will give further information. RD licences and tackle in Ashford *(see Medway and Hythe Sea Fishing Stations).*

SUNDRIDGE LAKES, Sevenoaks. 15-acre and 5 acre lakes. Stocked with large carp, roach and limited pike. St £69. Inquiries to Rod and Line Ltd, 70–72 Loampit Vale, Lewisham, SE13. Tel 01-852 1421.

LANCASHIRE AND CUMBRIA (Westmorland) streams

(For close seasons, licences, etc, see North West Water Authority, p 13–14 unless otherwise stated)

BELA. Cumbrian trout stream, flowing from Lily Mere to estuary of Kent at Milnthorpe. Much of its course is through low-lying country with heavy water. Size of fish better than in some northern streams; many dry-fly reaches. Salmon and sea trout below Beetham Mills private. One of the earliest of northern streams; trout fishing starts March 3.

Milnthorpe (Cumbria). Trout. Preserved by Milnthorpe AA and confined to members and guests. Association also preserves St Sunday's Beck from Deep-thwaite Bridge and Peasey Beck from Farleton Beck downwards and thence, from confluence of these streams, to Beetham Mills, which is as far as salmon run. Fishing below mills private. Sport very good in March, April, May and Aug. RWA licences and tackle from Atkinson's, Stricklandgate, Kendal (also Kent AA tickets) *(see River Kent).* Hotels at Milnthorpe: Cross Keys, Bull's Head, Coach and Horses; Wheatsheaf at Beetham.

Oxenholme (Cumbria). Bela, 2m E. Beehive Beck, 1m E. Old Hutton Beck, 3m SE. **Killington Reservoir;** large sheet of water, 3m E. Pike, perch and some big trout. Now privately fished.

CONDOR. Fishing station: **Galgate.** Brown trout and sea trout. No tickets.

DUDDON. Fishing station: **Broughton-in-Furness.** Sea trout, salmon. Dt from E A Clark, solicitor, for river from Duddon Bridge to Greety Gate, both banks. Millom & Dist AA has rights to 366 yds of north bank from Duddon Bridge, and permission on Mr Hagel's Hall Bridge stretch, reviewed annually; members only. Assn also has water on **Esk, Lickle, Annas, Irt, Lazy, Devoke Water** (salmon, sea trout, trout) and **Baystone Bank Reservoir** (fly only); members only. Close to Broughton-in-Furness, **River Lickle** joins Duddon on left bank. River rented by Millom AA. Members only. Applications for membership to hon sec.

Ulpha (Cumbria). Good sea trout and salmon, few brown trout. All river below down to Ulpha Bridge private. **Devoke Water** (large trout) may also be fished from here. Millom AA has rights, members only. Applications for membership to hon sec. *(See Cumberland—small streams).* Below this point Duddon runs into estuary. Hotel: Old King's Head.

KENT. Fast-flowing salmon and trout stream running into Morecambe Bay. Fishing reported much improved following pollution and drainage schemes. Salmon, sea trout, trout.

Kendal (Cumbria). Salmon, sea trout, trout. A few spring salmon with main run and sea trout moving up about June; fairly plentiful Aug onwards. Kent below Burneside preserved (together with **Mint,** both banks, from Mealbank to junction with Kent. Also about $\frac{1}{2}$m of **Sprint,** south bank). Thence south of the town to Basinghyll Bridge (both banks) held by Kent AA, wt £15 to May 31, £35 thereafter; dt £5 to May 31, £10 thereafter. RWA licence necessary. Tickets and licences from Kendal Sports *(see below).* Below is Levens Park fishery, private. Dt from Low Levens Farm for good stretch. Stainton Beck 2m; trout. Kendal Corporation owns Fisher Tarn; now privately leased. **Killington Reservoir** (ns Oxenholme), is property of British Waterways; pike, perch and trout. Fishing rights leased to Kent AA, wt £4.50, dt £2. Tackleists: Carlsons Fishing Tackle, Kirkland, Kendal, Kendal Sports, 28-30, Stramondgate, who issue Kent AA tickets and RD licences. Hotels: County, Woolpack, Seven Stars, Globe.

Burneside (Cumbria). Burneside AA water from a little below junction of Sprint up to Beckmickleing Wood near Staveley, including mill dams at Burneside, Bowston, and Cowan Head, which hold large trout (up to $1\frac{1}{2}$ lb); salmon and sea trout from July. *(See Sprint below.)* Permits and accommodation at Jolly Anglers Inn, st £25, wt £12, dt £5. Burneside Lakes (not assn): Skelsmergh Tarn, 2m NE; Gurnal Dubs, private fishing administered by Ellergreen Estates, 3m north.

Staveley (Cumbria). Kent; trout (small); salmon and sea trout in Sept and Oct. Staveley and Dist AA has rights on river, and on **River Gowan** and **Kentmere Tarn.** Wt £6 tarn, £8 river, from D & H Woof, 22 Main Street, Staveley. Hotels: Eagle and Child, Duke William, Railway.

MINT (tributary of Kent). Best fished from Kendal. Joins Kent about 1m above town; holds good head of small trout. Kent AA has lowest water *(see Kendal).*

SPRINT (tributary of Kent). Joins Kent at Burneside. Burneside AA *(see Burneside)* has about 1m of fishing from junction with Kent. Kent AA has $\frac{1}{2}$m (L bank only). Salmon and sea trout from Aug; brown trout small; banks much wooded.

KEER. Rises 4m above Borwick, runs into Morecambe Bay 3m below **Carnforth.**

Good sea trout and brown trout (no coarse fish). Carnforth AA has water; wt and dt on application to hon sec. Canal fishing for coarse fish in the vicinity, but not controlled by Carnforth AA.

LEVEN: Drains Windermere, and is joined by **River Crake** (from Coniston Water) at Greenodd, near Ulverston, before flowing into Morecambe Bay. Salmon, sea trout, trout. Both rivers strictly preserved.

Ulverston (Cumbria). Salmon, sea trout, trout. Ulverston AA has fishing on **Ulverston Canal,** $1\frac{1}{4}$m long, specimen tench, carp, etc; restocked; day and season tickets from Canal Tavern Inn, Bay Horse Inn, H Jackson and E Sharp, Sports shops. St £10, dt £1.50, concessions to OAP and jun. Match permits from AA sec. Lakes: **Knottallow Tarn,** (brown trout fishing, available on associate membership to visitors). **Urswick Tarn,** 3m S; coarse fishing. Apply Gen Burgoyne Inn, Little Urswick. Mere Tarn, 5m S (Furness FA; st only). Hotels: Armadale, Sun, Queen's, King's, Bay Horse, Lonsdale House. *Note: Guide book to fishing obtainable from Town Hall.*

Greenodd (Cumbria). Salmon, trout, sea trout; preserved by Lower Leven Fishery; waiting list closed. Crake: salmon, sea trout, trout *(see Crake).* Colton Beck; sea trout, salmon; private. Hotel: Armadale.

Newby Bridge (Cumbria). Salmon, trout; preserved by Leven AA down to Greenodd railway bridge; members only. Swan Hotel issues dt £1.75. Lakes: Windermere, 1m N; Bawtry Tarn, 2m NE; pike, perch; preserved by Furness FA. High and Low Dam, Finsthwaite; brown trout, coarse fish; dt from the Manager, Stott Park, Bobbin Mill, Finsthwaite, 2m S, **Bigland Hall** Sporting Estate. 12 acre coarse fish lake.

Lake Side (Cumbria). Salmon, trout. Some free fishing; other sections of the shore private. Inquire locally pike, perch, trout. Lakes: Windermere; pike, perch, char, trout. Bawtry Tarn 2m W *(see Newby Bridge) (see Westmorland lakes for Winderemere).*

TORVER BECK (tributary of Coniston lake), **Torver** (Lancs). Lakes: Coniston, 1m E; pike, perch and trout, Goat's Water, 3m NE. Beacon Tarn, 5m S. Hotel: Church House Inn.

CRAKE (tributary of Leven):

Greenodd (Cumbria). Crake; salmon, sea trout, trout. Dt for stretch at Lowick Bridge from W. Hall, Mill Farm, Lowick Bridge. **Rusland Pool River,** tributary of Leven; st £2 (jun £1) from Mrs P G Booth, Haverthwaite Lodge, Nr Ulverston, Cumbria LA12 8AJ. Tel: 0448 31228. Clitheroe FA has water; members only. Forestry Commission, Satterthwaite issues tickets, as do some farmers and landowners.

Coniston (Cumbria). Yewdale Beck, Torver Beck, $2\frac{1}{2}$m S. Crake; salmon, sea trout. Duddon, 8m; salmon, sea trout, (Millom & Dist AA water). Lakes: Coniston; pike, perch, char, trout and eels. Goat's Water, 2m W; Low Tarn, 3m NE. Esthwaite Lake, 4m; pike and perch *(see Hawkshead).* Char fishing in Coniston Lake very good from May to October. Lake free to holders of appropriate RD licence. Coniston and Torver AA issues permits for Yew Tree Tarn (rainbow and brown trout). Dt £4 and £2, according to date, from Raven, Gift and Sports Shop, Yewdale Road, Coniston.

GRIZEDALE BECK (tributary of Leven): **Hawkshead** (Cumbria). Forestry Commission, small brown trout; let to Grizedale AA; st £6. Wt £3.50 and dt £1 from Fern Cottage, Camp Shop, or Forestry Office, Grizedale. Reduced rates pre-June 30. Esthwaite Water; trout, pike, perch; preserved, but visitors can obtain tickets *(see English Lake District).*

TROUTBECK (trib of L Windermere): **Windermere** (Cumbria). Water on river given up by Windermere, Ambleside & Dist AA but fly fishing for trout on three tarns in the area (**School Knot, Moss Eccles,** and **High Arnside,** all stocked

regularly) available to visitors. St £12, wt £6, dt £3 from Raven, The Gift and Sports Shop, Coniston. *(For further details see entry for Ambleside, below.)* Hotels: Old England, Windermere, Stag's Head. Boats at Lakeside, Bowness, Millerground, Waterhead. Lake free to licence-holders *(see Cumbria Lakes).*

Ambleside (Cumbria) ns Windermere, 5m Windermere, Ambleside and Dist AA has trout fishing on **Rothay** and **Brathay,** streams running into the lake from the N, on **Rydal Water,** (chiefly pike and perch) and on tarns *(see Windermere entry.)* St £12, wt £6, dt £3. Jun & OAP $\frac{1}{2}$ price. Other waters near Ambleside: Scandal Beck; trout; preserved. Rydale Rock, 2m N Windermere; pike, perch and trout; free. Belham Tarn, 3m S. Yew Tree Tarn; Coniston AA. Hotels: Salutation, White Lion, Waterhead (boats).

Grasmere (Cumbria). Rothay; trout, Easdale Beck; trout. Lakes: Grasmere (now Winderemere, Ambleside & D. AA water); pike, perch and few trout. Rydal Water, 3m SE; perch, pike and few trout. Stream joining Grasmere with Rydal gives fair trouting. Easdale Tarn, 3m NW; good perch, trout. Codale Tarn, 4m NW; trout, perch. Hotels: Rothay, Prince of Wales (boats), Dale Lodge, Swan, Allonby (boats).

WINSTER. Parallel with Windermere for 6m. Joins the sea by **Grange-over-Sands.** Salmon, sea trout, brown trout, coarse fish. Wigan AA has extensive fishing in **Lyndale** area. Permits no longer issued for St Mary's College stretch. Brown trout and sea trout (late) may be taken in **River Eea.** Dt and wt from Commodore Hotel, Grange-over-Sands.

LANCASHIRE (lakes and reservoirs)

(see North West Water Authority, p 13–14, unless otherwise stated)

APPLETON RESERVOIR. Fishing station: **Warrington.** Coarse fish; Warrington Corporation, st and dt available from lodge near reservoir. At **Lymm,** near Warrington, is Lymm AC water; **Lymm Dam,** good carp, etc. St £17, dt £1, £2, from sec..

BARROW IN FURNESS RESERVOIRS. Barrow AA has trout fishing in five reservoirs. No tickets. Furness FA issues

season and day tickets for all waters, coarse and game, stocked and unstocked. Details from Hannay's (tackleist), 50 Crellin Street. *(See also Sea Fishing Stations.)*

BARNSFOLD WATERS. 7m NE of Preston. Trout, fly only. St and limited dt. Tel Ribchester 202.

BRYAN HEY RESERVOIR. 3m NW of Bolton. Coarse fish and trout. Dt £1.50

from Withnell Fisheries Ltd, 11 Kearsley Drive, Bolton BL3 2PG, Greater Manchester, and on bank.

BUCKLEY WOOD RESERVOIR, Rochdale. Leased by NWWA to Rochdale Walton AS. Inquire hon sec *(see also Mersey and Rochdale).*

BROWNHILL RESERVOIR. Between **Colne** and **Foulridge.** Feeder for Leeds and Liverpool Canal. Holds brown trout; preserved by Colne AA, tickets for members' guests only.

EARNSDALE RESERVOIR, Darwen. NWWA (S Rivers Div). Trout. Darwen AA has rights on reservoir; good fly water; st £32 dt £4.50; information from County Sports, Duckworth St, Darwen. Tel: 025 472187

HEAPEY LODGES. Chorley. 28 acres. Four reservoirs stocked with indigenous trout, and coarse fish of most suitable species, including a well established population of carp. Now Wigan AA water. St £12, juv £3.

NORTH WEST WATER AUTH RESERVOIRS. Rivington. These reservoirs which include **Upper and Lower Rivington, Anglezarke, Upper Roddlesworth** are about 35m north-east of Liverpool.

UPPER RODDLESWORTH RESERVOIR. This water now club managed by Horwich Fly Fishers Club. Club members and day ticket only, £6 *(no season permit),* concessions for OAP, juniors, disabled. Day ticket £4. Available from Andrew Leech, Fishing Tackle & Sports Outfitters, Leigh Lane, Horwich, Bolton. Lower Roddlesworth and Rakebrook reservoirs are managed by Withnell AC. Members only. Dt £1.50 from Brinscall Tackle Shop.

ANGLEZARKE RESERVOIR. This water now managed by Northern Anglers. Club members and day ticket only. Concessions for OAP, juniors, disabled.

Day ticket and membership details available from Andrew Leach Tackle Shop, Horwich.

UPPER RIVINGTON RESERVOIR. Mixed fishery. This water is now managed by Bolton AA. St £7.50, dt £1.50, from Andrew Leach *(see above).*

LOWER RIVINGTON RESERVOIR. Mixed fishery. This water is now managed by Greater Manchester Youth Ass. Dt only, £1.25 (conc for OAP, dis, juv), from A Leach *(see above),* and on the bank from bailiff.

OLDHAM RESERVOIRS. Oldham United AS leases six reservoirs from NWWA. **Lower Strinesdale, Castleshaw** and **Kitcliffe** (trout); **Upper Strinesdale, Ogden Reservoirs,** pike, perch, bream, roach, carp, tench, chub; some trout. St (trout) £52, (coarse) £5. Dt (trout) £4.50, (coarse) 50p, (Sundays £1). Tickets by post from sec or A Dyson, 7 Raven Avenue, Chadderton.

ORMSGILL LOWER RESERVOIR. Barrow. Trout, tench, carp. Furness FA water. Inquiries to Hannays, 50 Crellin St, Barrow in Furness.

PENNINGTON FLASH. Leigh. Good coarse fishing. Pennington Flash AA issues st £2.50 and dt 50p. Inquiries to G Unsworth, 142 Chestnut Drive S, Leigh, Lancs.

SABDEN RESERVOIR. Whalley. Trout (av 10 in), carp. Accrington and Dist FC water. Dt £4 from A Balderstones, 42 Townley Ave, Huncoat, Accrington. Tel: 0254 33517. Lancashire RD licence required.

WORTHINGTON RESERVOIRS. Wigan. 39 Acres, 3 reservoirs, one trout, two coarse fish. Wigan & Dist AA water. Assc. also controls several miles of **Ribble** and **Wyre.** Wigan tackleists: J A Blackledge, 4a The Wiend, Market Place; Bartons, Wigan Road, Hindley.

LEA or LEE

(For close seasons, licences, etc, see Thames Water Authority, p 16)

Walton's river; flows through Bedfordshire and Hertfordshire then along boundary between Essex and Middlesex to join Thames near Blackwall; 46m long. Building and canalisation have largely removed its charm, but still holds good coarse fish and occasional trout.

Tottenham (Middx). New Cut, at Tottenham Hale, $\frac{3}{4}$m stocked. Lee Navigation, at South Tottenham, stocked. Dt £1.80 at water, conc 90p. Roach and dace predominant; some chub, carp and bream. Best baits: hempseed, casters; TWA reservoirs close to Tottenham Hale (roach, perch, bream, pike; or stocked with brown and rainbow trout) *(see under London)*. Tackleists: Farrer, Seven Sisters Rd, N15; Don's, 239-246 Fore Street, Edmonton.

Enfield Lock (Middx). Fair sport with roach, perch, few bream and pike, and occasional carp.

Waltham Abbey (Herts). Good coarse fishing on **Lea Relief Channel** from Fisher's Green to Waltham Abbey. TWA has fishery $1\frac{1}{4}$m long able to accommodate about 250 anglers. St £14, dt £1.10 (concessions for OAP, regd disabled and juniors).From Tackleists: P & B Hall, 44 Highbridge Street, Waltham Abbey and Abbey Angling, Sun Street, Waltham Abbey. A $4\frac{1}{2}$ acre lake stocked with r and b trout is now available at Waltham Abbey. Limited rods available, no dt. Contact hon sec, Civil Service FS.

Cheshunt (Herts). Coarse fishing. Red Spinner AS has Cheshunt South Reservoir; carp and tench. Members only. Cheshunt AC has Friday Lake; members only. Kings Arms AC and Cheshunt Carp Club have Cheshunt North Reservoir.

Wormley (Herts). The famous **King's Weir Fishery** ($\frac{1}{2}$m R Lea, $\frac{3}{4}$m of Flood Relief Channel and $\frac{3}{4}$m of bank at Langridge Lake), available on dt (£1 and £2) and st £20. Tel: Hoddesdon 468394 for bookings.

Broxbourne (Herts). Leased by BT Committee from King's Weir Fishery boundary below Broxbourne bridge up to Dobbs' Lock above, including the **Crown Fisheries** and **Redlands Carthagena Fishery;** 2 lakes in 15 acres, stocked with coarse fish; $\frac{3}{4}$m of Old R Lea, 1m of Lea Navigation. St £15, juv, OAP £8. Tel: 0992 463656. "Leisure Sport" has group of lakes here totalling $125\frac{1}{2}$ acres. St £14 from LSA, Thorpe Park, Chertsey KT16 8PN. Tel: 64872.

Hoddesdon (Herts). ns Rye House or Broxbourne. On Lea, Stort and New River Lea: London AA has rights of Dobbs' Weir Fishery; large dace, bream, roach, pike, chub and perch, and a few trout. Dt 20p. Tackleist: C J Ross, 2 Amwell Street. Hotel: Fish and Eels.

Rye House (Herts). Roach, chub, dace, bream, pike, perch, tench, few trout. Rye House Bridge to October Hole is London AA water and October Hole to Ware public. West Ham AS controls "Forty Guinea" water, just above Fielde's Weir Lock to about 300 yds above Fish and Eels footbridge, both banks. Dt 15p (tow path only) from bailiff. Hotel: Ye Olde Rye House.

St Margaret's (Herts). Old River Lea. River fishing from towing-path.

Ware (Herts). Old River Lea. Fishing in Lea Navigation from towpath is public. There are roach, dace, bream and trout in the water, and "The Boom", where a side-stream comes in above the bridge, is a favourite place with anglers. This is a likely spot for a trout.

Hertford (Herts). For Lea, **Mimram, Beane, Rib** and **New River.** Lea is public from towing-path between Hertford and Old Ford Lock and Stort Navigation between Bishop's Stortford and Hoddesdon, excluding club waters, for which dt are obtainable (details on notice boards). London AA has stretch from Town Mill gate to junction with Lee Navigation ($\frac{3}{4}$m); members only. Tackleists: Brown Bros, Castle Street; Mecca Angling, 31 Railway Street. Hotels: Salisbury Arms, Dimsdale Arms, White Hart, Station. Trout, jack, perch, chub, roach and dace.

Hatfield (Herts). Hatfield AS has rights on river from Mill Green to Essendon (about $2\frac{1}{2}$m); including seven-acre broadwater (large carp and bream). Members only.

Cole Green, nr **Welwyn.** Lake stocked with carp, tench, roach and rudd. A second lake, at **Holwell Court,** is now available, stocked with carp. St £20, dt £2, from bailiff on bank. Contact Fishery Manager, Holwell Hyde Cottage, Holwell Hyde Lane, Welwyn Garden City.

Luton (Beds). Tring Reservoirs (10m); Grand Union Canal (10m); Great Ouse (20m). Clubs: Luton AC, Leighton Buzzard AC, Ampthill & Dist A & FPS. Information from tackleists: Anglers Corner, 73 Austin Road, or Wilds, 8-10 Bute St.

Fishing Clubs

When you appoint a new secretary, do not forget to give us details of the change. Write to Thomas Harmsworth Publishing, 13 Nicosia Road, London SW18 3RN. Thank you!

Tributaries of the Lea

STORT:
Roydon (Essex). Roach, dace, perch, pike, chub, bream. Between Roydon Station bridge and Mill bridge is ticket water; Dt £1.20 from Godfrey Davis Park Homes Ltd, Roydon Mill, Nr Harlow, Essex. Tel: 0279 2133. Fishery closes Nov 1 each year. Lychnobite AS leases Temple Farm Fishery, (about 2m of fishing). Dt from bailiff on water. Leisure Sport gravel pits at **Ryemeads**. St £13, concessions for jun, OAP, dis. Applications to LSA, Thorpe Park, Staines Road, Chertsey, Surrey. Tel: Chertsey 64872.

Burnt Mill (Essex). Stort. Controlled by London AA; strictly members only. Bishop's Stortford AS *(dt; see Harlow and Bishop's Stortford)* and Harlow AS (private) have water.

Harlow (Essex). Coarse fish. Harlow UDC has town waters. Inquiries to clerk of council. London AA has water here and at **Spellbrook** and **Thorley;** (available to associates). LAA grants facilities for Harlow residents on its water. Inquiries to Sec.

Sawbridgeworth (Herts). Good head of all coarse fish with many large roach; fishes best Sept onwards. Sawbridgeworth AS

has 1½m each side of railway station; dt from bailiffs; pike fishing (after Oct 1), limited number of st. Dt and tackle from The Pet Shop, Knight Street. Hotel: Queens Head (club HQ). Visiting parties welcome; apply hon sec for reservation.

Bishop's Stortford (Herts). Bishop's Stortford and Dist AS has coarse fishing to Spellbrook Lock (tickets) and has length at Harlow, Cam at Clayhithe, lakes, 10 acre gravel pit. Tickets from tackleist: Fins & Fur, 40a Hockerill Street, or hon sec. Hotels: Foxley, George, Hatfield Forest Lake (National Trust) *(see Essex (small streams and lakes))*.

ASH. Fishing stations: **Widford** (Herts) and **Hadham** (Essex); a few trout, pike, etc; preserved.

RIB: Trout, coarse fish. "Leisure Sport" fishery for st holders, inquiries to RMC House, Feltham, Middlesex. Fishing stations: **Standon, Braughing, Westmill,** all Hertfordshire. Abbey Cross AS has a stretch from Hertford to Watton Rd, nr Ware; strictly members only.

BEANE: This once-excellent trout stream has been largely ruined by abstraction. Some stretches still hold good fish, however.

MIMRAM: Trout, preserved.

LINCOLNSHIRE (small streams)

(For close seasons, licences, etc, see Anglian Water Authority, p 14–15)

GREAT EAU or WITHERN. Rises above Aby and flows some 12m to sea at Saltfleet; coarse fish; much free water; fishes best in autumn.

Saltfleet (Lincs), ns Saltfleet, 3m. Grayfleet, South Eau, and Mar Dyke; coarse fish; some free water. At Saltfleetby St Peters is pond on which fishing is available; dt, at shop near pond; no Sunday fishing. Sea trout in Haven in Sept; also flounders.

Louth (Lincs). Great Eau private above bridge on main Louth—**Mablethorpe** road, including Calceby Brook, Aby and South Ormesby Park; free below to licence-holders as far as Gayton lugs, thence ½m private to members of Mablethorpe, Sutton-on-Sea Dist AC (st £10), (also another ¾m stretch), thence free to Cloves Bridge. **Theddlethorpe** (Mablethorpe Dist AC), and free below

Cloves Bridge. Altogether 10m free fishing to RD licence holders; coarse fish, including good roach, bream, perch, pike, rainbow trout (few and mostly small) and grayling. **Lud** generally free below Louth to outfall at Tetney. Coarse fishing in ponds at **Grainthorpe, North and South Somercotes, Fulstow, Saltfleetby** and brick pits, Alfred Rd, **Sutton-on-Sea;** dt at adjacent houses. Parts of **Louth Canal** free to licence-holders from Louth to sea outlet at **Tetney;** part controlled by Witham and Dist. JAF; coarse fish; some private access; permission from farmers. Tackleists: Pet Shop, opposite Mablethorpe Station; Belas, Victoria Road.

STEEPING. Rises 5m above **Spilsby** (1m off on left bank), runs thence to **Wainfleet** and joins the sea 4m below near **Skegness** *(see also Sea Fishing Stations);*

coarse fish; largely free to RD licence-holders; applications for match lengths to RD after Jan 1. Croft AC has stretch at Haven House; tickets. Witham and Dist. JAF controls 20m from Wainfleet upstream, and **Wainfleet Relief Channel.**

Spilsby AA has **Ereby Canal;** good bream, tench, perch, etc; members only; confined to 13m radius; st and dt from hon sec or Higgs Bros (tackleists), Spilsby, who also issue licences.

LONDON (Thames Water reservoirs, etc)

Most of the waters referred to below are in the area termed Greater London. All are easily accessible from Central London. A number are rented by angling clubs and reserved for members, but at others fishing is available to the general public at modest charges on season or day ticket basis.

It seems appropriate to mention here two important angling bodies—first, the **London Anglers' Association,** which has water on several reservoirs as well as scores of miles on rivers, streams and lakes (125 fisheries in all). The Association now has about 9,000 full members through 300 affiliated clubs. It has offices at Forest Road Hall, Hervey Park Road, Walthamstow, London E17 6LJ (telephone number: 01-520 7477). For a brochure

Angling is a sport for everyone, but appeals especially to the young. This young man is trying his hand and his luck on the R. Rib at Standen Mill Pool Hertfordshire. *Photo: John Tarlton.*

and application form please send a stamped addressed envelope to LAA Forest Road Hall, Hervey Park Road, Walthamstow, E17 6LJ (Tel: 01 520 7477). Annual membership (associate) £15.50. (Jun, OAP, regd disabled) (£4.50).

The Central Association of London and Provincial Angling Clubs (HQ The Lord Raglan, St Martins Le Grand EC2) has about 120 affiliated clubs and fisheries on rivers, canals and lakes in the South of England. Day tickets issued for many fisheries. Full details from hon sec.

Among tackleists in Central London are: Hardy Bros, of 61 Pall Mall; C Farlow & Co Ltd, 5b Pall Mall *(advt p 3)*. Tackle dealers in the suburbs are too numerous to list. The Angling Trades Association is at 7 Swallow Street, Piccadilly (Tel: 01-437 7281).

(Tackleists in Metropolitan area listed under individual centres.)

Thames Water Reservoirs where fishing rights are let to clubs including the following: **King George's, Chingford; Queen Mary; Lambeth (No 4).** All to London AA. **Banbury, Walthamstow** to Civil Service Sports Council. **Cheshunt (South)** to Red Spinner AS.

Reservoirs open to the public for game fishing (stocked with rainbow or brown trout).

Walthamstow Nos 4 & 5. Barn Elms 5, 6 & 7 are all stocked with trout. Three are reserved for fly fishing only, in three others bait fishing and spinning, with certain restrictions, are permitted. Walthamstow 4 and 5 open for pike fishing 1 Dec to 1 Mar. Dt £8.30, ½ day £6, boat on Barn Elms 5 only, £4.50.

Comprehensive leaflet issued by TWA, supplied on request, by the Information Officer, Thames Water, Nugent House, Vastern Road, Reading. Tel: Reading 593538.

Reservoirs open to the public for coarse fishing.

Northmet Pit, Cheshunt, has pike to 35lb; dt £1.50, juv, OAP 75p. Contact Lee Valley Leisure Park *(advert below)*.

The Lee Valley Park contains some of the best fisheries and biggest fish in the country. There is a wide variety of river, gravel pit lake and reservoir coarse and game fisheries most of which can be fished on a day ticket basis.

For further information on day ticket waters, carp fisheries, trout fisheries, angling clubs, fishing competitions, angling instruction, disabled angling sites and fishing holiday facilities: **Contact Howard Pearce, Fisheries Manager, Lee Valley Park, PO Box 88, Enfield, Middlesex EN2 9HG. Tel: (0992) 717711.**

Walthamstow Nos 1, 2 & 3, E and W War-wick, High and Low Maynard, Coppermill Stream, New Cut, Lee Navigation ($\frac{1}{4}$m at Walthamstow). St, where issued, £30, £14 conc, dt £1.80, 90p conc. Comprehensive leaflet issued by TWA, supplied on request. See above.

LUNE

(For close seasons, licences, etc, see North West Water Authority, p 13–14)

Rises on Ravenstonedale Common (Westmorland) and flows through beautiful valley into Irish Sea near Lancaster. Excellent sport with salmon, sea trout and brown trout. Lower reaches also well-stocked with coarse fish. August and September best for salmon and sea trout.

Lancaster (Lancs). Salmon, sea trout, trout. NWWA has Skerton Fisheries. (Beaumont Beck to Scaleford—both banks.) Limited dt for salmon £4 (to 31 July), £6 (to end of season), night permits for sea trout £3. Above weir limited tickets for coarse fishing 80p. Matches can be booked on Sundays. NWWA licences and tickets from Darwen and Gough (Tackle Shop), 6 Moor Lane, Lancaster.

Halton (Lancs). Lune; salmon, sea trout, trout, coarse fish. NWWA has weir above and below weir, most of it on L bank; day permits for salmon £4 (up to 31 July) and £6 (1 August to end of season). Dt £3 for sea trout (May 1 to Oct 15, 8 pm to 4 am), from Mrs Curwen, Greenup Cottage, Hornby Road, Caton, nr Lancaster (Lancaster 77078). All charges subject to 50% reduction for OAP, juniors and reg disabled.

Caton (Lancs). Lancaster and Dist AA has fishing over 6 bank miles divided into three sections. Waiting list for membership. Wt £40; dt (pre-July) £5 (post July 1) £10, from Greenup Cottage, Caton. No dt Saturdays and Sundays, though Sunday fishing is allowed to members. Fly only when water level 1 ft 6 in or below. Worm prohibited in October. No maggot or grub fishing. Restrictions on threadline.

Hornby (Lancs). Salmon, sea trout, trout. Lancaster AA has Claughton stretch *(see Caton)*. No dt.

Whittington (Lancs). Salmon, sea trout ($\frac{1}{2}$ lb to 2 lb). Dt 75p from H G Mackereth, Whittington Farm.

Kirkby Lonsdale (Cumbria). Salmon, sea trout, trout. Trout and sea trout fishing are very good; average $1\frac{1}{2}$ lb; sea trout up to 8 lb. Kirby Lonsdale AA has about $4\frac{1}{2}$m of water. Visitors' tickets (Mon–Fri £20) to persons staying locally only (not caravanners or campers), from L Barrie, Gents' Outfitter, The Old Market. Below Kirkby Lonsdale & Dist AA water, Lancaster & Dist AA has water. Hotels: Royal, (can arrange salmon and trout fishing). Red Dragon, King's Arms, Sun, Fleece Inn. Casterton Hotel at Casterton, 1m upstream, is convenient for association waters. Salmon (best August, September); sea trout (June onwards), trout.

Barbon (Cumbria). Lune, 1m W Barbon Beck. Barbon is good centre for Kirkby Lonsdale AA water. Hotel: Barbon Inn.

Sedbergh (Cumbria). Sedbergh AA has about 2m on Lune and about 10m of tributaries **Rawthey, Dee** and **Clough.** Brown trout; salmon and sea trout from July. St £55 from G C Tomlinson, Ridge House, Cautley, Sedbergh, wt £20 (limited) dt £7 from The Sports Shop, Main Street. Manchester AA has stretch at **Firbank;** members only. Tickets for 9m on **Clough** from The Hive Garage, The Street, Garsdale. Hotels: The Bull, Oakdene.

Low Gill (Cumbria). Trout, sea trout and salmon (salmon and sea trout best at back end); about $2\frac{1}{2}$m both banks preserved by Manchester AA, which has water at Low Gill and Firbank. Membership: £140 pa. Blackburn AA also has water.

Tebay (Cumbria). Salmon and sea trout (August onwards best), trout (average 3 to lb). Telbay and Dist has 17m of good water; wt £30. Tickets from Tebay club secretary and hotels. Hotels: Cross Keys, Lune Valley Hotel, Black Swan, King's Head, Ravenstonedale.

Orton (Cumbria) ns Tebay. Trout (all season), salmon, sea trout. Pinford Lake, **Raisbeck;** r trout, dt £8 (4 fish) from tackleist J Pape, Market Place, Appleby. Accommodation at George Hotel. RWA licences: Davies, 8 North Terrace, Tebay.

Tributaries of the Lune

RAWTHEY. Trout, with sea trout and occasional salmon late in season. Sedbergh AA has good stretch on river and tributary **Dee;** visitor's st £55, wt £16, dt £6. *(see Sedbergh on main river).*
WENNING. Sea trout (good), brown trout, few salmon (late). Best latter part of season. Fishing station: **Bentham** (Yorks). Bentham AA has about $3\frac{1}{2}$m of water; fast stream, good sport; visitors' tickets: st £30 + £10 entrance fee, wt £16, dt £4 from hon sec, or Churchills, Station Rd, Bentham. Ingleborough Estate holds 5m. Wt (limited); apply Estate Office, Clapham; trout run 3 to lb. Blackburn AA has water; members

only. Hotels: The Coach House, Black Bull. Punch Bowl Hotel also has $\frac{3}{4}$m private trout and sea trout fishing and issues dt.
GRETA. Trout (4 to lb) and late run of salmon and sea trout. Fishing stations: **Ingleton** and **Burton-in-Lonsdale** (Yorks). Trout. Ingleton AA controls 6m of unbroken water on Greta, **Twiss** and **Doe;** st £20, wt £10, dt £4 from Berry's (newsagent), Main St, Ingleton, and hon sec. Sunday fishing on approx 3m, maps issued with permits. Accrington FC has Clifford Hall length at Burton; no dt. Hotel: Punch Bowl, Burton-in-Lonsdale (WA licences).

MEDWAY

(For close seasons, licences, etc, see Thames Water Authority, p 16)

Kentish river joining estuary of Thames at Sheerness through estuary of its own. Coarse fish (abundant bream) with few trout in upper reaches.

Maidstone (Kent). Free from towpath from Maidstone bridge to midway between East Farleigh and Barming Bridges. Maidstone Victory Angling and Medway PS have water at Barming, Teston, Wateringbury and Yalding. Permits from hon sec and local tackleists. **Pooh Corner trout fishery,** Rolvenden, nr Cranbrook, offers fishing on three lakes and professional casting and fishing tuition. Dt £10; evening (reduced limit) £5. Inquiries to I A G Thomson, tel 0580 241219. **Lambden Trout Fishery** is at **Gillingham;** tel: 023384 674. **Mote Park Lake** (coarse fish); dt £2.20 (non-residents) from A Sanders, 85 Bank Street; Pettitts, 18 Market Building (tickets and licences). Concessions to jun, OAP. Inns: Medway; West Kent; Rose and Crown; Queen's Head.
East Farleigh (Kent). Free on towpath side from Maidstone to notice-board midway between East Farleigh and Barming; thence mostly Maidstone Victory Angling and Medway Pres Soc water; tickets *(see Maidstone).* Inn: Victory.
Barming (Kent). CALPAC has water upstream and downstream of bridge. Inn: The Bull (no accommodation).
Wateringbury (Kent). Maidstone Victory Angling and Medway Pres Soc has most of towpath bank here and at **Teston;** tickets *(see East Farleigh and Maidstone).*

Medway Wharf Marina, Bow Bridge, has fishing for boat and caravan owners using their services. Tel: Maidstone 813927. Barking AS has a meadow; members only but open to visiting clubs. Inn: King's Head.
Yalding (Kent). Kent RD has about 200 yds upstream of Yalding Sluices, towpath side; no charge to licence-holders. Maidstone Victory Angling and Medway Pres Soc has towpath bank downstream of Railway Inn; tickets *(see East Farleigh and Maidstone).* Yalding AS has water; dt (weekdays only). New Studio AS has short length. Central Assoc of London and Prov AC has $\frac{3}{4}$m and one meadow at junction of Medway and **Beult;** dt from bailiff. Inns: Railway (tackle, but no accommodation); George; Anchor (boats).
Tonbridge (Kent). Tonbridge and Dist A & FPS has 9m of Medway, $1\frac{1}{2}$m of Eden and lakes. Dt for parts of Medway only at £1; from water bailiffs. Vacancies for membership; £7.50, ladies £3.50, concessions for OAP, from Mrs P Wolfe, 59 Hunt Road.
Tunbridge Wells (Kent). Royal Tunbridge Wells AS has coarse fishery at **Ashurst** and **Fordcombe,** trout waters on **Medway** from Forest Row to Hartfield, Withyham to Ashurst, and coarse fishing from Ashurst to Pounds Bridge (4m), also on

Teise below Finchlock's Bridge. Grayling and barbel in places. Fishing on two ponds also. membership limited. Annual subscription £28, concessions for ladies and juvs. Dt £4 to non-members, £2 to friends of members only. **Bartley Mill Stream.** *(See Lamberhurst entry below.)* Tackleist: S E Haward, 14/33 Goods Station Road.

Ashurst (Kent). Coarse fish, some trout, grayling, barbel to $9\frac{1}{2}$ lb. Tunbridge Wells AS has water *(see above)*. Guest tickets for members' friends only.

Fordcombe (Kent). Trout, grayling, coarse fish, barbel 10 lb. Tunbridge Wells AS has water *(see above)*.

Tributaries of the Medway

BEULT: Excellent coarse fishing; lower reaches noted for chub, bream and tench; trout higher. Gravesend Kingfisher A & PA (stretches at **Smarden, Hunton, Headcorn** and **Staplehurst;** members only); London AA has water at **Hunton** and **Linton;** members only. Lewisham Piscatorials and Dartford AA has fishing. CALPAC has water at Headcorn for members only. **Biddenden Trout Fishery** issues dt on lake 1m north of Biddenden. Tel: 058080 451.

EDEN: Coarse fish.

Penshurst (Kent). On Eden and Medway; coarse fish. Croydon AS has water on Eden and fishes CALPAC waters. Penshurst AS has rights from Ensfield to Pounds Bridge and from The Point on Medway to weir on Eden; members only. Dt £2 (Sundays: £3) at Salamans Farm for trout, grayling, chub, dace, etc. Hotel: Leicester Arms.

Edenbridge (Kent). Coarse fish. 8m controlled by Edenbridge AS (members only) also a mile at Penshurst. Short stretches rented by Holland AS, also Crawley AS.

TEISE: Joins Medway at Yalding. Trout, coarse fish.

Laddingford (Kent). London AA has water for members only at Mileham and Manor Farms. St £12; OAP, juv, £4.

Goudhurst (Kent). Teise Anglers and Owners' Association holds 5m of river; brown and rainbow trout; mainly fly only. Members only (£35 entrance fee, £95 sub). Season, April 3 to Sept 30.

Lamberhurst (Kent). Tunbridge Wells AS has trout water; members and friends only *(see Tunbridge Wells)*. **Hoathley** fishery (2m of Teise plus $\frac{3}{4}$m on **Bartley Mill Stream**) opened in 1982. Natural stock of trout, chub, roach, dace, etc, supplemented by b and rb trout from Bayham Lake. Fly, spinning and bait. Dt £2 from Hoathley Farm or Forge Garage, Little Bayham. Tel: Lamberhurst 890235 for advance bookings. **Bayham Lake** trout fishery near here. *(For details, see Kent Lakes, p 64.)*

MERSEY

(For close seasons, licences, etc, see North West Water Authority, p 13–14)

Forms Liverpool Channel and seaport. Main river polluted and of no account for fishing except in higher reaches. Some tributaries contain trout.

Liverpool (Merseyside). Liverpool and Dist AA has stretch on **Leeds & Liverpool Canal** and waters of **River Dee.** Northern AA has sole rights on **Lancaster Canal** including Glasson Branch; a stretch on Leeds & Liverpool Canal; stretches on R Dee, Worthenbury Brook and R Alyn; and is also allowed to fish several stretches on **Shropshire Union Canal.** 50m section of Shropshire Union Canal, starting from Ellesmere Port, directly controlled by BWF. St £7 concessionary, £1 to £3.50. At **Ormskirk** is **Hurleston Hall,** $4\frac{1}{2}$ acre, trout; tel: 0695 75901. Tackleists: Heslop and Dukinfield, 32 Smithdown Road; Skinners, 469 Rice Lane; Bob Thomas, 183 Breckfield Rd North, and 202 Walton Breck Rd; Wm Hitchell & Son, 47 Oxton Rd, Birkenhead; Frank Price, 42 Bridge Road, Litherland. **Stockport** (Cheshire). Stockport County Anglers have private water at Davenport; four pools; carp up to 10 lb. Stockport Waltonians AA also has private waters; coarse fish and trout.

Whaley Bridge (Derbyshire). River here known as Goyt; polluted. Dt (not Sundays), for one bank only. **Todd Brook Reservoir,** Whaley Bridge, stocked with trout and coarse fish. Dt 25p for **Bosley Reservoir,** near Macclesfield, from Harrington Arms on Macclesfield–Leek Road, and Mr J Arnold at 1 Lakeside

Estate, Bosley. Both waters hold roach, perch, bream, carp, pike, gudgeon *(see also Weaver).* **Peak Forest Canal** starts here; coarse, sport patchy. Lock pools at **Marple** stocked with carp and tench. Canal to Ashton Junction being opened and dredged. County Palatine AA has water on canal.

Tributaries of the Mersey

NEWTON BROOK (tributary of Sankey Brook):

St Helens (Merseyside). All brooks polluted. Lakes: **Eccleston Mill Dam, Eccleston Mere** and other local dams preserved by two works' clubs; members only. Dt for **Carr Mill Dam** from lodge; perch, pike, bream, roach. St Helens AA has waters in dams and canals and on the **Dee** and **Calder.** Limited st and wt from hon sec. Good carp, roach, chub, tench and dace in **St Helen's Canal** (Church Street length) and grayling in Blackbrook stretch; canal fishable all season.

BOLLIN:

Heatley (Cheshire). Occasional trout, roach, dace, pike. **Arden Brook,** 1m SE; **Mersey,** 1m N. Warrington AA has stretch of Bollin at **Bowdon.**

Ashley (Cheshire). Bollin, 1m N; trout, roach, dace, pike; Bollin and Birkin AA; private.

BIRKIN (tributary of Bollin):

Knutsford (Cheshire). Birkin, 4m; Bollin and Birkin AA has water; private. **Mere Hall Lake,** 3m; reserved for members of Mere Golf and Country Club. **Tabley Mere,** 3m. Now let to fishing clubs; no permits available. Toft Hall Pool, $1\frac{1}{2}$m S; occasional permits. Small Lake Pool, 3m E; Altrincham AA water. **Redesmere** and **Capesthorne Lakes** (6m S of Wilmslow on A34 road); Stoke AS waters; tench, king carp dt for Capesthorne stock pond only, £5 from A Bradley, Bailiff, East Lodge, Capesthorne (Tel. Chelford 861584). Tackleist: S Jones, Altringham Road, Wilmslow.

IRWELL:

Manchester. River polluted, but fair fishing (trout and perch) in three reservoirs at Tintwistle, Hadfield, 18m. These NWWA waters have now been leased to clubs. Enquiries to Fisheries Officer, New Town House, Buttermarket Street,

Warrington, tel: 53999. At **Poynton,** 10m out, Stockport & Dist FA has pool. St only. 18m from Manchester, at Northwich, is coarse fishing in Weaver *(see Weaver).* Northern AA issues st covering all its canals. Assn has much water, including parts of **Bridgewater, Macclesfield, Peak Forest, Lancaster Canals,** stretches on rivers in and out of the district, as far afield as the **Dee** and **Vyrnwy.** Wt and dt for many fisheries. Bolton & Dist AA has **Manchester, Bolton & Bury Canal,** from Hall Lane to Blue Wall length. **Warrington** AA has $16\frac{1}{2}$m of **Bridgewater Canal** as well as water on **Dee, Ribble, Severn** and tributaries and **Dane,** reservoirs, meres, etc. Association's **Shropshire Union Canal** water now BWF. No dt, but visiting anglers accommodated, if due notice given. Apply hon sec. St £8, concessions for ladies, juniors etc. Macclesfield Prince Albert AS has rights on canal from Buxton road bridge to Bosley Aqueduct (about 6m). Tickets from hon sec. Assn also controls **Turks Head Reservoir,** members only. Moss Side AS has water *(see Whaley Bridge).* Tackleists: Arrowsmiths, 1a Gorton Lane, West Gorton; Buckleys, 957 Oldham Road, Newton Heath. **Bolton:** tackleists; Steves of Bolton, 408 Bridgeman Street; Ben's Den, 78 Thickerford Road.

ROCH:

Bury (G. Manchester). Brooks polluted. Accrington and Dist AA has water on **Ribble, Lune, Wenning** and **Hodder;** st £47, wt £8, dt £4 (trout reservoir) and £2. Bury and Dist AS and has several small ponds and reservoirs including **Elton;** mostly coarse fishing, but some sport with trout on Northern AA waters. Bury AS mem £8, dt £1, juv $\frac{1}{2}$ price. Tackleists: Fisherman's Way, Boundary Street; Compleat Angler, 64 Bolton

Street; Angling Centre, 97 Rochdale Road, Belbeck Pet Supplies, 59 Belbeck Street; all Bury. Also Wood, Penny Street, Blackburn; Sports Shop, Blackburn Road, and Fisherman's Haunt, both Accrington.

Rochdale (G. Manchester). Rochdale Walton AS. Buckley Wood, 1m N (coarse and trout), dt only on application to hon sec. Rochdale and Dist AS has trout and coarse fishing at Castleton (dt 50p; visitors must be accompanied by member), and coarse fishing on Rochdale Canal, 3m from town; st £1, dt 12½p from tackleists (see below). Length of canal also held by Dunlop Cotton Mill Social Club; tickets from local tackleists. Hollingsworth Lakes, Littleborough; coarse fish; dt from tackleists: Towers of Rochdale,

52 Whitworth Road; Kay's, 18 St Marys Gate; W Pennine Angling Supplies, 204 Yorkshire Street, who issues tickets for fly-only trout fishery (fish to 12 lbs) and for coarse fishing in Calderbrook Dam. *For Rochdale Canal see also Calder (Yorks)–Hebden.*

TAME:

Ashton-under-Lyne (G. Manchester). River polluted. Water Authority reservoir Walker Wood, 2m NE; trout; st £180, dt £8, 10d £70. Tackleist: The Petman, 142 Stamford Street.

COMBS RESERVOIR:

Chapel-en-le-Frith (Derby). Combs Reservoir, 2m W; a variety of coarse fish and some trout; dt £1.50 and £2 (trout); Bailiff collects on bank; enquiries to C N Farley, Lakeside.

MIDLANDS (reservoirs and lakes)

ARLESEY LAKE. Church End, Arlesey, Beds. This lake, known nationally through the writings of the late Richard Walker, now a private syndicate water.

BLENHEIM LAKE. Woodstock, Oxon; excellent tench, perch, roach in summer; pike winter. Boat fishing only for visitors, Apply by letter to Estate Office, Blenheim Palace OX7 1PS for details of current charges. Tel: (during normal office hours) 0993 811432.

BODDINGTON RESERVOIR. Byfield (Northants); Banbury, 7m. 65 acres. Pike, bream, perch, roach, carp, tench; st £17 and mid-week 3-day ticket £9 from Principal Fisheries Officer, BWF, Willow Grange, Church Road, Watford, Herts WD1 3QA. (British Waterways Fisheries). Long waiting list. (Watford 226422.)

CLUMBER PARK LAKE. National Trust property, 4½m from Worksop; coarse fish (including pike); st £30, dt £1.50 (juv and dis 75p), from bailiff on bank. Licences and tackle from W Edgeley, Gateford Road, Worksop. Mr Edgeley also issues tickets for other lakes in area.

CASTLE ASHBY LAKES. Northampton 7m. Coarse fishing in four lakes totalling 19 acres. Pike and perch, roach to 2 lb, tench to 6 lb, bream to 11 lbs. St £20, OAP, juv £10 and dt £1 and £1.50 (night). Fishing dawn till dusk, enquiries to Water Bailiff tel Yardley Hastings (0601 29) 703. Menagerie Pond (specimen carp fishery). St £100; details from Estate Office, Castle Ashby, Northampton,

NN7 1LJ (tel 0601 29 232). Welland and Nene RD licence required. *(See also Nene.)*

CLAYDON LAKES. Buckingham, 6m. Upper and Middle Lakes at Middle Claydon, near Winslow, are Leighton Buzzard AC water; Danubian catfish, pike-perch, big carp. Members only. *(See also Ouse (Great).)*

COSGROVE PITS. Milton Keynes, 2m (Bucks); Northampton 12m. Coarse fish; dt at waterside from manager, Cosgrove Lodge Park, Milton Keynes. Great Ouse RD.

CRANFLEET CANAL. Roach, perch, gudgeon. Whole length from Trent Lock to Cranfleet Lock held by Long Eaton Victoria AS. Dt 70p on bank and from Bridge Tackle Shop. St £2.50 also from Bridge Tackle. *(See also Erewash Canal.)*

CRANSLEY RESERVOIR. Kettering (Northants) 2½m; Northampton 13m. Roach, perch, pike, large tench. Anglian Water Authority, Oundle Division. St £15, dt £1 from dispensing unit at reservoir.

DENTON RESERVOIR. Denton (Lincs). Excellent coarse fishing; held by Grantham AA; st £8, dt £1.25 (juv 50p) from hon sec (tel: 0476 75628), bailiffs and tackleists.

DRAYCOTE WATER, near Rugby (Warks) 600 acre reservoir, brown and rainbow trout. Season April 19–Oct 12. Dt £8, 8 fish limit; Evenings £5.20, 5 fish limit. St (full) £242, (Mon–Fri) £173. OAP, juv,

Anglers at the dam end of Clumber Park Lake, a good roach and bream water. *Photo: Bruno Broughton.*

dis, £121. Boats £6.30, engine £7.20 extra. After 4 pm £4.20, engine £5.30 ex. Bank anglers limited to 300. Information from Fishing Lodge (tel: 0788 811107). St, dt, advance bookings, from Kites Hardwick Filling Station, 300 yards from entrance on Banbury side. (Tel: 0788 812018).

DUKERIES LAKES. Worksop Welbeck and Clumber Lakes are fishable on a restricted issue of permits from the Estate Offices to members of the Worksop & District. AAA and to other approved applicants. Applications to Mr L Coe, 66 Kilton Glade, Worksop. The Association has rights on **Sandhill** Lake also.

EYE BROOK RESERVOIR. Caldecott (Leicestershire), off A6003 Uppingham-Caldecott Road. 400 acres good trout fishing. 25,000 caught each year, heaviest fish 1987 $9\frac{3}{4}$ lb. Fly only, st £155 (full), £117 (week days only), wt £25, dt £6. Boats £6 per day extra. Boat concessions after 12 noon and after 5 pm. Season April 1–Oct 31. Anglian Water Authority, licence required; tickets at reservoir hut (Rockingham 770264). Inquiries to

Corby (Northants) and District Water Co, Geddington Road, Corby, Northants NN18 8ES (Tel: Corby 64299).

FAWSLEY PARK LAKES. Daventry (Northants) $3\frac{1}{2}$ m; Northampton 12m. Two lakes; coarse fish; previously Northampton Nene AC water; present lessee unknown.

FOREMARK RESERVOIR. Melbourne 1m. 230 acre water opened for trout fishing by Severn-Trent WA in 1981. Stocked in 1987 with 25,000 fish. Brown, brook and rainbow trout. Season: April 2–Oct 15. St (full) £195 (Mon–Fri) £140, £6.30 (6 fish), evenings £4.20 (3 fish). Concessions to OAP, juv and disabled. R boats only, £5.70 weekends, £4.20 weekdays. Permits from Leicester Water Centre, Gorse Hill, Anstey, Leics, tel: 0533 352011 ext 265, or Mrs V Lawrence, Brookdale Farm, Milton, nr Burton on Trent, tel: 0283 702352.

GRAFHAM WATER. St Neots (Hunts). 1,600-acre reservoir stocked with brown and rainbow trout. Best brown 12lb 6oz., best rainbow 9lb. 40 boats available for hire. St £220, dt £8, boats £13. Part day boat also available. Special terms afternoons and evenings. Restaurant and bar. For full details, tel: Huntingdon 810531 (fishing lodge) or contact Pisactors Ltd, Grafham Water Fishery, Mander Park, West Perry, Huntingdon PE18 0BX. Note: Rod licence required.

HARLESTHORPE DAM. Clowne, Derbys. Trout, coarse fish. St £50, wt £14, dt £3 on site; also tackle and bait. Tel Chesterfield 810231.

LADYBOWER AND DERWENT RESERVOIRS, Bamford, (Derbshire). Severn-Trent Water Authority Northern Division, 43 Dimple Road, Matlcok, Derbyshire. Ladybower main fishery; Derwent no longer stocked. St £136, weekday £98. Wt £20, dt £6.30, evening £4.20, concessionary £3.20. Boat hire, £5.20, after 4 pm, £3.60. Limit, 4 fish up to May 31, thereafter 6 fish. Evening 2 and 3. Season Mar 26–Oct 15. Limited permits from warden for fly fishing on R Derwent below Ladyblower Dam. All prices include VAT. Enquiries to fishing office, tel: 0433 51254.

LINACRE RESERVOIRS, near Chesterfield. 43 acres, 3 reservoirs, 2 r trout, one b. St £90, from G Nixon, 4 Netherthorpe, Staverley, Chesterfield. Dt £6 (4 fish), £4 (2 fish) from Fishermans Supplies, Sheffield Rd, Chesterfield; or Peacock Hotel, Clythorpe.

NASEBY RESERVOIR, Northants. 85 acres. Carp to 19 lb, tench to 5 lb, rudd. St £15, from BWF, Willow Grange, Church Road, Watford, Herts. WD1 3QA. No juniors.

NANPANTAN RESERVOIR. 2m S of Loughborough. 8-acre coarse fishery. Stocked with carp. Dt £1.25 (concessionary 60p) from W H Wortley & Son, 45 Baxter Gate, Loughborough.

OGSTON RESERVOIR, near Chesterfield, Derbyshire. 203-acre water owned by Severn-Trent Water Authority. Large trout. Dt £5.25, conc £2.65 (limited), from STWA office, Dimple Road, Matlock and New Napoleon Inn, Woolley Moor. (Tel: 0246 590413).

PACKINGTON FISHERIES, Meriden (Warks). Excellent brown and rainbow trout fishing on 120 acres of pool, 4m of river. Dt £10, boats £5. Members' fees from £80 to £300, which includes boat charges. Season March 18–November 15. Fishing on Somers fishery for carp, tench, roach, perch, bream and rudd. St £35, dt £2.50. Concessions for juniors and OAP. Reduced rates for evenings.

Details from Packington Fisheries, Broadwater, Meriden, nr Coventry CV7 7HR (0676 22754). *(Advt below.)*

PITSFORD RESERVOIR, Northampton 5m. 750 acres. Anglian Water, Oundle Division. Rainbow and brown trout, fly only. St £135, mid week st £115, dt (8 fish) £5.30, wt £25. Evening £4 (4 fish). 50% reduction for juniors. Boats and permits from Pitsford Lodge, tel: Northampton (0604) 781350. Season 1 April to 29 October.

PATSHULL PARK FISHERIES, Burnhill Green, Wolverhampton WV6 7HY. 75 acre lake, well stocked with b and r trout; fly only. St £136.50, dt £8 (2 fish, other fish £1.20 each). Boats £4. Conc. Tel: 0902 700774.

RAVENSTHORPE RESERVOIR, Northampton 8m. 100 acres. Now managed by Mr Edward Foster in association with Ringstead Grange fishery (36 acres). Brown and rainbow trout, fly only. Dt £6 (6 fish limit), evenings: £4 (3 fish). Boats £8 (evening £4.50), dt £5 for winter season. Apply Fishing Lodge, Ravensthorpe (tel: 0604 770875). Season 1 April

PACKINGTON TROUT FISHERIES

Season Mar 18-Dec 13th
Lake or River

Day Tickets £10.00
Part Day Tickets available
BAG LIMIT 15 FISH

Venue for
Troutmasters Final 1987

Maxstoke Lane
Meriden, Nr. Coventry
Tel: Meriden (0676) 22754

Rutland Water on a memorable day. John Pawson nets a fish during the World Flyfishing Championship he helped win for England. *Photo: Peter Gathercole.*

to 29 October. For Ringstead Grange, tel: 0933 622960.

RUTLAND WATER, Leics. Stamford & A1 5m, Oakham 3m; managed by Rutland Trout, Whitwell Fishing Lodge. 3,000 acres, 17m of fishing bank, largest stocked trout fishery in Britain. Browns to 12 lbs and rainbows to 10 lbs. 65 motor boats. Competition facilities available, accommodation list. St £228 full, mid week £180. Wt £30, dt £7.50 (8 fish), £5 (4 fish). Package hol. with motor boat, £75. Juv 50%. Open 1 April to 29 October. Tel: Empingham (078086) 770. *(Advt p 81.)*

SHELSWELL LAKE, Buckingham 7m. Tench, perch, roach and pike, winter best; st £8, conc £3, from hon sec, Bicester AS and Allmonds Sports, Market Square, Bicester; boat available

at no extra charge. Bicester AS also has two stretches on River Ray; coarse fish; no tickets.

SHUSTOKE RESERVOIR. Shustoke; Coleshill 3m. Leased to Shustoke Fly Fishers by STWA. St £220, dt £8 (5 fish limit), boat £7, £3 $\frac{1}{2}$d; t on site from 12 Apr. Tel: 021 743 4040 or 0675 52370.

STOWE LAKES, Buckingham, 4m. Carp, tench, pike, roach, rudd and perch. Limited dt £2 by post (SAE) from C Hawkins, hon sec Stowe AC. Advance notice and alternative dates required *(see also Ouse (Great).)*

SULBY RESERVOIR. 1m Welford, 14m Northampton. Coarse fishing; excellent roach and bream and mirror carp. Limited st only, £17; concession to juniors. Applications to Principal Fisheries Officer, BWF, Willow Grange,

Church Road, Watford. Tel: Watford 26722.

STAUNTON HAROLD RESERVOIR, near **Melbourne,** Derbys. Severn-Trent WA coarse fishery, 209 acres, soon to be leased to a local angling club. Dt at present £1.10. No st. Inquiries to Leicester Water Centre, Gorse Hill, Anstey; Melbourne Tackle and Gun, 52/54 High St, Melbourne.

SYWELL RESERVOIR. Northampton 6m. Now a County Park. Large tench (6 lb or over), pike (over 20 lb), perch, roach and carp; members of Wellingborough and Dist AC only. St £4, conc £1; apply hon sec, warden or tackleists for details.

THORNTON RESERVOIR. Leicester 3m S of junction 22 on the M1. 76 acres. Trout, fly only. Leased to Cambrian Fisheries by STWA. St £165 and £130, dt £7.50, $\frac{1}{2}$ day £4.50. Boats £6 and £3.50. Tickets on site. Tel: 0530 230807.

TITTESWORTH RESERVOIR, near **Leek,** (Staffs). 184-acre trout water now leased

by STWA to Tittesworth Fly Fishers Ltd. Best r trout 1987, $11\frac{1}{4}$ lb, best b $9\frac{1}{4}$ lb. St, long waiting list. Dt £6 and boats £5, 6 fish limit, advance bookings inc., from fishing lodge at reservoir. Tel: Blackshaw 389 and 359. Concessions to jun, OAP and regd disabled.

TRIMPLEY RESERVOIR, near **Bewdley,** Worcs. Trout, fly only, from early March–July 31. Aug 1–Oct 15, mixed fishery; then coarse fishing until Feb 28. St £85 weekday, £60 weekend; mixed £35; coarse £12. There is a £13 joining fee. Dt for guests of members only. Write for details to sec, Trimpley AA.

WELFORD RESERVOIR, near **Welford,** Leics, 20-acre coarse fishery. Many specimen bream, pike, carp, tench, rudd and roach. St only £13 (Jun $\frac{1}{2}$ price) from BWF, Willow Grange, Church Rd, Watford or bailiff W Williams, Welford Grange Farm. Waiting list. Tel: Watford 26422.

NENE

(For close seasons, licences, etc, see Anglian Water Authority, p 14–15)

Rises in West Northamptonshire and flows to Wash. Good, all-round coarse fishery, slow-running for most part. Roach and bream predominate, the bream in particular running to a good average size. Excellent sport with carp in Peterborough and Northampton areas. Trout fishery in upper reaches.

Wisbech (Cambs). Centre of intricate system of rivers and drains; all waters well stocked with pike, bream, roach, perch and some good tench. Tydd Gote AC has water in **North Level Drain** at Tydd, **Middle Level** (good bream), **Popham's Eau,** 10m on **Sixteen Foot,** 6m on **Forty Foot,** 3m on **Delph,** and 6m on **Old Bedford;** st from hon sec. Wisbech and Dist AA sub-hires some waters. RD

licence and Assn wt required. Concession price for locals. **Great Ouse Relief Channel** provides 11m of good fishing from Downham to King's Lynn *(see p 90)*.

Peterborough. Excellent centre for roach, bream, chub, tench, carp, dace and pike. Peterborough AA now controls most of the N bank of the Nene from **Wansford** to the **Dog in a Doublet** and some

RUTLAND WATER

Europe's finest Trout Fishery

3,000 acres set in rolling Leicestershire countryside

RAINBOW and BROWN TROUT

Superb fishing lodge with full facilities including Tackle Shop and Refreshments.

FUNCTIONS ROOM. LICENSED BAR.
PARTIES AND PRESENTATIONS CATERED FOR.

For further information, write or telephone:
Whitwell Fishing Lodge, Whitwell, Oakham, Leics. LE15 8BL
Telephone: Empingham (078 086) 770

fishings on the S bank in the same area. The Association also has water on the **Welland** from **Spalding** to the "Kenulp Store", St £8, wt £2, dt £1.75, £4 divisional; dt **Tallington Lakes** £2.10, **Ferry Meadows Lakes**, £1.50, from tackle dealers and hon sec. Wansford AC waters now members only. At **Wansford** A1 road bridge, Stamford Welland AAA have ½m of south bank, downstream. Brotherhoods Sports Centre issue dt for their water on the Nene at **Warmington**, where Warmington AC also has stretch for members only (membership restricted). Grantham AA now too have water at Warmington. Apply John Bradshaw, New Lane, Stibbington, for dt on Nene. First-class sport in fen drains and brick pits, but many pits being filled in. Season tickets, Information and RD licences from tackleists: Webb, 196 Newark Avenue; Dogsthorpe, Gallyon, 3 Cumbergate. Dt from bailiffs on bank. **Orton Water** trout fishery is near Peterborough. Dt with boat £14.50 (5 fish limit), Tel: 0733 239995.

Cotterstock (Northants). Excellent fishing for roach, chub, bream, perch, tench, dace and pike held by Cotterstock AA here and at Tansor. St £3.50 and dt 80p from B Wing, Manor Farm and hon sec.

Elton (Northants). Leicester and Dist Amal Soc of Anglers has extensive stretches here and at **Nassington** and **Fotheringhay**. St £5, dt £1 from hon sec or bailiffs.

Oundle (Northants). Roach, bream, tench, dace, etc. Oundle AA has water; limited dt and st. Coventry AA has stretch at Stoke Doyle; members only. St £4, conc £1. Wellingborough Nene AC has 3m at Barnwell, just upstream of Oundle and 2-acre gravel pit (tench, pike, perch and rudd). Members only *(see Wellingborough)*. **Elinor Trout Fishery,** Aldwincle, 36 acre lake stocked b and rb. Dt £6, boats £5. St available. Inquiries to 40 North St, Oundle. Tel 73671 after 6.0 pm. Hotels: Talbot, Ship, Riverside (Oundle HQ).

Thrapston (Northants). Roach, dace, perch. Kettering, Thrapston & Dist AA no longer issue guest tickets; membership: £8 pa.

Rushden, Higham Ferrers and **Irthlingborough** (Northants). Coarse fish. With new sewage works completed, fishing now showing marked improvement. Rushden, Higham Ferrers AC have water at **Bletsoe** and **Harrold** on Ouse: barbel and

chub. Information, tackle and Rushden club cards (membership £6 pa) from Jack Leach, 26 Church St, Rushden and Webster, Corn merchant, Irthlingborough. **Ditchford Lakes** in the vicinity, well-stocked and with improved banks; excellent trout fishery at **Ringstead**, 36 acres, well-stocked with large fish. Dt £6.50, boat for two £7 extra, evening and junior tickets. Limit 6 fish, full day. Salmon included among the stock since 1984, advance booking recommended for week-ends and bank holidays. Tel: Thrapston 2351. Irthlingborough AC has several gravel pits. St £5. Not dt.

Wellingborough (Northants). Pike, perch, bream, tench, chub, roach, dace; strictly preserved by Wellingborough Nene AC from Ditchford Weir to one meadow below Hardwater Mill and water on **Great Ouse.** Club also has **Ditchford Lake** in conjunction with Rushden AA (coarse fish) and parts of **Ise Brook.** St £4 from hon sec. Northampton Nene AC has from Doddington up to paper mills, excluding Earls Barton AC water (1m) and water at Billing *(see Castle Ashby, Billing and Northampton)*. Tackleist: Watts, 4 Herriots Lane.

Castle Ashby (Northants). Pike, perch, bream, tench, roach; preserved for most part by Northampton Nene AC, which issues dt. Lakes on **CA Estate** (1¼m S); pike, bream, tench, perch, roach; dt from bailiff at waterside or estate office. *(See also Midlands Reservoirs.)*

Billing (Northants). Pike, roach, perch, bream, tench, chub; preserved by Northampton Nene AC, which issues dt for 1½m on both banks of river. Good coarse fishing at Billing Aquadrome. Seven lakes open from June 16 to Oct 16. St £15, wt £4, dt £1. All available on site. Tel: Northampton 408181 or 0933 679985.

Northampton (Northants). Pike, perch, bream, chub, roach, carp, etc; Nene AC controls north bank from Weston Mill to Clifford Hill Lock. Northampton good centre for lake and reservoir fishing in Ravensthorpe, Sywell, Pitsford, Grafham Water *(advt p 00)* and Draycote Reservoirs, Abington Park and Ovestone Park Lakes and Mackaness Gravel Pits *(see Midlands Reservoirs and Lakes)*. Hotels: Plough, Grand, Angel. Tackleists: Sportsman's Lodge, 44 Kingsthorpe Road, Kingsthorpe Hollow; Gilders, 148

Wellingborough Road; T H Thursby, Sheep Street.

Weedon (Northants). Pike, perch, bream, roach. **Grand Union Canal.** Northampton Nene AC has rights from Weedon to Yardley Gobion (16m); dt *(see Grand Union Canal)*. Lakes: **Fawsley Park** (two lakes); coarse fish (pike, roach, rudd,

etc); dt from Nene AC. Nene and Ouse licences needed for canal. Welland and Nene RD has stocked **Bugbrooke** reaches with trout ($3\frac{1}{2}$m in all between Heyford Mill and Harpole Mill); limited dt from Fisheries Officer. Nene AC has acquired **Hollowell Reservoir** and **Ecton Gravel Pits.**

Tributaries of the Nene

OLD RIVER NENE:

March (Cambs). Pike, perch, bream, rudd, roach, tench. Fen drains. **Old River Nene** mostly free to licence-holders. **Reed Fen** (south bank) controlled by March and Dist AA. **Twenty Foot** controlled by March Working Men's AC (tickets). **Popham's Eau, Forty Foot** and **Middle Main** (fished by Sheffield and Dist AS. Tackleist (and licence-seller): A Crowson (March) Ltd, Bridge House, who will give further information. Hotels: Griffen, Wades, Temperance.

Ramsey (Hunts). Pike, perch, bream, etc. Holme Brook. Wiston Brook. Lake: Ramsey Mere, 3m NE. Club: Ramsey AA.

WILLOW BROOK: Trout, coarse fish; preserved.

King's Cliffe (Northants). Willow Brook. Welland, 3m NW.

ISE:

Kettering (Northants). **Cransley Reservoir;** roach, perch and tench *(see Midlands Reservoirs and Lakes)*. **Wicksteed Lake,** also preserved water on Nene at Trapston, apply Kettering AA for st and dt. Licences, tickets, tackle and information from N Spring, 117 Wellington Street; Franks, 38 Wellington Street; Sports Stores, Gold Street. Hotels: Royal, George.

Geddington (Northants). Preserved by Duke of Buccleuch to Warkton. Barford

Bridge to Geddington is association water *(see Kettering)*.

STRECK:
Crick (Northants). Streck, 2m S. Lakes: Dunsland Reservoirs (pike, perch, etc), 3m SW; private.

Daventry (Northants). **Daventry Reservoir,** coarse fishery, pike, perch, etc; Daventry Dist Council water. **Drayton reservoir** BWF water; st £10, dt £1 from Banks and Burr, 27 Claremont Road, Rugby; also tackleist, Trinders Tackle, 70/72 High Street.

NORFOLK AND SUFFOLK BROADS
(Rivers Bure, Waveney and Yare)

(For close seasons, licences, etc, see Anglian Water Authority—Norwich Division p 14-15)

Rivers Bure, Waveney and Yare, their tributaries and Broads are among the finest coarse fisheries in England. They contain pike, perch, roach, rudd, tench and bream. Anglian Water—Norwich Division has access rights for fishing on some banks of tidal water which can be fished free. Some Broads are preserved and can be fished on payment. Rivers and most Broads very busy with boating traffic in summer, so early morning and late evening fishing advised. Best sport in autumn and winter. Boats essential for Broads.

BURE

Strong current from Yarmouth to little above Acle; upper reaches gentle and ideal for float fishing. The river contains a good head of coarse fish. Excellent roach, bream and pike etc, at Thurne Mouth, St Benets, Horning, Wroxham. Several Broads are connected and can be fished as well as tributaries Thurne and Ant.

Stokesby (Norfolk). Bream, roach, pike, perch. Strong tides and sometimes brackish; legering best; free.

Acle (Norfolk). Bream, roach, pike, perch. Tides often strong. River traffic heavy in summer. Inns: Queen's Head and King's Head, both 1m from river; Bridge Inn (close to river); Hermitage and the Thurne Lion at Thurne Mouth.

S Walsham and Upton. $3\frac{3}{4}$m R bank below **Ant** mouth, Upton Dyke and 1m Fleet Dyke free to licence-holders.

Horning (Norfolk); ns Wroxham, $3\frac{1}{2}$m. Good coarse fishing; free to licence-holders; boat almost essential; roach, rudd, bream, perch, pike, tench; river very busy in summer and early morning and late evening fishing gives best results. At **Woodbastwick** WA has about $\frac{1}{2}$m of right bank, tidal; free to licence-holders. Broads: **Ranworth** (tickets for Inner Ranworth from store on Staithe); **Decoy** (club water), **Salhouse** (dt issued); and **Wroxham** small charge—*see Wroxham*) upstream. Tackle, licences and bait at post office. Several boat yards. Hotels: Swan, New Inn and Petersfield House Hotel.

Wroxham (Norfolk). Roach, rudd, bream, pike, perch, tench; good pike and bream in winter; boats only. Boats from Wroxham Angling Centre, Station Rd,

Hoveton. Much river traffic, summer. Broads: **Bridge Broad,** boats only. **Salhouse Broad,** right bank, 2m SE dt issued. **Alderfen Broad,** specimen tench. Boats £5 per day from Wroxham Angling Centre *(see above).*Hotels: King's Head, Broads, Horse Shoes. Tackleists: Haylett's Tackle Shop, Station Road.

Coltishall (Norfolk). Roach, bream, perch, pike. Hotels: King's Head, Rising Sun.

Buxton Lamas (Norfolk). Pike, good bream and roach, perch. Enquiries to Clarke's of Market Place, Aylsham.

Aylsham (Norfolk). Trout, roach, rudd, dace and pike. Heavily weeded in summer; best Oct onwards. Above town are Aylsham and Dist AS preserves; apply hon sec. Tackle and bait from C Clarke, Market Place (also permits for local residents). Hotels: Ship, Black Boys, Plough and Shuttle, Marsham.

Bure Valley Lakes, nr Aylsham, 12 acres with r trout up to 9 lb, b trout up to $4\frac{1}{2}$ lb. Dt. £5 plus £1.25/lb fish caught. Tel: 026387 666.

Blickling (Norfolk). Trout upstream from Ingworth Bridge. Controlled by Blickling Flyfishers; permits for members' friends only. Part of river between Ingworth Bridge and Aylsham is trout fishing only. Dt for **Blickling Lake** (20 acres), from bailiff on bank; £2. No night fishing.

Tributaries of the Bure

THURNE: Slow-flowing, typical Broadland river; tidal below Potter Heigham. Coarse fish, good bream and roach. RD water at **Potter Heigham, Martham, Thurne Marshes.**

Thurne Mouth (Norfolk). Good roach, bream, perch. Hotel: Thurne Lion.

Potter Heigham (Norfolk). Popular centre; good roach and bream; fair-sized eels. Bure. 3m S. Broads: **Womack,** $1\frac{1}{2}$m; **Hickling Broad** and **Heigham Sound** (tench, bream, roach, perch); in all, approx 8m of tidal water free to licence-holders. Access points at Martham Ferry, Potter Heigham Bridge, Repp's Staithe, Thurne Lion dyke. Hotels: Bridge, Broads-Haven, Cringles, Broadland House. Boats from Herbert Woods; Bridge Hotel; Whispering Reeds Boatyard, Hickling; Arthur Walch, Nurses House, Martham. Licences, tackle, etc. from Ken Latham, Potter Heigham (Tel 388).

Martham (Norfolk). Rudd, tench, bream, roach, perch, pike; good bank fishing; **Heigham Sound** 1m free on AWA licence. good pike and other coarse fish. Closed Oct 1–Jan 31. Boats, Martham Ferry Boatyard; Beale, The Staithe, Hickling; and Whispering Reeds Boatyard, Hickling. Inn: King's Arms *(see also Hickling).*

Ludham. $2\frac{1}{4}$m of the river, upstream and downstream of Ludham Bridge, free to licence-holders.

ANT:

Irstead and Neatishead (Norfolk). Ant and Barton Broad. Good bream, perch, rudd, pike; also tench and roach. Fishing free. Hotel: Barton Angler Lodge Hotel, Neatishead (boats). Boats also from Cox, Barton Turf.

Stalham (Norfolk). River clear, slow-running and weedy in summer; roach, rudd, bream, perch, pike and few tench. Broads: **Barton,** 1m; rudd, bream and big pike; free fishing. **Hickling,** 3m by road; good pike, bream, etc. Sutton Broad overgrown. Tackle, bait, licences and information from Tracey Moore Sports, Unit 4, High Street. Hotel: Sutton

Staithe Hotel and Country Club. Inns: Swan, Grebe, Maid's Head, Harnser, Wood Farm.

Wayford Bridge (Norfolk). Upper Ant; head of navigation; fishing free to licence-holders; roach, rudd, perch, pike, tench, bream; boat advisable; river is narrow and fairly busy at times in summer; weedy and clear. Boats from Wayford Marina and Mixers Ltd, Catfield. Bait and tackle from Stalham. Good fishing also above the head of Ant Navigation in Dilham and North Walsham Canal, navigable to rowing boats as far as Honing Lock. Caravan site and food at Wood Farm Inn.

North Walsham (Norfolk). Ant, 1m E. Gunton Beck, 4m W. Lakes: **Wolerton Lake** 8m NW, **Hevingham Lake,** 9m W. Details from tackleist: Corner Tackle, 28 Market Place, who can advise on fishing in a number of waters in the district. Tel: North Walsham 403005; 405002 after hours. Hotels: Beechwood, Black Swan, Scarborough Hill.

SAW MILL LAKE: Fishing station: **Gunton** (Norfolk) near Cromer. 16-acre lake in Gunton Park, 3m; coarse fish; dt £2.50, from bailiff, on bank. Jun, OAP £1.25.

Horning (Norfolk), ns Wroxham. **Salhouse Broad;** too much traffic in summer, but good fishing in early mornings and from Oct to March. Dt issued. **Ranworth Broad** (tickets for Inner Ranworth from store on Staithe). **Malthouse Broad;** free. **Rollesby Broad;** free. **Decoy Broad;** now open only to clubs. Tackle, licences, bait at post office *(see also Bure).*

Ormesby, Rollesby and **Filby.** Fishing by boat only, boats available by the day or hour. These Broads are connected and undisturbed by motor cruisers and yachts; fishing good everywhere. Excellent pike in winter. Inn: Eel's Foot, Ormesby, boats £4.50, £3.50, accommodation, tel: 0493 730342. Boats also from W Tennant (Filby) and G Skoyles (Ormesby).

Salhouse (Norfolk). Salhouse Broad, 1m NE; few pike in winter.

Keep the banks clean

Several clubs have stopped issuing tickets to visitors because of the state of the banks after they have left. Spend a few moments clearing up.

Broads connected with the Bure

Wroxham Broad, 1m N; *(see Wroxham)*; Information and boat-hire from Wroxham Angling Centre, tel: Wroxham 2453. Decoy or Woodbastwick Broad, 2m NE; fishing on payment. Little Ranworth Broad, 3m E; good for bream. South Walsham Broad, 5m E; private; good bream and pike fishing; leave from owner.

Wroxham (Norfolk). Wroxham Broad, boat fishing only. Bridge Broad, boat fishing only. Salhouse Broad, right bank, 2m, SE. Alderfen Broad, Felmingham (trout in river, coarse fish in lakes); dt £5 from Wroxham Angling Centre, tel: Wroxham 2453. Hotels: King's Head, Broads, Horse Shoes.

Broads connected with the Thurne and (arranged under "Fishing Stations")

Potter Heigham (Norfolk). Hickling Broad *(see Hickling)*. Heigham Sounds; fine fishing in summer; pike fishing, roach and bream in winter (free). Pike fishing on Horsey (no live-baiting). Womack Water dredged and cleared of weed, and may be fished from quay below. *(For hotels, boats, etc, see entry under Thurne.)*

Hickling (Norfolk). Heigham Sounds, Horsey, Barton and Hickling Broads, bream, roach, pike, perch. All free except

Horsey dt from keepers. Licences from Post Office and stores; boats available. Accommodation: Pleasure Boat Inn; guest houses.

Martham (Norfolk). R Thurne. Bream.

Broads connected with the Ant:

Catfield (Norfolk). Barton Broad, 1m W; excellent bream fishing and noted for big pike. Hotel: Barton Angler, Irstead. Hickling Broad, 2m. Catfield Broad; overgrown.

WAVENEY

Flows along Norfolk-Suffolk border. Beccles is noted centre for roach and bream fishing, and reach between Geldeston Lock and St Olaves gives some wonderful sport with bream in most seasons.

Lowestoft (Suffolk). Oulton Broad and Waveney, which connects with Broad; bream, perch, roach, pike, etc; boats at Broad. Flounders and smelts in harbour and Claremont Pier. Good sea fishing in Oct, Nov and Dec from boats, piers and beach for whiting, cod and flatfish. Several Broads within easy reach as are following fishing stations: Beccles, Geldeston, Bungay, Somerleyton, Haddiscoe, Reedham, Cantley, Buckenham, Brundall. At Kessingland (5m S) visitors to wildlife, Country Park may have free river fishing. Much of River Hundred is Kessingland AC water. Tackleists: S G Hooks, 132 Bevan Street, who issue st £6 and wt £3 for several stretches. *(See Beccles and Bungay further on.)* Oulton Broad Angling Centre, Commodore Road. Oulton Broad (Suffolk). Broad gives good sport with eels to 5 lb, bream, roach, etc, but crowded with boats in summer. Bank fishing from Nicholas

Everitt Park. Waveney near; 2m of fishing at Barsham free to licence-holders; 170 yds at Worlingham; best from boat. Good perch and pike (best Oct-March); roach (good all season, best Jan, Feb, Mar), bream (moderate, best June-Nov); dace. North Cove; 400 yards with bream to 7 lb, big pike, st £2.50 from Post Office. Oulton Dyke (north side only); bream (excellent Aug, Sept, Oct); perch, roach, eels. Club: Oulton Broad Piscatorial Society. Fritton Lake, $2\frac{1}{2}$m N *(see Haddiscoe)*. Lake at The Villa, $2\frac{1}{2}$m N. Fishing free to licence-holders. Map of best fishing areas on Oulton from Publicity Manager, 7 Esplanade, Lowestoft, and tackleist Oulton Broad Angling Centre, Commodore Road. Hotels: Wherry, George Borrow, Golden Galleon.

Haddiscoe (Norfolk). New Cut: good coarse fishing; free. Lakes: Fritton; perch, pike, roach, rudd, tench; dt for bank fishing;

accommodation and boats at Fritton Old Hall. Other hotels: Crown, Queen's Head.

Burgh St Peter (Norfolk). Lakes: Fritton *(see Haddiscoe).* Hotel: Waveney House; licences, boats.

Beccles (Suffolk). Good roach, bream, pike, etc; best early or late in summer but especially good Oct onwards, when river traffic eases off. Boats may be hired at several places. 400 yd stretch at **Aldeby** is George Prior AC water, st £2 from S Hooks *(see Lowestoft).* **Aldeby Pits** coarse fishery is 5m from Beccles, on Waveney. Tackleists Crack Sport, 7 Blyburgate, issue st and dt for waters belonging to Beccles, Bungay Cherry, and Harleston and Wortwell clubs, on river and lakes. Charges range from st £17 to £5; dt from £1.50 to 50p. Hotels: King's Head, Waveney House. Tackle, licences, information and wt, dt, for Barnby and Cove AC waters in the vicinity from Crack Sports, 7 Blyburgate.

Geldeston (Norfolk). Good pike, roach, perch, bream, etc; free. Inns: Wherry (RD licences) and Geldeston Lock. Tackleist in Beccles (3m).

Bungay (Suffolk). Good roach, chub, bream, perch, pike and tench; fishes best at back end. Cherry Tree AC has several stretches and pit at **Ditchingham;** restocked with good tench and carp; members only; Broome Pits, dt on bank, 2 stretches at Ellingham Mill 4m from Bungay; subs £10 pa (ladies, OAP and juvs £5), wt £3. Permits from Hooks, Tackle Dealer, Lowestoft. Accommodation at Bungay Angling Centre, where membership cards may be obtained.

Homersfield (Suffolk). Pike, perch, roach (large), dace, tench. Licences from landlord, Black Swan Hotel. "Leisure Sport" gravel pit. See Fishery Agents.

Harleston (Norfolk). Waveney, 1m S; coarse fish. Harleston, Wortwell and Dist AC has about 7m on Waveney; st from hon sec; private pits stocked with tench, carp, perch, roach; visitors' wt, dt from G Denny (tackleist), Market Place. Hotel: Magpie.

Eye (Suffolk). Dove Brook; large dace. Fishing in Waveney at Hoxne, 3m.

Diss (Norfolk). **Waveney, Dove** and **Diss Mere.**

Broads connected with the Waveney
(arranged under "Fishing Stations")

Lowestoft (Suffolk). **Flixton Decoy,** 3m W. Large bream stocks (to 7 lb); also roach, rudd, tench, perch, pike and large eels. No bank fishing. Boats available from South Lodge, Flixton. Dt prices range

from £2-£1. *Tackleists and hotels, see previous Lowestoft entry.*

Belton (Suffolk). **Breydon Water;** salt estuary; no fishing. Fritton Lake, 2m S *(see Haddiscoe).*

YARE

Rises few miles from East Dereham and flows through Norwich to Yarmouth. Still one of the best Broads rivers for roach and bream; specially good for roach in middle reaches; bream in lower. Some trout stocking in upper reaches by River Authority which has water (some tidal) at Easton, Bawburgh, Buckenham Ferry and Postwick, Rockland and Langley. Permit required.

Great Yarmouth (Norfolk). Broads and rivers. Rivers Yare, Bure and Waveney fall into Breydon Water (Bure joined in upper reaches by Thurne and Ant). In all, some 200 miles of rivers well suited to boat and bank angling are within easy reach; some Broads are landlocked, strictly reserved for angling and free from river traffic; others connected to rivers, but mostly best fished from boat. Within 6m are **Filby, Rollesby** and

Ormesby Broads (136, 240 and 207 acres, respectively) forming part of the Ormesby group; also **Fritton Lake** (163 acres). Many other Broads easily accessible; also rivers Bure, Thurne, Ant and Waveney. Trout in Bure. Several miles of fishing at **Buckenham Ferry, Cantley, Rockland, Claxton** and **Langley** free to licence-holders. Also good sea fishing. Tackle, baits and further information from: King Street Tackle

Shop, 123a King Street; J Markham, 43 South Market Road and P Nicholls, 14, The Market Place, Loddon.

Reedham (Norfolk). Strong tide; legering best; roach, perch, bream, eels; free. Chet near, upstream. Hotel: Ship.

Cantley (Norfolk). Roach, bream, perch; bream and perch plentiful; fishing free to licence-holders; mostly by leger. Inn: Red House.

Buckenham (Norfolk). Bream, roach, perch, pike; boats at Beauchamp Arms; fishing free to licence-holders. Mouth of Hassingham Dyke is good spot. Lakes: Strumpshaw Broad, 1m NW. Buckenham Broad and Hassingham Broad, 1m SE; preserved. Rockland Broad, $1\frac{1}{2}$m SW on other bank of river; free.

Brundall (Norfolk). Roach, bream, perch in Yare. Fishing from riverside bungalows let by Blakes Holidays, Wroxham, Norwich NR12 8DH. Several reaches between Coldham Hall and Surlingham Ferry can be fished by boat. **Surlingham Broad** belongs to National Trust; fishing only fair in summer; water shallow and weedy; pike in winter.

Norwich (Norfolk). Good centre for Broads fishing. Roach and bream in vicinity. **Wensum** above city holds fine roach, perch, dace, grayling and pike. Good roach and bream fishing at **Rockland Broad**; 7m from Norwich; but poor access to banks. No boats now. Norwich AA has water on **Bure, Thurne, Ant** and **Yare, Ranworth Inner Broad** and **Woodbastwick Decoy** (fishing by boat only on last two waters); dt from hon sec and tackleists. 6m NW, at **Taverham**, seven lakes known as the Ringland Pits, carp, tench, bream etc. St from "Leisure Sport", RMC House, Feltham, Middlesex, dt from bailiff at lakes. St £4, dt £1.50, bait, licences and tackle from Gallyon, 9 Bedford St; C F Browne, Timberhill; John's Tackle Den, 16 Bridewell Alley. Hotel: Maid's Head and many others.

Bawburgh (Norfolk). Centre for Upper Yare; much free fishing. Badly weeded in summer, but good autumn onwards. Mostly controlled by River Division from Cringelford to Bawburgh. London AA has about 1m, members only. Trout and grayling as well as coarse fish, but most have gone downstream into stretch controlled by River Division.

Tributaries of the Yare

CHET:

Loddon (Norfolk); ns Norwich, 12m. Free coarse fishing in Chet from Loddon down to Reedham on Yare; roach, dace, bream, perch, occasional trout; this water now navigable and fishes best in autumn and winter when traffic finishes; licences, river and sea bait and tackle from P Nicholls, 14, The Market Place and W H Rager Ltd, Post Office, Loddon. Hotels: Swan, and Angel Inn, Loddon; White Horse, Chedgrave.

WENSUM: Coarse fish (good roach), some trout. Tidal through Norwich. $\frac{3}{4}$m stretch plus 65 acre fishery *(see Swanton Morley)*.

Costessey (Norfolk). Coarse fish. "Leisure Sport" have their **Taverham** gravel pits here. St £14, concessions for jun, OAP, dis. Applications to LSA, Thorpe Park, Staines Road, Chertsey, Surrey. Tel: Chertsey 64872.

Drayton (Norfolk). Free on permission of landowners; otherwise strictly preserved. Spixworth Beck, $2\frac{1}{2}$m NE; free adjoining Crostwick Common; also free fishing in Bure. Hotel: Red Lion.

Attlebridge (Norfolk). Good trout fishing here, some miles of water being preserved. Tud, 4m S; private. Lakes: Haveringland, $3\frac{1}{2}$m N; private. Hopground Lake, Honingham, 4m S; private. At **Reepham** $3\frac{1}{2}$ acre trout fishery. Fish to 15 lbs. Dt £9, st etc available. Enq to Norwich 870878.

Lenwade (Norfolk). Lenwade House Hotel has water. Other accommodation and information from Roberts, Common Lane.

Swanton Morley (Norfolk). Four lakes totalling 65 acres and $\frac{3}{4}$m river wellstocked OWR/Redland fishery. St £5, dt 60p from Chambers, Market Place, E Dereham; Mrs V Marsham, Waterfall Farm, Swanton Morley and from Kingfisher Tackle, Sheringham.

Hellesdon (Norfolk). Roach, chub, grayling, some tench. Good stretch of open water to New Mills.

Lyng (Norfolk). Fine roach, dace and some

trout. Dereham and Dist AC has water; excellent roach fishing; also **Wensum Pit;** good tench, pike, perch and bream; dt from Tackle Shop, Norwich Street, **Dereham.** Dereham and Dist AC also has lake (roach and perch) at **East Bilney;** dt from Bilney Hall; good trout, perch and roach. London AA has water for members only.

Elsing (Norfolk). RD has 1,270 yards of right bank.

North Elmham (Norfolk). Fishing in Wensum for pike, roach, perch, dace and few trout. Permission from riparian owners. London AA has $1\frac{1}{2}$m in three sections; members only. The Lake, Elmham Park, holds carp, large tench, rudd, roach and pike. Hotel: Railway, Dereham NR20 5HH..

Fakenham (Norfolk). Good trout and dace, some roach, grayling and pike. Fakenham AC has 4m. Dt £3 from Dave's Fishing Tackle, 1, Rear Norwich Street,

from whom bait and licences may also be obtained. Hotels: Crown, Limes.

TASS or TAES:

Swainsthorpe (Norfolk). Yare, 3m N. Lakes: Bracon Hall and Carlton Lodge, 2m W. All private.

BASS:

Wymondham (Norfolk). Yare, 4m N at Barford and 6m N at Marlingford; roach. Club: Wymondham AC. Tickets from the Horse Shoes Inn, Shropham. Lakes: Ketteringham Hall lake, 4m E; private. Shropham, 8m S; bream, tench. Tackleist: F W Myhill & Son, Fairland St (branches at Swaffham, Dereham and Thetford). Hotel: Abbey.

BLACKWATER: Trout; preserved.

Booton (Norfolk). Clay pits here hold carp (common, mirror and crucian), tench, perch, roach and pike; Aylsham and Dist AS has rights. St £2 and dt £1 from A Clarke, tackle dealer, Aylsham, or bailiff on bank.

Broads connected with the Yare
(arranged under "Fishing Stations")

Buckenham. Rockland Broad, $1\frac{1}{2}$m SW; good roach fishing and pike fishing in winter. R Dye, The Kilns Boatyard or tel: 05088 251/301, has some boats

available. Bed & breakfast nr Broad.

Brundall. Belongs to National Trust; shallow water grown up in summer, but good for pike in winter.

NORFOLK (small streams)

(For close seasons, licences, etc, see Anglian Water Authority, p 14–15, unless otherwise stated)

BABINGLEY RIVER. Fishing station: **Castle Rising,** ns North Wootton, 2m. Rises in the lake at Hillington Hall, and is 9m long. King's Lynn AA has water; no tickets. *See King's Lynn—Ouse (Great).*

GLAVEN. Rises 3m E of **Holt** and joins sea at **Cley,** 6m down. 1m at Cley.Fishing now held privately. No permits. At **Holt,** Edgefield Farm Trout Fishery, $5\frac{1}{2}$ acres. Dt £8. Inq to Gent, tel: Holt 2437. There are several small lakes in this area. **Letheringsett, Felbrigge Hall,** Booton at **Cawston,** Selbrigg at **Hemstead;** all

coarse fishing, dt on bank, £1, £1.50. Tackle: Sheringham. Tel: 0263 822033.

NAR. Rises above **Narborough** to enter the Wash at **King's Lynn.** At Narborough, five trout lakes. £2 per $\frac{1}{2}$ day session plus charge for trout taken. Inq to Narborough Mill, tel 0760 338005.

TASS. Rises N of **Wacton,** 11m S of **Norwich,** to enter Yare on outskirts of city. At **Swainsthorpe,** Taswood Lakes Fishery. Three lakes stocked coarse fish, carp and tench included. St £45, dt £2. Enquire Jean Smith, tel Swainsthorpe 470818.

Keep the banks clean

Several clubs have stopped issuing tickets to visitors because of the state of the banks after they have left. Spend a few moments clearing up.

OTTER

(For close seasons, licences, etc, see South West Water Authority, p 12)

Noted Devonshire trout stream flowing into English Channel immediately east of Exe. Mullet in estuary and some sea trout, with brown trout of good average size for West Country higher up, where hotels have some excellent dry-fly water.

Budleigh Salterton (Devon). Tidal. Free fishing from river mouth to Clamour Bridge (about $1\frac{1}{2}$m, both banks) to visitors staying in East Budleigh or Budleigh Salterton; RD licence necessary. Sea trout, brown trout, grey mullet plentiful but difficult to catch. Fishing on both banks from Clamour Bridge to Newton Poppleford. Sea fishing; bass, flatfish, etc, from extensive beach. *(see Sea Fishing Stations under Sidmouth).*

Ottery St Mary (Devon). Some good trout water in vicinity. Hotel Venn Ottery Barton, no longer has private fishing.

Honiton (Devon). Deer Park Hotel has 3m (both banks) of first-class trout fishing; trout up to 2 lb, average 1 lb; rods limited to six daily. Licences at hotel. Dt for non-residents (£20) when available. St £190, wt £45, river and small lake. Heaviest trout, 1985 — $5\frac{1}{4}$lbs. Otter Inn, **Weston,** has trout fishing, tel: 0404 2594. Monckton Court Hotel has 1m (both banks) available to visitors and guests; fly only. Dt for $\frac{1}{2}$m (both banks) from Cotterson Farm, **Awliscombe** and for $\frac{3}{4}$m (right bank) from Tracey House, Honiton. Mr Brimmicombe, c/o Ford's Shoe Shop, High Street, issues dts.

OUSE (Great)

(For close seasons, licences, etc, see Anglian Water Authority, p 14–15)

Rises in Buckinghamshire and flows north-east through Northamptonshire, Bedfordshire, Cambridgeshire, Huntingdonshire and Norfolk, entering the North Sea by The Wash. Coarse fishing throughout. Slow, winding river for most part. Lower reaches provide particularly good sport.

King's Lynn (Norfolk). Coarse fish of all kinds except barbel. King's Lynn AA has water on the Ouse from Ten Mile Bank to Denver Sluice; on the Wissey at Hilgay; on the **Relief Channel** Drain, 11m to Downham Market; on the **Middle Level** drain from St Germans to aquaduct, 8m. St £10, wt £5, dt £1.50; from tackleists or bailiffs R. Groom, 9 Church Road. Tackleists: Colin Stevens, London Road, F Harper, Railway Road, Downham Market. Hotels: Globe, East Anglian, Duke's Head.

Downham Market (Norfolk). Coarse fish, sea trout; tidal.

Hilgay (Norfolk). King's Lynn AA water on Ouse and **Wissey** *(see King's Lynn).* London AA has water on Ouse; dt from bailiffs.

Littleport (Cambs). Ouse and **Lark;** coarse fish, except barbel, good pike and bream, with roach and tench in parts. Preserved from Littleport Bridge to Ely (5m) by Ely Beet Sugar Factory and Littleport AC; permits for individuals and clubs, st £5, dt £1. Black Horse Inn at Sandhill issues dts. London AA controls 14m of water from Littleport Bridge to Southery (Norfolk), both banks. Dt from bailiffs.

Ely (Cambs). Free fishing from Lincoln Boatyard upstream to Newmarket Railway Bridge. Ely Highflyers have about 5m downstream from this and last mile of River Lark ("Queen Adelaide' stretch); dt and club-cards from Ely Trophy Shop, 21A High Street. Rosewell pits hired by Ely Beet Sugar Factory FC; dt (limited). Hotels: Lamb, Cutter Inn, Castle Lodge. Tackleists: Ely Trophy Shop; Thornton's, Broad Street.

Earith (Hunts). **Old West River.** Earith Bridge to Pope's Corner (Cambs); mostly hired by Histon AC, Cambridge Albion AS; good coarse fishing. **Old Bedford River** from Earith to Welches Dam and **New Bedford Level** or **Hundred Foot** (tidal) from Sutton Gault to Ox Willow Lode controlled by Cambridge Albion AS and Shefford AS; members only but dt issued by hon sec for Ivel. Ploughman's Pit (good carp, bream, pike; dt also from Airman public house) and lake at Oldfield Farm. St obtainable at local inns near the waters and

Cambridge tackleists. The **Hundred Foot** (Earith to Sutton Gault), rented by Cambridge FPS, tidal; practically all coarse fish, except barbel; dt £1, in advance, from hon sec or local inns for Cambridge FPS water. London AA has $6\frac{3}{4}$m on Hundred Foot from Adventurers' Drove, Oxlode, to $\frac{1}{4}$m above Welney on Hundred Foot and from Stokes Bridge to Welney on **River Delph;** members only. Cambridge Albion AS has stretch on Delph from Welches Dam to Chequers, Purls bridge. Hitchin AC and Letchworth AC share stretch of Old Bedford from Purls Bridge to Welches Dam, both banks; dt on water. Great Ouse Fishery Consultative Association rents water on **Counterwash Drain, Old Bedford River, Pingles Pit** (Mepal) and the **Hundred Foot.** Affiliated clubs have rights. Members of Sheffield AAS may

fish these waters, the **Delph** at Manea (Manea AC water) and the **Bedford River** from Purls Bridge to **Welches Dam** (Letchworth AA).

Over and Swavesey (Cambs). Bream, perch, chub, rudd, tench, pike, dace and zander. Over and Swavesey Dist AS has water. St £5 from all Cambridge tackleists. Punts for hire, £3.50 per day.

Holywell Ferry (Hunts). Hotel: Ferry Boat. Pike, bream, roach, rudd, chub, etc; free; boats available; good fishing, especially roach. Over and Swavesey Dist AS has water downstream on Cambridgeshire bank *(see Over and Swavesey).*

St Ives (Hunts). All coarse fish, barbel, bream and rudd predominant with dace, perch, rudd, chub in quantity; tench increasing. Ample bank fishing, but boats available. St Ives FP & AS has water; st, dt. Adjoining water held by

Fishing often bridges the gap between sport and fine art. These children, entranced by a fly-dresser at his craft, are attracted equally by the demonstration of manual dexterity, by the beauty and variety of the materials used and the delicacy of the finished product. Mr Stanley Woodrow holds his audience spellbound in the Salmon & Trout Association tent at a Home Counties Country Fair.

LAA, Houghton and Wyton and Hemingfords AS. Tackleist: Toys 'n Tackle, Bridge Street. Hotels: Golden Lion, Slepe Hall, Firs.

Godmanchester (Hunts). Good bream, roach, chub. Chance of carp and barbel. Godmanchester A & FPS has about 10m. Tickets from hon sec. St £5, dt 75p. London AA has Portholme Meadow (dt) and Berry Lane Meadows (members only). Boats from Huntingdon; no free fishing. Tackleist: Stansay Sports. Hotels: Black Bull, Exhibition, Bridge and George.

Huntingdon (Hunts). Chub, bream, roach and tench; good when boat traffic declines. Huntingdon AS has water below town. St £4, wt £2, dt 75p from tackleists. London AA *(see p 71)* has $4\frac{1}{2}$m of Ouse, stretch of **Alconbury Brook, Brampton Mill Pool** and millstream, and other water at **Brampton;** members only. Tickets issued for some waters; inquire hon sec. Tackleists: Ted's of Huntingdon, Ken Bradshaw, Old School Building, Walden Road.

Offord Cluny (Hunts). Chub, roach, bream, tench. Offord and Buckden AS has 4m of Great Ouse between Offord and Buckden; st £8 from hon sec; dt £1 from car park; hon sec or G Cooper, 5 Station Lane. Concessions for OAP, juniors, junior competitions run each season. Several sections are free of boat traffic at all times. Coach-party enquiries (40p per peg) to E Blowfield, 4 Monks Cottages, Huntingdon. Hitchin AC has short stretch; no dt. Letchworth AC also has meadow.

St Neots (Hunts). St Neots and Dist AS has extensive fishing from Barford Power Station with some gaps down to Wray House, Gt Paxton and Paxton Lake; good tench, chub, bream, roach and carp to 30 lb. St £9.50, wt £3.75, dt 75p (concessions for OAP, juniors and disabled) from hon sec and bailiffs. London AA has water at **Tempsford** and **Blunham** *(see Ivel)*. 30 acres of lake and $\frac{1}{4}$m of Ouse at **Little Paxton** available from OWR/Redland. 3 pits open. St £10, dt £1. Permits from Fishery Manager, I May, 5 Hayling Avenue, Little Paxton. Tel: Huntingdon 212059.

Biggleswade (Beds). Ouse, Ivel, Biggleswade, Hitchin & Dis. AC AA has 7m on mid Ouse at Wyboston, and 15 acre lake at Eaton Socon with large carp, tench, rudd, bream. St £16 from sec of local

tackleists. Arlesey Lake (4m S); syndicate water, members only.

Bedford (Beds). Some 4m water in town centre and above, free to Anglian Water rod licence-holders. Bedford AC controls most other fishing and issues limited dt at £1, st £12, concessions for OAP and juniors. Sunday fishing allowed; sport excellent. Hotels: Embankment, Swan, Lion. Tackleists: Dixon Bros, 95 Tavistock Street.

Felmersham (7m N of Bedford) Luton & Dist AA has $1\frac{1}{4}$m of river and two gravel pits, holding carp and tench. St £2.50, jun & OAP £1.

Sharnbrook (Beds). Wellingborough and Dist. Nene AC has $\frac{3}{4}$m upstream of **Harrold** and one field at **Pavenham.** Leighton Buzzard AC has water on left bank here. Ampthill AC has stretch on river at Dairy Farm, **Renhold.** Tickets *(see Olney)*. St £11 for Leisure Sport **Harrold** fishery. Apply LSA, Thorpe Park, Staines Lane, Chertsey, Surrey.

Newton Blossomville (Bucks). Coarse fish. Northampton Nene AC has water; strictly limited dt £2 from Old Mill, Newton Blossomville.

Olney (Bucks). Coarse fish, good bream. Leighton Buzzard AC has $\frac{3}{4}$m stretch at **Stoke Goldington,** from Gayhurst Spinney to brook, st £14.50; jun, OAP £4.

Newport Pagnell (Bucks). Good roach, bream, etc. Stretch fishes well in winter. Newport Pagnell FA has about 10m of river and nine gravel pits. St £10, dt £1 for members' guests only. At **Gt Linford** there is a complex of gravel pits holding bream, roach, tench and pike on which the fishing rights are now held by ARC. Luton & Dist AA has 8m of main river and a gravel pit. Inquire hon sec. Club has vacancies. St £2. **Vicarage Spinney** is 8 acre trout fishery near **Milton Keynes.** Dt and boats available. Tel: 0908 614969. Tackleist: Don Wills, High St. Hotel: Bull Inn (club HQ).

Stony Stratford (Bucks). Stony Stratford AS has 2m of Ouse following on 3m held by Deanshanger AS (members only; limit, 5m radius). Stony Stratford AC, st £2.50, dt 50p for accompanied guests. Galleon AA has water on **Grand Union Canal.** Dt from hon sec. Cosgrove Lodge lakes at Cosgrove (Northants); noted for roach, tench, bream, pike; dt on water. **Kingfisher Farm,** Deanshanger, has lakes of 36 acres. Trout, fly only. Dt £11.50, $\frac{1}{2}$ day £7.50. Boats £7, £4.

Buckingham (Bucks). Coarse fish, some trout. Buckingham and Dist AA has water. Members may now fish on ODAA water on Thames by Oxford. Joining fee £10, st £15, dt £3, from tackleist, Fish and Field, 62 Nelson St. Claydon Lakes, 6m; Leighton Buzzard AA; no dt. At **Mursley** Church Hill Farm has 2 lakes of 10 acres stocked daily with r and b trout. Dt £14, evening £8. Tel: 029672 524.

Tributaries of the Ouse (Great)

WISSEY:
Hilgay (Norfolk). King's Lynn AA have 2m of both banks down to Ouse. St £9, wt £5, dt £1.50. London AA issues dt for Five Mile House Farm.
LITTLE OUSE: Good bream, roach, etc; dace run large in some stretches.
Brandon (Suffolk). Bream (good), roach, dace, perch, pike (good), a few chub and zander. Stretches held by Brandon and Dist AC; limited number of visitors admitted. Licences and dt (40p) from Newmans DIY, Thetford Road. Thetford and Breckland AC has water above bridge, and London AA has a fishery here; members only. Hotels: The Ram and New Inn, Hockwood.
Thetford (Norfolk). Little Ouse and Thet. Roach, rudd, tench, chub and pike; and dace to specimen size. Fishing free from Barnham Common to first staunch. Thetford Breckland AC has several stretches and **Barnham Pit.**
LARK: Trout, grayling and coarse fish.
Mildenhall (Suffolk). From Bury St Edmunds to Lackford controlled by Bury St Edmund's AA; trout water; no permits. Lark APS has good water here. Tackleists: Stebbing's Sports; E Morley & Sons.
Bury St Edmunds (Suffolk). Coarse fish. Club: Bury St Edmunds AA. Tackleist: R Nunn, "Tackle Up", 49a St John's Street. For trout waters, A Woods, tel: 0284 612.
CAM: Coarse fish, mostly roach and bream.
Cambridge. Bream, roach, chub, dace and carp. Cambridge FP & AS leases west bank of Cam from Pike & Eel, Chesterton to Clayhithe; st £6, dt £1.50 from hon sec or local tackle shops. Concessions to OAP, juniors and disabled. Society also has about 4m of the **Hundred Foot River** from Earith Bridge to Sutton Gault and sole rights on whole of **Burwell Lode** and **Reach Lode,** plus 1m of Gt Ouse at **Barway** and 1m of **Lark** below **Prickwillow Bridge;** inquire hon sec for permits. London AA has water for members only at **Swaffham**

Prior. Cambridge Albion AS has two stretches at Wicken Fen, and Dimmocks Cote, also **Barnwell Pit,** Barnwell Bridge. **Cam** and **Granta** offer some free fishing to licence-holders. Cambridge tackleists: Gallyon & Sons Ltd, 66 Bridge Street, Thorntons, 46 Burleigh Street.
OLD WEST RIVER: Good stock of coarse fish; burbot taken on Histon AS stretch. St for rivers £6, dt for **Milton Lake** 65p. Large carp and other coarse fish.
Cottenham (Cambs). Willingham and Smithy Fen controlled by Histon and Dist AS. Waters also on **Cam** and **Lark.**
IVEL: Dace, roach and perch.
Tempsford (Beds). Ouse and Ivel. Biggleswade AC, now merged with Hitchin and District AA, has some water on both rivers. *(See also Blunham).* London AA has several miles on Ouse here and at Blunham; members only.
Blunham (Beds). Ouse (1m W). Tickets from hon sec, Blunham FC for Ivel. Below Blunham Bridge to Ouse held by Biggleswade and District AC. Club also has right bank of Ivel from Langford Mill to Broom Mill; no dt. Shefford AC has left bank. **Lower Caldecote** (Beds). Leisure sport has $\frac{3}{4}$m stretch, with trout, dace, chub, mirror carp and barbel to 3 lb.
HIZ (tributary of Ivel). Controlled by Biggleswade, Hitchin and District AA who have new 15 acre coarse fishery nearby, and 7m increase of water on Middle Ouse. Membership £16 pa, specimen perch, etc. *(See Midlands reservoirs, lakes.)* Club also has water on **Ouse, River Oughton** (trout, few chub, restocking under consideration; members only), and fishes waters of Great Ouse FCA and Ivel Protection Assn. St £16. Tackleist: Alan Brown, Nightingale Road, **Hitchin.**
OUZEL: Coarse fish.
Leighton Buzzard (Beds). Leighton Buzzard AC preserves various stretches above Leighton Buzzard and at Stoke Hammond, Water Eaton, Bletchley and Newport Pagnell but some stretches will

be temporarily lost by Milton Keynes development. Club also has several stretches on **Gt Ouse** (three at **Emberton** and others at **Stoke Goldington, Renhold** and **Sharnbrook**), five on **Thame–Shabbington** and **Worminghall** and 3m of **Grand Union Canal**. Also **Claydon Lakes, Tiddenfoot** and other pits. Annual membership £14.50. Concessions to jun & OAP. Leisure Sport has two gravel pits stocked with large pike, carp and catfish. St £12. Phone Chertsey 64872 for details. Tackleists: S L Pedder, 112 Victoria Street, **Dunstable;**

RELIEF CHANNEL: not strictly a tributary but included here because of the status traditionally enjoyed as an excellent coarse fishery in its own right, now re-established as such, after a difficult period with zander, by an intensive programme of investigation and re-stocking by AWA. Now rented to Wisbech & Dist AA which issues dt.

TOVE: Coarse fish.

Towcester (Northants). Towcester and Dist AA has water on river and three ponds; members only.

OUSE (Sussex)

(For close seasons, licences, etc, see Southern Water Authority, p 11–12)

Rises few miles south-east of Horsham and flows for 33 miles to enter English Channel at Newhaven. Tidal for 12 miles from mouth to point 4m upstream of Lewes. Coarse fish and trout, but notable for run of big sea trout.

Lewes and Barcombe Mills (Sussex). Sea trout (good), perch, bream, roach, dace, chub, carp and pike. Ouse APS has west bank to Barcombe Mills (about 4m) and east bank for 1m north of Lewes. Certain stretches also available above mills. Limited st only at £20, juv £12. Sea trout all time from May, but June–August best provided there is rain. Barcombe Mills Pool and side streams reserved entirely for sea-trout fishing and available to st holders at £2.50 a day (two rods daily) bookable in advance from hon sec. Trout fishing also available on 40-acre **Barcombe Reservoir** to st holders on payment of £6 day, 4 fish limit. Limited dt after July 1st. Full details from ticket sec, Ouse APS; The Old Barn Cottage, Peak Lane, East Preston. Hotels: Shelleys; White Hart; Crown (all Lewes). For Barcombe Mills: Angler's Rest, Anchor Inn.
Isfield (Sussex). Coarse fish, trout and sea trout. Isfield and Dist AC has about 12m of river between **Newick** and **Lewes.** Club

also has a stretch of **Uck** and six lakes. St £20 plus £5 joining fee, mt £5 from hon sec (sae please). No dt. Exchange ticket system with other clubs. Hotels: Laughing Fish, Isfield (club HQ), and Maiden's Head, Uckfield. *(For tackle see Haywards Heath.)*
Haywards Heath (Sussex). Coarse fish and trout. Haywards Heath AS has 12m of Ouse from **Ardingly** down to **Newick** (excluding stretch below **Fletching Mill**) and two lakes (**Balcombe Lake** and **Vale Bridge Mill Pond**). No dt but wt £2 for holiday visitors. Membership open to approved applicants £10 pa. Tackleists: Penfold's, High Street, Cuckfield.

UCK:
Isfield (Sussex). Coarse fish and trout. Isfield and Dist AC has water from here to **Uckfield** (members only). Several lakes in Sussex, Kent and Surrey. **Yew Tree Trout Fishery,** $5\frac{1}{2}$ acres, is at **Crowborough;** dt and boats. Tel: 089285 2529.

OUSE (Yorkshire)

(For close seasons, licences, etc, see Yorkshire Water Authority, p 14)

Forms with Trent the estuary of the Humber. Coarse fish, with some trout. Dunsforth, Beningbrough and Poppleton reaches noted for barbel and chub. Large bream present but difficult to catch. Most water held by Leeds and York clubs. Tributaries give excellent trout and coarse fishing.

Goole (N Humberside). Don enters Ouse here. Goole AA has stretch of **Derwent** from Wressle to Sutton; good roach, chub, pike, dace, few trout. No dt. Club also has water on **Selby Canal, Market Weighton Canal,** and local ponds. Memberships (£9, concessionary £4.50 pa) from Barry's of Goole Ltd, Westfield Avenue. Club has other waters on Trent, Derwent, and three ponds.

Acaster (N Yorks). Coarse fishing. Controlled by the Leeds Amalgamation. Tickets at Blacksmith's Arms, Naburn, and Manor Guest House, Acaster Malbis. Fishing mostly free below dam (tidal); fish include barbel; above dam, trout and coarse fish. Accommodation: Manor Guest House.

Naburn (N Yorks). On opposite bank to Acaster. York Amal also has water; members only. Below dam fishing free and water tidal.

York (N Yorks). Coarse fish; some free fishing on public waters. On left bank nearly all free except 8m from Rawcliffe Ings and Clifton Ings up to Aldwark. York Amalgamation has fishing on 80m of Ouse, Derwent, Nidd, Rye, Seven, and several still waters. St £18, dt £1.80 from local tackleists for lower **Nidd.** 4m on Rivers **Rye** and **Seven;** very good grayling and trout; $\frac{1}{2}$m on **Derwent,** all three fisheries members only. York Tradesmen's AA has rights on several becks, members only. Tackleists: Hookes Ltd, 28–30 Coppergate; G E Hill, 40 Clarence Street.

Poppleton, Beningbrough and Newton (N Yorks). Good barbel, pike, etc. York and Leeds Amalgamations have extensive stretches. Dt from Fox Inn, Nether Poppleton, and post office *(see York).*

Aldwark (N Yorks). Coarse fish. York Amal have privileges for $2\frac{1}{2}$m above and $\frac{1}{2}$m below Aldwark Bridge *(see York)* with exception of short stretch. Hotels: Three Horseshoes and Crown, Great Ouseburn; Bay Horse, Aldwark.

Low Dunsforth. From Low Dunsforth to Aldwark Bridge (about 4m right bank) fishing is in hands of Leeds Amal. Dt from Anchor Inn, Low Dunsforth; Anchor Inn, Whixley (Little Ouseburn); Crown, Three Horseshoes and Bay Horse (Great Ouseburn). Leeds Amal also has good length at **Hunterslodge** on opposite side below Aldwark bridge (left bank). Tickets as above.

Tributaries of the Ouse (Yorkshire)

DON (tributary of Ouse). Rises on Wike Head and flows through Sheffield and Doncaster to the estuary of the Ouse; much polluted in its lower reaches but efforts of water authority beginning to bear fruit. Elsewhere holds coarse fish. Some tributaries hold trout.

Doncaster (S Yorks). River polluted. **Thrybergh Reservoir,** near **Rotherham;** Rotherham MBC trout fishery. St £42, $\frac{1}{2}$ dt £2.30, conc £1.15 from on site. 34 acres of water. Rotherham MBC also has **Fitzwilliam Canal,** Rotherham 1m, dt £1.60. Doncaster & Dist AA has water on the **Idle** at Misson (10m) the **Torne** at Rossington Bridge to Pilfrey Bridge (18m) the **Trent** at Marton and Littleborough, the **S Yorkshire Navigation Canal,** lakes and drains. **Aire and Calder Navigation:** Castleford & Dist SAC has water between Cowick and Barnby Dun on New Junction Canal, also **Southfield Reservoir.** BWF Castleford Anglers have **Woodnook Reservoir.** St from Assn HQ and tackleists. Tackleists: M Potter, The Gables, Church Street, Armthorpe; F G Gale & Son, 26 Copley Road; W Argyll, 81 Call House Road; and Anglers Supplies, 148 High Street, Bentley.

Sheffield (S Yorks). Don polluted. **Damflask,** YWA reservoir, 5m W; trout. **Underbank,** corporation reservoir, coarse fishing and odd large trout. Tickets from attendant's office. For further information, see *"Yorkshire Lakes".* Sheffield Amal AS (membership books from Lord Nelson, Arundel Street) has three waters on **Trent,** at Besthorpe, Girton and North and South Clifton. Membership £7, juv £2.50. Dt £1.50. Sheffield and Dist AA has water on Rivers **Delph, Trent, Till, Don, Witham** and **Old Bedford River, Dearne and Dove Canal** at **Barnsley** (14m), **Stockwith and Chesterfield Canal** at **Staveley** (3m) and **Stockwith** (8m), **Idle** at **Haxey** (4m), and drains at **Keadby** in Wisbech district (Nene) and near **Chatteris.** Dt issued for most waters. **Stainforth and Keadby Canal** controlled by joint committee including Rotherham, Doncaster, Sheffield Amal, Sheffield and Dist and British Railways clubs. At **Staveley** urban district council have five-acre lake stocked annually with coarse fish; dt and st. Also Foxtone Dam; dt. Tackleists: Arthur Turner, 33–35 West Bar; Bennett's, 38–40 Howard Street, Sheffield; Ernest Stamford, 419 Attercliffe Common; W G Dawson, 70 Holme Lane.

DEARNE (tributary of Don):

Barnsley (S Yorks). Dearne; Barnsley Fitzwilliam AC; dt Sheffield and Dist AA has water on **Dearne and Dove Canal.** Barnsley Trout Canal fishes **Scout Dike Reservoir;** trout av $\frac{3}{4}$ lb; limited dt. **Wintersett Reservoir;** coarse fish; dt from bailiff. **Worsbrough Reservoir;** dt from Reservoir House, Red Lion Hotel, Ship Inn (good roach, bream, tench and pike). Other club: Barnsley and Dist AA. Tackleist: Field Sports Supplies, Pitt St.

Claycross (Derby). Lakes: Williamthorpe Ponds, 2m NE. Wingerworth Hall Lakes (two), $2\frac{1}{2}$m NW. Great Dam, $3\frac{1}{2}$m NW.

ROTHER (tributary of Don):

Killamarsh (Derby). Short Brook. Lakes: Woodhall Moor Dams, 2m E. Barlborough Hall Lake, 3m SE. Pebley Dam, 3m SE. Harthill Reservoir, 3m E. Woodhall Pond, 3m E.

AIRE: Issues from ground at Aire Head, half a mile south of Malham village. Its upper reaches contain quality trout and grayling, which give place to coarse fish between Steeton and Keighley, where Marsden Star AS has water, st £10, dt £1, conc. Tackle shop in Keighley. Lower reaches and others near large towns polluted. *(For Malham Tarn—see Ribble—Settle.)*

Leeds (W Yorks). Polluted. Adel Beck and Dam (private). **Roundhay Park Lakes,** 4m NE. Leeds and Dist ASA have fishing; dt from local tackleists. Larger lake (Waterloo) contains pike, perch, roach, tench, carp, etc; small lake stocked with carp, bream and roach. Leeds Amal has extensive fishing on Ouse and tributaries, canals and lakes, dt for many waters; full details from hon sec. Also trout at Pool and Arthington *(see Ouse (Yorks)—Wharfe).* At **Swinsty** and **Fewston,** 7m from **Otley,** are YWA reservoirs, containing trout; visitors' dt can be had at Reservoir Lodge, Fewston; no Sunday fishing. Minnow and fly only. Tackleists: Linsley Bros, 28 Kirkgate, Leeds LS2 7DR.

Bradford (W Yorks). Aire, 7m N. Bradford City AA has extensive rights here and on water on the canals at **Apperley Bridge** and near Skipton; on **Wharfe, Ure** and **Swale,** reservoirs and lakes. Bradford No 1 AA has water on **Wharfe, Aire, Swale, Ure, Nidd, Derwent, Leeds and Liverpool Canal,** and reservoirs. Addingham AA have water on **Wharfe** (Addingham, $1\frac{1}{2}$m; Denton and Ben Rhydding, $2\frac{1}{2}$m; trout and grayling) and three reservoirs holding trout and perch; members only st £85. Waiting list. Tackleists: W Carter, 15 Bridge Street; Knuttons, Barry Street; D Richmond, 110 Morley Street.

Bingley, Saltaire (W Yorks). Trout, coarse fish; Bingley AC has good coarse fishery; restocked annually. St £10 and dt £1.50. Club has good trout fishing on **Sunnydale Reservoir** (dt £1.50 from hon sec or Cullimores of Bingley); also two dams and beck. Trout waters are for members only. Excellent trout preserve in Myrtle Park; water restocked; dt 75p. Saltaire AA has water (being restocked); dt. From Bankfield Hotel downstream to Baildon Bridge (both banks, except Roberts Park) is Bradford No 1 water. Dt for 1m of **Harden Beck** which enters Aire at Bingley. Advance booking by letter to G R Reynolds, Goit Stock Estate, Harden, or by phone, Cullingworth 3810. Fly only. Tackleists: G A Cullimore, 29a Park Road.

Keighley (W Yorks). Trout, grayling, coarse fish. Sport improved after restocking. Keighley AC has 11m; st £10 (concessions to ladies, juniors, OAP) dt £2, £1.50 for R Aire only. Trout to $1\frac{1}{4}$ lb; best May–June and Sept. Club also has the **Leeds–Liverpool Canal** from Office Lock, Leeds, to Banknewton, **Whitefields Reservoir,** stocked with carp, tench, roach and perch, and, for members only, **Roberts Pond** (large tench, carp, pike) **Sugden End Reservoir,** Crossroads, (roach, perch, large carp and tench) and the **R Worth,** trout. *(See also Yorkshire lakes, reservoirs, etc.)*

Cononley (W Yorks). Trout, perch, chub, roach, dace, bream, grayling; dt after June 1, for Bradford City AA water £2 from Post Office or tackleists. Bradford No 1 AA also has water. Dt from tackleists.

Skipton (N Yorks). Trout, grayling, pike, chub, roach. At Skipton, Skipton AA has three miles of fishing, both banks; st

Grafham Water
Europe's Premier Trout Fishery

...Warren (Fishery Owner) and Brian Leadbetter (the ...ent world fly fishing Champion) discuss tactics ...re setting out for a days fishing.

1987, one of the best years since Grafham Water opened. Several hundred trout over 4lb have been caught. Privatisation has lead to many improvements in the facilities for fishermen, including larger quantities of bigger stock fish........

John Tiddy with part of his catch, showing three fish weighing over 7lb each — July "87".

...view from the Lodge restaurant.

The fishery now boasts of better boat facilities, earlier starting, its own Pub and Restaurant. Anglers enjoy the many variations of flyfishing that Grafham offers with traditional Loch style and dryfly fishing providing some of the best sport.

...licensed restaurant has a full a la carte menu ...oth English and Continental cuisine together ... a picturesque view of the harbour and ...fham Water.

...erything you need for a ...ood days trout fishing.

Piscators Limited
The Lodge — Grafham Water
Mander Park, West Perry,
HUNTINGDON,
Cambs. PE18 0BX
Tel: (0480) 810531 — Fishing
(0480) 810537 — Restaurant

WET FLIES AND NYMPHS

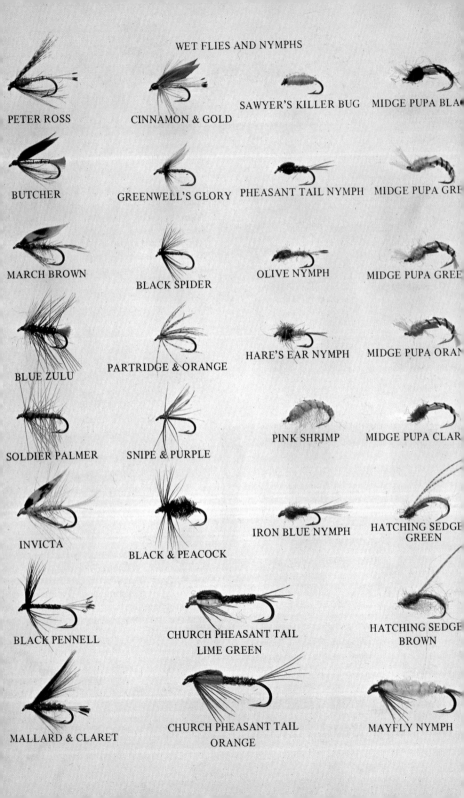

PETER ROSS

CINNAMON & GOLD

SAWYER'S KILLER BUG

MIDGE PUPA BLA

BUTCHER

GREENWELL'S GLORY

PHEASANT TAIL NYMPH

MIDGE PUPA GRE

MARCH BROWN

BLACK SPIDER

OLIVE NYMPH

MIDGE PUPA GREE

BLUE ZULU

PARTRIDGE & ORANGE

HARE'S EAR NYMPH

MIDGE PUPA ORAN

SOLDIER PALMER

SNIPE & PURPLE

PINK SHRIMP

MIDGE PUPA CLAR

INVICTA

BLACK & PEACOCK

IRON BLUE NYMPH

HATCHING SEDGE
GREEN

BLACK PENNELL

CHURCH PHEASANT TAIL
LIME GREEN

HATCHING SEDGE
BROWN

MALLARD & CLARET

CHURCH PHEASANT TAIL
ORANGE

MAYFLY NYMPH

£20 (entrance fee £27), wt £10, dt £3.50 (wt & dt, reduction for grayling only), issued by hon sec. Association also has rights on **Embsay Reservoir** (trout), and **Whinnygill Reservoirs** (trout and coarse fish) dt and wt. Bradford City AA water begins on both banks below Skipton water; about 7m in all. Assn also has canal near here. At **Kilnsey Park**, Skipton, are two trout lakes of 3 acres. Tel: 0756 752150. St, dt. Tackleist: Ken Wharton, "K Tackle", Water Street, issues st £17.25 and dt £2.30 for Aire below Skipton and 40p dt for **Leeds & Liverpool Canal**. Bradford No 1 AA has **Bradley Fishery**; roach, pike, chub, trout. St from hon sec. For **Earby Beck** (6½m SW), trout. Hotels: Devonshire Arms, Midland, Hole in the Wall (both latter can advise anglers).

Gargrave (N Yorks). Trout; was preserved hence down to Colne Railway Bridge by Aire Fishing Club, now defunct.

Bellbusk (N Yorks). Trout; preserved by private owners. Lakes: **Conniston House;** trout. **Eshton Tarn,** 2m NE; pike. **Malham Tarn,** 8m N; trout and perch; tickets *(see Ribble—Settle)*.

CALDER (tributary of Aire): Good coarse fishing from Brighouse to Sowerby Bridge.

Halifax (W Yorks). Calder 2m S. Clubs: Halifax and Dist AC (dams); Dean Clough AC (canal at Copley); Greater Elland AA (dams); Halifax Flyfishers'; no water. Ripponden Flyfishers'; good trout fishing in **Ryburn Reservoir**, Ripponden. Hebden Bridge AS; coarse fishing in canal; trout in beck. Brighouse AA and Bradford No 1 AA control 14m on Calder above and below **Brighouse;** heavily restocked and now provides sport with good-quality roach. St £14.95 + £13.80 joining fee from D B Arnett, 49 Templars Way, Bradford but 2-year waiting list. No dt. Brighouse AA also has water on canal and gravel pits. Ryburn AS; lakes near **Sowerby Bridge;** coarse, trout; tickets. Tackleist: A J Jewson, 1 Westgate.

Sowerby Bridge (W Yorks). Ryburn AS, has water on Calder and local dams and reservoirs. Top Willow Hall Dam and Lower Willow Hall Dam on dt.

Hebden (W Yorks). Hebden Bridge AS has water on Calder and **Rochdale Canal** (Callis Lock No 13 to junction with Calder and Hebble Navigation Sowerby Bridge) and on **Rivers Ryburn** and **Elphin,**

and **Hardcastle Crags Stream.** Dt for stream only of which club has several miles; being restocked. Membership open to Alderdale residents only. Canal also restocked. At **Todmorden** (Lancs) (4m away) the Todmorden AS (annual membership, £10) has about 6m of the **Rochdale Canal, Portsmouth Reservoir** and **New Mill Dam** (trout); members only. Dt £1.50 for **Calderbrook Bottom Dam, Littleborough.** Steve's Tackle Shop, Rochdale or Summit Store, Summit, Littleborough. **Calder and Hebble Navigation.** From Salterhebble Top Lock, through Brighouse, Lower Hopton Bridge, Thornhill, to upstream of Ganny Lock, the following clubs have water: Dean Clough AS, Mackintosh AC, Brighouse AA, Bradford No. 1, Slaithwaite AA, Thornhill C & BC, Unity AC.

COLNE (tributary of Calder):

Huddersfield (W Yorks). **Longwood Compensation Reservoir.** This, as its name implies, is compensation water known locally as **Oak Scar Reservoir.** Preserved and stocked by Huddersfield AA. It has good head of pike, perch, roach and gudgeon. Angling restricted to members of the association along with special annual permit-holders accepted by association up to 50 per season. No river fishing; no other details published.

Slaithwaite (W Yorks). Slaithwaite and Dist AC (st £10, dt £1) has rights on **Trent** at Sutton and Dunham, on **Rye** at Butterwick and on Rivers **Calder, Colne** and **Holme,** as well as several miles of canal and reservoir fishing; trout, coarse fish; dt (for canal) from D Rushforth, 22 Longwood Gate, Longwood, Hudds. No dt between Feb 28 and May 31. Dt some waters June 1–Feb 28. Apply hon sec for details.

HOLME (tributary of Colne);

Holmfirth (W Yorks). Lakes: **Holmstyes Reservoir;** trout (Huddersfield 8m) preserved by Huddersfield AA. St £38. **Boshaw Reservoir** (Huddersfield 8m); preserved as above. Holme Valley Piscatorials have water on the Sir John Ramsden Canal and Magdale Dam. Dt for the former 50p from tackle shops. Membership details from hon sec.

DERWENT: Rises in high moors and flows almost to coast near Scarborough where it turns south and enters estuary of Ouse. Its upper reaches, most easily reached from Scarborough, are trout and grayling waters *(see Ayton).* Lower down coarse fish predominate, barbel included.

Wressle (N Humberside). Coarse fish, mostly free.

Breighton (N Humberside); ns Wressle 1m. Bubwith 1m. Chub, dace, pike, etc; fishing free. Inquire Half Moon Inn.

Bubwith (N Humberside). Coarse fish; Howden & Dist AC has 4m of good mixed fishing on left bank to **Ellerton;** roach, perch, dace, bream, chub, eels and pike; flatfish lower down. Dt 50p and st £2.50 from White Swan Inn. Match bookings to hon sec.

Wheldrake (N Yorks). Tidal. Coarse fish. York AA has $1\frac{1}{2}$m right bank; dt from the Alice Hawthorne Inn.

Sutton-on-Derwent (N Yorks). Coarse fish. Cross Keys Inn; 2m tidal, 2m non-tidal; coarse fish below dam, trout above; dt and st. Further information from inn.

East Cottingwith (N Yorks); ns High Field, 4m. Coarse fish (pike and chub very good). York AA controls East Cottingwith Water (2m) and 10m of good coarse fishing on **Pocklington Canal.** Dt from secretary or Blue Bell Inn. At **Thorganby,** on other side of Derwent, Ferry Boat Inn can give permission for about 3m of river.

Pocklington (N Yorks). **Pocklington Canal.** Well stocked with bream, roach, perch, pike, etc *(see East Cottingwith).* York AA water. Dt from Canal Head; College Arms, Beilby; Melbourne Arms, Melbourne; and The Cottage at Coats Bridge.

Ellerton Landing (N Yorks). Mixed fishing. Hotel: White Swan, Bubwith.

Kexby (N Yorks); ns Fangfoss, 3m. Pike, chub, etc. York and Leeds Amalgamated Societies have water; members only. *(See also Stamford Bridge and Low Catton.)*

Low Catton (N Yorks). Coarse fish. Leeds and Dist AS has good length of water on left bank; members only. *(See also Kexby and Stamford Bridge.)*

Stamford Bridge (N Yorks). Excellent for roach, pike, chub, dace. York and Dist Amal has fishing on good length down to Kexby Brickworks; also pits. Dt at cafés in Stamford Bridge. *(See also Kexby and Low Catton.)*

Howsham (N Yorks). Coarse fishing. York and Dist AA has water on Derwent and Barton Hill Beck; Bradford No 1 AA has water; members only.

Kirkham Abbey (N Yorks). Coarse fish. Leeds and York Amalgamations have

water; members only.

Castle Howard (N Yorks). **Castle Howard Great Lake** contains specimen coarse fish, including pike, perch, tench, bream, roach and bank fishing only. For further details, see *"Yorkshire Lakes".*

Huttons Ambo (Yorks). Roach, pike, dace, barbel, grayling, perch and few trout. South bank held by Malton and Norton AC *(see Malton)* for 1m down and 1m up; no dt. North bank held by Huttons Ambo AC for 2m down and 2m up; membership, for people resident within 10m Malton, £3 pa.

Malton (Yorks). Coarse fish (mainly roach). Malton and Norton AC. Waters extend to 1m below Huttons Ambo. Membership discretionary, st £5.50, wt £3.50, dt 75p issued by hon sec and N & C Swift, Castlegate, Malton. Tickets from Malton Estate Office, Old Maltongate, for 3m of Derwent and Rye (trout and coarse fish). York and Dist AA has $5\frac{1}{2}$m at Old Malton to Ryemouth; st £18, dt £1.80. D S Johnson, 45 Mayfield Grove, Dring Houses, York. Tel: 704464. Costa Beck, 3m NE. Lakes: Castle Howard Park Lake, 5m W *(see Castle Howard).* Good deal of free water on Derwent and Rye. Tackleists: J Anderson & Son, Market Place (tickets for Malton AC waters); and C Swift, Castlegate. Hotel: Green Man.

Riddlington (Yorks). Derwent, 1m N. Coarse fish; Leeds Amal water. Scampston Beck, 1m E, private. Rye, 2m N. Costa Beck, 3m N.

Yedingham (Yorks). Coarse fish. Scartion Mere AC has $1\frac{1}{2}$m stretch, north bank only, on Marishes Lodge, Whitehalls and Crakehall Farms. Members only, who must reside in Scarborough area. The club also has water on Rye nr **Pickering** (6m), and Derwent at Wykeham Estate. Dt at Providence Inn for Leeds Amal waters. Inn also has private stretch. Foul Bridge Farm issue dt.

Ganton (Yorks). Chub, pike, dace, grayling; dt for 1m each way from Hay Bridge, from farm at railway crossing. Ruston Beck, 2m W.

Ayton (Yorks). Some good trout water. Scarborough Mere AC has **Scarborough Mere,** just outside town; coarse fish; st £10, dt £1; mere restocked regularly. About 2m trout fishing from Ayton towards Ganton controlled by Leeds Amal; no tickets.

Hackness (Yorks). Derwent AC, annual subscription £130, controls 10m of trout (brown and rainbow) and grayling fishing down to **East Ayton,** for part of which dt at £12 are available on main club water (from East Ayton to Hilla Green bridge on the Troutsdale Road) from July 1 to Sept 30. Farther up, above Langdale End bridge (3m both banks), dt available at £6 from April 1 to Sept 30. Fishing one fly only, wet or dry, is club rule on all water. Tickets from Scarborough tackleists: Pritchards, Eastborough (WA licences and club tickets, dt on lower water and dt and wt on upper water), and Grange Hotel (rods for residents on 8m of Derwent). Sunday fishing reserved for members and guests on lower club water, and all fishing between Hilla Green bridge and Langdale End bridge exclusively reserved to members and guests. Size limit for trout 10 in; limited three brace per day. No limit to size or number of grayling. Wading allowed.

FOSS BECK (tributary of Derwent). Fishing station: **Fangfoss** (Yorks); fishing private.

SPITTLE BECK (tributary of Derwent); **Barton Hill** (Yorks). Derwent, 2m E. Whitecarr Beck, 4m SE. Loppington Beck, 4m SE. Swallowpits Beck, 5m SE at Scrayingham. York and Dist AA have trout water **Barton Hill Beck.**

RYE (tributary of Derwent): Trout, grayling, other coarse fish.

Nunnington (Yorks). Permits for Holbeck Fishery (£5 top water, £2.50 bottom water) from Grice, the gamekeeper, Nunnington. Hotel: Worsley Arms, Hovingham.

Butterwick (Yorks). Trout, coarse fish. Slaithwaite AC has water; members only. St £10, dt £1 from D Rushforth, 22 Longwood Gate, Longwood, Hudds; or local tackleists.

Helmsley (Yorks). Trout, grayling; preserved above from Helmsley (road) bridge to Tylas Farm boundary and below to Nunnington (railway) bridge by Ryedale Anglers' Club; no tickets. Tackleist: Cooper & Son (ironmongers), Bridge Street. Hotels: Black Swan, Feversham Arms, Crown.

Hawnby (Yorks); ns Helmsley, $6\frac{1}{2}$m; Thirsk, 10m. Hawnby Hotel has 8m private fishing in Rye and **Seph**; trout; fly only on Rye; thigh waders and shortish rods advised; dt for non-residents £2.75, weekend £3, from hotel.

PICKERING BECK (tributary of Rye) and Costa Beck (chalk stream). Trout, grayling.

Pickering (Yorks). About 1m of free fishing in town; private above, preserved below (3m) by Pickering FA; fly only; membership limited to 90; st £45, entrance fee $1\frac{1}{2}$ times annual subscription. Water also on **Costa Beck** and **Oxfold Becks,** trout and grayling, and **Thornton-le-Dale** Beck. Two trout lakes. Dt for members' guests only, but hon sec pleased to assist prospective visitors. Club HQ: Bay Horse Hotel. Dt on lower Costa, **Rye, Dove** and **Seven** from farmers; 3–7m from Pickering, mainly coarse fishing. Scarborough Mere AC has 6m on Rye near Pickering. Hotels: White Swan, Black Swan, Forest and Vale, Crossways.

SEVEN (tributary of Rye): Trout, grayling; some coarse fish.

Newsham Bridge (Yorks). York and Dist AA has water on Seven and Rye; no dt.

Marton (Yorks). Private from mill to Marton; below Marton some free water; grayling, pike, chub, dace and a few trout. Tackleist in Malton, 12m.

Sinnington (Yorks). Seven AC has $2\frac{1}{2}$m downstream; trout and grayling; members only, long waiting list. Coarse fishing mainly below large weir and bottom farm. Upstream Sinnington AC has water; inquire hon sec. Waiting list for membership.

WATH BECK (tributary of Rye):

Slingsby (Yorks). Trout; preserved. Rye, 2m NE.

DOVE-IN-FARNDALE (tributary of Rye):

Kirby Moorside (N Yorks). Dove-in-Farndale, 1m E; trout; private. Dt for stretches downstream of Kirby Moorside available from some of the farms. Hodge Beck, in Sleightholme Dale, 1m W, trout only. Hotel: King's Head.

THORNTON BECK (tributary of Derwent):

Thornton-le-Dale (N Yorks). Trout and grayling; preserved. Pickering Beck, 3m W. Derwent, 3m S. Hotels: The Hall; The Buck; all Thornton-le-Dale.

WHARFE: Rises on Cam Fell and flows 60m south-east to join Ouse near Cawood. Trout in upper reaches, with coarse fish in increasing numbers downstream.

Ryther (N Yorks); ns Ulleskelf, 3m. Castleford and Dis ASA has water; mainly coarse fish. Ryther Arms will give further information.

Ulleskelf (N Yorks). Coarse fish; preserved by Leeds Amal; dt £1.50 from Golden Swan.

Tadcaster (N Yorks). Coarse fish (mainly chub and dace, but good head of barbel, perch and bream); trout (restocked); preserved by Tadcaster Angling and Preservation Association on both banks downstream, from road bridge to Sewage Farm (1m) and from road bridge to Grimston Park (2m); st £10; dt £1, OAP, juv 50%. Tickets from hon sec, The Bay Horse; Newsagent and Chris's Tackle Shop, Wharfe Bank.

Boston Spa (W Yorks). Trout, grayling, other coarse fish (chub, barbel and pike good; bream introduced). Most rights held by Boston Spa AC. Dt 85p from Lower Wharfe Anglers, Boston Spa. Spa Baths issue dt 90p for stretch from river bridge to Wharfedale Hall, S bank. Club members (who must live within 3m of Boston Spa post office) allowed 12 guests a year at current cost of dt and guest must fish with member on non-ticket waters. Club stocks water with trout and

grayling of 12 in or over. Limit two trout, one grayling, or vice-versa; trout 12 in. June best month for trout and August for barbel and chub.

Wetherby (W Yorks). Wetherby and Dist AC water (stocked with trout and coarse fish) extends from Collingham Beck to Wetherby Weir, south bank (about 350 yards in Collingham Wood, south bank is private). Club also has four fields between golf course and playing fields, north bank. This water is open for visitors on st (above weir), and dt. Members only below and on weir, but visitors may fish if accompanied by a member. Same charge as above. Dt 75p from: R Dee's, Market Place, Wetherby. No legitimate bait or lure barred. Trout limit 11 in. Hotels: Angel, Wetherby Turnpike.

Collingham (W Yorks). Wetherby AC has water here; trout and coarse fish (including barbel, grayling and good dace).

Arthington (W Yorks). Trout; left bank and much of right bank leased to Leeds and Dist Amal; rest preserved.

Pool (W Yorks). Trout, few chub; preserved by the Leeds and Dist ASA which has 5m of fishing from River Washburn to Castley Beck on left bank and about 3m on right bank. Dt from Leeds tackleists. Members of Leeds AA, small private club, can fish Harewood Estate preserves, 3m right bank, 2m left bank.

Otley (W Yorks). Otley AC hold 2m left bank and $2\frac{1}{2}$m right bank below Otley Bridge. Fishing for members only, no dt. Dt £1.50 available for Leeds & Dist ASA

Knotford Lagoon, near Otley; large carp and other coarse fish; stocked. Also some r trout. Bradford No 1 AA has three stretches here. At Yeadon (6m) Airboro' and Dist AA has **Yeadon Tarn;** roach, perch, carp, tench. Tackleists in Otley: A Agar, The Gun Shop & Angling Supplies, 36 Pool Road, Cross Green.

Burley and Askwith (W Yorks). Trout, grayling, chub, dace. Bradford clubs have rights for members only.

Addingham (W Yorks). Trout, grayling; Bradford City AA has water here; also Bradford No 1AA, no dt obtainable. Bradford Waltonians have $1\frac{1}{2}$m here and water at **Denton** and **Ben Rhydding;** also **Chelker Reservoir** near here. No tickets. Bradford No 1 AA has some left bank at Denton and right bank at Ben Rhydding. Keighley AC has water; dt from hon sec.

Ilkley (W Yorks). Ilkley and Dist AC and Myddleton AC have water. Ilkley membership restricted to ratepayers. St £25, wt £12, dt £3, juv, OAP £2 (April 15–Sept 30 inc) from Ilkley CB & Angling Centre, 6 Little Lane, Ilkley and Ilkley Library. Good trout, grayling and dace fishing (restocked annually) from Brook Street Bridge to Stepping Stones, both banks (abt 1m); worm and fly only; no Sunday fishing. Hotels: Wheatley (club HQ), Ilkley Moor, Troutbeck, Craiglands.

Bolton Abbey (N Yorks). Trout and grayling. Dt from Estate Office, Bolton Abbey for 5 miles stretch (both banks) from Barden Bridge to Kex Beck below Bolton Bridge. Fly only. Trout April 1–September 30. Grayling can be taken from 15 June. Grayling only Oct 1–Dec 31. Limit 4 trout of not less than 10 in. Grayling 4 fish limit over 10in. St £132.25, wt £27.60, dt £6.90. Evening t £4, conc; £3.45 dt. Some interference on Sundays and Bank Holidays due to public access. Furnished holiday cottages also available for fishermen. New 4 acre trout fishery 8m from Bolton Abbey, apply Estate Office. Fishing facilities available at the Devonshire Arms Hotel.

Burnsall (N Yorks); ns Skipton, $12\frac{1}{2}$m. Trout (av $\frac{1}{2}$ lb–1 lb; many large fish), grayling; preserved by Appletreewick, Barden and Burnsall AC from Linton Stepping Stones, below Grassington, to Barden Bridge, 7m. Dt for trout, June–Sept (excluding June and Sept week-ends) £9; wt £40, fly only during trout season; limit three brace; grayling dt £4 Nov to Jan (fly only). Waters restocked regularly with trout from $\frac{1}{2}$ to 1 lb and over. Waiting list. Tickets from Red Lion Hotel and Fell Hotel, Burnsall, or from river watcher, Bob Mason, Gnistone House, Main Street, Burnsall, Skipton BD23 6BU (Tel: Burnsall 650).

Bradford City AA has water at **Appletreewick;** members only. Dt for stretch at Appletreewick from New Inn (left bank only).

Grassington (N Yorks); ns Skipton, 10m. Trout (av $\frac{1}{2}$ lb), grayling (av $\frac{3}{4}$ lb); preserved by Linton, Threshfield and Grassington AC for $2\frac{1}{2}$m both banks (also in Captain Beck and Linton and Threshfield Becks until August 31); wt £25, dt £6 for fly-fishing only. Long waiting list for membership. No night or Sunday fishing. Trout season: April 1 to Sept 30 inclusive. Grayling only from Oct 1 to Feb 28; st £25, dt £5; fly only during Oct. Tickets from post office, or Devonshire Hotel, Grassington. Saltaire AA also has water at Linton and Threshfield; st, fishing best in May. Eller Beck, Hebden Beck, 2m E. Lakes: Blea Beck dams 4m NE. Hotels: Black Horse (Saltaire AA HQ), Wilson Arms, Devonshire and others.

Kilnsey (N Yorks); ns Skipton-in-Craven, 13m. Trout. Preserved by Kilnsey AC of 50 members, from 1m above Starbottom down to Netherside 2m below Kilnsey; st £275 from hon sec, wt £80, dt £15 from Keeper, T J Lambert at the Tennant Arms daily, between 9 am and 10 am (number limited, and none on Sundays or Bank Holidays). **Skirfare,**1m N; trout; preserved as Wharfe up to 1m below Arncliffe. Hotels: Tennant Arms, Falcon *(advt below).*

Buckden (N Yorks); ns Skipton, 19m. Trout. Bradford City AA has 2m; dt £3 from Dalesgarth Holiday Cott. Other fishing for guests at Buck Inn; dt issued.

SKIRFARE (tributary of Wharfe); well stocked with trout (3 to lb).

Arncliffe (N Yorks); ns Skipton-in-Craven, 16m. $2\frac{1}{2}$m on Skirfare and $1\frac{1}{2}$m on **Cowside Beck** available to guests at Falcon

Inn *(advt p 101)*. Dt fishing on Wharfe held by Kilnsey AC. *(See "Kilnsey", previous page).*

FOSS (tributary of Ouse): Trout.

Earswick (N Yorks). Free fishing on right bank. Owners are Joseph Rowntree Trust.

Strensall (N Yorks). Foss Navigation Cut, 1m NE. Whitecar Beck, 1m NE. York and Dist Amal has fishing here and at **Towthorpe** (ns Haxby); members only.

NIDD: Trout and grayling, with coarse fish from Birstwith downstream in increasing numbers.

Nun Monckton (N Yorks). Coarse fish. Bradford No 1 has 1½m reserved here, at **Ramsgill** and at **Summerbridge,** for members only.

Kirk Hammerton (N Yorks). Coarse fish. Following on Harrogate AA water *(see Goldsborough)*, almost all fishing downstream to where Nidd joins the Ouse controlled by Leeds and York Amalgamations. York Amal holds York side of river from Skip Bridge on Boroughbridge Road upstream for about 2m and also for about 1m above Hammerton Mill dam. Tickets from York tackleists; York Road Service Station, Mrs Abel, Crown Inn, Kirk Hammerton and Myers, Skip Bridge Filling Station.

Cowthorpe (N Yorks). Coarse fish, Harrogate AA water *(see Goldsborough)*. Stretch of 1m, one bank, belongs to Old Oak Inn, tickets issued; Sunday fishing. Licences and tackle available in Wetherby.

Goldsborough (N Yorks). Trout, grayling and mixed coarse fishing, including pike and barbel. Left hand bank at Goldsborough, Knaresborough Piscatorials. From Little Ribston downstream through Walshford Bridge to first meadow below Cattall Bridge belongs to Harrogate AA. Association also has both banks of **Crimple Beck** from confluence with Nidd above Walshford Bridge up to Spofforth. Waiting list for membership. Dt issued by hon sec to members' guests only. Water otherwise strictly preserved.

Knaresborough (N Yorks). Trout, grayling and coarse fish, including barbel. Practically all fishing in vicinity controlled by Knaresborough AC and Knaresborough Piscatorials. Former issues st and dt for good stretch upstream from Little Ribston village. Knaresborough Piscatorials provides st, wt and dt for visitors.

York Amal has good stretches here. Tickets from P H & J R Smith (tackleists), 28 High Street and M H & C Johnson, 4 Briggate; also from C J Fishing Tackle *(see Harrogate)*.

Ripley, Nidd Bridge (N Yorks). Trout, grayling and coarse fish. On right bank from about 300 yds below Harrogate–Ripon road bridge to Killinghall and downstream to Sewerage Works, about 2½m, held by Harrogate and Claro Anglers, who have full membership and long waiting list. Downstream for 2m river privately owned. At Killinghall both banks above and below Harrogate–Ripon road bridge held by Knaresborough AC, whose water continues about 2m up left bank and ¼m down; tickets for members' friends only. A further 2½m is held between Knaresborough and Little Ribston. St £20 and dt £1.50, available from Knaresborough tackle shops, issued for part of the water.

Birstwith (N Yorks). Trout and grayling above Birstwith Dam upstream to upper reaches of Nidd. Below Dam there are also coarse fish. Birstwith Private AC has some water on both banks between Hampsthwaite Bridge and about 1m above Birstwith Bridge, where their water joins that of Harrogate FFC. Two small stretches private. Club confined to small number of members; waiting list. No dt.

Darley (N Yorks). Trout and grayling water, strictly preserved by Harrogate Fly Fishers. No tickets. *(See Harrogate.)*

Pateley Bridge (N Yorks). Trout and grayling. From 1½m above Pateley Bridge down to **Summerbridge,** owned and rented by Nidderdale AC, who hold nearly all water, both banks, except short pieces here and there which are private; wt £21 and dt £3.50 (concessions to juniors). Ticket distr: Richmond's Shoe Shop, Pateley Bridge. Anglers must obtain tickets before beginning to fish.

Gouthwaite (N Yorks). River enters **Gouthwaite Reservoir,** fine sheet of water 2m long, well stocked with large trout and numerous grayling. Privately owned and fished; no permits. Below reservoir Nidd private.

CRIMPLE (tributary of Nidd). This river is about 12m long, very narrow and joins Nidd near Walshford Bridge, where for short distance there is reasonably good fishing. Harrogate AA has water *(see Nidd–Goldsborough)*. Permission to fish other water may be obtained from adjoining farmers. **Plumpton Lake:** mixed coarse and trout fishery, Plumpton.

Harrogate (N Yorks). Trout and coarse fishing, within easy reach of town in Nidd, Wharfe and Ure. Details from Information Bureau, Royal Baths. Harrogate Flyfishers preserve excellent trout and grayling water at Darley. Membership details from hon sec. Newby Hall coarse fishing, **Skelton-on-Ure**, dt £1.50. Tel: 09012 2583. Hotels: Crown, Majestic, Old Swan, St George, Cairn, Prospect. Tackleists: C J Fishing Tackle, 182 Kings Road; Linsley Bros, 4/6 Cheltenham Parade.

KYLE: Coarse fish.

Alne (N Yorks). Coarse fishing in Kyle up to Tollerton; York Dist AA has use.

Tollerton (N Yorks). Coarse fishing free down to Alne. Ouse at Aldwark, 4m W, and Linton Lock, 3m S and 7m NE, at Stillington.

URE (or YORE): Noted for grayling, but also holds good trout. Coarse fish from Middleham downstream.

Boroughbridge (N Yorks). Fine coarse fishing (especially chub and roach, bream increasing); few trout and grayling; taken by clubs. Numerous inns in town and at **Langthorpe, Aldborough** and **Roecliffe** where Bradford City AA has 6m (roach, perch, dace, pike, chub); no dt, limited privilege tickets for members only. Bradford No 1 AA also has Langthorpe stretch, left bank. Boroughbridge and Dist AC (HQ at Black Lion), issues dt (£1) (weekdays only) from June 1– Feb 27; available from Post Office, Black Lion Hotel and Sports Shop. Harrogate and Claro AC issue dt for water on north bank after June 1. Tickets from Three Horseshoes. Other hotel: Black Lion.

Ripon (N Yorks). Trout, grayling, pike, perch, chub, barbel, roach; preserved for 6m by Ripon Piscatorial Assn, for membership of which there is a waiting list. Association also has 2m **Ripon Canal** (carp, tench, bream) and 6m on **R Laver**. St £30, wt £6, dt £2. Ripon AC has 1m on Ure and 1m on **Laver** and **Skell**. Limited dt £2. These and Piscatorial Assn tickets from Hodgson, tackleists *(see below)*. **Lumley Moor Reservoir;** trout fly only; no dt. Lakes: Queen Mary's Ponds; coarse fish; Bradford No 1 AA. Dt for **Swinton Estate** trout fishery, Ripon, 100 acres, tel: 0765 89224

or 89713. Hotels: Spa, Unicorn, Studley Royal, Station, South Lodge. Tackleist: R C Hodgson, 7 Queen Street, who can give information.

Tanfield (N Yorks). Trout, grayling; preserved for about 5m, mostly both banks, by Tanfield AC. Guests must be accompanied by member. Full time bailiff employed. Long waiting list.

Masham (N Yorks); ns Ripon. Trout, grayling. $6\frac{1}{2}$m west bank belongs to Countess of Swinton's estate. A 2m stretch has been put at the disposal of Masham AC and is for members only. Rods limited on remaining waters; always waiting list. Yorkshire Flyfishers hold Clifton Castle water (about 2m left bank) above Masham. No tickets. Hotel: King's Head. **Leighton Reservoir** near here. *See Yorkshire Lakes.*

Cover Bridge (N Yorks); ns Ripon or Northallerton. Trout, grayling. East Whitton Estate issue dt on **R Cover** from Hallo Bridge to mouth. Mostly both banks. Fly only, £1.75. Tickets from Cover Bridge Inn, Middleham.

Middleham (N Yorks). Bradford No 1 AA has stretch, members only. Fishing may be had in Middleham Deeps and m upstream from Middleham Bridge both banks by dt from Old Horn Inn, Spennithorne. Leeds Amal water; excellent barbel, chub and grayling; few large trout; odd salmon. Dt £1 from Cover Bridge Inn for trout and grayling fishing on Cover.

Leyburn (N Yorks). Grayling, trout, coarse fish. Two dt available from Blue Lion, E Witton, for E Witton Estate water on Ure from Ulshaw Bridge to Harker Beck. $1\frac{3}{4}$m S bank. Fly only. Bolton FA and Thornaby AA have "members only" water here. Hotels: Bolton Arms, Golden Lion. Tackleists: Wray Bros, Town Hall (also licences).

Redmire (N Yorks). Trout, grayling; preserved by Lord Bolton. Restocked; fly only. All fishing now by st only (£100); numbers limited; apply Bolton Estate Office, Wensley, Leyburn. Trout best April, May and June; grayling Oct and Nov. Hotels: King's Arms, Redmire; White Swan, Middleham; Rose and Crown, Bainbridge; Wensleydale Heifer, Westwittom.

Aysgarth (N Yorks). Trout, grayling. Bradford AA has approx 2m from footbridge, both banks; Palmer Flatt Hotel has short stretch. Wensleydale AA water begins

The Ure, near Bainbridge. A fascinating river running through an unspoilt countryside. *Photograph by Bertram Unne.*

at Worton Bottom. Richmond & Dis AS has 1m west of Aysgarth.

Askrigg (N Yorks). Trout, grayling; preserved by Wensleydale AA. Tickets *(see Bainbridge)* from King's Arms or Victoria Arms, Worton. Hotel: King's Arms.

Bainbridge (N Yorks); ns Askrigg. Hotel: Rose and Crown (HQ of Wensleydale AA). Wensleydale AA water includes 6m on Yore, 2m of Bain, flowing from **Lake Semerwater,** and 2m trout water above lake; membership £5, st £15, wt £6, dt £2.50. Grayling only, st £2, dt £1 (Oct 1 to Feb 28). All maggot fishing prohibited in streams. Tickets from: Village Shop, Bainbridge and Rose and Crown, which also issues licences; also from King's Arms, Askrigg; Victoria Arms, Worton. Other accommodation at Greenways

Guest House; Victoria Arms, Worton.

Hawes (N Yorks). Trout, grayling; preserved with tributaries, from source of river downward about 8m (stock of big trout) by Hawes and High Abbotside AA; no sunday fishing; wt £12, dt £6 (grayling £3), from hon sec or Lowis, The Bridge. Below Hawes preserves Wensleydale AA has several miles of excellent water *(see Bainbridge).* Hotels: Crown, White Hart, Fountain, Board.

SWALE: Good chub and barbel water. Trouting best in upper reaches.

Helperby (N Yorks). Coarse fish; right bank from Swing Bridge to Myton Plantation controlled by Leeds Amal; dt from Golden Lion, Helperby. Dun Royal Hotel also issues tickets. Thornton Beck, 2m Sun Beck.

Topcliffe (N Yorks). Noted coarse fishing centre; especially good for chub and barbel. Thirsk AC and Bradford clubs have much water in this area; inquire hon secs. Hotels: Angel, Black Bull, which have water, hold small matches from Oct–March and issue dt £1.50. Assn of Teesside and Dist ACs has $1\frac{1}{2}$m at **Sand Hutton;** members only. **Cod Beck;** trout; preserved by Bradford City AA; apply hon sec for permits.

Pickhill (N Yorks). Coarse fish; trout. Thornaby AA has two fields (about 500 yds); members only *(see Thornaby under Tees)*. Leeds Amalgamation has a $\frac{3}{4}$m stretch at **Ainderby.** Northallerton and Dist AC have the Gatenby water, approx 3m.

Morton-on-Swale (N Yorks). Trout, grayling, pike, perch, roach, chub, dace, barbel, eels. Restocked with trout; fishing good. Northallerton AC has 4m both banks upstream of Morton Bridge reserved for members and 5m on east bank downstream for which wt £5 and dt £1 can be had from Mr J Grainger, Morton, and tackleist Pratt, Northallerton. Stockton AA has short stretch near here *(see Stockton-on-Tees).*

Langton (N Yorks). Trout, grayling, coarse fish; trout to 5 lb taken; Kirkby Fleetham AA has both banks downstream, linking up with Northallerton AC's water at Bramper Farm; fly only; no tickets. Richmond AC lease west bank upstream for $\frac{3}{4}$m, then Darlington Brown Trout Club water begins.

Catterick (N Yorks). Good mixed fishing; trout, grayling, dace, chub, barbel, few roach and pike. Trout from 8 oz to 1 lb; fast takers. Richmond & Dist AS has 14m of water on both banks, Richmond being the centre. Darlington Brown Trout AA has fishing downstream to Ellerton (north bank). Dt to visitors accompanying member. Thornaby AA has Thornbrough Farm 1m upstream from railway bridge above Catterick Bridge; noted grayling, trout and barbel stretch; members only. Also other fishings on Swale, **Ure, Tees** and **Eden.** Hotels: Farmers' Arms; Angel Inn. Licences and permits: E & B Langstaff, Parkgate, Darlington, who is also tackleist.

Richmond (N Yorks). Above town, trout; below, trout, grayling, chub, dace and barbel. Richmond and Dist AS preserves several miles: 6m above town and 4m

below; from $\frac{1}{2}$m above Marshe Bridge down to Brampton Scar, Brompton-on-Swale, mostly both banks. Trout above the falls; trout, grayling and coarse fish below. $\frac{1}{2}$m above Marshe Bridge, fly only. St £17.50, wt £10, dt £3. Jun $\frac{1}{2}$ price. From W Metcalfe (tackleist), Market Place. Dt Sunday above town during trout season, 50p. Spinning prohibited. Sand Beck, 1m S. Ash Beck, 1m N. Gilling Beck, 3m N. Colburn and Hipswell Becks, 2m S. Clapgate Beck, 4m W. Ravensworth Beck, 5m NW. Smelt Mill Beck, 4m N. Marske Beck, 5m W. Eller or Marrick Beck, 6m W; all trout. Skeeby Beck, $2\frac{1}{2}$m NE; trout and grayling; preserved. Aske Hall Park lake, $2\frac{1}{2}$m N; Forcett Park, 8m N; pike and perch, Calt Hole Tarn, 4m S.

Grinton (N Yorks); ns Richmond, 9m. Trout. Thornaby AA has whole south bank and part of north bank, from Isles Bridge to Grinton Bridge (about $5\frac{1}{2}$m); trout three to the lb. No tickets, but help given by hon sec to visiting anglers who write with SAE. Tackleists: F Fynn, 12 Varo Terrace, Stockton; or J W Wright & Son, 107 Park Gate, Darlington. *(See Thornaby under Tees.)*

Reeth (N Yorks). Swale; trout; Bridge bank only; $\frac{1}{4}$m downstream; st £4.90, wt £2, from Reeth Post Office. Black Bull Hotel has water for residents £1 day.

Muker (N Yorks); ns Askrigg, 8m. Trout; strictly preserved. Muker Beck; trout; Thwaite Beck, 1m W; trout; free. Summer Lodge Beck, 5m E; trout; preserved.

Keld (N Yorks); ns Kirkby Stephen, 12m. Trout; plentiful but small; preserved. *(See also Muker.)*

GUN BECK (tributary of Swale):

Husthwaite (N Yorks). Centre for good trouting on **Husthwaite Beck;** dt from York tackleists.

Coxwold (N Yorks). Pond Head Reservoirs (two), 3m SE; perch and pike. Hole Beck and Gun Beck preserved.

BEDALE BECK (tributary of Swale):

Leeming (N Yorks). Swale, 2m NE; preserved by Black Ox AC from A1 road to confluence with Swale, excepting only two small fields above Leeming Bridge. Trout and coarse fish. St £3 from Wrights Ltd *(see below).*

Bedale (N Yorks). Trout, grayling; private. Tackleists: Wrights Ltd, Market Place *(see also Leyburn).*

COD BECK (tributary of Swale); good trout water, but recent pollution of lower reaches has affected sport.

North Kilvington (N Yorks). Trout; preserved by Thirsk AC *(see Thirsk).*

Thirsk (N Yorks). Thirsk AC has water on beck; limited permits; trout restocked and coarse fish removed. York and Dist AA have $5\frac{1}{2}$ acre lake at **Sand Hutton, Park View.** Tackleists and licences: J Moss, Finkle Street. Hotels: Royal Oak, Three Tuns.

Sessay (N Yorks). Cod Beck, 2m W; Thirsk AC, Swale, 2m SW; Bradford club now has fishing on P J Till's farm (The Heights). Inn: Railway, Dalton.

Brawith (N Yorks). Trout; preserved. *(For Cod Beck Reservoir see Northallerton.)*

WISKE (tributary of Swale): Good coarse fishing ruined by pollution. Recovery in progress.

Otterington (N Yorks). Cod Beck, 2m E. Broad Beck. Sorrow Beck, 4m E.

Northallerton (N Yorks). Roach, dace, chub, pike; preserved: fishing good. Northallerton AC has fishing on Wiske (members only) and on several miles of water on the Swale at Morton Bridge; wt £5, dt £1 from Grainger, Morton on Swale, and Pratt. At Osmotherley is **Cod Beck Reservoir;** trout; fly only; fair fishing; one dt available from Hambleton DC offices. Tackleists: T Pratt, The Arcade.

PARRETT

(For close seasons, licences, etc, see Wessex Water Authority, p 13)

Rises in hills on border of Somerset and Dorset, and flows into Bristol Channel near Bridgwater. Roach, bream and dace predominate. Thorney-Middle Chinnock stretch and some of tributaries hold trout. Occasional salmon and sea trout run through into Tone.

Bridgwater (Som). River tidal here. Now a Marina. **King's Sedgemoor Drain** is also preserved by Bridgwater AA which has fishing about $\frac{3}{4}$m above Greylake Bridge, where 18 ft Rhine enters main and wider water, to Old Salt Works at Dunball. Good roach, rudd and pike; many tench. Bream, carp and perch being introduced to this water. St £10, wt £5, dt £1.50 from tackleists in area or L Williams, 7 Webbers Way, Puritan. Other Bridgewater AA fisheries; **Huntspill River, Cripps River, North Drain, South Drain, 18 ft Rhine, Westmoor and Southmoor Main Drains, Thorney Level, Bridgwater and Taunton Canal, Dunwear, Screech Owl, Taunton Road** and **Combwich Ponds** (mainly carp), and **Walrow Ponds** (carp, bream, roach, rudd, tench, perch) other ponds and drains. Season, weekly and day tickets, with concessions for jun, ladies, OAP. Permits cover all waters. Pocket maps from hon sec (see list of clubs at end of section). Bathampton AA has ponds near here; details from hon sec. Wessex WA reservoir at Durleigh, $1\frac{1}{2}$m from Bridgwater; trout; fly only *(see Somerset lakes, etc).* For tickets, licences, tackle, apply local tackle dealers.

Langport (Som). Parret and Yeo; pike, perch, carp, bream, roach, dace. South, East and West Fed hold large section from **Oath** to **Thurney,** and also has water on **Isle;** open to affiliated clubs.

Langport AA issues st, wt and dt, obtainable from A W Rule, Parret Close, Langport, tackleist.

Crewkerne (Som). Trout, coarse fish. Stoke-sub-Hamdon AA has trout fishing (with restocking) from Bow Mills to Hurdle Pool (trout av $\frac{3}{4}$ lb); members only; coarse fishing, 12 different species including 3 types of carp, from Hurdle Pool to Thorney Mill. St £4, concessions to jun & OAP, from local tackleists and committee members.

TONE: Trout above Taunton, coarse fish. Weedy in summer below Taunton but provides first-class coarse fishing in winter.

Taunton (Som). Fishing free at French weir and through Taunton. Taunton Fly Fishing Club has water on the Tone from Roughmoor to Wellisford (not continuous) which is mainly fly only but other baits and lures allowed in certain areas on a day ticket basis. St £25, mt £5 from Topp Tackle, 61 Station Rd.

Hillfarrance Brook (a Tone tributary—Hillfarrance to confluence with Tone). Trout, grayling—fly only—Members only. **Axe** (Chard Junction) $\frac{3}{4}$m single bank fishing below the village, fly only—Members only. Axe (Axminster) $\frac{1}{2}$m double bank fishing, Town Weir to Cloakham Bridge. Fly only—Members only. Annual subscription £18. Tickets for restricted areas available from Topp Tackle, 61 Station Road, Taunton. A A

Woodbury, High Street, Wellington. Mt £8.50, wt £3.50, dt £1.75 on coarse fishing waters in area controlled by Taunton AA. **Bridgwater and Taunton Canal** from Taunton to Durston—roach, rudd, tench, pike: a few bream and carp; weed in summer; **West Sedgemoor Drain** from Pincombe Bridge to Stathe (mainly bream and tench, but also roach, pike, perch, eels and carp); Curry Moor Drain; several long stretches on Lower Tone between Taunton and Athelney and local ponds. Hotels: Castle (which advises angling visitors on local facilities) County; George.

Wellington (Som). Trout, roach, dace; trout average $\frac{1}{2}$ lb. Wellington AA has water from Fox Bros' works 2m upstream; mt and dt from hon sec. Thereafter preserved by owners through Bradford to Taunton FFC water. RD licences from tackleists, A A Woodbury and Son, High Street.

Wiveliscombe (Som). Tone, Milverton Brook and Norton Brook; trout; leave from owners, banks bushed. Tackleists: Arthur Twigger, The Square; issues dt (bank only) for Clatworthy Reservoir and Wessex WA licences.

NORTON BROOK (tributary of Tone):

Bishops Lydeard (Som). Norton Brook and Bishop's Lydeard Brook; trout; leave from owners; banks overgrown. Taunton FFC have water on Norton Brook.

MILVERTON BROOK (tributary of Tone).

Milverton (Som). Trout; private; leave from owners; banks bushed.

YEO: Coarse fish, some trout.

Long Lode (Som). Good coarse fishing; permission from farmers.

Ilchester (Som). Mainly roach, dace, eels and some trout. Dt and st from A D Coles, greengrocer. Club: Ilchester AC. Hotel: Ivelchester.

Yeovil (Som). Trout (av 12 in), roach, chub, dace. Yeovil club waters on Yeo & Parret; trout and coarse fish (restocked). St from hon sec. **Sutton Bingham Reservoir,** 3m S; tickets; fly only *(see Somerset (lakes and small streams)).* Tackle, licences, permits and further information from Sports of Bond Street. Hotels: Mermaid; Manor; The Choughs.

ISLE: Prolific chub water; also roach, dace, etc.

Midelney (Som). Water down to junction with Parret held by South, East and West Wessex Fed of Anglers *(see also Langport).*

Isle Brewers (Som). Roach, chub, dace, some trout from Fivehead Road to Hambridge; private.

Ilminster (Som). Roach, chub, dace, trout. Ilminster AA water; dt and wt from hon sec or tackleists (see below). Bathampton AA also has water here; inquire hon sec. Tackleists: T Clapp, West Street.

RIBBLE

(For close seasons, licences, etc, see North West Water Authority, p 13–14)

Rises in the Pennines and flows 56 miles into the Irish Sea between St Anne's and Southport. Good coarse fishing lower down, between Great Mitton and Preston. Also coarse fishing in Long Preston Deeps. Best salmon, sea trout, brown trout and grayling fishing is between Settle and Great Mitton. Above Settle there are only brown trout. Tributary Hodder has good salmon, sea trout and brown trout fishing throughout length but much affected by water abstraction. Upper waters impounded in Stocks Reservoirs. Its main tributary, the Loud, also provides good trout and sea trout fishing.

Preston (Lancs). Coarse fish, few salmon and sea trout. 2m Federated Anglers (Preston Centre) water through town; st £3, dt £1, including other waters on Ribble and **Wyre, and Lancaster Canal** (Preston to Natland). **Twin Lakes** Trout Fishery, **Croston,** 12 acres, r and b trout, best r 12 lb. Full st £256, dt £12 (4 fish). Tel: 0772 601093. Further information from tackleists in Preston; C Calderbank, 33 Moor Lane; Ted Carter, 87/88 Church Street and hon sec. Local to

Southport is **Hurleston Hall** trout fishery, dt £10, on site. Robinsons, 71 Sussex Rd, Southport, will answer queries.

Samlesbury (Lancs). Coarse fish, few salmon and sea trout. Coarse fishing tickets for 2m from Samlesbury Hall, Ribchester. Several miles preserved by Federated Anglers (Preston Centre) and Ribble and Wyre FA, dt from hon sec.

Longridge (Lancs). Ribble, 3m SE. Hodder, 5m NE. Salmon, sea trout and trout. Loud 2m N. Most of right bank preserved by Loud and Hodder AA. Visitors' tickets issued if accompanied by member. Prince Albert AS, Macclesfield, own several miles below M6 bridge. Warrington AA has short stretch at **Hurst Green.**

Mitton (Yorks); ns Whalley, 2m. Salmon, sea trout, trout and coarse fish. Lancashire RD has much water on Ribble and **Calder.** Dt from J Hoyle, Filling Station, Hill Crest. *(see Clitheroe).*

Clitheroe (Lancs). Clitheroe AS fishes 3m of Ribble, 4m of **Hodder** and 1m of **Lune.** Townson Bros have fishing on Ribble and Hodder; Charbury Trading Estate, Clitheroe. **Stocks Reservoir** trout fishery, Slaidburn, well stocked with b and r trout, has st £115, wt £42 (3 fish per day), dt £7 (3 fish). Boats £5, ob £5. Tel: 0468 61305, 02006 602, or contact Bentham Trout Farm, Low Mill, Bentham, near Lancaster. Tel: 0468 61305. The Inn at Whitewell, also on the Forest of Bowland, offers fishing to guests. By the A59 between Clitheroe and Accrington, **Whalley Abbey** trout fishery. St and dt. Phone 025 4822211 for details. Lancashire FFA have 4m; tickets only to members' friends. **Blackburn** and Dist AA have several miles on Ribble and other fisheries on **Lune, Wenning, Aire, Gilpin** and reservoirs. Some dt; apply hon sec. Ribble Valley Borough Council issues st £12, wt £6.50 and dt £2.25 for water below Edisford Bridge. From Council offices 9-5 all the year round; from Warden caravan site at the bridge April-October. Concessions for OAP & jun. Two rods on Hodder for residents of Red Pump Hotel, Bashall Eaves; dt issued. Some permits from Rectory, Stoneyhurst College. Tackleists: Ken Varey, 32a King Street, Clitheroe; Harry Le-Moine, 22 Accrington Road, Blackburn. Hotels: Inn at Whitewell, Roefield; Bounty Inn, Slaidburn, tel: 02006 246.

Chatburn (Lancs). Ribble, 1m W; good trout, occasional salmon and sea trout. Several miles of river preserved by Clitheroe AA; limited visitors' tickets through members only.

Sawley (N Yorks). On Ribble; ns Chatburn, 2m. Salmon, sea trout, trout and grayling. Trout and salmon fishing good. Several miles preserved by Yorkshire FFC (visitors' tickets through members only). Inn: Spread Eagle.

Gisburn (N Yorks). Trout, salmon. Stocks Beck: Gisburn AA.

Long Preston (N Yorks). Ribble, 1m W. Trout, grayling, odd salmon, coarse fish. Several miles of water preserved by Blackburn and District AA; visitors' tickets through members only. Settle AA also has water *(see Settle).* Malham Tarn, $3\frac{1}{2}$m NE. Hotels: Boar's Head (fishing for residents), Maypole.

Settle (N Yorks). Settle AA has $7\frac{1}{2}$m of good trout and grayling fishing in Ribble between Langcliffe, Settle and vicinity of Long Preston. Wt £30, dt £6 at Royal Oak Hotel. Fly only; limit $1\frac{1}{2}$ brace. Water stocked yearly. Hotel: Royal Oak, from which Settle AA tickets are obtainable during licensing hours. **Malham Tarn** is 6m from Settle and holds large trout. Dt available *(see Yorkshire Lakes, reservoirs, etc).* Further north are Manchester AA's waters. Other hotels at Settle: Fulcon and Golden Lion.

Horton-in-Ribblesdale (N Yorks). Trout; preserved from source to Helwith Bridge, including all tributaries, by Manchester AA. Fish passes erected at Settle Weir, but few fish ascending. Assn also has **Newhouses Tarn** (fly only); trout. No

tickets. Annual membership: £110. Hotel: Crown Inn.

Tributaries of the Ribble

HODDER: Good salmon and trout water. **Higher Hodder Bridge** (Lancs and Yorks). Salmon, sea trout, trout, grayling and coarse fish *(see Clitheroe on Ribble)*.

Chipping (Lancs). Hodder, $1\frac{1}{2}$m E. Salmon, sea trout and grayling. Loud, 1m SE. Trout and sea trout. About $\frac{1}{2}$m of Hodder below Doeford Bridge on right bank and several miles of **River Loud** are preserved by Loud and Hodder AA; tickets if accompanied by member. Hotel: Derby Arms.

Whitewell (Lancs). Salmon, sea trout, trout, grayling. "The Inn at Whitewell" has four rods on 6m of the Association water. Mt from £40, dt from £8. Tel: 02008 222 for details. The Red Pump Hotel, Bashall Eaves, has two rods 8m further down the river.

Slaidburn (N Yorks); ns Clitheroe, $8\frac{1}{2}$m. Hodder; salmon, sea trout and trout; all preserved. Hotel: Bounty.

CALDER: Mostly polluted but RD issues dt (limited) for stretch from Mitton Wood to Calder Foot, north bank. Some club water.

Whalley (Lancs). West Calder. Ribble, 2m W; salmon, sea trout and coarse fish. Marsden Star AS has Chew Mill Farm stretch *(see Colne)*. Hodder, 2m W; salmon, sea trout and trout. Sabden Brook, 2m E. Park Brook, 3m SW. Dean Brook, 4m W. Crowshaw Reservoir, 5m NW.

Barrowford (Lancs). Pendle Water; trout. Marsden Star AS has from Quaker Bridge to Bardisn Lane Bridge, also **Barrowford Reservoir** coarse fishery. Colne Water (polluted) and Pendle join near Barrowford to form Calder (polluted). **Leeds and Liverpool Canal** runs through district *(see Colne)*.

Burnley (Lancs). Local waters mostly polluted. Burnley AS leases **Lea Green**

Malham Tarn, showing the boathouse, and the adjacent limestone cliffs which give this water its unique character. *Photo: Bruno Broughton.*

Reservoir, but tickets available only to local ratepayers; trout. Reservoir at **Hapton** stocked with rainbow trout; dt from Trevor Hughes, Egerton Road, Fallowfield, Manchester 14. Tickets for **Leeds and Liverpool Canal** from Northern AA and local tackleists: Littlewoods, Parker Lane; Mack's, 33a Parliament Street; H McLoughlan, 33a Parliament Street.

COLNE (tributary of Calder). Much pollution but holds some trout and coarse fish.

Colne (Lancs). Colne; trout. Water held by Colne Water AS. **Leeds and Liverpool Canal** held by Northern AA (Lancashire side of Mile Tunnel) and Marsden Star AS (Barnoldswick to Bank Newton); pike, trout, tench, bream, roach, rudd, perch; st and dt for waters held by both

clubs. Marsden Star AS: (other waters on **Calder, Aire, Earby Beck** and **Greenfield Reservoir**) st, wt, and dt from local tackleists. *For Colne AS and reservoirs see Foulridge.* Tackleists: D W & D Foden, Post Office Buildings, Barnoldswick; Colne Angling Centre, Windsor Street; Jackson's Tackle Shop, Albion Street, Earby; Boyces, 44 Manchester Road, and Wally's Tackle Shop, Forest Street, both **Nelson.**

Foulridge (Lancs). Four British Waterways Fisheries reservoirs: **Lower (or Burwains), Upper, Slipperhill, White Moor.** Only Lower fishable by ticket; match bookings from G R Sutton, The Anchorage, Foulridge, dt £2.15 from bailiff on bank, match-bookings 0282 863993, (Mrs Peate). trout, pike, roach, perch, bream, gudgeon. Other reservoirs let to clubs members only. *(See also Colne.)*

ROTHER

(For close seasons, licences, etc, see Southern Water Authority, p 11–12)

Rises near Rotherfield and reaches the sea at Rye Bay. Mostly coarse fish, with trout in upper reaches and tributaries but runs of sea trout increasing. Mullet and bass in estuary. Mullet also abound in lower reaches of Tillingham and Brede in season.

Rye (Sussex). Near mouth of Rother; coarse fish. Rye and Dist AS has 3½m upstream from Starlock to Wittersham. Club also has water on **Brede, Tillingham** and various drains on Romney Marsh. Memberships (£10), wt £5, dt £1.50 from hon sec. Ashford and Dist APS have water on **Royal Military Canal;** dt £1; also Clive Vale AC at Winchelsea. Romney Marsh *(see Kent–small streams)* is close by. Several clubs have water, including Hastings, Bexhill and Dist (Freshwater) AA; st £12–£13, dt £1.25. Tackleist: C A Robins, 22/23 Landgate.

Wittersham (Sussex). Clive Vale AC have good stretch at Blackwall Bridge. Dt £2, only in advance, from hon sec or local tackleist.

Newenden (Sussex). Large bream, chub and roach; preserved by Rother FA which controls about 12m from Robertsbridge to Iden.

Bodiam (Sussex). Trout (small), coarse fish. Fishes best in Sept onwards. Rother FA has 12m. No individ dt, but applications from clubs may be accepted. Rye AS has water from Iden downstream; dt issued. Visiting clubs should apply in advance to hon sec. Kent RD has stretch from Iden Bridge to Scots Float (right bank only).

Hotels: Castle, Justins. Anglers catered for.

Etchingham (Sussex). Hastings, Bexhill and Dist AA has water on the Rother down to **Iden,** the upper Rother in Burwash, more on the **Brede,** many miles of dyke and drains noted for pike, bream, tench and rudd on **Romney Marsh** between **Gulderford** and **Appledore,** 10 acres of coarse fishing at **Hastings,** with many carp to 10 lb, tench, pike; dt £1.25, from hon sec or local tackleists. St (confined to people living within 25m of Hastings or Bexhill) £12–£13. At **Burwash** are **Lakedown Fisheries,** 14 acres, trout, tel 0435 883449.

Stonegate (Sussex). Wadhurst AS has trout water; dt to members' friends only. Hotel: Bridge.

Tenterden (Kent). River now improving after decline due to dredging. Tenterden and Dist AA has many miles on Rother and tributaries; no day or period tickets. Tackleists: N Warwick.

BREDE: Rother tributary. Coarse fish, a few small trout; controlled by Rye and Clive Vale clubs. No dt. St £11 from Clive Vale hon sec or local tackleists. Fishing stations: **Rye, Winchelsea.**

SEVERN

(For close seasons, licences, etc, see Severn-Trent Water Authority, p 15–16)

Longest river in England. Rises in Wales (N Powys) and flows 180m into Bristol Channel. Fair salmon river, with commercial fisheries near mouth; spring salmon in January/April and May. Average size good. Some trout and grayling in upper reaches, but river notable chiefly for coarse fishing, especially for chub in the upper reaches and barbel in the middle river. Shad runs up river in May and are taken on rod and line, principally at Tewkesbury Weir.

Sharpness (Glos). Coarse fishing in the **Gloucester and Berkeley Canal** from Severn Bridge to Hempstead Bridge, Gloucester (about 16m); bank licence from any bridge house.

Gloucester (Glos). Gloucester United AA controls several miles of Severn from Haw Bridge to Ashleworth, st £8, dt £1, from tackleists *(see below)* and Haw Farmhouse. Assn also has water from **Lower Lode** to **Deerhurst**, on gravel pit at **Saul** and on **Gloucester Sharpness Canal**. **Gloucester and Berkeley Canal** provides 15m of good coarse fishing; st, dt from bridge keepers. At Little Witcombe, nr Birdlip, 5m SE; **Witcombe Reservoirs** managed by Cambrian Fisheries. Fly only; brown and rainbow trout. St £184 and £92, guest tickets for friends of members. Tel: 0452 864413. Tackleists: F Harvey & Co, 13 Barton Street; Allsports, 126/128 Eastgate Street (dt for Wye salmon fishing); Jeff Aston, 78 High Street; Rod & Gun Room, Alvin Street. Hotels: New County, Fleece, New Inn.

Tewkesbury (Glos). Salmon, twaite and coarse fish. Avon: coarse fish. Below weir shoals of big bream; match weights over 70 lb, 1987. Birmingham AA has stretches at Bushley, Ripple, Uckinghall, Severn Stoke, Deerhurst, Chaceley, Apperley and Maisemore. Tewkesbury AA water on Severn (400 yds above weir to Lower Lode—Ham bank): **Avon** (Healings Mill to Abbey Mill) and **Mill Avon** (Abbey Mill to Lower Lode—both banks); full membership limited to 3m radius of Tewkesbury Cross, otherwise limited membership; dt £1 and st £8 from R Danter *(see below)*. Hotels: Swan (Trust House), Bell, Hop Pole. Tackleist: R Danter, Tackle Shop, 31 Barton Street.

Ripple (Worcs). Bream, pike, perch, chub, dace, roach. Ripple Brook, Avon 2m E; chub, dace, roach, pike, perch. Birmingham AA has 3m. Severn Meadow and Cowscroft, below ferry, a STWA day ticket fishery. BAA St £13.50, conces-

sionary £3.75.

Upton-on Severn (Worcs). Chub, barbel, bream, roach, dace, perch and pike. R bank for 1500 yds above old railway embankment free to SWTA licence-holders. Upton-upon-Severn AA has Upper Ham. Free parking. Dt £1 from G Shinn, tackleist, 21 Old Street. Birmingham AA has two stretches, about 3m in all; members only. Hotels: King's Head, Swan, The Inn, Star (Assn HQ).

Worcester (Worcs). Pike, barbel, chub, dace, bream, roach, salmon, trout, etc. Left bank for 640 yds of Upper Ham, **Kempsey**, and right bank from Worcester Bridge to notice board at **Diglis Weir** free to STWA licence-holders. Worcester & Dist United AS has more than 5m in four stretches, including the salmon fishery below Diglis Weir. St £40, dt £4–£4.50 issued. Honorary members' books issued by hon sec or through tackleists (below); society also has stretch of **Worcester-Birmingham Canal**, from Blackpole Bridge to Commandery, 1½m on **Avon** and two meadows on **Teme** at Powick. Teme, 2m S; coarse fish, trout, salmon. Birmingham AA has stretches at Severn Stoke, Hallow, Grimley and Holt Fleet, rights on Worcester and Birmingham Canal from King's Norton to Blackpole (near Worcester); bream, roach, perch, pike. Hotels: Star, Great Western, Commis, Pack Horse. Tackleists: Al's Tackle, Malvern Road, Worcester; W Richardson, St John's; F Durrant & Sons, Mealcheapen Street.

Lincombe and Holt (Worcs). Holt, Fleet and Wharf Hotels issue dt for water below bridge. Good perch at Lincombe. Whitmore Reans CAA has **Seed Green** and **Larford** fishing.

Stourport-on-Severn (Worcs). At confluence of Severn and Stour; also **Staffordshire and Worcestershire Canal;** coarse fish. Lyttelton AA has 1½m plus new stretch 1m upstream; wt £4, juv £2, dt £1.25 from hon sec. Birmingham AA has water. Hampstall Cider House, Astley Burf, issues dt. Severn Valley Fisheries have stretch below bridge in Stourport, dt from John White. Tackleist: J White, Raven Street, where Lyttelton AA tickets are sold during opening hours.

Bewdley (Worcs). Salmon, trout, excellent head of coarse fish in general, barbel exceptional. Kidderminster AA has 2m, $\frac{3}{4}$m of water above and below town, and 1m below Stourport at **Winnalls**. St £10, from local tackleists: Whites, Stourport; Lewis, Bewley; Stevens, Cradley Heath; Storey, Kidderminster; Hingley, Stourbridge. Birmingham AA waters in vicinity. Cards for both clubs from S R Lewis, tackleist, 2 Sevenside South, who runs own riverside guest-house and issues tickets for private pool; carp, pike, etc.

Upper Arley (Worcs). Salmon, trout, grayling, chub, dace, pike, etc. Dowles Brook, 3m S. Birmingham AA has stretch. Hotels: Valentia, Harbour and Unicorn (last two issue dt).

Hampton Loade (Salop). Pike, perch, chub, dace, trout, salmon.

Bridgnorth (Salop). Salmon, trout, barbel (good), chub, pike, etc. Whitmore Reans AA rents a stretch here of about 1m. Bridgnorth AS has water (st £6, wt £5, dt—excluding Sundays—£1) and Birmingham AA has stretches at Bridgnorth, Knowle Sands, Danery, Quatford and Eardington. Salopian Fly FA has good stretches on **Worfe** at **Worfield** (3m NE); trout; members only. **Willey Park Pools** at **Broseley** (5m) and pools at **Ticklerton** are also on club card; rainbow, brown and some American brook trout. Membership limited. Approx 6m and 8m S, on Kidderminster Road, **Pool Hall** and **Shatterford** dt trout fisheries, including also carp pools. Details of prices and limits on application. Tackleists: Jeffries, Whitburn Street; Hardwicks, Northgate. Hotels: Falcon, Fosters' Arms (both Low Town); Ball, King's Head (both High Town).

Coalport (Salop). Chub, barbel, pike, etc, fewer roach and dace than are found farther downstream. Some free water. Rowley Regis and Dist AS has stretch on right bank. No tickets.

Iron Bridge (Salop). Fish species—as Coalport; good fishing on association waters by permit; 750 yds of fishing free to SWTA licence-holders. Hotel: Tontine.

Berrington (Salop). Severn, 1m N; chub; dace, pike, trout, salmon. Cound Brook,

$1\frac{1}{2}$m SW; trout; private. Tern, $2\frac{1}{2}$m N; two pools; private. Hotels: Fox; The Bell.

Atcham (Salop). STWA issues dt £1.25 for water above bridge (both banks) and 3m on R bank below, obtainable at Atcham Service Station. Macclesfield Prince Albert AS has members only fisheries here, at Bicton, Melverley, Longnor, Royal Hill, The Isle, Welshpool and Newton. Also fishings on the rivers **Gam, Vyrnwy** and **Banwy**.

Shrewsbury (Salop). Chub, pike, perch, roach, barbel, dace, a few trout; fishing free or by ticket. Spring salmon fishing; best months Mar, Apr and May. Extensive fishery above and below town mostly controlled by council. Permits from local authority. Wt for Dithering-ton AS water, 1m below weir, from Ebrall Bros *(see end of entry)*. Sabrina AC has 3m above town and water at **Mytton**, on the **Cound Brook** and **Netley Hall Pools** at **Dorrington**. St £12, peg-fee for matches, 90p. Birmingham AA has stretches at **Underdale, Pool Quay** and **Buttington Bridge.** Coventry AA has salmon and trout water on the Vyrnwy at **Meiford;** no tickets. Whitmore Reans CAA fishes Bicton Farm water, **Montford Bridge,** and $1\frac{1}{2}$m at **Alberbury.** Condover, Onny, Stapleton and Sheinton Brooks all private. Hazeldine Anglers control $\frac{3}{4}$m of ticket water at Montford Bridge. Sec, 8 Dudley Rd, Sedgeley, Dudley. Tackleists: Ebrall Bros, Smithfield Road; Chris Partington's Vintage Tackle Shop, 103 Longden Coleham; who will supply information.

Pentre (Salop); ns Shrewsbury, 2m NW. Good coarse fishing. Dt £1. Hotel: Royal Hill Inn, Kinnerley.

Melverley (Salop). Two meadows on L bank, about 700 yds, free to SWTA licence-holders.

Llandrinio (Montgomery). Chub, dace, trout, salmon; leave from farmers. Birmingham AA has short stretch at Llandrinio Bridge. Liverpool and Dist AA has water on main river at Leighton Bridge and on **Vyrnwy,** at Houghton, Mrs Edwards Farm, st £7, salmon licence £10 extra, from J Johnson, 97 L'pool Road, Maghull L31 2HG. Canal; coarse fish, tickets *(see Welshpool).* Maerdy Brook, 2m SW. Arddleen Brook, excellent trout, dace and chub. Hotel: Golden Lion.

Welshpool (Powys). Salmon, trout, coarse

fish (inc grayling). Trout small in streams, few but big in river. Welshpool and Dist AC now in Montgomeryshire AA which has 60m of coarse and game fishing in Severn, **Camlad, Vyrnwy, Banwy.** Also **Black Pools,** Welshpool, fly only. **Shropshire Union Canal** (coarse fishing). Ticket 50p. The Leighton Estate waters (leased to Crewe AA; members only), adjoin those held by STWA below Cilkewydd Bridge (free to licence-holders). Sylfaen Brook is preserved. Some permits are available for **Maesmawr Pool** (5m NW). Bank and boat fishing (dt £9 and £4) on Marton Pool, Marton, 5m SE. Good coarse fishing. Apply to Site Manager, Marton Pool Caravan Park. Tackle and WA licences from A E Bond, Hall Street and C D Millington, 3 Church Street. Hotels: Westwood Park, Welshpool; Bear, Newton; Black Lion, Llanfair Caereinion.

Forden (Powys). Montgomery, 3m. Trout. salmon, chub, dace, etc. Birmingham AA has extensive stretch. **Camlad;** trout, grayling. Montgomeryshire AA has water on river; tickets *(see Welshpool).*

Montgomery (Powys). Severn, 2m; trout, salmon, grayling, chub, pike and perch. Lion Hotel, Caerhowell has 400 yards of Severn; dt. **Camlad,** 2m N; good trout, grayling, chub. Montgomeryshire AA has water; tickets *(see Welshpool and Newtown).* Warrington AA, st £8 + £6 entrance, has ¾m and other waters at **Caersws, Dolwen, Fron** and **Llanidloes.** Also **Vyrnwy, Dee,** canals and pools. Herbert Arms, Cherbury, has 1½m; dt. Tackleists in Welshpool and Newtown.

Abermule (Powys). Severn and **Mule;** salmon, trout, grayling, coarse fish; mostly private but dt for some lengths. Dolforwyn Hall Hotel has ½m stretch and offers special discount to anglers booking. Water not always fishable in summer. Montgomeryshire AA has 1¼m of Severn and water on **Mule;** dt from hon sec. *(See Welshpool.)*

Newtown (Powys). Salmon, trout, grayling, pike, chub, dace, ½m by car-park

for STWA licence-holders. Newtown and Dist FC, Llanfair Caerinion FC and Welshpool AC form Montgomeryshire AA, covering some 60m of coarse and game fishing on Severn and tributaries, brooks, canal and lakes. St £11, wt £5, dt £2 for all waters, except Fachwen Trout Pool, £5. Apply hon sec and local tackleists *(see also Welshpool).* Birmingham AA and Prince Albert AS have stretches here. Here and at **Penarth** ½m fisheries free to STWA licence-holders. Tackleists: The Postmans Shop, 15 Shortbridge Street. Hotels: Bear, Elephant and Castle.

Caersws (Powys). Maesmawr Hall Hotel has 3½m on Severn free to guests. Trout, coarse fish, some salmon. Montgomeryshire AA has waters on Severn and brooks; dt from hon sec and limited for club's trout pool (Fachwen Pool, Aberhafesp). Caersws AC has water here and at Red House. ST £40, no dt.

Llandinam (Powys). 4m of trout and grayling fishing on both banks. Dt £4, OAP, juv £2 from Lion Hotel or Llandinam Post Office, Caersws.

Llanidloes (Montgomery). Trout, salmon, pike, chub, dace, grayling. Llanidloes AA has about 20m fishing on upper Severn, **Afon Clywedog** and other tributaries. St, wt and dt from hon sec. Montgomeryshire Fedn of Angling Assns (address in Welsh section) or tackleists. STWA has 600 yds on R bank for which dt is issued. **Llyn Clywedog** provides first-class sport with brown and rainbow trout; dt, wt, st *(see Powys Lakes in Welsh section for further details).* Warrington AA has water downstream. Red Lion Inn has 2m trout fishing at Llandinam. At **Trefeglwys** (4m N) is caravan park with 40m of fishing (trout and coarse) on **Trannon,** Severn and **Dulas.** Best months for trout; April–July. Nantgeifr Reservoir, 3m NE; trout. Hotels: Lloyds, Unicorn, Queen's Head, Angel, Temperance, Royal Oak, Red Lion.

Tributaries of the Severn

LEADON: Trout, coarse fish (some barbel introduced.

Upleadon (Glos). Trout; preserved from Upleadon Church to M50 motorway by Gloucester AC.

Ledbury (Hereford). Ledbury AA has trout water, no dt. Castlemorton Lake; coarse fishing; free, but RD licence necessary. **AVON:** The principal tributary of the lower Severn. Roach, chub, dace and perch dominate higher reaches; bream and pike, the latter patchily distributed, below Evesham. Barbel beginning to appear.

Tewkesbury (Glos). Confluence of Avon and Severn, connected also by "Mill Avon". Weirs and weir-pool fishing, including twaite shad during the spawning run. Cheltenham club controls 10m of Avon from **Bredon** up and at **Nafford**. Good coarse fishing, pike included. St, wt, dt (Mon to Sat only) from hon sec, from Mrs Stayt, Boon Street, or the Bell Inn, both Eckington.

Twyning (Glos). Chub, dace, roach, pike, perch, bream. White Swan Piscatorials preserve left bank of river from near Bredon Church to four meadows below Twyning lane. Club also has water on Severn at **Bewdley; Mease** at Harlaston; **Tern** near Wellington (Salop); and **Lugg** near Hereford; members only. Birmingham AA has stretches at **Mythe Farm, Twyning, Bredon, Eckington.** Cheltenham AC has about 10m of the **Avon** running through **Bredon, Strensham, Eckington, Birlingham** and **Nafford.** Coarse fish. St £8, wt £4 and dt £1 for part only. Mon–Sat only, from Bell Inn, Eckington. Other water for members only.

Pershore (Worcs). Pike, perch, roach, dace, chub, bream. STWA licence-holders may boat-fish free from mouth of **Piddle Brook** to **Pomona Works Meadows,** and at **Wyre Mill.** Worcester United AS has water nearby *(see Worcester).* Birmingham AA has water here, at **Nafford, Birlingham, Pensham, Bredon** and **Mythe Farm.** Some free water in recreation ground. Tackleists: W L Brown, 3 High Street; H Heritage, 17 Boat Lane. Hotel: Angel.

Evesham (Worcs). Pike, perch, bream, roach, dace, chub. Evesham AA has water in town, wt £3.50, dt £1 from bailiff on bank; E Huxley has stretch at Hampton Ferry accommodating 160 anglers. Dt £1 from café or bailiff's office on bank; matches booked at £1.30 per peg. Birmingham AA has fisheries here and at **Charlton, Chadbury Meadows, Cropthorne** and Fladbury. **Hampton Playing Field, Waterside** and **Workman Gardens** (overnight only), reserved for local anglers; permits from Council and tackleist: J Heritage, Boat Lane. Near Evesham is **Black Monk Fishery,** with two spring fed lakes in 10 acres, stocked with trout. Dt £5 plus £1 per fish to 5

fish limit. Lenchwick, Worcs WR11 4GT.

Stratford-upon-Avon (Warwick). Recently dredged. A stretch of the Avon preserved by Corporation. Birmingham AA has stretches at **Milcote, Avon Meadows, Welford, Barton, Bidford, Marlcliff, Salford Priors** and **Cleeve Prior. Bidford Grange** has $2\frac{1}{2}$m stretch at Bidford with cottage and caravan to let. Tel: 0789 773376. Good chub and dace and also water on **Stour** (2m S). **Stratford Canal** provides good coarse fishing. Dene, 5m NE. Tackleist: Coopers, 37 Greenhill Street. Permits for a number of waters in the district; RWA licences. Hotel: Salmon Tail, Evesham Road.

Leamington (Warwick). Bream, chub, dace, roach, pike, perch. Avon at **Barford, Wasperton** and **Guy's Cliffe** preserved by Royal Leamington Spa AA; annual membership, £5. **Leam;** roach, dace, chub, pike, perch, carp; leased by Leam AA. Royal Leamington Spa AA has $12\frac{1}{2}$m in **Warwick Canal;** coarse fish (good carp and tench in June, July, Aug); dt £1 (canal only). 10m south, **Bishop's Bowl Trout Lakes.** 40 acres of flooded limestone quarries. Fish of high average size. Dt £9. Punt £4. Evening and winter season terms available. Tel: 0926 613344. Tackleists: F Cooper, Clarendon Street; Cartwright, Regent Place; Rook's, Clemens Street; Norris, 24 Russell Terrace. **Chesterton Mill Pool;** trout fishery, dts. Tel: 0926 22471 or 613235.

Rugby (Warwick). Centre for **Draycote Water** (trout). *(See Midlands Reservoirs.)* Rugby Fed of Anglers has water on **Avon, Grand Union canal,** on part of **Stanford Reservoir, Newbold Quarry,** 25 acres, $1\frac{1}{2}$m from town centre; tench, carp, pike. St £8 (£2 juv), dt £1 canal, £2 quarry, from Banks & Burr *(see below)* or bailiffs. **Oxford Canal** is now BWF water. Coventry AA has water on **Grand Union Canal.** Details from tacklelists. Details of **Foxholes Fishery** at **Crick** (three lakes stocked with carp, tench etc) apply R Chaplin, Gt Arbour Close, Kenilworth. For **Stemborough Mill,** 4 acre trout fishery at **Lutterworth,** tel: 0455 209264. Tackleists: Banks & Burr, 27 Claremont Road; C Donald, 155a Bilton Road. Hotels: Three Horseshoes, Rugby; Dun Cow, Dunchurch; Albany, Crick.

ARROW joined by the **Alne** at Alcester;

flows into Avon at Salford Priors: Coarse fish, some trout.

Salford Priors (Worcs). Arrow and Avon; coarse fish.

Wixford (Warwick). Pike, perch, roach, dace, chub and bream; dt for about 1m of water from Fish Hotel. Harvington FC water L bank above bridge. Lakes: Ragley Park, 1m NW.

Redditch (Worcs). Redditch AC has water at **Fladbury, Binton** and **Wood Norton.** Inquire hon sec. Good fishing in **Lodge Pool,** tench and carp, and **Arrow Valley Lake,** a local authority leasure park. Dt on site. Tackleists: Powells, 28 Mount Pleasant. Hotels: Royal, Southcrest.

Alvechurch (Worcs). Barnt Green FC has rights on **Upper and Lower Bittell Reservoirs, Arrow Pools** and **Canal feeder. Lower Bittell** and **Mill Shrub** trout (fly only) remainder coarse fish. Guest tickets only issued by members to their friends. *(See also Salwarpe-Bromsgrove.)*

STOUR (tributary of Avon): Coarse fish, trout.

Shipston (Warwick). Shipston-on-Stour AC has about 12m; members only. Tickets (limited) for High Furze from E Draper, 37 Station Rd, Shipston-on-Stour. Stocked with trout by Severn RD. Knee Brook (2½m S); landowner issues ticket. Hotel: George.

LEAM (tributary of Avon): Coarse fish.

Eathorpe (Warwick). Coventry Godiva AS has fishery here; coarse fish. Good winter fishing; st. *(See also Leamington entry).*

HAM BROOK (tributary of Leam): Coarse fish.

Fenny Compton (Warwick): Good pike, bream, tench, roach in **Oxford Canal** (no longer London AA water). **Claydon.** Stoneton House Lake, 2½m NE. Farnborough Hall Lake; fishing good, but by invitation only.

SOWE (tributary of Avon):

Coventry (W Midlands). Excellent trout and coarse fishing on **Packington Estate, Meriden.** More than five miles of river fishing and 160 acres of lakes. Rainbow and brown trout; also coarse fishery 2m off. *For details see Midlands (reservoirs and lakes).* Coventry AA has extensive fishing on rivers, canals and reservoirs and coarse fishing in **Trent, Nene, Thames** and **Warwickshire Avon.** Rivers are for members only, but dt for canals and reservoirs may be had from tackleists in Coventry area or hon sec.

Canal waters include stretches on **Coventry Canal, Grand Union, Ashby Canal** and **Oxford Canal.** Dt £2 from bailiffs for Assn's **Napton Reservoirs,** noted bream, carp, tench and roach water; STWA licence needed. Tackleists: W H Lane & Son Ltd, 31/33 London Road.

BRAUNSTON CANAL: Coarse fish; sport only fair.

Braunston (Northants). Tickets for canal from Coventry AA; obtainable from Coventry tackleists. Hotel: Old Ship Inn.

TEME: Trout and coarse fish, with a few salmon; has acquired reputation for grayling.

Worcester (Worcs). Worcester St John's AS has some water. Worcester and Dist UAS has two meadows *(see R Severn).*

Broadwas (Worcs). Trout, grayling, chub, dace. Birmingham AA has stretch of left bank.

Leigh Court (Worcs). Trout, chub, dace, grayling, pike, perch, salmon. Bransford AS and local clubs rent Leigh to Powick; members only.

Tenbury (Worcs). Good trout, grayling, coarse fish. Salmon run from Feb to end of season, following removal of obstructions at Worcester (April, May, June best). Peacock Inn has ½m one bank (mainly bottom and spinning water). Limited dt for Tenbury FA water; fly only; tickets from hon sec. Dt for ¾m at **Ashford Bowdler** (near Ludlow) from Mrs Wall. Birmingham AA has water here, near Ludlow, below Eastham Bridge, and on **Ledwyche Brook.** For **Kyre** carp pool, apply S Lewis, 2 Severside S, Bewdley. Tackleist: W E Bunce, 61 Teme Street. Hotels: Royal Oak, Swan, Crow.

Ludlow (Salop). Trout, grayling, chub, dace, roach, perch, pike. Ludlow AC has ¾m both banks above town, also about ¼m of **Corve.** Flyfishing on upper part of Teme water; dt (limited) available to visitors resident in the area. Trout water restocked annually. Best months: June and July. Excellent grayling. Birmingham AA has fishing here and on several other stretches on Teme. **Ledwyche Brook,** 1½m E; trout, grayling, chub, etc; landowners sometimes give permission on this water. Hotels: The Feathers, Angel, Bull, Bull Ring Tavern, Charlton Arms, and Exchange.

Bromfield (Salop). Trout, grayling, chub, pike, all water strictly preserved by Earl of Plymouth Estates, who also own some

5m of **Corve.**

Leintwardine (Hereford). Birmingham AA has water on **Clun** here and at Aston and Broadward; members only.

Bucknell (Salop). Trout, grayling, chub; preserved by landowners. **Redlake Brook;** trout and eels. Licence to fish Redlake from Messrs Prince & Pugh *(see Knighton).*

Knighton (Powys). Trout; strictly preserved except for 1m free to licence-holders. Tackle, licences from Messrs Prince & Pugh. Hotels: Swan, Norton Arms.

ONNY: Good trout, grayling, chub, etc.

Plowden (Salop). Trout, chub; strictly private. Plowden Club has 4m running through Plowden Estate.

Craven Arms (Salop). Grove Estate water, N of Craven Arms, $1\frac{1}{2}$m. Onny, $3\frac{1}{2}$m. Quinney and Byne Brooks, preserved and strictly keepered by Midland Flyfishers; trout, grayling; members only; no tickets; club also has water from Stokesay Castle Bridge to Bromfield. Stokesay Pool; pike, chub. Bache Pool, Bache Farm; carp; dt from farm. Dt for trout and grayling fishing on 150 yards of Onny from Mrs Maund, 1 Onny Cottage, The Grove. Tackleist: W H Miller, Market Street.

SALWARPE: Trout, coarse fish. Birmingham AA has two stretches, one at confluence with Severn (becoming a notable pike fishery) and another above at **Porter's Mill.**

Droitwich (Worcs). Trout above, coarse fish below; leave from landowners. Severn 6m W. Droitwich and District AS has water at **Holt Fleet;** dt from hon sec to members' guests only. Noted chub waters. Society also has **Heriotts Pool** (large carp). Dt (open to all) from Talbot Hotel, High Street. Some coarse fishing in canal; Birmingham AA members only. 1m W of town, **Westwood Park,** 60 acre lake, first-class coarse fishery stocked with big tench, roach etc. Dt (bank) £1.50, boat for one £3.50, for two, £5. Tackleist: D Walsh, Queen Street. Hotels: Worcestershire Brine Baths; Raven; Chateau Impney.

Bromsgrove (Worcs). Tardebigge Reservoir rented to Bourneville Club (messrs Cadburys) for many years. Limited st for local anglers. Upper and Lower Bittel Reservoirs owned by Barnt Green FC; members only *(see also Arrow—Alvechurch).* Hewell Grange Lake; permits for local clubs. *(See also Worcester and Birmingham Canal.)*

STOUR: Polluted and fishless.

Stourbridge (Worcs). **Staffordshire and Worcestershire Canal;** coarse fish. Tackleist: Riley's, Lower High Street *(see also canal).*

Brierley Hill (W Midlands). Stour, 3m S, polluted. **Himley Park Lake;** coarse fish; Dudley Corpn issues dt. Clubs: Brierley Hill AC (no water) and various works clubs. Tackleist: Maybury, Church Street (tickets and WA licences).

Dudley (W Midlands). Lakes: Pensnett-Grove Pool, Middle Pool, Fenns Pool, 3m SW *(see Brierley Hill).* Himley Park Lakes and Common Pool, 4m W. Dudley AS has 3m between **Bewdley** and **Stourport** (Severn). Plenty of fishing in canals within 6m radius. Lodge Farm Reservoir; Dudley Corporation. At Parkes Hall, Coseley, $2\frac{1}{2}$m away, is good pool for which dt can be had; coarse fish (Dudley Corporation). Tackleist: Peter Gordon, 84 High Street.

SMESTOW (tributary of Stour): Polluted.

Wolverhampton (W Midlands). Smestow, 2m W; polluted. Some fishing in Penk at Penkridge. Whitmore Reans AS (hon annual membership £6, juv £2) preserves water on **Penk, Tern, Roden** and **Severn,** and local canals. Dt £1 from hon sec. Most local water on Severn held by Birmingham AA; permits from tackleists, Patshull Pool, Pool Hall (2m away). Further information from local tackleist: Fenwicks, Pitt Street.

TERN: Coarse fish, some trout.

Grudgington (Salop). A few trout and coarse fish. White Swan Piscatorials *(see Twyning—Avon, Severn)* have a fishery here.

Marsh Green (Salop). Whitmore Reans CAA fish Mr F Evans water at Isombridge Farm, near Wellington.

Hodnet (Salop). Tern. 1m E; a few trout and coarse fish. Strine Brook, 2m E. Lakes: Rose Hill Ponds, 4m NE. **Hawkstone Park Lake,** $3\frac{1}{2}$m; excellent tench and carp water (40 lb bags not uncommon) and large roach, rudd, pike and eels; private preserve of Wem AC, membership closed.

Market Drayton (Salop). Trout, pike, roach, dace; private. Several private lakes and ponds in neighbourhood. At **Great Sowdley,** 7m SE, are canal reservoirs; Stoke AS; perch, pike, roach, tench, carp. Warrington AA controls $2\frac{3}{4}$m of **Roden** at **Shawbury.**

MEESE (tributary of Tern); Trout, coarse fish.

Newport (Salop). Meese, 1m N; trout; private. Lakes: Chetwynd Park Pond, 1m N. Minton's, Limekiln and Wildmoor Pools, 3m S. Moss Pool, $1\frac{1}{2}$m NE. Whitmore Reans CAA has 2m of right bank at Wood Farm, **Caynton.**

REA: Trout, grayling; preserved but leave sometimes given.

Minsterley (Salop). Trout, grayling, Minsterley Brook. Habberley Brook, 3m SE. Lake: Marton Pool, 7m SW. **Lea Cross;** Warrington AA fishes on 1,000 yds stretch.

SHELL BROOK (tributary of Roden):

Ellesmere (Salop). Shell Brook, 2m NW; preserved. Halghton Brook, 4m N. Roden, 6m SE. Lakes: **Ellesmere Meres,** noted for bream (12 lb plus). Ellesmere AC (st £10), issues wt £5, dt £1.50 for **Whitemere** and **Blakemere** (bank fishing only). Sunday fishing is allowed. Boats available on most assn waters for members only. Ellesmere AC members may fish 4m stretch of **Shropshire Union Canal;** coarse fish. Tickets from tackleists: Clay & Sons, 5a Scotland Street; Steve's Tackle, High St, Ellesmere. Hotels: Black Lion, Bridgewater, Red Lion (Ellesmere AC HQ); tickets *(see also Shropshire Lakes).*

PERRY: Trout, preserved.

Baschurch (Salop). Perry, 1m W; trout; some leave from landowners.
Lakes: Birch Grove, $1\frac{1}{2}$m NE. Berth Pool, 1m NE. Fennymere Pool, 2m E. Marton Pool, 2m NE.

Ruyton Eleven Towns (Salop). Warrington AA fishes on Platt Mill Farm stretch.

VYRNWY; Provides sport with trout, grayling, coarse fish and salmon.

Llanymynech (Salop). Trout, salmon, grayling, roach, perch, pike, chub, etc. For Lord Bradford's water at Lower House Farm inquire of agent, Llanymynech. Warrington AA has short stretch; members only. The Lion Hotel issues st £5, mt £2, wt £1 and dt 50p for good stretch now held by Northern AA, and canal. Other hotels: Bradford Arms, Cross Keys, Dolphin.
Good trout fishing at **Lake Vrynwy** *(see Lakes in Welsh section).*

Llansantffraid (Powys). Warrington AA has 800 yds here.

Meiford (Powys). Montgomeryshire AA has water; here and at **Maesbrook;** restricted to 12 rods; dt 60p from hon sec.

MORDA (tributary of Vyrnwy):

Oswestry (Salop). Severn, **Vyrnwy, Tanat, Dee, Ceiriog, Perry, Morlas, Morda, Clywedog Reservoir.** Many good trout lakes and carp pools, and excellent fishing in **Shropshire Union Canal,** all within easy reach. Most river fishing preserved, but Oswestry AS has good water, game and coarse (including carp). St £6.50 (20% reduction for local residents); no dt. Lakes: Meres at Ellesmere give good coarse fishing. Lake Vyrnwy (18m), good trout; proprietor of Lake Vyrnwy Hotel will give particulars *(see also Powys Lakes in Welsh section).* Tackleist (and WA licences): J Ellis, Regal Stores, Oswestry. Hotels: Bear, Queen's, Wynnstay. Morton Lodge Hotel, Morton, can arrange fishing on Tanat, Vyrnwy and local pools.

TANAT (tributary of Vyrnwy): Trout (good average size), chub and grayling, but fewer than there used to be.

Llan-y-Blodwel (Salop). Horseshoe Inn has $1\frac{1}{2}$m (dt £2.50), and Green Inn, Llangedwyn, has short stretch; dt issued (3 rods only); fly only.

Llanrhaiadr-y-Mochnant (Powys); ns Llanfyllin, 7m—Moch; trout; free. Tanat, 1m; trout, grayling, chub, etc; 6m from Llangedwyn to Llangynog strictly preserved. No dt.

CAIN (tributary of Vyrnwy): Trout, coarse fish.

Lanfyllin (Powys). Trout. Hotel: Bodfach Hall, which caters for fishermen and has 200 yds. Guests may fish adjoining $\frac{1}{4}$m free of extra charge. Hotel also has boat on Lake Vyrnwy (10m); trout. Warrington AA has two stretches near **Llansantffraid.**

BANWY (tributary of Vyrnwy): Trout, grayling, chub, pike, dace and chance of salmon here and there.

Llanfair-Caereinion (Powys). Montgomeryshire AA has about 4m trout fishing on Banwy and Twrch *(see under Welshpool on main river for permit details).* Permits from Wynnstay Hotel or hon sec. No maggot fishing; some Sunday fishing for st holders. Birmingham AA have stretch here and at Foel. April–June fly only on upper reaches. At Cyffronydd Warrington AA has 610 yds. **Maesmawr Pool** lies 5m NE; strictly limited permits from Maesmawr Hall. Hotel: Wynnstay Arms.

Llangadfan (Powys). Trout; Montgomeryshire AA has good stretch; dt from hon sec.

A Hard Day's Fishing?

Relax
with a good book!

BLENHEIM BOY — Richard Passmore, and its sequel **MOVING TENT**
(each £10.95)
The first is the story, sometimes grim, often hilarious, of a Blenheim Bomber gunner who led a charmed life in the first year of the War in that beautiful, dangerous blue sky. The second is its sequel.

Blenheim Boy "rings with the love of flying, as well as the excitement, peril and humour" — *Daily Mail*
Moving Tent: "often extremely moving, frequently hilarious, always elegantly written" — *The Kriegie*

NEVER STOP THE ENGINE WHEN IT'S HOT — Air Chief Marshal Sir David Lee (£11.95)
A light-hearted tale of a life on the North West Frontier of India flying with the RAF in the early 1930s — a life that few will remember.
"Delightful" — *Sunday Express*

LADIES WITHOUT LAMPS — Eve Williams (£9.95)
A delightful and humorous tale of a VAD in the War who was far too inclined to cross swords with Matron — in England, Australia and Hong Kong.
"You'll enjoy reading it" — *Grimsby Evening Telegraph*

CHRISTMAS ISLAND CRACKER — Air Vice Marshal W E Oulton (£14.95)
An intensely fascinating account of the planning and execution of the British Thermo-Nuclear tests in the Pacific in 1957, by the man who was charged with masterminding this secret and massive operation. Only the author knew the whole picture. Only now can the story be told.
"A splendid, first-hand account, racily told, of an event that has changed Britain's political history"
— *H Chapman Pincher*

YES, YOUR EXCELLENCY — V E O Stevenson-Hamilton (£10.95)
A tale, brilliantly told, of the glitter of Government House in the Punjab in 1935; and of the horrors of massacre on Partition and Independence of India in 1947.
"We still have some among us who actually led the sort of lives which Kipling and Maugham could only try to portray"
— *Daily Mail*

ANGEL VISITS — FROM BIPLANE TO JET — Frank Griffiths   (£9.95)
During the war Frank Griffiths secretly piloted the country's top boffins while
they tested their brilliant inventions (radar in particular).
> "Frank Griffiths was absolutely super. His book deserves to
> be read by anyone with an interest in aviation adventure"
> *— Radio Clyde*
> "I found myself laughing with some incredulity at the many
> and varied accounts contained within"
> *— British Airline Pilots Assn Journal*

MEMOIRS OF AN ACCIDENTAL AIRMAN — F F Rainsford   (£10.95)
Fred Rainsford was at the very centre of responsibility in the Air Ministry
during the Berlin Airlift; an operation that probably prevented a third world
war. But earlier he was engaged in bombing Libyan targets to prevent Germany
supplying their North African troops. Later, he was to become no mean
diplomat. A delightfully told tale.
> "A marvellous story, very well told"
> *— (The late) Lord Boothby*

THURSDAY IS MISSING — Richard Passmore   (£10.95)
A story, told with a touch of magic, of the author's childhood in the slums of
Liverpool between the Wars.
> "Highy readable"   *— Home Valley Express*

THE BURGOYNE DIARIES — Gerald Achilles Burgoyne   (£11.95)
These stunning First World War Diaries were found in an old trunk by the
author's daughter:- a fascinating and horrifyingly vivid account from the Royal
Irish Rifles trenches south of Ypres in that glutinous campaign.
> ". . . can be unhesitatingly recommended"
> *— Royal Irish Ranger*

WITH A BUSLOAD TO NEPAL — Eve Williams   (£9.95)
A thoroughly amusing account of a not-uneventful bus journey to Nepal; by
the intrepid 65-year-old author. Through the now closed Afghanistan.
> "A rich combination of humour and descriptive accounts of
> an incredible journey"   *— Epsom Advertiser*

PRINCELY PAGEANT — Christopher Armstead   (£10.95)
The one-time Mint Master, Superintendent of Stamps, Chief Electrical
Engineer, Director of State Workshops, Warden of Weights and Measures and
Currency Officer to His Exalted Highness, The Nizam of Hyderabad and Berar
(once the richest man in the world) tells his humorous tale.

*(prices are subject to change
without notice)*

**ORDER through your
BOOKSHOP.**

**Thomas Harmsworth Publishing
13 Nicosia Road, London, SW18**

SHROPSHIRE LAKES

ELLESMERE LAKES. Fishing station: **Ellesmere.** Excellent coarse fishing in Ellesmere (noted for bream), **Crosemere, Newton Mere, Blakemere, Whitemere** (bream of 12 lb 4 oz taken). Controlled by Ellesmere AC who issue dt £1, bank fishing only, on **Whitemere, Blakemere. Colemere** now Stoke AA water. Dt also for **Hardwick Pool** (1m) noted tench water from Clay, 5a Scotland Street.

PEATSWOOD LAKE. Market Drayton 1m. Brown and rainbow trout av 1 lb 6 oz. Two lakes, $5\frac{1}{2}$ and 2 acres approx. Strictly private, Peatswood FF; membership closed.

WALCOT LAKES. Lydbury North, 3m NE of Clun. Two extensive lakes, one controlled by Birmingham Anglers' Assn. Tench, pike and other coarse fish. *For membership details, see "Birmingham", under Rea (tributary of Trent).*

SOMERSET (streams, lakes and reservoirs)

(For close seasons, licences, etc, see Wessex Water Authority, p 13)

AXE. Rises on Mendips and flows 25m NW to Bristol Channel near Weston-super-Mare. A few trout in upper reaches and tributaries, but essentially a coarse fish river, containing a mixture of the usual species, with roach now predominating.

Weston-super-Mare and Bleadon (Som). Weston-super-Mare AA has $8\frac{1}{2}$m of Axe, 4m of **Brue** at Mark, near Highbridge, stretches of **Old Glastonbury Canal, Old Bridge River, Congresbury Yeo** and **North Drain,** and two ponds (good carp), with trout and chub fishing in tributaries **Spring River** (Cheddar Yeo) and **Crooked River.** Club also has rights on 8–10m of fishing on **Parret** and **Isle** as members of SE and W Wessex Federation of Anglers. St £8.50, wt £3.50, dt £1.50. Cheddar AC has 6m stretch upstream of **Clewer.** Inquire hon sec. Tackle, tickets, licences from Maroli Pet Shop, 19 Orchard Street. Tickets also from hon sec. Many hotels *(see Sea Fishing Stations).*

Brinscombe (Som). Bristol Amalgamated has three fields here and further waters at **Clewer** and **Weare.** St from hon sec and tackleists *(see Bristol).*

BRICKYARD PONDS: Pawlett. Bristol Amalagamated tench fishery. St from hon sec or tackleists *(see Bristol).*

BRISTOL RESERVOIRS:

Chew Valley, Blagdon and **Barrow** reservoirs provide some of the best lake trout fishing in Europe, with a total annual catch of 46,000 fish of high average size. Season and day tickets available. WWA licence required for all waters. Details as follows:

Barrow Reservoirs—Barrow Gurney. Open April to Oct 15; brown and rainbow

trout; dt (bank) £4.30, st £120 (concessionary £57), fly only.

Blagdon Lake—Blagdon. Open April to Oct 15; noted brown and rainbow trout water; dt £13 (pulling boat) or £7 (bank) per rod per day; st £320 (concessionary £180), fly only.

Chew Valley Lake—Chew Stoke. Open April to Oct 15; noted brown and rainbow trout water where fish run large; dt £15.50 (motor boat) or £6 (bank) per rod

Trout fishing in the Mendip Hills
Bristol Waterworks Company

Enjoy superb trout fishing in the beautiful setting of the Mendip Hills.

Chew Valley Lake, Blagdon and the Barrows are within easy reach of the M4 and M5. For permits, boat reservations and information phone or write to:

The Recreations Officer
Bristol Waterworks Company
Woodford Lodge, Chew Stoke
Bristol, BS18 8XH

Telephone Chew Magna 332339

per day; st £245 (concessionary £135); evening bank from May 1 (3 pm) £3.50 (2 brace limit), fly only. For all waters apply to: Bristol Waterworks Company, Recreations Department, Woodford Lodge, Chew Stoke, Bristol BS18 8XH (Chew Magna 332339). Bank dt from self-service kiosks at all waters. Reduced charges for boats after 3.0 pm. Concessions for juvs (under 17), OAP and registered disabled. All prices incl VAT. *(Advt p 120.)*

Cheddar Reservoir—Cheddar. Opened as general coarse fishery in 1974. Bank fishing £2, st £16 (concessions for OAP/jun/reg disabled). Permit information (Chew Magna 332339). Wessex Water Authority Rod Licence is required; annual £8.20, weekly £2 (concessions for OAP/jun/reg disabled).

WESSEX WATER AUTHORITY RESERVOIRS, managed by the Fisheries and Recreations Dept, Box 9, King Square, Bridgwater TA6 3EA. Licence-fee included in permit charge: concessions for jun and OAP. St from above address; dt from dispensing units at reservoirs. There is a season ticket at £220, covering all the reservoirs.

Clatworthy Reservoir. 12m from **Taunton** in Brendon Hills; 130 acres brown and rainbow trout; fly only; $2\frac{1}{4}$m bank fishing. St £165; dt £6. Boats (limited) £6, incl fishing permit. Season March 29–Oct 12.

Durleigh Reservoir. 2m W of **Bridgwater.** 77 acres; brown and rainbow trout; fly only. St £165. Dt £6. Boats £6. Season

March 21–Oct 12, then Oct 18–Nov 16.

Hawkridge Reservoir. 7m W of **Bridgwater.** 32 acres. Brown and rainbow trout; fly only. St £132, dt £6. Season March 29–Oct 12. No boats.

Otterhead Lakes. About 1m from **Churchingford** nr Taunton. Two lakes of $2\frac{3}{4}$ and 2 acres; brown and rainbow trout; fly only; no boats. St £116, dt £6. Season March 29–Oct 12.

Sutton Bingham Reservoir. 3m S of Yeovil. 142 acres. Brown and rainbow trout; average $1\frac{1}{4}$ lb; fly only; st £165; dt £6. Boats £6. Season March 22–Oct 12.

CHARGOT WATER, Luxborough. 3 ponds. Trout; fly only. Dt from Colonel Sir E Malet Bt OBE, Chargot Farms.

DONIFORD STREAM (Swill River at Doniford) and **WASHFORD RIVER, Taunton.** Trout; strictly preserved.

HORNER WATER. On National Trust Holnicote Estate; upstream from Newbridge to Pool Bridge (4m) excluding Nutscale Reservoir; fly fishing, trout. Dt, wt. Licences, tickets and tackle from John Lynn & Co. **Porlock.** (Tel 862427).

WIMBLEBALL RESERVOIR. 4m NE of Dulverton. Rainbow and brown trout. 374 acres. Fly only. Season: May 1–Oct 31. SWWA water. Dt £6, evening £4, boats £5.50 (£4 half day). Wheely boat for disabled. Concessions jun and OAP. 5 fish limit. Tackleist: L Nicholson, High St, Dulverton. Hotel: Carnarvon Arms.

YEO. Fishing station: **Congresbury.** Tidal. Good fly water for trout; a few coarse fish. Bristol Amalgamated have water here and at **Wrington.**

STOUR (Dorset)

(For close seasons, licences, etc, see Wessex Water Authority, p 13)

Rises in Wiltshire Downs and flows through Dorset, joining Hampshire Avon at its mouth at Christchurch. Noted coarse fishery (roach especially good), salmon up to Wimborne, trout and grayling patchily distributed. Salmon not numerous, but large. River best for coarse fish in winter.

Christchurch (Dorset). Avon and Stour. Salmon, pike, perch, chub, roach, tench, dace. *(See also "Avon".)* Dt and wt on stretch between Iford Bridge and Wick Ferry. Wt £7.50, dt £2.50, juvs half-price from Davis (address below), from where tickets may be obtained for local stillwater trout and coarse fisheries, and for the Avon at Ringwood. Coarse fishing can be had on Royalty Fishery waters *(see Avon).* Sea fishing from

Mudeford in Christchurch Bay is fair. Tackleist: Davis (Bargates) Ltd, 75 Bargates, who sell tickets for various fisheries in the district. Hotel: King's Arms, Christchurch.

Throop (Dorset). Throop fisheries (Christchurch station $2\frac{1}{2}$m); $5\frac{1}{2}$m of top quality coarse fishing, with occasional salmon and sea trout. Strictly preserved. Barbel to 13lbs, chub to $7\frac{1}{4}$lbs, roach to $2\frac{3}{4}$lbs in 1985. Also a mill pool stocked with roach, bream, carp and tench. Coarse fishing: st £48.50, ft £22, wt £13.80, dt £3.70 (reduced rates for pensioners and for juveniles; special rates for clubs; booking essential); for tickets, RD licences and all inquiries apply to Glen

Sutcliffe, Manager, South Lodge, Holdenhurst Village, Bournemouth. Tel 0202 35532.

Hurn Bridge (Dorset). Stour and Moors; no angling. Preserved now as a bird sanctuary.

STOUR (Dorset)—Tributaries

Wimborne (Dorset). Good chub, roach, dace and pike. Some trout, small runs of salmon and sea trout. Red Spinner AS has water at Barford and Eyebridge; about 9m in all; members only. Hon sec, Wimborne and Dist AC will also be glad to give information. Wimborne Club has about 12m in Wimborne, Longham and Charlton Marshall areas; 2m of Stour, five coarse fish and two trout lakes plus two new lakes of 9 acres, also 2m of trout-stream. Membership £18 pa (entrance-fee £5) wt £10, dt £2. The Old Mill, Corfe Mullen, issues tickets for about 1m (one bank only) and has accommodation. Tackleist: Minster Sports , 8 West Street, Wimborne BH21 1JP (information). Hotels: Griffen, King's Head, Three Lions, Greyhound.

Sturminster Marshall (Dorset). Southampton PS has about 2m here. Coarse, a few trout; no tickets. The Old Mill Guest House, Corfe Mullen, issues dt; free fishing for residents.

Shapwick (Dorset). Coarse fish. Southampton PS has several miles of fishing here; no tickets issued. Durweston AS has fishing. Strictly limited issue of dt from Post Office, when open. No matches.

Blandford Forum (Dorset). Fine roach, chub, dace, perch and pike; best Oct onwards. Blandford and Dist AC have most fishing from **Durweston** Bridge to **Crawford** Bridge. Tickets from hon sec or A Conyers (tackleist), West Street.

Also club membership forms and RD licences (Tel Blandford 2307).

Sturminster Newton (Dorset). Chub, roach, dace, pike, perch, tench, bream; fishing good. Sturminster and Hinton AA has 7m above and below town. For st £9, wt £4 and dt £1.25 apply club secretary or Sports Shop. Hotels: Crown, Marnhull; White Hart; Swan Hotel, Fiddleford Inn; Cottage Guest House, Sturminster Newton, Romaynes, Lydlinch; Old Post Office, Hinton St Mary.

Stalbridge (Dorset). Stalbridge AA (membership £6 pa) has 2m of Stour and 1m on **Lydden**. Wt £3, dt £1.50 from Corner Cottage Tackle Shop.

Gillingham (Dorset). Trout and coarse fish; Gillingham and Dist AA; Assn membership £15 pa, and dt £1.50 for coarse fishing only from Hussey, Station Road, Gillingham. Fishing for tench, bream, rudd etc, in **Turner's Paddock Lake** now included in Assn. membership, but no dt. Hotels: Royal, Red Lion.

Stourton (Wilts). **Stourhead New Lake** on Stourhead (western) Estate at Stourton, near Mere. Coarse fishing: June 16 to March 14; dt issued. Apply M Bullen, The Laundry, Gasper, Stourton. Hotel: Spread Eagle.

MOORS: As Allen.

Verwood (Dorset). Allen and Moors. Moors trout in parts, otherwise mainly roach; Ringwood club has water. *(See Ringwood under "Avon".)*

STOUR (Kent)

(For close seasons, licences, etc, see Thames Water Authority, p 16)

Rises in two arms north-west and south-east of Ashford, where they join. From junction river flows about 30m north-east and east to sea beyond Sandwich. Good coarse fishing lower down. Trout fishing restricted to club members in upper reaches.

Sandwich (Kent). River fast-flowing from Minster to Sandwich (Vigo Sluice); good fishing for bream and roach; few perch and tench; sea trout and grey mullet.

Private fishing from Richborough Road, upstream. Sandwich and Dist AA has 1m; dt from hon sec. Sandwich AA also has **Reed Pond** (now private). **Stonar**

Lake (stocked, carp and roach) and North and South Streams, **Lydden** (coarse fish; dt). Tackleists: Pretts, The Chain. Hotels: Red Lion, Ramsgate Road (dt for mullet); Bell; Haven Guest House. *(See also Sea Fishing Stations.)*

Grove Ferry. Stour and Little Stour. Betteshanger Colliery Welfare AS has 6m on Stour from **Plucks' Gutter** to **Stonar.** Roach, bream and mullet (Red Lion stretch, June–Aug). Society also has stretch at **Minster.** Tickets from hon sec, Red Lion or bailiff on bank. Canterbury AA has water on Stour *(see Canterbury).*

Canterbury (Kent). Trout, coarse fish. Free within city boundary, except for municipal gardens stretch. River from city boundary to **Grove Ferry** private for members of Canterbury & Dist AA. St £23; dt on bank £1.50 for stretch from Grove Ferry Bridge to **Plucks' Gutter. Fordwich** and **Vauxhall lakes,** members only. **Westbere** leased by Brett Ltd, Wincheap, Canterbury. Hotels in Canterbury: County, Falstaff, George and Dragon, Chaucer, Abbots Barton. Hotels on water: George and Dragon, Fordwich, Fordwich Arms, Grove Ferry, Dog and Duck, Stourmouth. Permits from bailiff on bank, tackleists or hon sec at headquarters, "Riversdale", 14 Mill Road, Sturry, nr Canterbury. Tack-

leists: Greenfield's Road and Gun Store, 4–5 Upper Bridge Street (bait, licences).

Wye (Kent). Pike, roach, etc; private but some permission from owners. Hotel: King's Head.

Ashford (Kent). Ashford AS holds **River Stour** between **Ashford** and **Wye** (members only) and **Royal Military Canal;** 16m between **Iden Lock** and **West Hythe Dam.** Coarse fish; wt and dt. Water level fluctuates during winter due to land drainage, thus making fishing at times difficult. Cinque Ports AS has water. St £7.50 (+ entrance fee of £2.50), ft £3.75, wt £2.50, dt £1 from J B Walker, 5-Marine Walk Street and Light Railway Restaurant, Hythe. Ashford Working Men's Club has a pit; good tench, carp, rudd; members only; no dt. Tackle and licences from Ashford Sports, North St, and Ironmongers' Stores, Beaver Road. Hotels: County, Kent Arms.

LITTLE STOUR: Same fish as main river, but overgrown in places.

Plucks' Gutter (Kent). Dog and Duck Inn issues dt, also from bailiffs on bank.

WANSUM. Roach, bream and tench, many fish of high quality caught. Wansum AC has water and issues dt £1. From hon sec or King Fisheries, tackleists, 34 King Street, Margate.

STOUR (Suffolk)

(For close seasons, licences, etc, see Anglian Water Authority, p 14–15)

Coarse fish river forming border between Suffolk and Essex. Some sea trout in semi-tidal waters below Flatford. Experimental restocking with salmon and sea trout was carried out by Essex RA.

Manningtree (Essex). Tidal; roach, dace, perch, pike and occasional sea trout (fish of 9 lb caught). Sea trout and coarse fish between RD notices at **Flatford Mill.** (Elm Park, Hornchurch and Dist AS waters). Club: Lawford and Manningtree AC. Hotel: White Hart.

Dedham (Essex). Coarse fish, fine bream, carp, pike and dace in mill pool. St £6, dt £1 for **Clovers Mill** waters from Clovers Mill Ltd, Gunhill, Dedham, Colchester, Essex. Tackleist in Colchester: K D Radcliffe, High Street.

Nayland (Suffolk). Bream, chub, dace, perch, pike, roach, tench. Colchester APS has water here and at **Wormingford, Wiston, Boxted, Langham, Stratford St Mary** and **Flatford.** St £14, no dt.

Colchester PS has rights at **Boxted;** no tickets. Colnes AS has stretches at **Little Horkesley** and other fisheries in area. Dt 50p. Mill pools private. Essex RD has trout fishery on tributary **Box:** dt from River Conservatory (limited to three rods daily). **Hadleigh** and Dist AS has water on tributary **Brett:** coarse fish; no dt. Brett fishes best in winter.

Bures (Essex). London AA controls a good deal of water here and in **Clare, Cavendish** and **Sudbury** areas. Also **Bures Lake;** members only, but some waters available to associates at Bures. Dt from F Staples, 25 Nayland Rd, Elm Park. Hornchurch & Dist AS has stretch, members only. Moor Hall and Belhus AS has excellent 5 acre lake at **S Ocken-**

den. Members only (st £15 + £40 entrance.) Hotels: One Bell; Eight Bells; Horseshoes.

Sudbury (Suffolk). Sudbury AA (now affiliated with London AA) control approx 12m on Stour and carp fishery; dt from hon sec or I Whitehart, Arthur Hall Cottage, Melford Rd. St £13, dt £1.50.

SURREY (lakes)

ENTON LAKES. Witley. Enton Fly Fishers' Club has four lakes stocked with trout; members only; no tickets; apply secretary for membership details.

FRENSHAM PONDS. Farnham (4m). Farnham AS has rights on Great Pond and Little Pond, leased from Hambledon Rural District Council; coarse fishing; permits from hon sec and bailiff. "Leisure Sport" gravel pits at Yateley. Coarse fish. Tel: Chertsey 64872.

OLD BURY HILL LAKE. Nr. Dorking. Coarse fish, especially tench and pike. St £25, dt £2. Boat: £2 extra. Concessions to jun, OAP. From Fishery Manager, Lake View. Tel: Dorking 883621.

RIPLEY. Papercourt fishery, Sendmarsh. Pike, bream, tench etc, a Leisure Sport restricted permit fishery. St £19, £2 key deposit. Applications to LSA, Thorpe Park, Staines Road, Chertsey, Surrey. Tel: 64872.

TRILAKES. Sandhurst. Mixed fishery; well stocked with tench, carp (common and crucian), bream, rudd, roach, perch, pike, eels, trout. Dt £3 from fishing hut. Car park, toilets, licenced café. (Tel 0252 873191).

VIRGINIA WATER. Virginia Water, Johnson Pond and Obelisk Pond, Windsor Great Park fishable by season ticket only; coarse fish; st £13.50. Early application advised in writing, to Crown Estate Office, Windsor Great Park (sae).

WEY FARM LAKE. Ottershaw. Coarse fishing. St £12, dt £1 from manager, 88 Beech Road, Brookwood.

WILLOW PARK, Ash Vale, nr Aldershot. Three lakes acres, stocked with a variety of species. Dt £1 from 2, Park Road, Farnborough.

WINKWORTH LAKES. Winkworth, nr Godalming. National Trust property. Trout fishery (fly only) managed by Winkworth Fly Fishers. St £96. Details from hon sec. *(See Club List.)*

WIREMILL POOL. Nr Lingfield. Coarse fish include tench up to 6 lb, bream up to 7 lb, roach up to 3 lb, carp up to 6 lb. In process of being resold.

YATELEY. Nr Camberley. Thirteen "Leisure Sport" lakes stocked with pike, carp, tench, roach and perch. Large specimens recorded. A restricted permit fishery. St £20 + £2 key deposit. Concessions to jun, OAP, dis. Applications to LSA, Thorpe Park, Staines Road, Chertsey, Surrey KT16 8PN. Tel: 64872.

SUSSEX (lakes and streams)

ARDINGLEY RESERVOIR. Ardingley, nr Haywards Heath. 180 acre trout water. Fly only to Oct 31. St £250 and £200. Dt £3.50 to £8. 2, 4 and 6-fish limits. Enq to Colin Simpson, The Lodge, Ardingley Reservoir, W Sussex. Tel: 0444 892549.

CHICHESTER LAKES. Chichester (Sussex). Chichester and Dist AS has three gravel pits; roach, rudd, carp, tench, bream, chub, perch, pike; members only except for wt from hon sec or treasurer or local tackleists *(see below).* Society also shares stretch of **Rother;** from Arundel Town Bridge upstream to S Stoke. St £10 + £10 entrance, concessions for jun and OAP. Wt £7. Tackleists: C G Daughtry, 44 The Hornet, Chichester and Fisherman's Den, Canada Grove, Bognor.

DARWELL RESERVOIR. At Mountfield, **Robertsbridge** (Tel: Robertsbridge 880 407); brown and rainbow trout to 6 lb; 180 acres; leased from Southern Water Authority by Hastings Flyfishers Club; st £115, dt £7, self vending service at fishing lodge; boats £6.50 day extra, to be booked 48 hrs in advance from bailiff. Fly only; limit 6 fish, 4 fish in Apr; season Apr 3–Oct 31. Take precise care over approach route down small lanes.

FARTHINGS LAKE. Nr Battle. Carp, tench, bream, roach, rudd. St £15 and £10 from Bury Hill Fisheries, Lakeview,

Old Bury Hill, Dorking. Dt £1.50 on site after 9 am, and from Stills Garage and Surridge Newsagents, Battle.

FURNACE BROOK TROUT FISHERY Nr. Herstmonceux. Brown and rainbow trout from 2 lbs up. Dt £10. St available. Phone 0435 830298 or 830151 for details.

FEN PLACE MILL. 2m SW of E Grinstead. 14 acres of stillwater trout fishing on three developed hammer ponds. Brown and rainbow trout av $2\frac{1}{2}$ lb weight. All amenities. St and dt for members' guests. Tel 0342 715466.

GREAT SANDERS RESERVOIR. At Sedlescombe (Tel: Sedlescombe 248); 57-acre water containing brown and rainbow trout; av 1 lb. (Details as for Darwell Reservoir.)

MILTON MOUNT LAKE. Three Bridges (Sussex). Crawley AS water (st £20); mostly carp; dt. Crawley AS also has Tittermus Lake (pike, tench, carp, roach, perch) and **Sandford Brook** (trout; fly only) in Tilgate Forest; Roffey Park Lake, near Colgate (carp, roach, tench, perch, gudgeon); New Pond, Pease Pottage (carp and crucian carp, tench), the Mill Pond, Gossops Green, and Furnace Lake, Felbridge (carp and crucian carp). These are for members and friends only. At **Buchan Park** nr Crawley, Crawley AS has lakes; dt £2 from hon sec; carp, pike, etc.

CLIVE VALE RESERVOIRS: ECCLESBOURNE RESERVOIR. Hastings. Good carp, tench, roach, bream and rudd. Tickets issued by Hastings Clive Vale

AC. St £11 from hon sec. Dt £2, no juv, from Owens corner shop, Hastings.

PEVENSEY LEVELS. Marshland drained by various streams into **Pevensey Haven** and **Wallers Haven;** good coarse fishing on large streams (pike, roach, rudd, perch, bream, carp and tench), most of best waters rented by clubs. Fishing stations: **Eastbourne, Hailsham, Pevensey.** Compleat Angler FC has substantial stretches on one bank of **Wallers Haven,** good fisheries on both banks of **Pevensey Haven** and water on **Langney Haven** and **R Cuckmere.** Tickets, st £15, dt £1 from hon sec or Compleat Angler, 22 Pevensey Road, Eastbourne. Good coarse fishing on Old Haven ($3\frac{1}{2}$m) controlled by Hailsham AA *(see also Cuckmere)*; dt from hon sec. Lydd AC also has water; dt from bailiff on bank.

SCARLETTS LAKE. 3 acres, nr E Grinstead. Good coarse fishing, carp incl. Dt £3 at waterside. St £30 from lakeside or Jackson, Scarletts Lake, Furnace Lane, Cowden, Edenbridge, Kent. (Tel: 034 286 414). OAP, juv, dis, 50%.

WEIR WOOD RESERVOIR. Forest Row (Sussex), $1\frac{1}{2}$m; **East Grinstead,** 4m; 280 acres. Re-stocked with trout for 1986 season, after some years as a coarse fishery. Fly only April 2 - Oct 31, thereafter any legal rod & line method. St £275, mt £80, wt £30, dt £2 to £8. 2, 4 and 6-fish limits. Enq in writing to The Lodge, Weir Wood Resevoir, Forest Row, Sussex. Tel: 08833 715242 (evenings).

TAMAR

(For close seasons, licences, etc, see South West Water Authority, p 12)

Rises in Cornwall and follows boundary between Devon and Cornwall for good part of course, emptying finally into Plymouth Sound. Holds salmon, sea trout, brown trout of fair size—pounders not uncommon—and grayling.

Milton Abbot (Devon). Endsleigh FC has 9m. Limited wt and dt (£112–£175 and £16–£25) for guests at historic Endsleigh House. Average salmon catch—251; 90% taken on fly. Good car access to pools. Apply to Manager for more details.

Lifton (Devon). Tamar, **Lyd, Thrushel, Carey, Wolf;** trout, sea trout (late June to end Sept); salmon (May, to mid-October). Hotel: Arundell Arms, which has 20m of excellent water in lovely surroundings; 23 individual beats, also 3-acre trout lake, brown and rainbow trout

to 9 lbs. Licences and tackle at hotel, fly fishing courses (beginners and semi-advanced) by two resident instructors. Dt (when there are vacancies) for S & ST £9—£15, according to date; for brown trout, £8.50 *(advt p 127).*

Launceston (Cornwall). Salmon, sea trout, trout. Permits can be obtained for some parts of Tamar, **Ottery, Kensey, Inney** and **Carey** from Launceston AA, which has about 14m of fishing in all. St (full) £40, st (part of fishery only) £20. Visitors' tickets: Dt (S) £9 and £7, (T) £4.

Fishing the salmon fly on the beautiful Quarry Pool on the R Tamar, near Lifton, Devon. *Photograph by John Tarlton.*

Wt (S) £25, (T) £15. Entrance-fee, concessions for juniors. Lakes and ponds: **Stone Lake,** $4\frac{1}{2}$ acres coarse fishing, dt £1.30, tel: 083786 253. **Tredidon Barton Lake,** dt £2, tel: 056686 288. **Alder Quarry Pond,** $4\frac{1}{2}$ acres, coarse, dt, tel: 056683 444. **Dutson Water,** coarse fishing, tel: 0566 2607. Tackleist: Tony Kennedy Sports, Church Street.

Hotels: White Hart (RD licences), Eagle House, Race Horse Inn, North Hill. Launceston Publicity Committee issue booklet listing accommodation.
Bridgerule (Devon). Farmers may give permission. **Tamar Lakes** here: SWWA waters for which tickets are issued. (*See Cornwall: lakes.*) Hotel: Court Barn, Clawton, Holsworthy.

Tributaries of the Tamar

TAVY: Rises in Cranmere Pool on Dartmoor and flows about 17m before forming estuary below Buckland Abbey. Excellent salmon and sea-trout river.
Tavistock (Devon). Tavy, Walkham and Plym FC; limited membership. Salmon, sea trout and brown trout permits for visitors on Bridge; main river and on **Meavy, Plym** and **Walkham.** Comprehensive: st £20, wt £8, dt £4. Brown trout only; st £10, mt £5, wt £4, dt £2. Fly only. Available from tackleists Barkells, 15 Duke Street, Tavistock. Hotel: Bedford (salmon and trout fishing on Tamar and Tavy). Hotel: Endsleigh.
Mary Tavy (Devon). Brown trout; late run

of salmon and sea trout. Fishing mostly privately owned; riparian owners sometimes give permission. Plymouth & Dist Freshwater AA has rights at **Peter Tavy** (members only).

Yelverton (Devon). Good centre for Tavy, Walkham and Plym FC waters. Salmon, sea trout, dt £4. Brown trout, dt £2, from Rock Stores, Yelverton, or tackleists in Tavistock and Plymouth. Hotels: Rock, Devon Tors and Dartmoor Inn (last two issue RD licences).

WALKHAM (tributary of Tavy): Upper reaches rocky and overhung, but downstream from Horrabridge there are many

Fly fishing in Devon

nice pools. Peal run from July onwards.
Horrabridge (Devon). Salmon, sea trout, trout. A good centre for Tavy, Walkham and Plym FC waters.
INNEY: Trout.
Launceston. Farmers give permission *(see*

Launceston under Tamar).
LYD: Trout, sea trout, some salmon.
Lifton (Devon). Arundell Arms *(advt p 127)* has fishing for salmon, sea trout and brown trout, also on main river and other tributaries.

TAW

(For close seasons, licences, etc, see South West Water Authority, p 12)

Rises on Dartmoor and flows 50m to Barnstaple Bay, where it joins estuary of Torridge. Salmon (best March–May) with sea trout (peal) from July onwards. Brown trout and good coarse fishing in places.

Barnstaple (Devon). Bass and mullet in estuary. Salmon, trout, peal, roach and dace. Salmon best March, April, May; peal July, August. Barnstaple and Dist AA has water immediately below New Bridge (some free water below this), on **Yeo** (trout and sea trout), and on ponds at **Lake Venn** and **Swimbridge** (carp, tench, bream, rudd, perch). Visitors' tickets for salmon, trout and coarse fisheries from local tackleists *(see below)* or hon sec. Coarse fishing in ponds: visitors may become assn members which entitles them to fish ponds (Mon–

Fri only). Tickets limited and not weekends or Bank Holidays. C L and Mrs Hartnell, Little Bray House, **Brayford,** have about 1m (both banks) of **Bray;** small trout only; dt £2. For other trout fishing see tributary Yeo. East and West Lyns, Badgeworthy Water and Heddon are accessible, as well as fishing on Wistlandpound and Slade Reservoirs. Tackleists: E Gale & Son, 59 High Street, who produce a useful booklet on fishing in the area; E Stacey, Bear Street.
Chapelton (Devon). Salmon, peal, trout, dace. Taw mostly private down to New Bridge. Barnstaple and Dist AC water below *(see Barnstaple).*
Umberleigh (Devon). Salmon, peal, trout; preserved. West of England Centre of Game Angling has 5m on Taw, Bray, Mole, Yeo. Tel: 0805 23256/22114 *(also see Torrington).* Rising Sun has $3\frac{1}{2}$m of water (seven beats, including first fishing above tidal water) for which dt are issued when not required for residents; fly only after April 30. Sunday fishing is allowed; salmon best March, April, May and September; peal July, August and September. Brochure, giving charges, etc, on request. Wt £66 and dt £15 nonresidents, £10 residents only. Other hotel: Northcote Manor, Burrington.
South Molton (Devon). Taw and Mole; salmon, trout, peal. South Molton AC has water on Taw and **Mole** ($\frac{3}{4}$m both banks); fly only; dt issued. Permits from hon sec. Rumbos, 6 The Square, issue permits for several stretches. Fortesque Arms no longer has any fishing on this river. In March, April and May there are salmon throughout water, and occasional fish in Sept. Sea trout July on.
Eggesford, Chulmleigh (Devon). Fox and Hounds hotel has $2\frac{1}{2}$m of private sea trout and brown trout fishing on Taw.

RISING SUN

UMBERLEIGH   North Devon

FOR SALMON AND SEA TROUT

Brochure with plan of water available on request.
Tel: High Bickington 60447

This comfortable old inn is the first hotel on the River Taw with fishing above tidal waters and caters specially for fishermen. It has $3\frac{1}{2}$ miles (7 beats) of exclusive water, with three huts and a well-equipped rod room. There is usually a fine Spring and Autumn run of Salmon and excellent Sea-trout fishing in July, August and September. The cooking is personally supervised, there is a good cellar, and guests are assured of every attention.

SSSH.......

....man fishing

All Severn-Trent trout fisheries
are pleasant, inviting and regularly
stocked with good, healthy fish.

A day permit will put you in the picture.

Ladybower Reservoir, Derbyshire.

SEVERN TRENT WATER Brochure available on request.

BROWN MARABOU

SHREDGE

MACLAREN

MURDOCH'S BUTCHER

DOG NOBBLERS.

Stocked with trout from May 1st. Sea trout best June–Sep. Fly only from May 1 to Sep 30. Wt £50, dt £10, $\frac{1}{2}$dt £7. Salmon fishing available March–April. Full details from Hotel.

Coldridge (Devon). Taw Fishing Club has water from Taw Bridge to Hawkridge Bridge; very good trout fishing; complimentary for members guests only.

Lapford (Devon). Salmon, sea trout, trout. Dt £3. Contact J O Yates, Gemini, Lanham Lane, Winchester; or R Drayton, 46 Godfrey Gardens, Bow, Crediton.

North Tawton (Devon). Trout. Burton Hall Hotel has about 4m of water here; trout; occasional sea trout and salmon. Free to guests; dt issued subject to hotel bookings. K Dunn, The Barton, also issues dt for about 1m.

Sticklepath (Devon). Trout. Dt £1 from Mr & Mrs P A Herriman, Davencourt, Taw Green, S Tawton, for $\frac{1}{2}$m downstream. Accommodation: Taw River Inn.

YEO (Barnstaple): Sea and brown trout. Barnstaple and Dist AA has water on Yeo, wt and dt from Barnstaple tackleists. *(See Barnstaple.)*

MOLE:

South Molton (Devon). Sea and brown trout, some salmon. Dt £1, contact A W Youings, Garramarsh, Queens Nympton, tel: 07697 360. Hotel: George.

BRAY (tributary of Mole):

North Molton (Devon). Trout, sea trout, few salmon; ns South Molton, 2m. Poltimore Arms Hotel has 2m of fishing on Bray; fishing good. Cdr R H Dean, Little Bray House, **Brayford,** issues dt for about 1m of river.

TEES

(For close seasons, etc, see Northumbrian Water Authority, p 14)

Rises below Cross Fell in Pennines, flows eastwards between Durham and Yorkshire, and empties into North Sea near Middlesbrough. Once notable salmon river, but destroyed by pollution. New sewage works have improved the situation. Salmon and sea trout are again running in favourable conditions. Brown trout to $2\frac{1}{2}$ lbs in the upper reaches. Well stocked from Middleton-in-Teesdale down to Blackwell; coarse fish from Winston down to Preston Park. River tidal to Worsall.

Middlesbrough (Cleveland). River polluted. NWA reservoirs **Lockwood** and **Scaling Dam** in vicinity. Stocked with trout; dt £4.50 on site. Local tackleist: W P Adams, 9 Princes Rd. *(See Yorkshire lakes, streams, etc.)*

Stockton (Cleveland). Trout; grayling, coarse fish on one of best stretches of river. Stockton AA has over 10m at **Gainford, Winston, Dinsdale, Middleton-on-Row,** nr Darlington, **Aislaby,** nr Yarm, and on **Swale,** nr **Ainderby** (Moreton-on-Swale); no tickets. For reservoirs see Middlesbrough. Tackleist: F and K Flynn, 12 Varo Terrace.

Thornaby (Cleveland). Trout, grayling and coarse fish. Thornaby AA has $1\frac{1}{2}$m below Leven Beck mouth at **Ingleby Barwick** (coarse fish; tidal), $4\frac{1}{2}$m at Croft (trout, grayling, dace, chub, roach, perch, pike, gudgeon), and stretches on **Leven, Wear, Eden, Swale** and **Ure.** Annual membership: £14. Concessions. No tickets but applications to secretary will be sympathetically considered. Thornaby AA are allied with Teeside &

DAC. Tackleists: F & K Flynn, 12 Varo Terrace, Stockton; J W Wright, 107 Parkgate, Darlington.

Eaglescliff, (Cleveland). Coarse fishing at Preston Park, free from top of park downstream. Yorkshire bank in Yarm free fishing. **Leven** joins just below Yarm. Trout and coarse fish. Middlesbrough AA to falls; Thornaby and Yarm AA together up to Hutton Rudby. Excellent brown trout fishing; occasional sea trout.

Yarm (Cleveland). Tidal good coarse fishing; occasional trout. Yarm AA, strong team club with $5\frac{1}{2}$-6m tidal water, are members of Ass of Teeside & Dist ACs, with 10m water; st £41.50, dt £1.50; limited dt from tackleist, Flynn, Stockton.

Croft (Durham). Fair head of trout, grayling and coarse fish. Free fishing for 200 yds upstream of road bridge. Thornaby AA has downstream; 7m both banks.

Darlington (Durham). Trout, grayling, coarse fish. Richmond AS has water (apply to hon sec). Darlington Brown Trout AA has water beween Middleton and Croft, also on **Swale.** Dt for members' guests only. Stockton AA has water at **Winston** *(see Stockton).* At **Whorlton,** 4m T J Richardson, Whorlton Farm, issues strictly limited permits for stretch. Tackleists (and licences): E & B Langstaff, Parkgate; Adams, Duke Street.

Piercebridge (Durham). Trout, grayling, dace, chub, gudgeon. Tickets available for Raby Estates water *(see Darlington)*; otherwise preserved, Clow Beck, 3m S of Darlington; part is Darlington AC water; otherwise preserved. Forcett Park Lake, 8m SW; pike, perch; private, occasional winter permits.

Gainford (Durham). Trout, grayling, coarse fish. Up to Winston, most of the water held by Stockton AA. No tickets. Alwent Beck, 1m W; trout; private. Langton Beck, 2m N.

Barnard Castle (Durham). Trout, grayling. Barnard Castle FFC has from Tees Viaduct to Baxton Gill, near Cotherstone; private club water. Barnard Castle AS has from a point above Abbey Bridge to Tees Viaduct; private club water, but

some dt to visitors staying locally. Darlington FFC has 2m above and below Abbey Bridge (1m below Barnard Castle). Water holds some big grayling; members only. Other fishing on permission from riparian owners. Grassholme, Selset, Balderhead, Blackton and Hury reservoirs, 5m NW; dt obtainable *(see Tees Valley Reservoirs).* Hotel: King's Head, Market Place.

Mickleton (Durham). Trout. St £15, wt £6, dt £3 for S bank between Cronkley Bridge and Lune Fort from Turnbull & Parkinson, 152 Front Street, Chester-le-Street; Cleveland Arms; J Raine & Son, Horsemarket; all Middleton-in-Tees-dale.

Middleton-in-Teesdale (Durham). Trout (plentiful but small); Turnbull & Parkinson, 152 Front Street, Chester-le-Street, issues limited st £15 (or pro rata) each for about 9m of Upper Tees; fly only. Wt £6, dt £3. Reduced charge for juniors.

GRETA: Trout.

Bowes (Durham). Mostly private, but inquire of Richardson's Tackle Depot, Barnard Castle, for possibilities.

TEIGN

(For close seasons, licences, etc, see South West Water Authority, p 12)

Rises on Dartmoor, 5m south-west of Chagford, and flows 30m south-east to the sea through an estuary beginning below Newton Abbot. Best known as sea trout river; salmon incidental bonus. Principal tributary is Bovey. Salmon, sea trout (peal) and brown trout. A spring river. Teign usually fishes best for salmon from late March to early June.

Dunsford (Devon). ¾m single bank; salmon, sea trout, brown trout; dt £3.50 from Stepps Bridge Hotel, tel: 0647 52313.

Newton Abbot (Devon). Salmon, sea trout, trout; preserved by Lower Teign FA from Sowton Weir to Teignbridge (excluding stretch from New Bridge to Preston Footbridge). Three separate beats. Dt (three per beat) £8. Assn also has 3m on Bovey *(see Bovey).* Tickets from Drum Sports *(see below).* Newton Abbot FA has five lakes at **Rackerhayes** and six at **Preston;** coarse fish, including carp and tench. Exeter AA has Bluewater Pool at **Bovey Tracey;** coarse fishing. **Trago Mills** is 600 yds coarse fishing, dt £2.75, OAP, juv £1.75. G Mole, tel: 062682 462. Tackleist: Drum Sports, 47a Courtenay Street, Newton Abbot; Doel Sports, Bank Street,

Teignmouth. Hotels: Globe, Queen's, Tavistock Inn (RD licences).

Chudleigh (Devon). Salmon, sea trout, trout; Lower Teign FA has water *(see Newton Abbot).*

Moretonhampstead. Manor House Hotel no longer leases fishing here.

Chagford (Devon). Trout, sea trout, Upper Teign FA preserves about 12m in all, fly only before June 1 on some parts and for whole season elsewhere; size limit 7 in. Tickets: Drum Sports, 47a Courtenay St, Newton Abbot, or Bowdens, The Square, Chagford. Gidleigh Park, Country House Hotel, has 1m of river. St £12, wt £5, dt (S and MT) £4 from hotel. Dt (T) £1.80 from hotel and The Angler's Rest, Fingle Bridge, Drewsteignton. Fernworthy Reservoir, 3½m (trout) *(see Devon lakes, streams, etc).*

Tributary of the Teign

BOVEY: Salmon, sea trout, trout.
Bovey (Devon). On Bovey and Teign. Fishing above Bovey preserved by land-owners and below by Lower Teign FA. No tickets. Lakes: Tottiford and Kennick Reservoirs; trout *(see Devon lakes,* *streams, etc).* Hotels: Manor House, one mile from North Bovey (water on Bovey and Bowden, and salmon and trout fisheries on Teign); Glebe House, North Bovey.

TEST

(For close seasons, licences, etc, see Southern Water Authority, p 11–12)

Rises from springs in the chalk near Overton, above Whitchurch and flows via Stockbridge and Romsey to enter Southampton Water. Salmon run as far as Romsey. Before the era of the rainbow, the brown trout Mecca of the whole civilised world. Now considered by some to have been spoilt to some degree by the introduction of the former.

Romsey (Hants). Trout and grayling fishing good; salmon fishing good below the town, all preserved by the different land-owners. **Broadlands Estate** lets salmon rods and $\frac{1}{2}$ rods, a named day per week for two for £728 and a named day for two per fortnight for £368. Trout fishing is £700 and £360 (2 brace), dry fly only. There is also an excellent stillwater coarse fishery. St £35, wt £12, dt £3. Golden orfe a special feature. Enquiries: Fisheries Manager, Estate Office, Broadlands, Romsey SO5 9ZE. Tel: 0794 513052 or 517888. Dt for residents from Council Offices, Duttons Road, for Romsey Memorial Park; limited to two rods daily. Salmon, few small trout, grayling, coarse fish. Good trout fishing at **Two Lakes,** near Romsey *(see Hampshire streams, lakes, etc).*

Stockbridge (Hants). Greyhound Hotel has water; dry fly and nymph only. Fish average 3 lbs. St (2 rods) (one day per month) £330. Dt £30.

Houghton (Hants). Bossington Estate lets rods by season. (Tel 0794 388265; waiting list.)

Fullerton Bridge (Hants). Trout (av 2 lb 8 oz). Season mid-April to end of Sept. Leckford Estate controls 7m of main stream and carriers from Fullerton Bridge to Longstock Grange. Dry fly only. Waiting list. Inquiries to Leckford Estate Ltd, Stockbridge (Stockbridge 634).

Whitchurch (Hants). Trout; strictly pre-served. No tickets are granted. Fish numerous, but not so large as farther down. Hotel: White Hart.

Keep the banks clean

Several clubs have stopped issuing tickets to visitors because of the state of the banks after they have left. Spend a few moments clearing up.

Tributaries of the Test

ANTON: Trout, grayling.
Andover (Hants). Anton joins Test at Testcombe Bridge. Trout and grayling; all strictly preserved. At **Rooksbury Mill**, Rooksbury Road, a first-class trout fishery offering a choice of st terms, from £70 to £375, a £15 (5 fish) dt and boats £6. Tel: 0264 52921 for full details *(advt p 131)*. Andover AC preserve worked-out gravel pits at **Charlton**, 1m NW, flooded by Anton; king carp, common carp, dace, perch, roach, rudd, tench. Apply sec for dt. Tackleists: Cole & Son, 67 High Street. Hotels: Star and Garter, White Hart, Junction, George, Anton Arms, Globe Central.

PILL HILL BROOK: Trout, grayling.
Amport and Monxton (Hants). Trout and grayling. Nearly as long as Anton, but pure chalk-stream. Monxton Mill reach greatly improved and contains full head of locally bred brown trout averaging 14 oz, with occasional heavier fish. Fishing preserved by landowners, who occasionally give permits. Dry-fly only.
DEVER: Trout, grayling.
Sutton Scotney (Hants). All strictly preserved. Dever joins Test at Newton Stacey.
BOURNE:
St Mary Bourne (Hants). All strictly preserved. Bourne joins Test above Longparish.

* *Test and Itchen Fishery Association compiles register of rods to let; inquire hon sec; address in club lists.*

THAMES

(For close seasons, licences, etc, see Thames Water Authority, p 16)

Second longest river in England. Tidal reaches much recovered from pollution and fish returning in considerable numbers. Salmon are running again in modest numbers; rainbow trout are caught quite regularly in the freshwater tideway. Barbel, flounders, smelt and odd trout taken at various points. River worth fishing from Southwark Bridge upstream. Above Teddington Lock boat traffic largely spoils sport in summer, except in weir pools, but fishing can be good early and late. River fishes well from October to March. Holds good stock of coarse fish, with excellent bream and barbel in some stretches. Large trout found in weir pools, but catching them ("Thames trouting") is separate and difficult art. Among famous tributaries are Kennet, which comes in at Reading and is one of best mixed fisheries in England. Trout and coarse fish run large. Higher up, Coln, Evenlode and Windrush are noted trout streams, but for most part are very strictly preserved and fishing difficult to obtain. Fishing on Thames open up to City Stone at Staines. Above, permission often necessary and lock-keepers and local tackleists should be consulted. Weir permits at £7 per season issued by Thames WA. Thames Angling Preservation Society, (membership fee £2) founded in 1838, has restocked seven tributaries—now keeps close watch on water quality and fish stocks in whole Thames basin. Not a fishing club; a fishery preservation society supported by anglers, membership details from secretary, A E Hodges, The Pines, 32 Tile Kiln Lane, Bexley, Kent DA5 2BB. London Anglers Association (LAA) HQ, Forest Road Hall, Hervey Park Road, London E17 7LJ, has numerous fishings on Thames and elsewhere. St £15.50. Dt £1 (concession to OAP and juniors), issued for some waters. Several reservoirs in which fishing is allowed (coarse fish and trout). *(See London—Reservoirs, etc.)*

Isleworth (G London). Tidal. Dace, roach, bream, perch, eels, etc; free from towpath or boats. Fly-fishing for dace on shallows when tide is down. Reach down past Chiswick Eyot can be good for roach, dace; towpath only; free. *Note: Many gravel pits and streams in Thames Valley and elsewhere are available on* *season ticket from* **Leisure Sport, Angling**, Thorpe Park, Staines Lane, Chertsey, Surrey KT16 8PN. Tel: 64872. Tackleists: Hounslow Angling Centre, Bath Road *(see also Colne-Wraysbury).*
Richmond (G London). Half-tidal. Down to Isleworth is fishing for roach, dace, bleak, bream, perch; free from towpath

or boats (boatmen on towpath). Notable recent catches include two trout by members of Barnes and Mortlake AS. In Richmond Park **Pen Ponds** hold perch, carp, bream, roach and pike. Permit (£4) from park superintendent at his office in Richmond Park (enclose sae). Tackleist: Edgar Thurston & Co Ltd, 360 Richmond Road, Twickenham. Hotels: Castle, Bird's Nest, Pigeons, White Cross.

Twickenham (G London). Coarse fishing; free from boats and towpath. Deeps hold barbel, roach, bream, carp. Corporation allow fishing from Radnor, Orleans and Terrace Gardens. Dt for **Kennet** at Newbury, from White House Inn and bailiff. Tackleist: Guns and Tackle, 81 High Street, Whitton. Hotels: Bird's Nest, White Swan.

Teddington (G London). Thames holds barbel, dace, chub, roach, bream, pike, perch; fishable from boats but none available on spot; free fishing from towpath. Hotels: Anglers', Clarence, Railway.

Kingston (G London). Canbury Gardens, is very popular stretch and has yielded large carp, bream, perch and roach. Tackleists: Morgan's, 17 High Street, Hampton Wick.

Hampton Court (G London). Thames, **Mole;** coarse fish. Good roach, chub, barbel, etc, in Molesey Weir. Much free fishing from towpath; for RWA licence-holders. Several boatmen near bridge. **Bushey Park Ponds;** roach, tench, pike. **Home Park Ponds** and **Long Water,** Hampton Court, hold eels and tench; permission from park superintendent (send sae if apply by post). St £1, ½ price for OAP and young people 10–17. Tackleists: E C Cheeseman, 11 Bridge Road, East Molesey.

Hampton (G London). Hampton Deeps hold bream, pike, perch and sometimes a good trout; free fishing from towpath and boats. Inns: Ye Old Red Lion, Bell.

Sunbury (Surrey). Excellent for all-round angling; free. Fine weir and weir shallows, barbel, chub, dace, bream and occasional trout may be taken. Tackleist: Wilson Webbs, Thames Street. Hotel: Magpie.

Walton-on-Thames (Surrey). Bream, barbel, perch, dace, chub, carp and pike; perch and pike in backwater; free; boats available. Club: Walton AS (water on **Mole,** Cobham). Boats: Rosewell's, River Bank. Tackleist: Walton Cycle Shop, Bridge Street. Hotels: Anglers', Riverside; Weir, Riverside; Swan, Manor Road.

Shepperton (Surrey). Pike, barbel, perch, bream and carp; free; boats available. Ashmere Club has well stocked trout lake; members only. Two Leisure Sport gravel pits, similarly stocked: St £13. For full details phone Chertsey 64872. Hotel: Anchor.

Weybridge (Surrey). Thames, **Wey** and **Bourne Brook;** pike, trout, bream, perch, barbel, roach, etc; free fishing in Thames only. Byfleet AA has six stretches of Wey; pike, dace, roach, chub, carp, barbel, bream, perch; st £10. Six local clubs have rights on **Wey Navigation Canal** from Thames Lock to Walsham Lock and have formed Wey Navigation Angling Amalgamation; dt from hon sec. Hotels: Ship, Thames Street; Lincoln Arms, Thames Street; Oatlands Parks; Blue Anchor. For fishing in Basingstoke Canal *(see Hampshire streams, etc)*.

Chertsey (Surrey). Pike, perch, chub, roach, bream, occasional trout; free fishing from boats and towpath. Thorpe Water Park here, HQ of the **Leisure Sport Angling Service,** with fisheries in many parts of Lowland England. St from £11 to £32 for individual fisheries. Group permits also issued. Write to LSA, Thorpe Park, Staines Road, Chertsey KT16 8NP. Tel: 64872. Club: Addlestone AA, which has water at **New Haw, Wey** and **Bourne** and a gravel pit at Laleham; dt to members' friends only. Leisure Sport have two stretches of **Wey** at **Addlestone.** Several boat yards. Hotels: Cricketers, Bridge.

Staines (Surrey). Good coarse fishing; free from boats and towpath. Penton Hook good for barbel and chub. "Leisure Sport" gravel pits, pike, carp, tench, etc; st (retricted) £17 + £2 key deposit. Concessions to jun, OAP, dis. Applications to LSA, Thorpe Park, Staines Road, Chertsey. Tel: Chertsey 64872. Clubs: Staines AS (stretch opposite Runnymede; members only). Tackleist: Tackle Dept Johnson & Clark, High Street. Hotels: Packhorse (Middlesex bank); Swan (Surrey bank). *(See also "London Reservoirs".)*

Laleham (Surrey); ns Staines. Barbel, dace, roach, pike, perch. Inn: Three Horseshoes.

Wraysbury (Bucks). Coarse fish, as above.

Hounslow Piscatorials have stretch of **Wraysbury River.** "Leisure Sport" gravel pits, 138 acres here, and 90 acre lake at **Kingsmead;** tench, bream, pike to 35 lb. St £14, concessions to jun, OAP, dis. Applications to LSA, Thorpe Park, Staines Road, Chertsey, Surrey KT16 8PN. Tel: 64872. **Queen Mother Trout Fishery,** Horton Road, Horton, **Slough.** 475 acre trout fishery, st on application, dt as follows: £10, $\frac{1}{2}$ day £7, evening £5. Boats: £5, £3.50, £2.50, outboard £6, £4.50, £3.50. Limit, 8 fish, $\frac{1}{2}$ day 5 fish. There are also 2 and 4 hour sessions. Concessions for OAP, dis, juv. Rod sharing for beginners. Tel: 0753 683605.

Windsor (Berks). Fishing from south bank below Windsor Bridge and north bank to Eton–Windsor road bridge, by TWA licence only. Dt issued for club waters near Maidenhead; inquire tackleists. Old Windsor AC (st £10) issues dt £1 for Romney and Albert Bridge fisheries. From local tackle dealers and bailiffs on bank. Much river traffic in summer. Punts available. Council offers fishing on one meadow. Fishing can be had in Windsor Great Park ponds and Virginia Water *(see Surrey Lakes)*. New TWA trout fishery on **Datchett Reservoir.** Details from controller on site. Tackleists: Windsor Field Sports, St Leonard's Road.

Boveney (Bucks); ns Windsor, 2m. Coarse fish. Backwater good for pike, and weir pool for trout and barbel. Towpath free. LAA Eton Wick fishery here.

Bray (Berks); ns Maidenhead, $1\frac{1}{2}$m. Weir pool good for trout, and free from boat or punt. Bray Mill tail from 1m above lock to lock cut private. Towpath free. Hotel: Hinds Head.

Maidenhead (Berks). Roach, pike, perch, chub, barbel, dace, chance of trout. Some free fishing from My Lady Ferry down to Boulter's Lock cut. Clubs with water include Maidenhead and District AS, dt for Downey. Boveney reaches from bailiff. Boats: Andrew Bros; Bushnell Ltd. Tackleists: Jack Smith, 4 High Street; Angling Services, 41 Clare Road. Hotels: Skindles, Thames, Bell, Bear, Riviera.

Cookham (Berks). Cookham & Dist AC has all water from Odney weir pool to London AA water at Spade Oak ferry *(see Bourne End)*; no tickets; members only. Hotels: Ferry, Royal Exchange, King's Arms, Bell and Dragon, Crown.

Bourne End (Bucks). Wide, open water with some shallow stretches, good for fly fishing. London AA has water here; dt from bailiffs. Stretch also available to associates.

Marlow (Bucks). Usual coarse fish, including barbel; good spot for Thames trout. Marlow AC has water; no tickets but open for competitions. Little free water. The Compleat Angler Hotel has fishing from grounds, free for residents, non-residents at hotel's discretion.

Hurley (Berks). London AA has fisheries at Frogmill Farm and Hurley Flats. Dt issued for $1\frac{1}{2}$m. Other water at Hambledon; members and associates only.

Henley (Oxon). Pike, roach, perch, tench, bream, eels. Good roach swims by Hambledon Lock. Barbel and trout at Hambledon Weir. Chub fly-fishing below weir and at Marsh Lock (upstream). Remenham AS has fishing from Henley Bridge downstream on Berks bank to within $\frac{3}{4}$m of Hambledon Lock. Tickets from bailiff. On Oxon and Bucks bank water controlled by society for members only. Also from end of Henley Promenade upstream to Marsh Lock, bridges and meadows upstream from Marsh Lock. London AA has stretches for members. Free water from Henley Bridge up to end of Promenade only (north bank), and on Marsh Lock bridges only (not weir). Tackleist: Parrots Riverside. Boats: Hobbs, Parrott. Good accommodation for anglers at Anchor Hotel, Friday Street. Other hotels: Catherine Wheel, Little White Hart.

Wargrave (Berks). Thames and Loddon; good coarse fishing and some trout in **Loddon.** London AA has Loddon Bridge meadow and Loddon Marsh fishery above Sindlesham Mill; members only.

Sonning (Berks); ns Twyford. Bank and boat fishing. Good stretch for Thames trout, especially Shiplake Hole. Much fishing from **Shiplake** to Sonning Bridge on Oxfordshire bank controlled by Shiplake and Binfield Heath AS; members only. Mill Tails preserved by Lord Phillimore. Guests at White Hart can fish private stretch of $\frac{1}{2}$m on Berkshire bank towards Shiplake. London AA has water for members only at Sonning, Lowfield and Mapledurham. Reading & Dist AA has Sonning Eye fishery (lake and river); dt from bailiff, Lake View.

A Southern English river where anglers coming and going quietly are the only human intruders. The result: perfection. *Photograph by Graham Swanson.*

Reading (Berks). Most coarse fish. Free to RWA licence-holders from towpath from Sonning Bridge up to Horseshoe Bridge; thence Huntley and Palmer AC water to Kings Meadow (members only). Reading Borough Council controls the fishing on Kings Meadow, Christchurch Meadow and Thames-Side Promenade. The fishing from Thames-Side Promenade to Scours Lane is controlled by Thames Water Authority. There is some free water on the **Kennet** from Horseshoe Bridge to County Weir (adjacent to Inner Distribution Road). Fishing upstream of County Weir is controlled by Reading and District AA. No dt for any Reading and District AA waters. Farnborough AS has good trout and coarse fishing on **Whitewater** at Heckfield (8m). Countryside Club, 109 Upper Woodcote Road, Caversham Heights, Reading, has trout and carp fishing let on a family st basis; At Bradfield, **Pang Valley trout lake**, approx 6 acres, stocked with rainbow trout. Dt £12.50, 4 fish limit, from tackleist Turner (*see below*). Leisure Sport has coarse fisheries available on permit at **St Patrick's Stream, Twyford** and **Theale** (52 acres), apply LSA, Thorpe Park, Chertsey, tel: 64872. **Deans Farm**: 60 acre gravel pit and $\frac{1}{2}$m of Thames bank controlled by Reading and Dist AA. Carp, tench, pike, etc. St £10 or £5. No day tickets available on this fishery. Tackleists: Reading Angling Centre, Northumberland Avenue; T Turner & Son Ltd, 21 Whitley Street and Tulls Tackle, 258 Kentwood Hill (Tilehurst).

Tilehurst (Berks). Elthorne Alliance and Reading and District AA control the fishing on the Oxfordshire bank. Free fishing from towpath to Caversham (*see restrictions under Reading*). Roebuck Hotel has private stretch on south bank.

Goring (Oxon). Pike, bream, roach, chub, perch and (in weir pool especially) barbel and a few trout; best fish taken from weir pool, fishing from weir or boat. Other fishing can be had from towpath above and below lock. London AA has R bank from Beetle & Wedge Hotel to Cleeve Lock; Gatehampton Farm and Hartslock Wood fisheries on L bank. Members only, but $\frac{3}{4}$m available to associates. Hotel: Leathern Bottle.

Pangbourne and **Whitchurch** (Berks). Thames and **Pang**. Trout, perch, pike,

roach, bream, chub, dace. River fishes well in winter; free fishing $1\frac{1}{2}$m above and below Whitchurch Bridge; good coarse fishing; boats available. Weir pool private. Pang holds trout, especially near Tidmarsh, but is strictly preserved; trout at its mouth. Pangbourne and Whitchurch AS has local fisheries. Trout in pits at **Theale** (2m); dt issued. Carp and tench in local ponds.

Moulsford (Berks). All coarse fish. London AA has water here; members only. Hotel: Beetle.

South Stoke (Oxon). London AA controls the water from footbridge above railway bridge down to Beetle and Wedge ferry and second meadow below the ferry down to Runsford Hole; members only.

Wallingford (Oxon). Usual coarse fish. Local club: Jolly Anglers, who have four stretches (good bream in summer, chub in winter); st £7, wt £4.50, dt £1.50 (concessions for juniors), from Castle's, 45 St Mary's Street and Wallingford Sports Shop, High Street. Boats at town landing stage.

Cleeve (Oxon). Usual coarse fish. Landlord of Leathern Bottle issues dt for 1m upstream of Cleeve Lock, including ferry.

Benson (Oxon); ns Wallingford. Usual coarse fish. Club: Benson AA. St £6, wt £3, dt £1 from Peter Aldridge, The Garage, Crown Square.

Shillingford (Oxon). Wallingford AA has water upstream; dt from hon sec. Shillingford Bridge Hotel has good pike fishing on $\frac{1}{4}$m (both banks) free to guests; boats available.

Little Wittesham (Berks). Thame comes in here.

Clifton Hampden (Berks). Clifton AA has water. Tickets for holidaymakers from hon sec, Abingdon & Oxford AA, st £10, dt £1.50. Oxford and Dist AA also has water. Inn: The Barley Mow.

Appleford (Berks). London AA controls from just above the railway bridge down to beginning of Clifton Hampden cutting; both banks, then a short stretch on R bank only; members only.

Culham (Oxon). All water except weir pools controlled by Abingdon & Dist ARA. Other clubs: Culham AC and Sutton Courtenay AC. Sutton Courtenay AC has pits. No day tickets.

Abingdon (Oxon). Bream, chub, pike and barbel good. Tickets from Town Clerk's office for $1\frac{1}{2}$m controlled by Council.

Details from Stratton Lodge, Bath Street, Abingdon. Fishery includes weir, but must be fished from bank. St £5, dt 50p. Abingdon and Dist ARA, now member of Abingdon & Oxford Anglers Alliance, have water here. Annual subscription of £10 covers three clubs. Wt £1.50. Covers well-stocked river and lake fishings. Permits from hon sec, Abingdon and Dist ARA. Tackleists: I. Hayden, East Street, Helen Street. Hotel: The Upper Reaches. The Alliance trout section has lake at **Standlake**, Oxon, st £40, entrance fee £15. Members and their guests only. R H Williams, 2 Holyoake Rd, Oxford, OX3 8AE. Millets Farm Fishery at **Fyfield** has 2 lakes in 7 acres, stocked with b and r trout. St, dt, conc for OAP, dis. Orchard Way, Fyfield, Oxon.

Sandford-on-Thames (Oxon). Pike, bream, roach, perch, etc. Oxford and Dist AA has water here; members only.

Iffley (Oxon); ns Oxford. Thames (or Isis). From here to Folly Bridge is Oxford and Dist AS water; no tickets. Inn: Isis Tavern.

Oxford (Oxon). Thames (Isis), **Cherwell** and **Oxford Canal.** All coarse fish. N Oxford AS has water on Thames, at **Gostow** and **Carrot's Ham,** Cherwell, canal, and carp and tench fishing in **Dukes Lake** and **Pickford Lake.** Their best water is **Seacourt Stream** at Carrot's Ham, with many species. St £10 (concessions for juniors, OAP), dt £1 for Thames. Holiday visitors should apply for permits to hon sec. The N Oxford AS and Oxford & Dist AA now issue joint ticket. Oxford Alliance controls about 70m of river-bank, plus gravel pits. Oxford and Dist AA has fishing in **Clifton Hampden, Iffley, Sandford** and **Godstow** areas; members only. Good Thames backwater sport near Oxford available in season on day basis from David Corke, Frenches Cottage, Long Wittenham. London AA issues dt for 3$\frac{1}{2}$m from **Claydon** to **Fenny Compton.** Boats for Thames from Salter's Folly Bridge. For limited dt for private trout lake, contact J C Bonham, Dorchester Road, Drayton St Leonards. 4$\frac{1}{2}$m W of Oxford, **Farmoor Reservoir** no. 1 leased by Farmoor Flyfishers. Members only. Reservoir no. 2 is trout and coarse fishery. Dt £7.50; part dt £5.75. Boats full day £5; part day £4. Facilities for disabled. Reduced charges for OAPs. Phone Oxford 863033 for advance bookings. Hotels: Cherwell, Oxford; Swan, Islip; Prince of Wales, Cowley Road (Oxford APS HQ).

Eynsham (Oxon). Good coarse fishing; large bream. Good centre for Thames trout. Hotels: Ye Talbot Inn, Railway, Red Lion. Oxford Angling and Pres Soc has water *(see Oxford).* Eynsham Weir fishing available to holders of weir permits; likely place for trout.

Bablockhythe (Oxon). Ferry Inn issues dt £10 for 1$\frac{1}{2}$m on north bank downstream. Water upstream on north bank (and some on south bank) is Appleton and Tubney AS as far as Oxford APS water.

Newbridge (Oxon). Near Witney. Good coarse fishing (bream increasing), few trout in the **Windrush.** Newlands AC has Longworth Fishery on right bank and two gravel pits. St £8 + £4 night fishing supplement; concessions for OAP, juniors. Hotels: Rose Revived ($\frac{3}{4}$m water on Thames and Windrush; good coarse fish, some trout) and May Bush ($\frac{1}{2}$m water on Thames). Other fishing preserved by Abingdon AA and Witney AS (members only). Stroud AA have 1m of Thames (dt Batemans Sports, Stroud. Tel: 4320). Tackleist: D State, t/a Bob Bridgeman, 76 High Street, Witney, who can give further information.

Tadpole Bridge, Buckland (Berks). Coventry & Dist AA has water here. Good chub and barbel; good pike in weir-pool. Trout Inn issues dt for own stretch. Accommodation at Trout Inn (caravans, camp sites). At **Pyreford,** Walton-on-Thames AS has a mile of river and a lake. Dt for members' friends only.

Radcot (Berks). Thames trout; bream, chub, barbel and roach. Radcot AC has 5m. St £7, mt £4, wt £3, dt £1.50. Apply hon sec or Swan Hotel. Clanfield AC also has water here. Clubs catered for. Tents and caravans. (Tel Clanfield 220). Anchor Inn, Eaton, Hastings has 3m of fishing. Dt and st. Clubs welcome; tents and caravans. (Tel Faringdon 99121044).

Lechlade (Glos). For Thames, Coln and Leach. Dt for coarse fishing £1.50 and for weir pool trout fishing (£2.50) from Trout Inn, whose fishery extends upstream from St John's Bridge to Murdoch Ditch. LAA has extensive fishery at **Buscot.** Dt issued. Stroud AA controls 2m Thames; dt £3 from Batemans, Sports, Stroud.

Cricklade (Wilts). Thames known here as

Isis. Isis AC has water on main river, tributaries **Ray** and **Churn** and 12 acre

gravel pit at **South Cerney** (Glos), carp to 30 lb. St £12.50, dt £2.

Tributaries of the Thames

MOLE: Coarse fish, some trout.

Esher (Surrey). Chub, roach, dace, etc. Epsom AS has 1m at Garson Farm (no dt), $\frac{1}{2}$m at Wayne Flete and $\frac{1}{2}$m on Wey at **Weybridge**. St £10, conc £4, from sec or Winslo Tackle, Gilders Rd, Chessington. Other club: Banstead AS ($\frac{3}{4}$m at Hersham; members only). Tackleist: Weybridge Guns & Tackle.

Cobham (Surrey). Walton-on-Thames AS has $1\frac{3}{4}$m of Mole (good chub water); and one lake holding pike and carp, roach, tench and bream. St £25, dt £3, from membership sec. Tickets to members' friends only.

Leatherhead (Surrey). Dace, chub, roach and perch. Hotel: New Bull.

Dorking (Surrey). Coarse fish. Dorking AS has about $4\frac{1}{2}$m; chub, roach, perch, dace; dt (part of water only) or st from S C Fuller (tackleist), South Street. Leisure Sport Angling has two gravel pits stocked with carp; at **Newdigate**. St £12. Full details from LSA, Thorpe Park. Tel: Chertsey 64872. Dt also available for **Old Bury Hill Lake**. Good pike; boats; *(see Surrey Lakes)*. Hotels: White Horse, Bell, Arundel.

Betchworth (Surrey). Coarse fish. Carshalton and Dist AS has water; strictly members only.

WEY: Coarse fish, trout higher up.

Weybridge (Surrey). Wey Amalgamation have water here *(see Thames)*. St £5, dt 50p, juv 50%; from bailiff. Weybridge AC, Addlestone AC and Leisure Sport *(see entry for Chertsey)* have stretches here.

Woking (Surrey). Roach, chub, pike, etc. Woking and Dist AS has rights on 23 miles of river bank and two ponds (perch, carp and tench) at Send; dt for members' guests only. New members welcome; details from hon sec. At **Old Woking** Walton-on-Thames AS has 1m of Hoe Stream plus small lake holding tench and carp. Tackleist: Surrey Anglers Supplies, Station Road, Addlestone.

Wisley (Surrey); ns Ripley. Ponds: Wisley Mere, Hut Pond, and several other ponds on Ripley and Ockham Commons; carp, pike, perch, roach.

Guildford (Surrey). Guildford AS has about $9\frac{1}{2}$m; inquire hon sec of club HQ, Guildford Trades and Labour Club, Mount Street. At Clandon Park are some lakes, also on Broad Street and Whitmoor Common (carp to 19 lb in Britton Pond). At Shamley Green **Willinghurst Trout Fishery**, 7 lakes totalling about 12 acres. St £300, dt £14, $\frac{1}{2}$dt £10.50 + VAT. Apply J M G Syms, Willinghurst, Shamley Green. Tel: 0483 275048. **Albury Estate Fisheries** are at Albury. 9 acres, 4 lakes, b and r trout. St £402, dt £14. Limits 4 or 6 fish. Tel: 048641 2323. Powder Mills Fishery, **Chilworth,** under same management; tel: 0483 570419. Tackleist: S R Jeffrey & Son, 134 High Street *(advt below)*. Hotel: Angel.

Shalford (Surrey). Wey; bream, roach, pike, etc. **Tillingbourne**; trout; strictly preserved. Inns: Parrot, Victoria, Sea Horse, Percy Arms, Chilworth.

Godalming (Surrey). Godalming AS has Wey from Eashing Bridge (Stag Inn) to

GUILDFORD - SURREY

Large stock of Tackle by all the leading makers
also
GUNS - CARTRIDGES
and all
SPORTS EQUIPMENT

JEFFERY'S are specialists in everything for the Angler

JEFFERY'S *of* GUILDFORD

134 High Street, Guildford. Tel: 505055

Broadfield Bridge (about 8m); grayling, coarse fish and trout; society also has Broadwater Lake (11 acres) which holds good carp, tench and perch; (no boats or camping) and limited fishing on Busbridge Lake. St £15 (long waiting list). Dt for accompanied guests £2 from tackleist Allchorne. At Milford, Enton Flyfishers' Club has four trout lakes *(see Surrey Lakes).* Peper Harow Flyfishers have about 2m of Wey and three ponds (brown and rainbow trout); rods limited; st £160, no dt. Tackleists in Farncombe: Patrick's, St John Street; F J Goodman & Sons, Silo Road. Other tackleists: A & G Allchorne, 10 Bridge Street, Godalming; Atkinson, New Road, Milford. Hotels: Broadwater, Farncombe Manor, Lake, King's Arms (Godalming AS HQ).

Frensham (Surrey). Farnham AS has trout water below Frensham Mill. Mill Lane Lake, 8 acres (large tench), **Frensham, Great and Little Ponds,** roach, perch, carp, etc; open membership for coarse fishing. St £23 (joining fee £20), dt £2, (conc), from The Creel, Station Rd, Aldershot.

Haslemere (Surrey). Coarse fish. Surrey Trout Farm is here.

Farnham (Surrey). Farnham AS provides sport for trout and coarse angler. Trout at **Frensham;** stocked, but only open to members' guests. Coarse fishing at Farnham, Frensham, **Elstead, Bagshot Lea Pond, Lodge Pond, Stockbridge Pond** at **Tilford,** and **Loddon** at **Aborfield.** Tickets for some; apply hon sec for details. Note: all waters heavily fished early in season.

Alton (Hants). Trout; preserved. Hotels: Swan, Crown.

COLNE: Coarse fish, some trout.

Iver (Bucks). Long stretch of river and two adjacent lakes held by "Leisure Sport". *(See next entry).*

Wraysbury (Bucks). Blenheim AS has $1\frac{3}{4}$m on **Colne Brook;** coarse fish and occasional trout. Also gravel pits; good carp and crucian carp. Members only. Civil Service AS has Poyle Park Fishery, **Colnbrook** *(see Thames, Wraysbury);* Hounslow Piscatorials have water on **Wraysbury River** (trib of Colne); much improved; roach, dace, chub, Twickenham PS and Staines AC have gravel

What next? Will the dog feel obliged to live up to his 'retriever's' image? It looks rather like it. Setting: the R Dunn, in Berkshire. *Photograph by Eric J Chalker.*

pits; no tickets. Wraysbury 1m "Leisure Sport" fishery. St £14, conc to jun, OAP, dis. Applications to LSA, Thorpe Park, Staines Road, Chertsey, Surrey. Tel: 64872.

West Drayton (G London). Trout, pike, perch, bream, dace, roach, tench, chub. West Drayton Fishery now open following diversion of Colne for new 40-acre reservoir. Entrance in Trout Road. Dt on site (Iver Heath 4607). Grand Union Canal is near.

Uxbridge (G London). Pike, perch, roach, dace and bream. Fishing free on Uxbridge Moor. London AA holds long stretches of **Grand Union Canal,** on which dt are issued (£1). **Osterley Park Lake** holds bream, tench, etc; for details and permits apply the Superintendent of Parks, The Store Yard, Hyde Park, London W2. St £6, reductions for OAP and young people 10–17. **Farlows Pit, Iver,** holds roach, tench, carp, bream, pike; limited number of st.

Denham (Bucks). Colne; coarse fish *(see Harefield).* Blenheim As has 3m of **Grand Union Canal;** roach, dace, bream, tench, perch, gudgeon; dt and st at small charge.

Harefield (G London). Blenheim AS has 2m (canalised); roach, dace, bream, perch; dt from bailiff. **Savay Lake,** Moorhall Road. A 52 acre gravel pit stocked with specimen coarse fish. St £25 from P Broxup, Fishery Manager, 309 Shirland Road, W9; dt £2 from newsagents, Peverills, Harefield, or Balfours, Denham. Concessions for junior and OAP.

Rickmansworth (Herts). Trout, chub, dace, roach, pike, perch. "Leisure Sport" stretch and two gravel pits. Inquiries to LSA, Thorpe Park, Staines Road, Chertsey, Surrey. Tel: 64872. St £19 + £2 key deposit. Blenheim AS has $1\frac{3}{4}$m of **Grand Union Canal;** good roach and bream; fishing now much improved after pollution; dt from bailiff on water. Watford Piscators have $1\frac{1}{2}$m canal (restocked); dt from bailiff: **Batchworth Lake** and **Bury Lake;** dt on site. Other clubs have private waters. **Croxley Hall,** four lakes in 20 acres: trout. St, dt. Tel: 0923 778290. Tackleist: E Sears, 28 High Street. **Gade;** trout; preserved. **Chess;** trout, strictly preserved. North Harrow Waltonians have water in river and lake; members only.

Watford (Herts). Good coarse fishing in

Gade, canal and lakes. Ticket waters: Batchworth and Stocker's lakes; Elstree and Tring reservoirs *(see Aldenham and Tring under Herts and Middlesex reservoirs and lakes)* and Grand Union Canal *(see under Grand Union Canal and Gade).* London AA issues dt for canal from Hunton Bridge to Tring. Free fishing in Gade in Cassiobury Park. Further information from tackleists: Pet's Pantry, High Street and St Alban's Road; and from Watford Piscators. Hotels: Maldon, Clarendon, Rose and Crown.

CHESS: Brown and rainbow trout—one of few British streams where rainbows spawn naturally.

Chorleywood (Bucks). Chess; trout.

Chesham (Bucks). Brown and rainbow trout. Private. Tackleist: Cox the Saddler, 23, High Street. Hotel: George and Dragon.

Latimer (Bucks). Upper river and two lakes (13 acres in all) available for trout fishing; brown and rainbow; average $2\frac{1}{4}$ lbs; daily restocking; boat available. Fly only. Season: April 2 to Sept 30. St £311, $\frac{1}{2}$st £168. Dt £13, evenings £7. Advance booking essential. Details from Latimer Park Lakes Chesham, Bucks, (02404 2396) where full details can be obtained.

GADE: coarse fish.

Boxmoor (Herts). Boxmoor and Dist AS has private water at Westbrook and Berkhamstead AS now controls Pixies meres; members only; no tickets. St £200 for gravel pit trout fishery. Inquiries to R Hands, 23 Sebright Rd, Boxmoor, Hemel Hempstead, tel: 0442 64893 or to Boxmoor Trout Fisheries Ltd, 29 High St, Hemel Hempstead.

Berkhamsted (Herts). Visitors can fish London AA water on Grand Union Canal; coarse fish, dt £1 on water *(see also Grand Union Canal).* No free water. Club: Berkhamsted and Dist AS. Hotels: King's Arms (Trust House), Crown, Swan.

LODDON: Coarse fish.

Twyford (Berks). Twyford Charvil and St Patrick's stream, held by Leisure Sport Angling. St £16, concessions to jun, OAP, dis. Applications to LSA, Thorpe Park, Staines Road, Chertsey, Surrey. Tel: 64872.

Arborfield Cross (Berks). Farnham AS has three stretches here; coarse fish *(see Wey—Farnham).* Dt from bailiff (see notices on water). Cove AS also has water near here at **Shinfield** and on **Hart**

and **Whitewater;** members only *(see also Fleet).* Farnborough AS has water at **Winnersh** *(see Basingstoke Canal).* At **Binfield** is Felix Farm Trout Fishery, 7 Caswall Close. Tel: 0734 345527; st, dt.

KENNET: One of England's finest mixed coarse fisheries; upper reaches noted for trout and grayling.

Theale (Berks). Water west of point 1m upstream of Bridge House (Wide Mead Lock) strictly preserved; few trout and coarse fish. Englefield Lake, 2m. Pike, and fine tench and carp (private). Reading and Dist AA has water on lower Kennet, Holybrooke and backwaters, about 10m in all; association controls from Wide Mead Lock east through Theale to Fobney. No dt. "Leisure Sport" gravel pits at Theale and **Burghfield.** 101 acres. Roach, bream, tench and pike. St £15 Theale, £19 Burghfield. *(See Twyford entry, above, for details.)*

Aldermaston (Berks). Coarse fish and few trout. Old Mill issues permits for about 1m of water; dt £3.50, club bookings £65 inc. Nr Reading London AA has 2m on **Fisherman's Brook;** coarse fish; members only. Off Aldermaston—Kingsclere Road, a chain of eight Leisure Sport gravel pits, fishable by restricted permit. Carp, tench, other coarse fish. St £19. Con, jun, etc. Applications to LSA Thorpe Park, Chertsey. Tel: Chertsey 64872.

Thatcham (Berks). Fishing between Reading and Thatcham controlled chiefly by Reading & Dist AA, an association of affiliated clubs. No dt on Association water, but membership available through affiliated clubs. Details from hon sec *(see club list).* Controls also six lakes and water on Kennet & Avon canal. Thatcham AA also has water. Piscatorial Society has water; strictly members only.

Civil Service AS has Ham Bridge Fishery; $2\frac{1}{2}$m; trout, coarse fish; members only. Hotel: Swan.

Newbury (Berks). On Rivers Kennet and **Lambourn** and **Kennet and Avon Canal;** trout and coarse fishing. Newbury & Dist AA, Thatcham AA, Civil Service AA, Piscatorial Society, CALPAC and Reading and Dist AA all hold water in this area. St for Newbury & Dist AA £15. Dt £1.50 for members' guests only. Tackleists: Field and Stream, 109 Bartholomew Street and Nobby's, Kingsbridge Road.

Hungerford (Berks). Kennet and **Dunn;** trout, grayling; strictly preserved. **Hungerford Canal** fishing in hands of Hungerford Canal AA (3m). Frequently restocked with rainbow trout and coarse fish from local rivers. Excellent fishing. Recent captures: tench $7\frac{1}{2}$ lb, roach 3 lb 2 oz, bream 5 lb 6 oz, trout 6 lb 14 oz; st and dt from hon sec or Lamb Inn. Accommodation at Home Café, Red Lion, Three Swans, Bear, Lamb Hotel (Canal AA HQ).

East Hendred Brook (Berks). Clearwater Fish Farm has 200 yds of double bank stocked with trout. St £125, dt £7; evenings £2.50 per hour; fly only, no lures. Peter Austin, Clearwater Fish Farm, East Hendred, Wantage OX12 8LN.

Lockinge (Oxon). 2m E of Wantage, **Lockinge Stillwater Trout Fishery.** Av 2 lb. St £365. Enq. to Lockinge Trust, Ardington, Wantage. Tel 0235 833200.

Marlborough (Wilts). Trout at Axford. Marlborough and District AA has fishing rights in **Kennet and Avon Canal** from Milkhouse Water to Burbage Wharf and Bruce Tunnel to Little Bedwyn. Excellent roach regularly restocked. Club also fishes Brimslade Farm Water. St £10 wt £7, dt £1, £2 entrance fee. Piscatorial Society has water at Axford; strictly members only. **Wroughton Reservoir,** near **Swindon,** stocked with brown and rainbow trout. Eight dt per day, £6. £1.20 extra for punt. Booking with Thames Water, 17 Bath Rd, Swindon. Tel: 24331. No Saturday fishing. Bristol AA has **Tockenham Reservoir,** near Swindon, members only. Tackleists: H Duck and Leathercraft, both High Street; Tackle Box, Gorse Hill, Victoria Road, Swindon. Hotels: Aylesbury Arms, Savernake, Castle and Ball, Crown (Marlborough AA HQ).

THAME: Coarse fish.

Dorchester (Oxon). Thames and Thame. Coarse fish; good chub and dace, and carp quite numerous. Dorchester AA has water; dt from hon sec or Fleur-de-Lys.

Thame (Oxon). Roach, bream, perch, chub. Leighton Buzzard AC has stretches at **Shabbington, Worminghall, Ickford** and **Waterperry.** Tackleist: Seal Seam (Thame) Ltd, Chestnuts Yard.

Eythrope (Bucks). Roach, bream, perch, chub, good dace. Aylesbury Dist and Izaak Walton AA has water (4m from Aylesbury), members and friends only. Blenheim AS ¾m at **Stone.** Tackleists: S G Waters, Cambridge Street, and H Cobbold, Britannia Street (both Aylesbury).

CHERWELL: Coarse fish.

Islip (Oxon). Cherwell and Ray; good chub, roach, perch and pike fishing may be had in the Cherwell. Preserved by Oxford Angling and Preservation Society, st £8.50, dt £1.50. The Bicester AS has 1½m on Cherwell Northbrook, and ½ acre carp pool, 2m Bicester. Good

accommodation at either of the inns or in the village. Inns: Red Lion, Swan. *(See also Oxford.)*

Heyford (Oxon). Preserved by Banbury and Dist AA; tickets from hon sec.

Banbury (Oxon). Banbury AA (HQ Reindeer Inn, Parsons Street) has fishing at Cropedy, Nell Bridge, Clifton, Somerton, Heyford and Bletchington. Canal also. St, wt and dt for river, canal and **Clattercote Reservoir.** Tickets from The Suitcase, 3a Church Lane. Coventry AA hold stretch in Aynho area; members only.

EVENLODE: Trout, coarse fish (roach and dace especially).

Hanborough (Oxon). Red Spinner AS rents 10 to 12m of the Evenlode; trout (restocked annually), dace, roach, chub, pike; strictly members only. Glyme Valley Fly Fishers have 1½m of the **Glyme** nr Wooton restocked yearly with trout. St £185; ½ rod £95. Members only. Good fishing on **Blenheim Park Lakes,** property of Duke of Marlborough. Excellent tench, perch and roach, with pike in winter. Boat fishing only. *(See Midlands lakes, reservoirs, etc.)* Nr Chipping Norton, **Salford Trout Lakes;** 5 and 3 acres stocked with r and b trout. St £147 (55 fish per season), dt £12 (4 fish limit), ½dt £7. N Colston, Larches Farm, Chipping Norton. Tel: 0608 3209/2524.

WINDRUSH: Trout, grayling, coarse fish (dace up to 1 lb and 2 lb roach not rare).

Witney (Oxon). Large trout; preserved below; leave must be obtained from the proprietors; good hatch of mayfly. Witney AS (HQ Eagle Vaults) has water *(see Minster Lovell and Newbridge).* No dt and membership £10 pa restricted to county as a rule, but outside applications considered; apply hon sec. Club now has

THE SWAN HOTEL, BIBURY

GLOUCESTERSHIRE
Tel: Bibury (028 574) 204
A.A.★★★   R.A.C.★★★

Famous Old Coaching Inn, carefully modernised.

All rooms with private bathroom and colour TV.

300 yards of the River Coln facing the Hotel. Dry Fly Trout fishing only.

BIBURY TROUT FARM

Bibury, Cirencester, Gloucestershire

Rainbow Trout bred on the River Coln. High quality fish available for restocking. Farm open to Visitors 9am - 6pm or dusk daily. Fishery open April to September.

Telephone: Bibury (028574) 215

water on gravel pits at Stanton Harcourt (carp, tench, etc). Tackleist: R Bridgeman, 76 High Street.

Minster Lovell (Oxon); ns Witney. Cotswold Flyfishers have 10m at **Swinbrook** and **Stanton Harcourt;** trout (restocked yearly), fly only; membership limited; no dt. Witney AS has water on Windrush at **Worsham** (1m above village; trout retocked yearly) and on Thames at **Newbridge** and **Standlake;** trout, grayling, coarse fish; fishing much improved *(see Witney).* **Linch Hill Fishery,** Stanton Harcourt; Willow Pool stocked with large carp; Stoneacres Lake mixed trout and coarse fishing. 10 acre Christchurch lake, carp. St £20, dt £2, concessions; tel: Oxford 882215. Hotel: Old Swan Inn (no fishing).

Burford (Oxon). Burford AC (st £5) holds

water in vicinity; trout restocked yearly and coarse fish. 14 day permits on sale at Royal Oak, Witney Street. TWA licence now required. Hotels: Cotswold Gateway, Lamb, Bay Tree, Bull, Winters Tale.

COLN: notable dry fly fishing for trout of good average size; grayling.

Fairford (Glos). Trout; excellent; April 1 to Sept 30. Dry fly only upstream. Well stocked. Tickets can be had for $1\frac{1}{2}$m from Bull Hotel, Market Place. Size limit 12 in; bag $1\frac{1}{2}$ brace per rod; trout of $1-1\frac{1}{2}$ lb plentiful. St £350 dt £12 (reduction for residents). Other hotel: Hyperion House, London Street. Nearest tackleist at Lechdale, 4m.

Bibury (Glos). Coln: trout. Swan Hotel *(advt p 142)* has 300yds facing hotel free to residents: dry fly only.

TORRIDGE

(For close seasons, licences, etc, see South West Water Authority, p 12)

Rises near Cornish border of Devonshire and joins the Taw estuary at Appledore, to flow into Bideford (also termed Barnstaple) Bay. Salmon, sea trout (peal) and brown trout (small).

Bideford (Devon). Two reservoirs, at **Gammaton** 2m on east side of river, stocked with brown and rainbow trout; leased by Torridge Fly Fishing Club; st £60 from hon sec, written application only, dt £4.50 from hon sec or Gales, Tackleist, Mill Street. Concessions to juniors. **Weare Gifford,** salmon, sea trout, brown trout; dt from A Hooper, Post Office. At **Jennetts Reservoir,** new SWWA coarse fishery. Carp and tench. Dt £2, from Tackle Box, Kings Shopping Centre, Cooper St, Bideford. Hotels:

Royal, New Inn, Tanton's, Ring o'Bells, Market.

Torrington (Devon). Salmon, sea trout, brown trout, 9 beats available over 7m from Manor Mill Hotel, Town Mills, tel: 08052 2114. Dt £8. W of England Centre of Game Angling, Orford Lodge, has beats of 2m on Torridge, **Taw** and smaller waters, offering a wide variety of excellent fishing. Tuition is the principle object of the operation, but fishings, when possible, are made available on wt and dt basis. Phone John Gawesworth,

0805 23256 for bookings. Lower Torridge Fishery has 7 beats on 5m of water from Torrington to Blinsham, 5 beats fly only. From May 1, apply C R Rowe, Oak Tree Cottage, Stafford Way, Dolton, Winkleigh, Devon. Tel: Dolton 389. Best months for salmon, March, April, May; for sea trout, July, Aug, Sept. Fishing lodge and occasional day rods on **Beaford** stretch; contact Group Capt P Norton-Smith, Little Wareham, Beaford, Winkleigh; tel: 08053 317. Coarse fishing at **Darracott Reservoir**, open all the year. Dt from The Fisherman's Retreat Sports, 7 South Street, Torrington.

Woodford Bridge (Devon). Brown trout (av 8-9 in). Woodford Bridge Hotel, Milton Damerel has 7m of brown trout fishing and 2m of salmon and sea trout water free to residents at hotel. Dt for non-residents as available: S & MT, £12, brown trout £8. Tel 040 926481.

Shebbear (Devon). Devil's Stone Inn has $2\frac{1}{2}$m of salmon, sea trout and brown trout fishing on Torridge; fly and spinning; excellent dry-fly trout water. Nearest beat 2m. RD licences and tackle, and angling instruction available. Dt sometimes issued to non-residents.

Sheepwash (Devon). Half Moon Inn has 8m of salmon, sea trout and brown trout fishing on Torridge. Banks cleared to facilitate fly fishing on all beats. Spinning allowed to April 30. Five upper beats stocked regularly with 1 lb brown trout; fly only. Season opens March 1. Dt £6. Brochure on request from Charles Inniss. *(Advt below.)*

Hatherleigh (Devon). Torridge, Lew, Okement; salmon, sea trout, brown trout. Tackleists: Pengelly D.I.Y., The Square, Holsworthy. Hotel: New Inn, Meeth ($\frac{1}{2}$m on Torridge; dts for salmon and trout).

POLLUTION

Anglers are united in deploring pollution. To combat it, urgent action may be called for at any time from any one of us. If numbers of fish are found dead, dying, or seriously distressed, take samples of both fish and water and contact the office of the Director of Scientific Services at the appropriate Regional Water Authority.

Tributaries of the Torridge

LEW: Sea trout, trout.
Hatherleigh (Devon). W of England Centre of Game Angling *(see Torrington)* have 2m here.

OKEMENT:
Okehampton (Devon). Torridge and Dartmoor streams accessible. Trout fishing, wt £1, from Hill Barton Farm, tel: 0837 454.

8 miles of excellent Salmon, Sea and Brown Trout fishing on R. Torridge. Banks well cleared and fishing easy to approach. Regular stocking of Upper Beats with 1 lb. Brown Trout. First class food and every comfort.
Ashley Courtenay recommended.
BLACK TORRINGTON (040 923) 376

TRENT

(For close seasons, licences, etc, see Severn-Trent Water Authority, p 15–16)

Largest river system in England. Rising in Staffordshire, Trent drains much of Derbyshire, Nottinghamshire and Lincolnshire, and empties into Humber. A hundred years ago, one of England's principal fisheries; now recovering its status following massive effort at water-quality improvement by RWA. The tide-water, in particular, now fishing excellently. Some famous trout-holding tributaries, notably Dove, Wye and Derwent.

Gainsborough (Lincoln). Pike, perch, roach, chub. There are a few fish to 3m below Gainsborough. Tidal. Lincoln & Dist AA has stretches to accommodate 60 and 70 match pegs respectively at N Clifton and Laughterton Marsh. St, dt. Goole AA has fishing at **Church Laneham**. No dt.

Torksey (Lincoln). Pike, roach, chub. Fossdyke Navigation; good coarse fishing; managed by BWF, through whom matches should be booked; runs from Torksey through Saxilby to Lincoln *(see also Lincoln—Witham).*

Dunham (Notts). Sheffield and Dist AA have two lakes and left bank of Trent. Dt £1.50 from Bridge Garage, Dunham. This fishing is leased from STWA.

High Marnham (Notts). Nottingham Fedn has stretch above power station; dt and matches; tidal.

Sutton-on-Trent (Notts). Tidal water. Pike, roach, dace, chub. Sheffield and Doncaster associations have joint rights on $3\frac{1}{2}$m of Ossington Estate. Sheffield Amalgamated AS has sole right of Newcastle Fishery, about 6m. Heavily match-fished.

Collingham (Notts). Club water. Trent 2m W; pike, carp, barbel, roach, dace, chub, perch, bream; dt from King's Head, Royal Oak. Collingham AA has 4m from Cromwell Weir to Besthorpe gravel pit; dt £1.50 from bailiff on bank. The Fleet of Besthorpe can be reached by bus from here; all round coarse fishing; a noted resort for eels. Between Holme and **Winthorpe** are several waters of Worksop AAA. At Besthorpe Wharf is Newcastle Fishery; dt 50p. Sheffield AAA. Hotels: Royal Oak, King's Head, Grey Horse.

Muskham (Notts). Nottingham PS preserves from Fir Tree Corner (Kelham boundary) to Crankley Point, both sides, including gravel pits; members only.

Averham, Kelham (Notts); ns Newark, 2m. Very good coarse fishing; preserved by Nottingham PS for members only— roach, dace, chub (excellent fly water) —from railway bridge at Averham to South Muskham boundary on both sides of the river.

Newark-on-Trent (Notts). Roach, dace, pike, chub, bream. Newark and Dist Piscatorial Federation has water on Trent Dyke and Trent at **Winthorpe**. Dt £1.50 from bailiffs. Sheffield and Dist AA have lake at Winthrope, dt £1.50 from Mrs Potter, The Level Crossing, Winthrope. Trent preserved below by Nottingham PS; no tickets. **Newark Dyke**; Nottingham Piscatorial Society has a good deal of water on north bank; no tickets. **Cromwell Lake**, just off Newark By-Pass; 29 acres, trout, tench, bream, roach, carp, pike. **Farndon Gravel Pit:** Newark and Dist PF; dt from bailiff. Tackleists: C Smith & Sons Ltd, Clinton Arms Yard, Newark-on-Trent and G M Purvis, 41 Castle Gate, who will be pleased to give local information. Hotels: Britannia Inn, Farndon Ferry.

Farndon (Notts): ns Rolleston or Newark. Trent RD's Newcastle fishery. Nottingham Piscatorial Society has north bank (tickets as Rolleston), south bank let to Nottingham AA; dt issued.

Rolleston (Notts). Nottingham Piscatorial Society water from Greet mouth to Staythorpe power station; good roach and chub; dt from some tackleists and Rolleston Post Office. No permits on bank. Greet, trout; strictly preserved. Nottingham AA has water at Farndon Ferry (opp Rolleston); dt from bailiff; matches can be arranged in advance.

Fiskerton (Notts). Good roach and chub fishing. Bromley Arms has water here and beyond Hazleford; dt. The Greet enters Trent at Fiskerton; trout; strictly preserved.

Hazleford (Notts); ns Bleasby. Hazleford Ferry water, Fiskerton, now rented by Star and Garter Hotel; dt for about 1m water from Hotel, fishing free from hotel grounds for guests.

Hoveringham (Notts). Coarse fish. Nottingham PS has stretch to Willow Holt; members only. Dt for Nottingham AA stretch, £1.20.

Gunthorpe (Notts); ns Lowdham. Good coarse fishing; roach, dace, chub.

Burton Joyce (Notts). Chub, roach (mainly), dace. Nottingham and Dist Fedn has good stretch for which dt issued (matches arranged, booked in advance after Nov 1 for following season); tickets from bailiff, hon sec, Stoke Ferry Boat Inn, Lord Nelson. Nottingham AA has from Colwick Viaduct downstream for one field.

Shelford (Notts). Shelford Fishery (dt from bailiff) on south bank (Lord Carnarvon's waters) is in hands of Nottingham AA. Matches arranged in advance.

Radcliffe-on-Trent (Notts). Roach, chub, dace and gudgeon, with perch, pike and tench in Lily Ponds. From Stoke Weir down to Gunthorpe, Nottingham AA; dt. From Stoke Weir up to Radcliffe Ferry, including Lily Ponds, Nottingham Fedn; dt. Fedn also holds from Radcliffe Ferry upstream (members only) and water below Radcliffe railway bridge *(see Burton Joyce)*. Accommodation at Chestnuts Club.

Nottingham (Notts). Good mixed fishing. Several miles in city free. Nottingham AA has water at **Shelford, Chilwell** and at Britannia Inn, **Farndon.** St £12, dt £1.20 from hon sec and tackle dealers. Nottingham Piscatorial Society has fishing at **Rolleston, Fiskerton** and **Farndon;** dt from tackleists only. Long Eaton Victoria AS; **Thrumpton Fishery** and from **Erewash mouth** to **Attenborough;** dt from hon sec, Regal Club. Nottingham and District Federation of Angling Societies comprises upwards of 68 clubs; water at **Burton Joyce** and **Stoke Bardolph.** West Bridgford British Legion AC has some water on Trent; st

and dt from hon sec. Lake in **Wollaton Park** may be fished by dt from Parks Superintendent, Wollaton Park; bream, tench, roach, pike, perch at **Colwick Park,** a coarse fishery operated by STWA and Nottingham City Council. St £18.50, dt 80p, concession for OAP, juniors. Tickets from the Lodge. Tackleists: Tom C Saville Ltd (mail order specialists) Unit 7, Salisbury Square, off Ilkeston Road *(advt below).* Walkers of Trowell, 9–15 Nottingham Road, Trowell; Redmayne & Todd, Carrington Street; T Watson, 1 Oak Street, Carrington; A Tizley, 55 Kirkewhite Street East; C Smith & Sons Ltd (Newark); Anglers' Shop, 198 Ilkeston Road.

Wilford (Notts). **Clifton Fishery** from Beeston Weir to Man of Trent; Nottingham AA; dt issued. From railway bridge down is Nottingham AA water; members only.

Beeston (Notts). Chub, roach, dace, bleak, gudgeon; preserved by Nottingham AA. Dt for stretch to Beeston Weir from hon sec. Assn also has water on **Beeston Canal.**

Thrumpton and Long Eaton (Notts). Roach, bream, dace, chub. Long Eaton Victoria AS has Thrumpton Ferry field. St £7. No matches. Coventry & Dist AA also has water here now, dt from local tackleists. Canals: Long Eaton Victoria AS has lengths in **Erewash Canal** and **Cranfleet Canal;** coarse fish, also Grange Pond (in Long Eaton) 2½ acres coarse fish. Long Eaton and Dist AF has water on Trent at Trent Lock, on **Soar** at **Kegworth** and on Erewash Canal. Tackleists: Horseshoe Sports Depot, Station Road; and Bridge Tackle Shop, Derby Rd; Long Eaton.

SERVICE ● QUALITY ● VALUE EXPERTISE ● RELIABILITY
THAT'S WHAT YOU WANT – THAT'S WHAT **WE** GIVE
Plus! LOWEST DISCOUNT PRICES!!!
SEND £1 TODAY FOR OUR 128-PAGE **GAME-FISHING CATALOGUE**
— WE STOCK **EVERTHING** for the **GAME ANGLER** —
TOM C. SAVILLE LTD.
UNIT 7, SALISBURY SQUARE, MIDDLETON STREET,
off ILKESTON ROAD, NOTTINGHAM NG7 2AB
Open Monday to Friday only (closed Sat.)   24-hr. Answering Service. Tel: 0602-784248

Chellaston (Derby). Trent, 1m SW, at Swarkestone. Derby AA has water below, and upstream, through **Ingleby** and **Twyford,** to above **Willington.** Stretches are held on both banks, with few breaks. Most species of coarse fish present. Club also has 14m on **Trent and Mersey Canal,** and lakes. St £20 d £1.50; concessions for OAP, juniors. From hon sec, Rising Sun, Willington and Derby tackle dealers.

Burton-on-Trent (Staffs). Good free fishing for roach and chub at Newton and Willington. Burton Mutual AA fishes **Dove** at **Tutbury** to confluence with Trent, and Branstone gravel pit; members only. Birmingham AA has six coarse fishing pools at Bretby. Good pools at Barton and Walton. Dt £1.25 for STWA **Claymills** river fishery, from The Poplars, Burton-on-Trent. Tickets for canals, various stretches on the R Trent and a variety of other waters from tackleists Mullarkey, 184 Waterloo Street. Hotels: Queen's, Station and Midland.

Alrewas (Staffs). Perch, dace, roach. Birmingham AA has water here and at **Yoxall.** Trent and Mersey Canal, dt from keeper. Tame, 2m SE; chub, dace. Mease, 3m SE.

Rugeley (Staffs). Usual species. Rugeley and Brereton AS has about 1m on Trent and water on **Trent and Mersey Canal** from Armitage to Wolseley Bridge. From here to Colwich held by British Waterways (dt from them); roach, pike, perch. Tickets available from Manton, Bow Street (tackleists). **Blithfield Reservoir,** 4m NE; trout; South Staffs. Water Co allows fishing on season permit only. Inquiries to: Recreations Office, Blithfield Reservoir, Abbots Bromley, Staffs.

Colwich (Staffs). Not the best part of the river, but some coarse fish. Sow, 4m W; controlled by Stafford Anglers. Blyth 5m E; preserved. Sherbrook and Oakedge Pools preserved by Lord Lichfield. Rugeley and Brereton AS has water on canal; roach, pike, chub, perch; dt and st at small fee *(see also Rugeley).* Hotel: Lamb and Flag.

Great Haywood (Staffs); ns Colwich, 1m. Usual species. **Trent and Mersey Canal;** roach, pike, chub, perch; length held by Shugborough Park FC (no tickets). Hotel: Clifford Arms.

Stoke-on-Trent (Staffs). Stoke City & Dist AA has fishing on **R Sow, R Roden, Trent & Mersey Canal,** from Aston Lock to Burston and in city between Wieldon and Etruria Road Bridges; **Shropshire Union Canal** (200-peg match-venue, enq invited) and **Knighton Reservoir.** Coarse fish. St £9 (reductions for ladies, juvs, OAP) from mem sec D Deaville, 1 Churston Place, Sneyd Green. Tel: 267081. Tackleists: Abbey Pet Stores, 1493 Leek Road, Abbey Hulton; H and J H Durber, 8 William Clowes Street, Burslem; J Birks, 293 Uttoxeter Road, Longton; Coopers, 30 Pall Mall, Hanley; Tackle Box, Hartshill Road, Stoke-on-Trent; P W Lovatt Sports Shop, 7 Brunswick Street, Newcastle; and others.

Trentham (Staffs). Lake in Trentham Gardens; area about 70 acres. Village about 3m from Stoke-on-Trent on main road London to Manchester. Fishing tickets at Lodge Gate. Trentham Hotel 1m. Catering available in Trentham Gardens, caravan site.

Weston-on-Trent (Staffs). Coarse fishing in **Trent and Mersey Canal;** chub, roach, bream, perch.

Tributaries of the Trent

IDLE: Excellent coarse fishing in parts.

Misterton (Lincs). Trent and Idle. Coarse fish: Sheffield and Dist AA has 4m of water on Idle for members only.

Misson (Notts). Doncaster and Dist AA has from Newington to Idlestop, about 10m. Good roach, bream, perch, pike; st and dt from tackle dealers. Assn also has Black Drain and Bandspinner Drain. Sheffield and Dist AA also has stretch of Idle; members only. *(See also Misterton.)*

Retford (Notts). Poulter, 4m S. Meden, 4m S. Maun, 4m S. Idle above Retford private. Retford AA controls a stretch of the **Chesterfield Canal** from Ranby to West Retford bridge, $5\frac{1}{2}$m, famous for chub, match weights up to 50 lb. Limited membership. From Woodcocks Bridge to Church Lane bridge, Clayworth and left bank at Mattersley belong to Worksop and Dist Anglers' Association. Tackle Shop at Carolgate.

TORNE and NEW IDLE. Doncaster and Dist AA has 18m from Rossington to Pilfrey Bridges, also **Ring Drain** alongside and water on **Stainforth and Keadby**

Canal; dt from E Drury, Candy Corner Pumping Station, Finningly, nr Doncaster.

Althorpe (S Humberside). **Sheffield and South Yorkshire Canal;** coarse fish; about 14m of water above and down to Trent; good fishing; rights held by Sheffield, Rotherham and Doncaster associations. Other fishing stations for canal are **Thorne** and **Crowle.**

Crowle (S Humberside). Excellent centre for coarse fishing. **Stainforth and Keadby Canal, Torne** and **Ring Drain,** are $\frac{1}{2}$m from Crowle Central Station; Doncaster AA; roach, tench, bream, perch, carp, pike. Three Drains on A18; Sheffield and Dist AA; roach, perch, tench, carp. Licences, association books and dt from hotels or hon sec (enclose s/a envelope). Hotels: South Yorkshire, Crowle; Friendship Inn, Keadby. Tackle shops in Doncaster (17m) or Scunthorpe (10m).

RYTON (tributary of Idle); Coarse fish.

Scrooby (Notts). Ryton. From Bramshall's farm to junction with Idle, 2m; dt from Pilgrim Fathers and the garage, Scrooby.

Worksop (Notts). On Ryton and **Chesterfield Canal;** coarse fish. Worksop and Dist AA has 11m of canal from W Retford Bridge to Drakeholes Basin. St only from G March, 262 Kilton Road. Lakes: Dukeries Lakes *(see Nottinghamshire lakes and canals)* especially **Clumber Park Lake** (National Trust), where dt and st can be had; and **Sandhill Lake;** trout, coarse fish; *(see also Midlands reservoirs, lakes).*

MAUN (tributary of Idle): Polluted.

Tuxford (Notts). Maun, 3m NW polluted. Bevercotes Beck, 3m NW. Idle, 4m NW. Poulter, 4m NW. Meden, 4m NW. Lakes: Haughton Decoy and lower ponds, 3m NW.

Mansfield (Notts). Sand Hills Quarry, Worksop; trout, coarse fish; dt. Other dt waters (coarse fishing): Vicars Pond, Clipstone; Wellow Pond near Ollerton. Mansfield AA has water on **Witham, Trent** and gravel pits and lake; members only. Tackleists: R and M C Dibble, 40 Belvedere Street.

Sutton-in-Ashfield (Notts). Lakes: Lawn Dam. King's Mill Reservoir, 1m NE; tickets on bank. Hardwick Lakes, Hardwick Hall, are 6m W. Hotels: Nag's Head, Denman's Head. Tackleist: H Burrows, 91 Outram Street NG17 4AQ.

DEVON: Coarse fish.

Bottesford (Notts). Smite, 3m NW at Or-

ston. Car Dyke, 5m NW. Bottesford AA preserves 5m of **Grantham Canal** at Bottesford, Muston and Woolsthorpe-by-Belvoir; st and dt from Bull Inn and Rutland Arms, Woolsthorpe-by-Belvoir (on canal bank); and from hon sec and from bailiffs on bank. Good coarse fishing, with pike over 20 lbs.

Belvoir Castle (Leics). Between Melton Mowbray and Grantham. Belvoir Lakes, 3m SE, and Knipton Reservoir, 4m SE (coarse fish); st £40, $\frac{1}{2}$st £25, dt £3 from Estate Office, or keeper, Belvoir Castle, Grantham, also a chain of carp lakes, st only. Also **Nottingham and Grantham Canal** on which Bottesford and District AA has water. Other stations on canal are **Long Clawson, Harby, Hose** and **Stathern.**

GREET: Trout; coarse fish; preserved.

Southwell (Notts). River private. Trent, 3m SE at Fiskerton. At Oxton, 5m SW, Nottingham Fly Fishers' Club has a trout lake at Gibsmere; strictly members only, long waiting list. Greet FC, too, has trout fishing. Cromwell Fly Fishers, 20 Norwood Gardens, Southwell, has a lake north of Cromwell.

NUT BROOK no longer a fishery.

West Hallam (Derby). Lakes: **Mapperley Reservoir,** 2m N, **Shipley Park Lakes, Lescoe Dam** and stretch of Erewash Canal all NCB waters. St £7. juv, dis, £3 from D Allsop, 27 Hardy Barn, Shipley, Derbys. Dt £1 from park rangers.

SOAR: Very popular coarse fishery with anglers in the Leicester area.

Ratcliffe (Notts); ns Kegworth. Good coarse fishing. Long Eaton & Dist AF administrate Lockington Estate and Ferry fisheries. Members only *(see immediately below for other details).*

Kegworth (Derby). Roach, dace, bream, tench, chub, perch. From Kegworth Bridge up to Kegworth Lock held by Long Eaton Victoria AS. Dt and st. Nottingham AA has from noticeboard below Kegworth Bridge to Kingston Dyke (members only). Long Eaton AF has good stretch down to Ratcliffe; st and dt from Anchor Inn. Soar AS has water here *(see Loughborough).*

Normanton-on-Soar (Leics). Good coarse fishing. Recently restocked by Loughborough Soar AS *(see Loughborough).*

Loughborough (Leics). Coarse fish; sport much improved through efforts of STWA; preserved by Loughborough Soar AS from above Kegworth to

Barrow-on-Soar Weir and Shallow Lock (also canal same length); st £9, dt £1 (concessions to OAP and juniors); Sunday fishing permitted. Tackleist: Wortley & Sons, 45 Baxtergate (licences and permits). Tickets also from Mrs E Gee, 9 Pasture Lane, Sutton, Bonnington; Rose & Crown, Zouch, hon sec and tackleists. **Proctor's Lake and River Fishing,** The Park, Barrow-on-Soar (5m SE). Dt issued *(see Barrow).* Hotels: King's Head and Central.

Quorn (Leics). Roach, bream. Quorn AS has rights on stretches of river and 1m of canal; they now have joint ticket with Leicester & Dist AS, st £6, juv £2.50; inquire hon sec. River fishes best in autumn and winter.

Barrow-upon-Soar (Leics). About 3m river and canal fishing; good roach and bream; recently restocked. Fishes best autumn and winter. Leicester and Dist ASA Water Navigation AC, previous tenant, now disbanded. Quorn AC has water in area. **Proctor's Lake and River Fishing,** The Park (Quorn 2323). Caravanning and camping and fishing facilities. Dt from machine at entrance.

Tackleist: Webster and Barnes, 68 High Street.

Leicester (Leics). Coarse fish; recently restocked by Trent RD. Much water in Leicester district held by Leicester and Dist Amal Soc of Anglers; includes fishing on Soar canalised, **Wreake, Eye Brook, Nene,** and canals. All on dt or st from local tackleists or bailiffs. Leicester AC (Soar and canal; dt and st). Leicester AC (water on **Grand Union Canal**) and Wigston AS (canal; tickets from C Burnham, Blaby Road, S Wigston). Kibworth and Dist AS fishes **Leicester Canal;** some good coarse fish but boat traffic ruins summer sport. Thornton (7m W), Cropston (5m NW), Saddington (10m SE) and Swithland (6m). Reservoirs all preserved. Quenby Hall Lake, 7m E; preserved. Exceptionally high quality coarse fishing in five lakes totalling 20 acres in **Mallory Park.** St £100 (covering all five lakes) from Marks and Marlow, address below. The Pool, Groby, 5m NW; bream, tench, roach, pike; dt from house at pool. Quorndon Brook, 6m NW, at Bradgate Park; trout; preserved. Hotels: Grand, Royal, Hermitage

One does not need access to exclusive waters to catch splendid fish. This nice net of early morning tench was taken from a day ticket gravel pit near Birstall, Leicestershire. *Photo: Bruno Broughton.*

(Oadby). Tackleists: John Adams, Humberstone Gate; N Woodward, Braunstone Gate; Marks & Marlow, 39 Tudor Road; "The Aquaria", Melton Road; J C Townsend, Humberstone Road.

Narborough (Leics). Hinckley and Dist AA has water here containing trout and grayling; permits from permits sec.

WREAKE (tributary of Soar): An attractive coarse fishery on which Leicester and Dist ASA has extensive coarse fishing rights.

Syston (Leics). Roach, bream, pike, perch, chub, dace; greatest part preserved by Leicester and Dist ASA, between Syston and Melton Mowbray; dt. *(See Leicester above.)*

Ashfordby (Leics). Roach, perch, dace, pike, chub. Mostly Leicester ASA water; dt £1 from E Edwards, G Rainbow, bailiffs. Ashfordby SOA has water on Wreake and pits at **Frisby** (1m). Members only; no dt. Dt for **Holwell Works Reservoir** from E Madden, "The Limes", Ashford-by-Valley.

Melton Mowbray (Leics). **Knipton Reservoir,** 8m N, at Branston. Melton Mowbray Society of Anglers (dt from club HQ at Rutland Arms, King St; affiliated to Leicester and Dist ASA) has water; also preserve tributary Eye. Tackleist: John F Green, 27 Nottingham Street.

DERWENT: Noted trout and grayling water in upper reaches; downstream coarse fish come into their own.

Sawley (Derby). Coarse fish. Pride of Derby AC has from Wilne Weir to mouth of Derwent (south bank), 750 yd stretch on north bank, and both banks of Trent above confluence to Red House on one bank and Sutton's Eaves on other. Also canal from Derwent Lock to Trent and **Trent** to Sawley Lock. Further water on Trent below Sawley Weir towards lock house and including the island and several ponds. Members only (st £16 are issued to anglers living in 16m radius of Derby only; long waiting list, applications to hon sec). Tackleists issue dt for other clubs' waters. Inn: Harrington Arms, Old Sawley, Long Eaton (permits for local waters).

Borrowash (Derby). Coarse fish. Earl of Harrington AC waters *(see Derby).*

Spondon (Derby). Coarse fish; preserved by Earl of Harrington AC *(see Derby).* Chaddesden Brook, 1m NW, and Locko Park, 2m N. Private.

Derby (Derby). Coarse fish, Earl of Harrington AC has Derwent from Borrowash Bridge through to Midland Station. St and dt from hon sec. Derby Corporation issues st and dt for Derwent from Darley Abbey to Derby railway station. Corporation also issues tickets for **Alvaston Lake, Markeaton Park Lake, Allestree Park Lake** and Derwent in Darley Abbey Park (dts from keeper). Locko Park Lake and Chaddesden Brook private. "Leisure Sport" gravel pits in **Attenborough Nature Reserve.** Bream, tench, roach. St £14 from LSA, Thorpe Park, Chertsey, Surrey. Tel: 64872. Other clubs: Pride of Derby AA *(see Sawley)*; Derby RIFC (water on Derwent, **Trent, Dove, Ecclesbourne;** canals). Derby AA (Derwent, 1m of **Big Shrine** at **Borrowash,** canal, dt). Derby Federation has water at **Duffield,** from Milford Bridge to Little Eaton. Trout and coarse fish. Tackleists: Anglers Corner, 355 Osmaston Road; Artisan Angling, 141 London Road; Blount, 80 Shaftesbury Cres.

Duffield (Derby). Coarse fish, trout and grayling. Derbyshire AF water. Dt for trout and grayling from Bridge Inn, Duffield.

Belper (Derby). Grayling, pike, trout, coarse fish; 8m held by Belper AC. Dt £1.50 from Hendersons Quality Tackle, Bridge Street. Earl of Harrington AC has $^3/_4$m of trout fishing on **Ecclesbourne** at Turnditch (3m W); fly only; members only *(see Derby).* Black brook, Holbrook Road, 2m SE.

Ambergate (Derby). Few trout, pike, coarse fish. Belper AC has water downstream streams; Alderwasley Ponds, 2m NW. **Butterley Reservoir** and **Codnor Park Reservoir;** roach, bream, tench, carp, pike; Ripley and Dist AA; st £6, dt 80p from hon sec, keepers and tackle shops. Loscoe Dam; dt from keeper. Hotel: Hurt Arms.

Whatstandwell (Derby). Mostly grayling and trout, with former predominant. Dt £1 from Derwent Hotel, which has $^1/_4$m fishing; rather overhung with trees, but plenty of fish and good wading in low water. Dt £1. Homesford Cottage Inn stretch now let to Cromford Fly Fishers; no tickets.

Cromford (Derby). Trout; fly only; preserved below road bridge (both banks), as far as and including Homesford Meadows, by Cromford Fly Fishers;

Trotting the redworm for grayling in Derbyshire. Some say they feed more freely when snow is on the ground. *Photo: Bruno Broughton.*

members only, no tickets. St £100 + £100 entrance fee; 3 year waiting list. Above bridge, Derbyshire CC AC water. No tickets. Cromford Canal too overgrown for fishing. Hotel: Greyhound.

Matlock (Derby). Trout (some rainbows), grayling and coarse fish. Matlock AC issue wt and dt; dt from Midland Hotel (Matlock Bath); water at Matlock and Matlock Bath; trout and coarse; about 1m.

Rowsley (Derby). Trout, brown and rainbow; grayling. Darley Dale Fly-fishing Club has rights on Derwent from $\frac{1}{2}$m north of Rowsley bridge to $\frac{1}{2}$m north of Darley Bridge; fly-fishing only; no dt; stocked with brown trout. Two dt available to guests at Peacock Hotel, **Rowsley.** £15. Two dt on similar terms for guests at Grouse and Claret Hotel for $\frac{1}{2}$m north of Rowsley Bridge. Peacock Hotel, Rowsley also have rights on Duke of Rutland's fishery on **Wye** for guests; rainbow trout; dry fly only. Water not stocked but fish plentiful; limit three brace. Dt £15. Sunday fishing. Haddon Estate has several waters: **River Bradford** from Lathkill junction to Bradford Village (small stream fishing); **Bradford**

Dams (limit 4 over 10"); **Wye** from Rowsley through Bakewell (double bank) and Upstream (single bank). All dry fly, brown trout only; dt £10 from Estate Office, Haddon Hall, Bakewell.

Baslow (Derbys); nr Bakewell, 4m. The Cavendish Hotel, originally the famous Peacock, has 6 rods on the Chatsworth and Monsal Dale fisheries. $6\frac{1}{2}$m of the Derwent, by courtesy of Chatsworth Estate. Brown trout and grayling; $4\frac{1}{2}$m of the **Wye,** brown and rainbow trout. Dt are £18. Priority booking for residents. For full details, phone Baslow 2311.

Hathersage (Derby). Trout, grayling; preserved by the Derwent FFC; also at Bamford and Grindleford (members only).

Bamford (Derby). Trout, grayling. Derwent FFC has water below Bamford Mill; also from Bamford Mill to Yorkshire Bridge; members only. Peak Forest AC has 9m of **River Noe** upstream from Mytham Bridge; fly fishing. Members only; subscriptions £225 + £50 entrance fee. Tel: 0246 434592.

Ladybower. Centre for **Ladybower and Derwent Reservoirs;** trout; fly only *(see*

Midlands reservoirs and lakes). Hotels: Ladybower Inn, Yorkshire Bridge Inn, Ye Derwent Hotel, Bamford (1m), Anglers' Rest (1m), Marquis of Granby, Bamford (2m), Rising Sun, Bamford (2m).

AMBER (tributary of Derwent): Trout, coarse fish.

Alfreton (Derby). Ripley AA has water for members only. St £6. Dt 85p issued for reservoirs at **Butterley** and **Codnor Park** for pike, perch, roach, tench, bream, and carp; tickets from keepers. Sheffield Trout Anglers have water on Amber at Wingfield. Hotels: George, Castle. Also fair fishing in Derwent at Ambergate, 5m SW.

WYE (tributary of Derwent): One of few rivers in which rainbow trout breed. Also holds good brown trout.

Bakewell (Derby). Peacock Hotel, **Rowsley**, has 6m; rainbow trout and grayling. Dt £15, 3-day ticket £33, 5-day ticket £55. Hotel now has self-catering flat available. Trout. Fishing preserved by The Duke of Rutlands Haddon Hall Estate.

Monsal Dale (Derby). 4½m double bank. Excellent trout fishing. Membership £400. Dt £15 is now available, in advance, from keeper. 4 rods per day only. Applications to Chatsworth Estate Office, Edensor. Dt for residents at Cavendish Hotel, Baslow.

Buxton (Derby). River private. Brown and rainbow trout fishing in **Lightwood** and **Stanley Moor** reservoirs; Buxton Fly-fishers' Club; limited dt from hon sec. Dove *(see Dove)*, Manifold *(see Manifold)*, Derwent *(see Rowsley up to Ladybower)*, Lathkill; trout; private. Hotels: Palace, St Ann's, Old Hall, Leewood, Buckingham, Hartington, Grove, Portland.

DOVE. Dovedale waters, where Izaak Walton and Chas Cotton fished, are now more of historic than sporting interest. Heavily overfished. Good sport with trout and grayling elsewhere. In lower reaches, where polluted Churnet enters Dove, angling is improving. Stretches below Uttoxeter, Doveridge, Marchington, Sudbury, etc, also improving.

Uttoxeter (Staffs). Trout, grayling. Uttoxeter AA preserves good deal of water between Rocester and Uttoxeter; no permits.

Rocester (Staffs). Trout, grayling above town; grayling, few trout below. Chur-

net; fishing spoilt by pollution, but improving; private.

Ashbourne (Derby). Several miles of R **Henmore** and **Bentley Brook,** both tributaries stocked with trout and grayling, and two small lakes controlled by Ashbourne Fly-Fishers' Club. St only; no dt. In **Dovedale** 3m of good trout and grayling fishing can be had by guests at Izaak Walton Hotel. Dovedale (dt £6) fishing best before tourism build-up in May. Charles Cotton Hotel *(see Hartington)* and Crewe and Harpur Arms *(see Longnor)*. Hotel in Ashbourne; Green Man; hotel at Mayfield, 2m SW (Staffs); Royal Oak. Tackleist: Foster Bros.

Hartington (Derby). Trout. Charles Cotton Hotel has about 250 yds of the River Dove; residents only. Proprietor will give data about stretches available from farmers.

CHURNET (tributary of Dove): Mixed fishery spoilt by pollution for some years, but improving.

Cheddleton (Staffs). Endon Brook, 1m NW. West Brook, 1m SE. Pond by Wetley, 3m S. Club has canal *(see Leek).*

Leek (Staffs). Trout, coarse fish; preserved above Leek town by landowners. Fishing improving as pollution decreases. Leek and Morland's FC has water on canal at Leek and Cheddleton. **Crakemarsh** (coarse fish) and stretches on the **Dove, Manifold** and parts of Churnet between Rudyard and Leekbrook. St £11, dt £1, from Club for visitors to area. Contact hon sec or tackleists in the Potteries. **Rudyard Lake** is 3m NW; very good bream, with roach, perch and pike; dt. Punts on half and full day from water bailiff Lake House, Rudyard, near Leek or from BWF. Match lengths pegged. **Tittesworth Reservoir:** 189-acre Severn-Trent WA trout fishery. *(See Midlands reservoirs and lakes.)*

MANIFOLD (tributary of Dove): Offers visitors one or two opportunities for sport with trout and grayling.

Longnor (Staffs). Buxton, 7m; trout. Dove, 1m E; trout, grayling. Fishing (fly only) can be had from the Crewe and Harpur Arms; 8m on Manifold; dt £2; waders necessary; limited to guests; non-residents may fish if all rods not taken. Part of Hoo Brook and Manifold is National Trust property; trout restocked.

MEASE. Coarse fish. Fishing stations are: **Measham** (Leics); **Snarestone** (Leics); and **Ashby-de-la-Zouch** (Leics); **Netherseal**

(Derby); **Edingale** and **Harlaston** (Staffs); Birmingham AA has water at last three. Willesley Park Lake, 1m SW. Ashby Wolds Reservoir, 4m W. Barrat Pool, 4m SW. Coleorton Ponds, 3m E. Staunton Lake, 4m. Hotels: Queen's Head, Royal.

SEAL BROOK (tributary of Mease):
Over Seal (Leics). Lakes: Ashby Wolds Reservoir, 1m N.

TAME: After a long history of pollution, much recovered under the care of the Severn-Trent WA. Fish now present in many stretches. Further improvement scheduled.

Tamworth (Staffs). Tributary Anker holds roach, pike and perch. Dt issued for Castle Pleasure Grounds, Tamworth Corporation water; other dt from Warren Farm, Amington. Mease; roach, chub, dace; Haunton, Harleston; dt from W T Ward and Harleston Mill. Lakes: Drayton Park, 2m S; Middleton Park, 4m S; Canwell Heath, 4m SW; Cuttle Mill, 5m SW; good carp water. Local clubs: Lamb AC; Fazeley Victory AC; Birch Coppice AC; Tamworth WMC; which fish Coventry and Birmingham Canals; some tickets available. Tackleists: L Bates, Amington Road; H Greenway, Lichfield Street; S Mulvey, Watling Street, Wilnecote. Hotels: Albert (fishing in Anker); Castle; Peel.

Kingsbury (Warwicks). County council water park, including specialist pike and carp fisheries, also lakes stocked with a variety of coarse fish. New fishery, Mill Pond, 12 acres; carp, tench. St £7.50-£40 from CC offices, Warwick; dt £1 for some of the fisheries on site.

Sutton Coldfield (W Midlands). Lakes: Bracebridge Pool, 2m NW; Blackroot Pool, 1m NW; Powell's Pool; all in Sutton Park; dt £1.25 (50p juv) from keepers. St £16. Local clubs: Sutton Coldfield AS has fishing on rivers and lakes. Membership applications to hon sec. Permits for members' guests only.

ANKER (tributary of Tame): coarse fish; best sport in winter.

Polesworth (Warwick). Coventry AA has 3m; good pike fishing. St from hon sec. Assn also has 7m on canal; dt from Association, bailiffs and tackleists.

SENCE (tributary of Anker): small stream, but good trout and grayling in places, as well as chub, roach and dace. Members only. Coventry and Dist AA has 1½m at **Sheepy** and on the Crown Estate at **Gop-** sall between Shackerstone and Heather *(see Narborough)*.

BOSWORTH BROOK (tributary of Sence): Trout; preserved.

Market Bosworth (Leics). Bosworth Brook, 1m North; trout; preserved by owner of Bosworth Hall. Sence, 3m W. Tweed, 3m SW. Coventry AA has 4m of canal here; good tench *(see also Shenton, below)*. Lakes: The Duckery, Bosworth Park, 1m S; pike, etc. Gabriel Pool, 3m NE.

TWEED (tributary of Sence):
Shenton (Warwick). Coventry AA has water on canal; association membership books required; obtainable from Riley's Sports, 37 Queens Road, Nuneaton.

BOURNE BROOK (tributary of Bourne). Fishing station: Plough Inn, **Shustoke**, Warwicks. Trout fishing in Avon Division STWA Shustoke Reservoir *(see Midlands reservoirs and lakes)*.

BLYTH (tributary of Tame): Coarse fish. Centres: **Coleshill** (Warwicks) (chub, perch, pike, roach); **Packington** (trout, *see Midland Lakes*); **Hampton-in-Arden** (Warwicks) (chub, dace, roach); **Solihull** (Warwicks). **Earlswood Lakes,** 6m SW; ticket for three lakes (coarse fish); on bank from bailiff. **Olton Mere** coarse fishing; apply to sec, Olton Mere Club.

REA (tributary of Tame): Polluted and fishless.

Birmingham (W Midlands). Birmingham AA, formed from a number of local clubs, controls water on river, canal and lake throughout the Midlands and into Wales. St £13.50, Ladies, juniors, OAP, regd disabled £3.75, covering salmon, trout and coarse fish. The club-card gives details of all fishing rights, which include water on **Severn and tributaries, Trent and tributaries, Wye and tributaries,** canals, lakes and ponds. A detailed guide with excellent maps is issued price 30p from Assn HQ, 100 Icknield Port Road, Rotton Park, Birmingham B16 0AP. White Swan Piscatorials own or rent waters on the **Severn, Avon, Teme, Mease, Tern, Rea, Lugg, Ithon, Hereford-shire Arrow** and numerous pools. St £32 + £32 entrance fee; limited. Game Fishers' Club has water on **Lugg, Rea, Monnow** and several brooks. Trout and grayling. Both clubs restrict day permits to members' guests only. St £50. Reservoir at **Edgbaston** fishable on permit. **Park Lakes:** coarse fishing on 14 lakes and pools in city. For details, Dept of Recreation, Auchinleck House, Five

Ways B15 1DS. St £11, dt £1.10; juv £5.50, 60p; from park keepers. Special st for pensioners available. Tackleists: W Powell, 35 Carrs Lane; H Greenway, 5 Warren Farm Rd, Kingstanding and at Pipe Hayes, Tyselely, Shard End and Tamworth; Bate, 16 Colmore Circus; Simmons & Priddy, 9 Stratford Rd, Shirley; Brooks, 958 Bristol Rd S; A Clissett, Cotterbridge; Keeling, New Market Hall, Bull Ring Centre; J Hickman, 211 Station Rd, Stetchford; Allmarks, 43 Waterloo Rd, Smethwick and Hagley Rd W, Quinton. Many hotels.

Lifford (Birmingham). Bourne Brook, 2m N. Cole, 2m E. British Waterways reservoir. Good coarse fishing. Dt from parkkeeper.

FORD BROOK (tributary of Tame). Fishing stations: **Pelsall** and **Walsall** (W Midlands). Brook polluted. Lake: Hatherton Lake; pike. **Sneyd Reservoir** (British Waterways); rented by Swan AC. Walsall and Dist AS has **Hatherton Canal. Park Lime Pits;** carp, bream, roach, perch, pike; dt and st for small charge. **Aboretum Lake;** bream, tench, roach, perch, pike; dt. Tackleists: R Wallace, 35 High Street, Walsall.

SOWE: Coarse fish, some trout.

Stafford (Staffs). Upstream of town; perch, pike, dace, roach, chub. Downstream; perch, roach, bream, chub, occasional trout. Free for about $\frac{1}{4}$m upstream of town on left bank only; remainder pre-

served by Izaak Walton (Stafford) AA. This association has fisheries on the Sowe, the **Penk, Trent & Mersey Canal, Shropshire Union Canal** and **Hopton Pools,** the latter containing carp and tench as well as the more widely distributed coarse fish. Apply hon sec for annual membership, wt and dt. Hotels: Swan, Station, Vine, Royal Oak, Garth, Tillington Hall.

Great Bridgford (Staffs). Sowe, Whitmore Reans AA has water; st only, apply hon sec. Izaak Walton (Stafford) AA has about $1\frac{1}{2}$m *(see Stafford).*

Eccleshall (Staffs); ns Norton Bridge, 3m. Trout; preserved. Offley Brook. Lakes: Oatland Pond, 4m W. Cop Mere, 2m W. All private.

PENK (tributary of Sowe):

Acton Trussell (Staffs); ns Stafford. Coarse fish. **Staffordshire and Worcestershire Canal.** Stafford AA has water *(see Stafford).* Whitmore Reans AA has water here on canal and on Penk at **Rickerscote.** Dt £1 from hon sec. Annual membership, £6, juv £2.

Radford Bridge (Staffs). Izaak Walton (Stafford) AA has water here *(see Stafford under Sowe).* Tickets from ATC Stores (tackleists).

Penkridge (Staffs). Whitmore Reans AA has water here; also on Whiston Brook and Staffordshire and Worcestershire Canal. Hotels: Litteton Arms, Fox and George, White Hart.

TYNE

(For close seasons, licences, etc, see Northumbrian Water Authority, p 14)

Formed by junction of North and South Tyne at Hexham, and empties into North Sea at Tynemouth (Northumberland). Once famous salmon river, became badly polluted but now reported to be improving for salmon and sea trout; trout fishing fair. Pike are increasing in lower reaches (below Hexham) and dace in the North and South Tyne.

Newcastle-upon-Tyne (North'land). Pollution abating. **Whittle Dene Reservoirs,** trout fishery 11m W of city, leased to West Water Angling. Dt £8 at fishing hut at reservoir, 6 fish limit, self service. Tel: Humshaugh 405. George Hotel has fishing at **Chollerford.** Tackleists: J Robertson, 101 Percy Street; Bagnall & Kirkwood, Grey Street. R.S. Tackle, 36 Collingwood Street. *(For Northumbrian Anglers' Federation water see Prudhoe.)*

Ryton (Durham). Occasional salmon; trout,

coarse fish. Federation water *(see Prudhoe).*

Wylam (North'land). Federation water. Local association: AA, which has about $1\frac{1}{2}$m below Federation water; no tickets. Few salmon; trout, coarse fish.

Prudhoe (North'land). Trout, coarse fish; occasional salmon; water at **Bywell, Ovingham** and **Wylam** preserved by the Northumbrian Anglers' Federation; st £25; 14-day visitors ticket, £20, covers all species. From all Newcastle tackleists.

Mickley (North'land). Trout, coarse fish; occasional salmon; Federation water *(see Prudhoe)*. Lakes: Whittle Dene Reservoirs, 5m N.

Stocksfield (North'land). Trout, coarse fish, few salmon.

Corbridge (North'land). Trout and dace; trout plentiful but small with runs of sea trout and salmon. Corbridge Riverside Sports Club has 3m on south bank; membership restricted to persons living locally; dt to members' guests only. $\frac{1}{4}$m free on north bank. Licences from Waltons, Middle Street. Newcastle's **Hallington reservoirs** (8m N) now private. Derwent Reservoir (trout) 10m S *(see Derwent)*. At Allendale (12m SW)

visitors staying locally may have dt for **East Allen** (trout). Information and licences from D Lowes, Middle Street. Hotels: Dyvels, Station Rd; Angel, Main Street; Wheatsheaf, St Helen's Street; and those in Hexham.

Hexham (North'land). Trout (av $\frac{3}{4}$ lb), coarse fish; salmon improving. Salmon fishing at Tyne Green, near town. Spring and October. St £10, dt £1.50, juv, OAP £5 and £1.50 from Tynedale DC Recreation Dept, Prospect House, Hexham. All other salmon water preserved. **Hallington Reservoirs,** 7m N; private. Club: Hexham AA has water; no tickets. Hotels: Beaumont, Beaumont Street, County, Priestpopple; Royal, Priestpopple.

Tributaries of the Tyne

DERWENT: Few trout. Trout average about $\frac{1}{4}$ lb, but hard to catch owing to plentiful feed; early months best.

Swalwell (Durham). Some pollution. Winlaton Mill to Lintzford, 5m, held by Axwell Park and Derwent Valley AA; few trout; membership restricted to 30, but dt available

Shotley Bridge (Durham). Derwent, 1m W; trout and grayling. Derwent AA preserves about 14m of river from Lintzford to **Derwent Reservoir** (trout, *see Durham Reservoirs)* and one bank above reservoir to Baybridge; membership restricted: long waiting list. Hotel: The Lord Crewe Arms, Blanchland.

NORTH TYNE: Useful trout water, with one or two salmon.

Chollerford (North'land). Trout, coarse fish. The George Hotel, Chollerford has $\frac{3}{4}$m bank fishing upstream of bridge. Trout average $\frac{1}{2}$ lb. St £25, dt £1.50, juv 75p. Free to guests.

Bellingham (North'land). Trout, salmon sea trout; runs have improved since 1965; best July–Oct. Bellingham AC has 5m water above and below town. Membership limited to 60; st £30, wt (for holiday-makers staying in Bellingham only, all months except Oct) £12, Mon-Sat incl. No dt. Hotels: Rose and Crown, Cheviot, Black Bull, Riverdale Hall.

Tarset (North'land). Trout.

Kielder (North'land). Major NWA reservoir opened in 1982. Stocked with brown and rainbow trout. St £120, concession-

ary £60, dt £3 and £1.50, evening £2.50. Motor boats £10. Fly and worm. Fly fishing only at **Bakethin Reservoir;** dt £4.50. Boats £5 per day. Concessions for both waters to OAP, juniors and regd disabled. Tickets on site.

REDE: Trout and pike, with few autumn salmon.

Otterburn (North'land). Percy Arms, has 1m near hotel, salmon and sea trout. Residents only. Wt £10, dt £3. Excellent trout fishing on **Sweethope Lake, Kirkwhelpington** April 1 to Sept 30; brown trout, some rainbows; average 8–9 oz; fly only; limit five brace; rods limited to five a day; gillie available. Permits at W Woodburn. **Sweethope Lower Lough;** pike, small perch. For Sweethope Loughs tel: 0830 40349. Dt (bank only) from Swallow Hotels (as above). Good burn fishing. Otterburn Tower Hotel has $3\frac{1}{2}$m on Rede. Northumbrian AF has water on Rede and Durtrees Burn; also 2m (both banks) **River Font.** Dt £2.50 for **Fontburn Reservoir** (unstocked) on site.

SOUTH TYNE: One or two clubs issue tickets for trout and salmon fishing on this river.

Fourstones (North'land). Trout and occasional salmon. Newbrough and Fourstones AA has $2\frac{1}{2}$m of north bank only; no visitors' tickets.

Haydon Bridge (North'land). Trout and occasional late salmon. South Tyne AA preserves $3\frac{1}{2}$m of water. No spinning before June 1. Wt for visitors staying in parish £18, from J O Moore, 24 Struther Close. 10 pools. Hotel: Anchor, adjoins river.

Haltwhistle (North'land). Brown trout, sea trout, salmon. Haltwhistle and Dist AA has 7m on main river and 7m on Haltwhistle Burn; wt £5–£25 from Greggs Sports Shop, Market Place. Tackleist: K

Stott, Lees Hall Gate. Hotels: Grey Bul Railway, Featherstone, Manor House Wallace Arms.

Alston (Cumbria). Enjoyable sport wit trout at 4 or 5 to lb. Alston AA ha water; mt £25, dt £2 and wt £8 from ho sec, or Struthers, Newsagents, From Street.

WANSBECK

(For close seasons, licences, etc, see Northumbrian Water Authority, p 14)

Northumberland trout stream which fishes well under favourable conditions of water but opportunities for visitors are few.

Morpeth (North'land). Brown trout; preserved by Wansbeck AA for 5m; members only; limited to residents. Dt for tidal stretch on Ashington side of Wansbeck from Wansbeck DC. Information on water in town from AA sec.

Tackleists: Sports Shop, Newgate Street Morpeth; McDermotts, 112 Station Road, Ashington. Hotels: Waterford Lodge, Queen's Head, Angler's Arms Weldon Bridge.

Tributary of the Wansbeck

BROOKER BURN:
Longhirst (North'land). Wansbeck, 2m S; trout, free. Lyne, 2m N.

WAVENEY

(See "Norfolk and Suffolk Broads", p 84)

WEAR

(For close seasons, licences, etc, see Northumbrian Water Authority, p 14)

Rises on Kilhope Moors in extreme west of Co Durham and enters North Sea a Wearmouth. In former years river was noted for salmon, but fishing ruined by pollution in lower reaches. With closure of many colleries and energetic restocking by water authority the position is much improved, and sea trout stocks in particular have risen in recent years. Brown trout fishing upstream from Chester-le-Street, although difficult, is well worthwhile. Tributaries Browney and Rookhope are improving. Bedburn preserved.

Chester-le-Street (Durham). Sea trout, brown trout (stocked by club) coarse fish. AC (annual membership £23 + £4 joining fee) has good water. St £5, dt £1, from F Armstrong, North Burns; Photo & Sports, Front Street. New members welcomed, ladies included. Concessions for jun.

Durham (Durham). Trout, sea trout. Durham City AC has 1½m on river, and stillwater fisheries stocked with coarse fish. St £22 + £10 joining fee. Concessions to jun + OAP. Dt for

friends of members only. Ferryhill AC has fishery at **Croxdale** and Willington AC has water; dt from Bond's Stores, High Street, Langley Park. Bear Park, Cornsay and New Branspeth Assns all have water on **Browney**, 4m W of Durham; limited dt; restocking. North-West Durham AA has trout water on two reservoirs: **Waskerley** and **Smiddy Shaw**. Tackleist: N Telfer, 43 North Road.

Bishop Auckland (Durham). Sea trout, brown trout, grayling, salmon. Bishop Auckland & Dist AC controls some 20m of water on Wear, **Browney** and **Swale**. Bait fishing for grayling restricted to worm. St £48. Dt £5—£20, according to date from Windrow Sports, Fore Bondgate; hotels, post offices and other tackleists in the area. Further details from hon sec. Other club water in area is **Witton Castle Lakes**, 21 acres trout fishing; dt £10-£6. Hotels: Castle, Queen's Head, Wear Valley.

Wolsingham (Durham). Trout, sea trout (good). Wolsingham AA has water; members only (st £31, limited for visitors). Long waiting list. No dt. At Hag bridge, **Eastgate** (about 8m W), Northumbrian WA has stretch; dt £3, £2, conc £1.50 *(see Stanhope)*. North-West Durham AA has **Waskerley** and **Smiddy Shaw Reservoirs**. **Tunstall** an NWA fishery.

Frosterley (Durham). Trout, sea trout. About $1\frac{1}{2}$m water belongs to Frosterley AC; members only, who must reside in area.

Stanhope (Durham). Trout, sea trout. About 2m water (both banks) belongs to Stanhope AA; limited st for visitors, £10, local st £4, from hon sec. Sea trout June onwards. Northumbrian Water Authority has 2m. Dt (limited) from West End Filling Station. Hotels: King's Arms, Phoenix.

Upper Weardale (Durham). Trout, sea trout (Sept and Oct). Upper Weardale AA has about 6m of water; st £13, wt £6, dt £2.50, juv 50%, from Post Office or Golden Lion at St John's Chapel. Water re-stocked annually with fish up to 12 in; no Sunday fishing. For **Burnhope** reservoir tel: M Graham, Alston 81263.

Tributary of the Wear

BROWNEY: now free of pollution; trout.

Lanchester (Durham). Langley Park AA lease river at Langley Park. Trout only. St £12, dt £1.50, limited.

Burn Hill (Durham). Waskerley, Tunstall, Hisehope and Smiddy Shaw Reservoirs; close together on moors between Stanhope and Consett. *(See above and under Durham Reservoirs.)*

WEAVER

(For close seasons, licences, etc, see North West Water Authority, p 13-14)

Rises south-west of Cheshire and flows into Mersey estuary. Sport has benefited from recent restocking. Most species of coarse fish, trout in the upper reaches.

Northwich (Cheshire). Good coarse fishing held by Northwich AA. Water on Weaver, **Dane, Trent and Mersey Canal** (about 17m, being restocked); **Billinge Green Pools; Petty Pool Mere; Great Budworth Mere; Pickmere Lake**. Comprehensive st (all waters); st £10, wt £3 Exceptional concessions to OAP and regd disabled, from Box 18, Northwich. River, meres and pools. Tackleists; Hyland's Pet Stores; Firthfields Pet Stores. Hotels: Railway, Salter, Woodpecker and Railway (Hartford).

Minshull Vernon (Cheshire). Weaver 1m W. Wheelock, 1m E. Ash Brook, 3m. Weaver from New Bridge to Church Minshull rented by Winsford & Dist AA. Stockport & Dist AF has water on **Rochdale Canal**, Weaver and the lake in

Drinkwater Park. Dt on bank. Crewe LMR Sports AS has Sandhole Pool (coarse fish) and good tench water at Warmingham ($\frac{1}{2}$m); some permits *(see Crewe)*.

Worleston (Cheshire). Coarse fish. Weaver. Pool Brook (of little account) and Wistaston Brook.

Crewe (Cheshire). Weaver $2\frac{1}{2}$m W. No fishing in Crewe, but Crewe LMR Sports AS has 3m of Weaver near Nantwich (4m away) on Batherton Estate. **Sandhole Pool** (1m), and **Doddington Hall Pool** (5m), rights on **Shropshire Union Canal** and stretches of **Severn, Weaver** and **Dane**, as well as good bream, tench and pike fishing on **Hortons Flash**. Guest tickets are not issued for any of these waters. Dt for Macclesfield Canal; coarse fish *(see also Congleton)*. Tackleists: Wooldridge's, High Street; Jenk's 109 West Street.

Nantwich (Cheshire). Trout, grayling, dace, roach, chub. Nantwich AS controls nearly all Weaver near Nantwich; st only; water starts on Reaseheath Estate and stretches SE of town for 7m mainly on both banks, broken at Batherton Mill. Society also has stretch on **Dove** at **Doveridge** and **Severn** at Trewern. Other clubs with water near Nantwich are Pioneer AA, Amalgamated Anglers and LMR Sports (all Crewe), Wyche Anglers and Winsford and District AA; **Dane,** (Croxton Lane to King Street), Weaver; flashes; pools; st, dt from hon sec. These 4 clubs are members of Cheshire AA. Winsford Club's pools contain fine tench, carp, bream and pike. Weaver is chalk stream here; well stocked with roach, dace and chub. Middlewich AS controls 6m of **R Dane,** coarse fish, trout on **Bostock** lengths only. St £8.50, dt £1.50, juv st £2.50 from sec or Dave's

Tackle Shop, Middlewich. Permits c **Doddington Hall Lake** (7m) issued c yearly basis to clubs by Crewe LM Sports AS £3.50 *(see Crewe)* an Wybunbury AA £6.50; also waters o Howbeck Brook; members only. Boa on all waters. **Shropshire Union Can** controlled by BWF: dt £1 from bar ranger; st £5 from tackleist. Other wate within 10m of Nantwich are: Big Mer Quoisley Mere (boats), Osmere, Blak mere (boats), Combermere (boats Tackleist: J & A Tackle, 36 Pepp Street, Nantwich. Hotels: Lamb, Crow Three Pigeons.

Audlem (Cheshire). Adderley Brook. Bi chall Brook, 2m NE. Lake: Woolfa Pool, 2m NE. Hotels: Lamb, Crowr *(For club water see Nantwich.)*

Wrenbury (Cheshire). Nantwich AS ha water in area; no tickets. Marbur Brook. Sale Brook, 2m S. Baddile Brook, 2m N. Hotel: Combermere Arms Burleydam, Whitchurch.

Tributaries of the Weaver

DANE: Good trouting in upper reaches, but difficult to come by. Coarse fishing, with odd trout and grayling lower down.

Congleton (Cheshire). Trout, dace, roach, chub, gudgeon and occasional grayling and perch. From Radnor Bridge towards Holmes Chapel partly controlled by Prince Albert AS, Cheshire AA, Grove and Whitnall AA and Warrington AA. St for Cheshire AA stretch at **Somerford-booths** from secretary or Crewe tackleists. Assn also has water on Severn. Above Congleton controlled by Congleton United AS and syndicates. Moreton Hall Lake, 2m SW, private. **Macclesfield Canal** controlled by Corbridge AS; roach, perch, tench, bream, pike; recently dredged; st and dt at small charge from bailiff.

Bosley nr **Macclesfield** (Cheshire). Trout, dace, roach, chub; private. Lake: **Bosley Reservoir;** dt 40p from Harrington Arms; roach, pike, carp, perch, few trout; Moss Side AA water.

Macclesfield (Cheshire). **Langley Bottoms and Lamaload Reservoirs** (trout; fly only) controlled by Prince Albert AS, a nationally famous club with many fisheries in the NW of England and in Wales. These include stretches on the R

Dane, the **Severn,** the **Ribble, Wye, Towy Teifi, Cothi, Banwy, Twymyn, Tren Dove-Winster, Vyrnwy, Lledr, Dulas Dysinni, Dee, Dovey, Mawddach an Lune; Marbury Mere,** Whitchurch, Isl **Lake,** Shrewsbury, **Langley Bottoms** an **Lamaload** Reservoirs, Macclesfield an others. St £30 + £20, long waiting list. D issued for a few of their waters.

Teggsnose Reservoir (trout, coarse fish) i Macclesfield Waltonian AS water; n tickets. Other clubs: Macclesfield Fly fishers' Club (12m on Dane and **Clough** strictly preserved; no tickets), and Mac clesfield and District Amalgamated Soci ety of Anglers. **Macclesfield Canal;** goo carp, pike, roach, etc; st and dt from tackleists. County Palatine AA ha water. **Bosley Reservoir;** dt from Harrington Arms, Bosley and bailiff, Lakeside Estate. **Redesmere** and **Capes thorne;** roach, bream, tench, perch, pike, mirror and crucian carp; dt from bailiff East Lodge, Capesthorne *(see Cheshir lakes, meres, etc).* Other waters in area **South Park Pool;** carp, roach, perch, pike; dt **Knypersley Pool** controlled by Cheshire AA; st and dt issued. Tackleist Ray Newton, 5-7 Park Green; licences and canal tickets.

WHEELOCK (tributary of Dane): **Sandbach** (Cheshire). Wheelock and brooks polluted. Pool at Hassall is Holly Bush AA water. Taxmere (2m); carp, bream, roach, tench, pike, perch; dt from I F McDonald, 49 Welles Street, Sandbach, or Johnson's *(see below)*. Elworth Anglers have much subsidence water; residents only. Tackleist: B Johnson, Bold Street. Hotels: Wheatsheaf, Old Hall.

ARTLE BROOK:
Keele (Cheshire). Artle, 1m W. Lake: Madeley Manor, 1m W. Doddington Pool (permits only); coarse fish.
MARBURY BROOK:
Malpas (Cheshire). Holywell Brook, 2m NE. Weaver, 3m NE. Marbury Brook, 3m SE. Moss Meres, Capel Mere (Cholmondeley Park), 3m NE and Barmere, 3m SE.

WELLAND

(For close seasons, licences, etc, see Anglian Water Authority, p 14-15)

Rises near Market Harborough and flows through Lincolnshire Fens to the Wash. Coarse fishing very good, much of it controlled by clubs. Bream and roach plentiful and run to good size in most areas and pike, perch, dace, chub, with some carp and tench, also taken. River stocked with trout in upper reaches. Fen Drains hold roach, bream, tench and pike, but few fish in North and South Drove Drains.

Spalding (Lincs). Welland, **Lincolnshire Drains;** good coarse fishing. Spalding FC preserves Counter, North, South and Vernatts Drains; pike, perch, roach, carp, rudd, bream, tench; also **River Glen** from Guthram Gowt to Surfleet village bridge and **New River** from Spalding to Crowland *(tickets, see Crowland)*; dt on recommendation of members only. Welland, from Spalding to The Deepings, provides 12m of good fishing for pike, perch, chub, roach, dace, bream and tench; st and wt at small charge from licence distributors. **Coronation Channel** also fishable (east bank reserved for matches). RD arranges matches on 12m of accessible water between Spalding and Crowland. Worksop and Dist AAA now lease 2½m, both banks, at Spalding. Tickets from R Ball, Fishing Tackle Shop, Hawthorne Road; or M Tidwells, Fen Lane.

Cowbit (Lincs). Pike, perch, dace. Spalding FC water *(see Spalding)*.

Crowland (Lincs); ns Postland, 3m. Pike, perch, dace. Nene, 2m SE at Black Horse Mills. New River from Spalding to Crowland preserved by Spalding FC; pike, roach, perch, dace, rudd, bream, tench; tickets from R Ball, or M Tidwells *(see Spalding)*.

Deeping St James (Lincs). Chub, dace, roach, tench, bream, trout, pike; preserved. Deeping St James AC controls Several Fishery at Market Deeping *(see entry below)*. Hotels: Bell,

Goat, Waterton Arms.
Market Deeping (Lincs). Several Fishery controlled by Deeping St James AC. Extends 6½m from Market Deeping to Kennulph's stone, on Deeping high bank, also on **Welland, Folly River,** Peakirk and **Maxey Cut.** Notice boards erected. St £6 (trout: members only, waiting list), dt £1, but not issued for all waters. For matches, inclusive of pegging. Apply J Cran, 53 Castle Drive, Northborough, Peterborough PE6 9DL. Tickets from tackleists Pets Pantry and N Clark, both Deeping St James. Fishing opens June 16 to Mar 14. Glen, 4m N, at Kates Bridge. Hotels: Bull, New Inn, White Horse, Vine, Three Tuns.
Stamford (Lincs). Chub, dace, roach, pike, perch; fishing free to RD licence holders on N bank between Town and Broadeng Bridges; approx 1¼m. Elsewhere preserved by Stamford Welland AAA. Approx 18m of water, stretching from Barrowden to Tallington. St £6, members only, from hon sec or tackleists. Lakes: Burghley Park, 1m SE (bream and tench, some rudd), Tuesdays, Thursdays and Saturdays only; permission to fish island side of **Burghley Lake** from hon sec or Tackleists: Bob's Tackle, Foundry Road. Dt £2. (No Sunday fishing).
Ketton (Leics). Oakham AS has water here and on **River Chater;** members only; coarse fish *(see also Midlands Reservoirs)*.
Rockingham (Northants). Eye Brook Reser-

voir; good trout fishing *(see Midlands reservoirs and lakes)*. Hotels: Falcon; Central (both Uppingham, 5m N); Castle Inn, Caldecott.

Market Harborough (Leics). **Saddington Reservoir** is Saddington AA water. Enquiries to hon sec. Market Harborough and District Society of Anglers has about 6m of **Grand Union Canal** *(see English*

Canals section), good for tench, bream, carp early in season; roach Nov–March; membership cards £2.50, dt 50p from Sports & Toys, 7 St Mary's Road; Wilkinsons, 26 Coward Street; or bailiffs on bank. Hotels: Angel, Peacock, Grove. At Lutterworth is **Stemborough Mill Trout Farm,** well stocked with r trout. Dt £8 (6 fish). Tel: Leire 209624.

Tributaries of the Welland

GLEN: River free from Surfleet village to reservoir, coarse fish; trout above Bourne.

Surfleet (Lincs). Glen free below village. Preserved above by Spalding FC *(see Spalding)*.

Pinchbeck (Lincs). Permits issued by Welland and Nene RD. River Welland, 2m SE at Spalding; also Coronation Channel.

Counter Drain (Lincs). Counter Drain; coarse fish; Spalding FC.

Bourne (Lincs). Glen holds trout upstream; landowners sometimes give permission.

GWASH: Fair trout and grayling stream. Private fishing. Stamford Welland AA have $\frac{3}{4}$m at Stamford.

CHATER:

Luffenham (Leics). Roach and dace. Stamford AA has stretch near junction with Welland. Oakham AA has water on river; members only *(see also Stamford)*.

EYE BROOK: Good head of roach, dace and chub; trout upstream.

Uppingham (Leics). Welland, 3m SE, at Seaton. Chater, 3m N. Gwash, 4m N at Manton. Eye Brook Reservoir *(see Rockingham)*.

WITHAM

(For close seasons, licences, etc, see Anglian Water Authority, p 14–15)

Rises south of Grantham and flows northward to Lincoln, then south-eastwards to Boston, where it enters the Wash. Above Grantham noted mainly for trout, mainly private. Between Grantham and Lincoln it is a good mixed coarse fishery, with chub dace and roach, mainly private clubs. From Lincoln to Boston it is entirely embanked with excellent roach and bream fishing. The fishing rights for the majority of this length are leased to the Witham and District Joint Anglers' Federation. Members of affiliated associations have free fishing. Otherwise, temporary members, day-permits price £1 are available from their bailiffs on the bankside or local tackle shops. Match bookings to Secretary, R Hobley, 6 Gunby Avenue, Lincoln. Main fishing accesses are **Washingborough, Bardney, Southrey, Stixwold, Kirkstead Bridge to Tattershall Bridge** (road alongside), **Chapel Hill, Langrick Bridge and Boston.**

Boston (Lincs). Angling facilities exceptionally good; at least 100 miles of good coarse fishing (pike, perch, dace, tench, roach and bream) in Witham, **South Forty Foot Drain,** and **Hobhole, Maud Foster, Sibsey Trader** and **West Fen Drains,** within easy reach. Witham and Dist JAF holds 30m between Lincoln and Boston, also tributaries. St and dt for Boston & Dist AA from local tackleists Burdens, Northend, Swineshead; Gon' Fishing, Main Ridge; Morleys, Wide Bargate; Don Whites, West Street. Match bookings for Witham JAF to Fed secretary; for Boston AA waters to hon sec.

Lincoln (Lincs). Good coarse fishing. Witham fishes best from Aug–Oct with bream predominant. Lincoln is HQ for Lincolnshire Anglers Fedn and Lincolnshire Rivers Anglers Consultative Assn. Witham and Dist JAF has **Sincil Drain** to Bardney Timberland Delph, Billinghay Skerth, Kyme Eau. Lincoln AA has excellent coarse fishing on **Trent, Till, Old River Witham,** drains, dykes and **Hartsholme Lake** (good bream and carp). Membership books £6 from tackleists, concessions to jun, OAP. Dt £1. 11m **Fossdyke Canal** between Torksey and Lincoln now BWF managed *(see Boston and Torksey—Trent).* **Lincoln Fisheries,** Doddington Road, Hartsholme: Two eight-acre lakes; stocked with carp, tench, bream, roach, pike. **North**

Hykeham; Richmond Lakes, 40 acres, coarse; dt £1.50, on bank. Tel: Lincoln 681329. **Butterley Aggregates Lake;** 200 acre coarse; dt 80p on site. Off A15 north of Lincoln, **Toft Newton Reservoir;** Now leased by AWA to Gerald Denton. Enquire Normanby-by-Spital 453. At **Tattershall, Castle Leisure Park,** 3 lakes, 60 acres coarse fishing. Dt £1.50. Tel: Coningsby 33193. **Willow Holt Lake,** 10 acres, coarse; dt £1, on site. Tel: Woodhall Spa 4311. Lincoln tackleists: South End Pet Stores, 447 High Street; G Harrison, 55 Croft Street; Paul Andrews Tackle, 291A Newark Road; J Wheater (Gunmakers) Tentecroft Street; Boundary Pet Stores, 6 Bunkers Hill. Newport Tackle Shop, 85 Newport, Lincoln.

Grantham (Lincs). Grantham AA has good coarse fishing on Witham, **Grantham Canal** and **Denton Reservoir;** st £8. Dt £1.25 for reservoir and canal from hon sec and local tackleists. Concessions for jun and OAP. (Note: Grantham AA is a member of the federation of Midlands clubs. This federation, which includes Peterborough, Wreake, Birstall, Boston, Oakham, Newark, Asfordby and Deeping St James Clubs, has been established to protect fisheries in area and leases waters on **Bourne Eau** and the **Glen.**)

Long Bennington (Lincs). Chub, roach, perch, grayling, etc. No dt.

Tributaries of the Witham

SOUTH FORTY FOOT DRAIN:
Good coarse fishing. Much water leased by Boston and Dist AA, dt £1. Matches booked through D G Wootton, Myyorn, Hall Lane, West Keal, Spilsby, Lincs.

Centres are **Boston, Wyberton, Hubberts Bridge, Swineshead** and **Donington.**
RIVER BAIN: Trout above Horncastle; chub and dace below. Private fishing.
Horncastle (Lincs). Rivers Bain and

Waring; trout, roach; preserved. Tupholme Brook 7m NW. Horncastle AA has an old brick pit in Hemingby Lane and about $1\frac{1}{2}$m on canal from Bath House to lock pit; no dt for canal but st covers canal and brick pit (from hon sec). **Revesby Reservoir;** 2 lakes, 42 acres, coarse fish; contains big pike; apply at estate; tel: 065886 395, dt limited and not granted Sundays. Tackleist: Hargreaves, Market Place. Hotels: Bull, Red Lion, Rodney.

FOSSDYKE NAVIGATION: Fossdyke held by BWF. Centres: **Lincoln, Saxilby** and **Torksey.** Good coarse fishing.

HOBHOLE DRAIN, EAST AND WEST FEN DRAINS: All canalised lengths of river forming part of fen drainage system. Hold good stock of coarse fish (bream, roach, perch, pike, tench), and include following waters: Maud Foster, Sibsey Trader, East Fen Catchwater drains, West Fen, Kelsey and Bellwater drains. St £5 and dt £1 from Boston tackleists and D G Wootton, Myyorn, Hall Lane, Spilsby, Lincs PE23 4BJ. Match-pegs 80p. Hobhole and West Fen drains may be fished on AWA licence only. St covers also fishing on **Witham, Steeping, Steeping Relief Channel, Glen, Bourne Eau, South Forty Foot** and **Swanholme Lakes.**

SLEA: Rises west of Sleaford and enters Witham at Chapel Hill. Trout in upper reaches. Coarse fish, particularly roach, elsewhere. Suffering from abstraction, RD trying to augment flow. Private fishing throughout length. Tackleist: Slingsby. Hotel: Carr Arms.

WYE

(For close seasons, licences, etc, see Welsh Water Authority, p 17–18)

Most famous of English salmon rivers. Rises on south side of Plynlimmon near source of Severn and enters estuary of Severn 2m south of Chepstow. About 55 years ago this river, owing to over-netting and other misuse, had deteriorated so much it hardly paid netting interests to operate. Through careful conservation and control of nets, river today produces larger rod catch of salmon than any other English or Welsh river and is outstanding example of benefit of proper control of commercial fishing. Most of rod fishing in private hands, but there are several hotels and one or two associations with rights on river. Richard Harris & Stokes *(advt below)* have more than 30m under management. Salmon run large. Sea trout fishing of no account, but coarse fishing in lower reaches exceptionally good. No free fishing. Licences may be obtained from distributors in most villages and have usually to be produced when obtaining tickets or other permits to fish. Good brown trout fishing in Upper Wye and tributaries.

Tintern (Gwent). Tidal; mostly eels and flatfish, though salmon sometimes taken. Tintern AC has **Angidy;** members only. Rose and Crown Inn.

Redbrook (Gwent). Chub, dace, pike, perch, salmon. *(See Monmouth.)*

Monmouth (Gwent). Wye holds salmon, pike, trout, grayling, chub, dace; preserved. Birmingham AA has water on Wyastone Leys Estate; salmon rights excluded. **Monnow;** trout, grayling, chub, dace; Monmouth Dist AS has water.

The Wye at its loveliest; flowing through Llanwrthwl, Powys.

Trothy, trout; preserved. Brockweir to Livox Quarries, trout and coarse fish; St £16, wt £6, dt £2.

Symonds Yat (Hereford). Salmon, trout and coarse fishing all preserved. $1\frac{1}{2}$m both banks between **Goodrich** and Symonds Yat controlled by Newport AA. Good S water; members only. Enquiries to hon sec. Birmingham AA has about 1m, both banks, above Saracen's Head Inn.

Kerne Bridge (Hereford). Chub, dace, pike, perch, salmon, trout; preserved. Castle Brook, Garron, 2m; trout. Luke Brook, 2m. Lammerch Brook, 5m.

Ross (Hereford). Salmon, trout, grayling, roach, large pike and chub and good dace. Ross AC has coarse fishing; wt £5, dt £1.50. Permits may be obtained at G & B Sports, Broad Street. Enq V R Hepburn. Tel: 64255. Town water available to visitors at small charge. Garron, Gamber, 6m, and Monnow, 9m, are very good trout streams; landowners sometimes give permission. Salmon fishing available through Ross AC. Hotels: Pengethley, Royal (Trust House). Ross AC will be pleased to help visitors; send sae if writing.

Hereford (Hereford). Salmon, trout, grayling, other coarse fish. Hereford and Dist AA holds water on Wye and **Lugg**. Tickets (Wye only); dt and wt for trout and coarse fish only. When vacancy occurs, special membership may be granted to visitors for salmon, trout and coarse fish, or for trout and coarse fish only. Membership applications to hon sec. Tickets from tackleists *(see below)*. Birmingham AA also has water on **Lugg** at Bodenham, Marden, Mordiford and Lugg Mill. Longworth Hall Hotel, **Lugwardine**, has trout and coarse fishing on Wye (outside salmon season) and a short stretch on the **Lugg**. Mt £34, wt £9, dt £1.50. Advance booking recommended. For other fishing inquire Garnons Estate Office, Bridge Sollars; W Jones, Carrier Cottage, Whitney-on-Wye; and Red Lion, Brewardine. Local tackleists: Hattons (also fishery agent, pleased to give information), 73 St Owen Street (2317); Mrs Perkins, Commercial Road. Hotels: City Arms, Green Dragon, Kerry Arms, Booth Hall. Red House Farm, Eaton Bishop, caters for anglers.

Bredwardine (Hereford). 8m salmon, trout and coarse fishing available (Moccas can be fished from here. Other fishing in area from Mrs Lewis, Bronydd Farm, Clyro.

Glasbury-on-Wye (Hereford). Salmon, trout, chub, dace, grayling, pike. Fishing in Wye and Llynfi preserved. Llangorse lake is accessible.

Builth Wells (Powys). Salmon (best March, April and May); trout (av $\frac{1}{2}$ lb), grayling, chub, dace, pike. Groe Park & Irfon AC have $2\frac{1}{2}$m on **Irfon & Wye**, including some double bank, with seven salmon catches. Club stocks with takeable trout. Wt (S) £20, (T) £10, 3-dt (S) £12, (T) £6, juv 50%. Dt for **Caer Beris Lake** ($2\frac{1}{2}$ acres) £4.50: from M Morgan, 23 Garth Road. Several local hotels have GP and IAC permits. Tackle and permits: M Morgan, Glanbran, 23 Garth Road. Elan Estate Reservoirs accessible *(see Rhayader).* Cueiddon, Duhonw, Baili and Edw preserved. Pencerrig Country House Hotel has 3m; wt £2.10.

Newbridge-on-Wye (Powys). Salmon, trout, grayling, chub, dace, pike, roach; preserved, Ithon; trout; preserved. Accommodation and further information at New Inn.

Rhayader (Powys). Wye; trout (av $\frac{1}{2}$ lb; Wye record, $10\frac{1}{2}$ lb, caught at Rhayader Bridge), salmon. Marteg, trout (3m). For further information apply hon sec, Rhayader AA, which has 4m on Wye and 16-acre lake (Llyngyn) (trout; fly only); wt £10, dt £3. Jan $\frac{1}{2}$ price. There is Rhayader AA water at **Doldowlod. Elan Valley** and **Claerwen Reservoirs.** (3–6m W) Claerwen Res and streams controlled by WWA. St £30, dt £1. **Caban Coch, Garreg Ddu, Peny-Garreg** and **Craig Goch** (total area: 850 areas) controlled by Elan Trout Fisheries

Water) subject to bookings, at Red Lion Hotel (500 yds from river. Tel: Moccas 303). St £350 (one day per week), wt £130, dt £20. *(Advt above.)*

Whitney-on-Wye (Hereford). Salmon, trout and coarse fish. Whitney Court fishery now privately let. The Rhydspence Inn has private fishing available to guests.

Hay-on-Wye (Hereford). Salmon, trout, pike, perch, chub. Tackle, RD licences and information from H R Grant & Son, 6 Castle Street. Hotels: Crown has fishing on **Llynfi,** Swan. Llangorse Lake

Assoc. St £15, dt £1.50. From Ranger, at new Visitors' Centre below Caban Coch dam, and Mrs Powell, Newsagent, West St, Rhayader. Spinning on Craig Goch; other waters fly only. Hotels: Royal Oak; Lion; Castle; Elan Valley (fishing arranged on Wye, **Elan, Marteg** and lakes) *(advt p 164)*; Lion Royal (1m on Elan); Vulcan Arms. Tackleists: E R Davies, West Street, Rhayader; M

Power, Garth House, Rhayader.
Llangurig (Powys). Trout, March 1 to Sept 30; fly only. Salmon, March 1 to Oct 25; fly and spinning. Black Lion Hotel has 8m of water on Wye for its guests. Dt and wt for residents, and for non-residents. Best months May/June and Sept. Blue Bell Inn has 8m also. Dt and wt.

Tributaries of the Wye

TROTHY: Trout, some assn water.
Dingestow (Gwent). Trout; preserved. Glamorgan AC, Cardiff, has 6m fishing. Inquiries to the hon sec. Monmouth and Dist AS has water. St £16, wt £6, dt £2.
MONNOW: Good trout and grayling stream. Monmouth. 1m N **Osbaston fishery**, leased by Cwmbran AA. Salmon, trout, coarse fish. St and dt from Pontnewydd, Pontypool and Cwmbran tackleists.
Skenfrith (Hereford). Trout, chub, dace. Birmingham AA has fly fishing here. The Priory Hotel has 300 yards; free to guests.
Pontrilas (Hereford). Trout, grayling; preserved by owner of Kentchurch to 3m below here, thence by private owners to within 1m of Monmouth.
Pandy (Gwent). Trout, grayling; private throughout and strictly preserved. Honddu: trout; strictly preserved. Hotel: Pandy Inn.
HONDDU (tributary of Monnow): Trout.
Llanfihangel Crucorney (Gwent). Trout only, preserved. No tickets issued.
Llanthony. Fishing for trout in unstocked water can sometimes be arranged at Abbey Hotel; small charge.
LUGG: Trout and grayling, with coarse fish in some stretches.
Mordiford (Hereford). Trout, grayling, etc; Birmingham AA has good stretch here, also water at Tidnor, Lugg Mill, Bodenham, Dinmore, Marden and Moreton. Inn: The Moon.
Longworth (Hereford). Longworth Hall Hotel has trout and coarse fishing, and on **Wye**, outside salmon season. Mt £34, wt £9, dt £1.50. Advance booking recommended.
Lugwardine (Hereford). Preserved by Hereford and District AA *(see Hereford)*.
Leominster (Hereford). Trout, grayling, pike, perch, dace. Above town Lugg

preserved by landowners. White Swan Piscatorials also have water; otherwise preserved by landowners. **Pinsley Brook;** trout, grayling; landowners sometimes give permission. Ridgemore Brook. Stretford Brook, $1\frac{1}{2}$m. Humber Brook, 3m. Puddleston Brook, 4m. Hotels: Royal Oak (where fishing can be arranged for guests); Talbot.
Kingsland (Hereford). Lugg. Arrow, and Pinsley Brook; trout, grayling. Fishing generally preserved by landowners. 2m from Kingsland is River Arrow at Eardisland. Accommodation: Angel and Mortimer Cross.
Presteigne (Powys). Lugg, Arrow and Teme afford excellent trout and grayling fishing, generally dry fly; preserved but landowners may give permission. At **Walton,** fly fishing for trout in 4-acre lake reserved for tenants of holiday cottages, boat available. Wt £10, children usually fish free of charge. Details from Mrs A Goodwin, Hindwell Farm, Walton, Presteigne. Tel: New Radnor 054421 252.
FROME (tributary of Lugg). Trout, preserved.
Ashperton (Hereford). Frome, $2\frac{1}{2}$m Leddon, $2\frac{1}{2}$m. Lakes: Devereux Park Lakes, 4m.
ARROW (tributary of Lugg): Trout, grayling, dace; but few opportunities for visitors.
Pembridge (Hereford). Trout, grayling, dace; preserved by landowners. White Swan Piscatorials have a stretch at Ivington. Inn: New Inn.
Kington (Hereford). Trout; preserved. Inns: Swan, Royal Oak.
LLYNFI: Trout, grayling, etc; preserved.
Glasbury-on-Wye (Hereford). Lynfi enters Wye here. Trout, grayling, chub. Fishing good, but mostly preserved. Hotel: Maesllwch Arms.

Talgarth (Powys). Llynfi. Dulais brook. Rhiangoll; trout. Treffrwd, 2m. **Llangorse Lake** (pike, perch) can be fished from here (4m); boats available. Hotel: Castle. Visitors' tickets from local association.

IRFON: Salmon, trout, grayling, chub.

Llangammarch Wells (Powys). Excellent trout fishing April, May, June, and September, and good spring and autumn salmon fishing. Lake Hotel has about 5m of Irfon and nearby streams (**Garth Dulas, Chwefri,** etc), and some rods for salmon fishing on Wye negotiated each year and charged accordingly. Also $2\frac{1}{2}$ acre trout lake (brown and rainbow; fish average $1\frac{1}{2}$ lb) in grounds. Lake and rivers restocked annually. Fly only on some beats. Wt and dt for residents only. Salmon dt from £6, trout £3.50. Cammarch Hotel has $3\frac{1}{2}$m of trout and salmon fishing on Irfon and about 4m of **Cammarch** and Upper **Dulais.** Dt £3.50 trout, £7 salmon. Best salmon Sept–Oct. Best trout Apr–June, Sept. Licences and tackle at both hotels.

Llanwrtyd Wells (Powys). Trout. 3m of association water. Lakes. Hotel: Neuadd Arms ($1\frac{1}{2}$m of fishing) Llwynderw.

ITHON: Trout, chub, few salmon. Good hotel and assn water.

Llandrindod Wells (Powys). Llandrindod Wells AA controls 5m of trout fishing close to town. Grayling also (plus large eels). Available to visitors on st £17, wt £10, dt £3. Concessions for OAP, juv. Joining fee £2. Limit five brace per day. Sunday fishing; spinning allowed after August 1; waders essential. Tackleists: G Selwyn & Sons, Park Crescent (Tel: 2397), Wye Authority licences and association tickets. Hotels: Metropole, Commodore, Glen Usk, Mostyn.

Penybont (Powys). Trout, chub, autumn salmon. Aran, 10m; trout. Clywedog Brook, 1m; trout. Camlo, 1m. Dulas, 2m. Llandegley Brook, 2m. Edw, 3m. Hotel: Severn Arms, which has 6m of trout fishing (on Ithon) free to residents. Dt for non-residents. Fish run 3 to lb average. Licences at hotel; tackleists in Llandrindod.

Llanbadarn Fynydd (Powys). Upper Ithon. New Inn has $3\frac{1}{2}$m trout fishing; free to guests (fly only); also rough shooting.

Exclusively a man's sport? Gillian Clifford, holding a double-figure Hornsea Mere pike, demonstrates otherwise. *Photo: Bruno Broughton.*

WYRE

(For close seasons, licences, etc, see North West Water Authority, p 13–14)

From Churchtown downstream coarse fish and brown trout. Above Churchtown limited amount of salmon fishing and good sea trout and brown trout fishing.

Fleetwood (Lancs). Sport in estuary improving as pollution lessens; flatfish mostly.

St Michael's (Lancs). Mainly brown trout and coarse fish. Local club: St Michael's AA; dt from Miss G Martin, Bridge Cottage and C Calderbank (Preston). Dt for Northern AA waters from Miss Martin, as above. Hotel: Grapes.

Churchtown (Lancs). Salmon, sea trout, trout and coarse fish. Ribble and Wyre FA controls good deal of water between Churchtown and Garstang at St Michael's and at Great and Lower Eccleston; st £3 and dt £1 from hon sec.

Garstang (Lancs). Salmon, sea trout, trout and coarse fish. Garstang AA preserves 3m both banks. Fly only. No dt. Wt £10 for temporary residents in area from hon sec or Mille Roberts, Fishing Tackle & Guns, Garstang. Hotels: Royal Oak, Eagle and Child, Crown.

Scorton (Lancs). Salmon, sea trout, trout, coarse fish. Wyresdale Anglers have 7m water; no tickets.

YARE

(See Norfolk and Suffolk Broads, p 84)

YORKSHIRE (lakes, reservoirs, canals and streams)

(For close seasons, licences, etc, see Yorkshire Water Authority, p 14, unless otherwise stated)

BRANDESBURTON PONDS. Twenty coarse fish ponds. Hull and District AAA retain two of these, plus 20 acre carp lake at **Newport,** members only, st £10 from J Haldenby, 1 Grebe Road, Newport, Brough, N Humbs.

BURTON CONSTABLE LAKES. In grounds of Burton Constable Hall; excellent coarse fishing for roach, bream, perch, tench, carp and pike. St £20, mt £10, wt £5 from Warden, Old Lodge, Sproatley, nr Hull. 25 acres of fishing. Season 1 Mar–31 Oct.

CASTLE HOWARD GREAT LAKE. Fishing station: **Malton.** Specimen pike, perch, tench, bream, roach and eels. Dt £1.50, weekend £1.75, OAP and children 50%, from C Burr, bailiff, Fishing North Lodge, Coneysthorpe, York. Close season Feb 28 to May 31. Sunday fishing.

CHELKER, SILSDEN and WINTERBURN RESERVOIRS. Trout; let to Bradford Waltonians; no tickets. Waiting list. *(See also Bradford.)* Near **Silsden** and **Ilkley.**

DAMFLASK and UNDERBANK RESERVOIRS. YWA, Southern Division. Damflask, 5m from Sheffield. Underbank 10m. Both stocked with trout (2 fish limit) and coarse fish, pike to 34 lb.

Season: March 25 to following Jan 31. Dt £2.80 sold from machines at reservoirs. Concessions.

DOE PARK RESERVOIR, Denholme. 20 acres. Trout, coarse fish; let to Bradford City AA; dt £2, Mon–Fri incl.

WHINNYGILL, and EMBSAY RESERVOIRS. Let by YWA to Skipton AA. Trout and roach. St £27 + £20 entrance fee. Dt (Embsay—trout) £4, (Whinnygill—trout and coarse fish) £2. Assn also has fishing on R Aire.

FEWSTON, SWINSTY and THRUSCROSS RESERVOIRS. YWA North & East Division. Trout. Fly only at Fewston and Swinsty; any legal method (limit 4 fish) permitted at Thruscross. St from YW North & East Div, dt from machine at Swinsty Moor Fishing Office *(see also Leeds).* Near **Harrogate** and **Otley.**

HEWENDEN RESERVOIR. Between **Keighley** and **Bradford.** Trout, pike, roach, bream. Central Division AC. St £3.50 + £2.50 entrance fee from hon sec, A R Healey, 49 Green End Road, E Morton, nr Keighley, W Yorks. Waiting list.

HORNSEA MERE. Fishing station: **Hornsea.** Yorkshire's largest inland water (472 acres). Very good pike, carp, bream, rudd, perch, roach, tench. Hornsea Mere Marine Co (Tel 3277). Dt £1.60, evening (and junior) 50p, punts £3.50 day (limited boat and bank fishing).

LEEMING RESERVOIR. Fishing station: **Oxenhope.** 20 acres; good trout fishing, brown and rainbow. Bradford City AA; dt £3, Mon–Fri.

LEIGHTON RESERVOIR. Masham, N Yorks. 105 acre water-supply reservoir on the Swinton Estate stocked with large rainbow trout (some very large) for season and day ticket fishing. St available, dt £8, evening £4; concessions. 1987 rod average 2·5 fish. A branch of the Salmon & Trout Association cooperates with the Swinton Estate in the management of this water. Phone Ripon 89224 for further details.

LEVEN CANAL. Beverley 6m. 3m of good coarse fishing. Hull and Dist AA. Dt from tackleists.

LINDHOLME LAKE. 12m E of **Doncaster.** 18 acre fly only trout fishery. St (35 visits) £75. Extra visits by arrangement. Bag limit. Severn-Trent licence required. Inquiries to Epworth 872015.

MALHAM TARN. 6m from **Settle.** A Nature Reserve leased from National Trust by the Malham Tarn Field Centre. Boat fishing only, for trout with fly, and for perch with worm. Fish may run large. Weekdays £6 plus £4 per rod (£2.25 juv, accompanied by adult). Weekdays and Bank holidays £8 + £4 per rod. Bookings and detailed information from Warden or Secretary (Tel Airton 331). Phone bookings recommended. Seasons May 1 to Sept 30 for trout; July to October 31 for perch. Accommodation available at Centre.

MARKET WEIGHTON CANAL. Fishing stations: **Newport** and **Broomfleet.** 6m long; bream, perch, roach, pike. Water leased by YWA. Dt available locally.

MOREHALL RESERVOIR. Sheffield 7m. YWA. Southern Division. Trout, fly only; dt £3.30 from machine at reservoir.

NOSTELL PRIORY LAKES. Foulby, nr Wakefield. Well-stocked with pike, carp, bream, tench and roach. St £35 each lake, £75 all three, dt £2.50, ½ day £1.50. Various concessions. Details from J Austerfield, Head Bailiff, Foulby

Lodge. Tel 0924 863562.

SCOUT DIKE, Penistone. 16m from Sheffield. YWA (Southern Division). Trout 2 fish limit; st £16.50. Dt £3.30 sold from machine at reservoir.

SEMERWATER LAKE. Fishing station Bainbridge. Trout, perch, bream and rudd. Water ski-ing at weekends. Dt £2.50 for Wensleydale AA waters (west side and 2m of River Bain near lake from Rose & Crown, Bainbridge *(see Yore— Bainbridge).*

SHIPTON LAKE. Shipton-by-Beningbrough. Tench, perch, roach, trout, pike. Bradford City AA. Strictly members only.

STAINFORTH AND KEADBY CANAL. Controlled by joint committee including following clubs: Rotherham, Doncaster, Sheffield Amal, Sheffield and District and British Railways. Polluted by seepage from Don, but reported improving. Coarse fish.

TEES VALLEY AND CLEVELAND RESERVOIRS. This group of reservoirs, managed by the Northumbrian WA, includes both stocked and wild waters. **Grassholme, Selset, Scaling, Hury** and **Lockwood Beck** are retained by NWA, trout, fly only on Lockwood Beck and Selset. St £200, dt £5, concessions 50%. **Cow Green** now let to North Country Anglers. Fly and worm, native b trout. Self service t from fishing lodge. For **Balderhead,** hon sec Willington & Dist AC. For **Blackton,** hon sec Felling Fly FC.

THORNTON STEWARD RESERVOIR, Masham. Season: March 25 to Sept 30. Trout, fly only. 4 fish limit, dt £4 from Finghall Sub-P.O.

WORSBROUGH RESERVOIR, Barnsley. Coarse fish. Barnsley AS has rights and on ½m of canal. St £6, dt £1. Fishing June 1 to Feb 28. Dt £1 from bailiffs walking the bank. Sunday fishing to assn members only; hempseed and bloodworm barred.

ULLEY COUNTRY PARK. Sheffield; 9m. Rotherham MBC, Grove Road, Rotherham. 33 acre coarse fishery. Season: June 1 to Feb 27. Dt £1.60 on sale at reservoir. Enquiries to Dept of Amenities & Recreation, Grove Road, Rotherham.

ENGLISH CANAL FISHING

When the previous edition of "Where to Fish" went to press British Waterways and their fishing club tenants were, as then reported, locked in conflict over the future management of our canals. As predicted, the conflict was resolved by amicable compromise, with 900 of the 1100 miles of canal owned by the Board remaining in the hands of the clubs, as do a number of the 92 operational supply reservoirs also owned. 200 miles of canal and some reservoirs (shown below or in the appropriate geographical section of the book) are directly managed and available to all comers by day or other ticket.

Stocking is adequate; the quality of the fishing governed, as elsewhere, by water quality. Facilities for anglers in wheelchairs have been introduced in places; competitions can be arranged on directly controlled waters on application to the Fisheries Officer.

With matters thus stabilized and the improvements noted it has been decided to expand this section of the Directory. 770,000 anglers over the age of 12 fish British Waterways fisheries regularly. They form an important part of the coarse fishing on offer in England and Wales. Roach, perch, bream, eels, pike, carp, tench and other coarse fish are to be found. On some canals, one may even catch the odd trout! Canal and lock cottages are to left for holidays on some stretches.

British Waterways canals are divided into regions which have the following addresses: London, Gloucester areas; Willow Grange, Church Road, Watford, Hertfordshire WD1 3QA (tel: 0923 226422). Nottingham, Birmingham areas; The Locks, Hillmorton, Rugby, Warwickshire CV21 4PP. Northwich, Castleford and Wigan areas; Chester Road, Nantwich, Cheshire CW5 8LB (tel: 0270 625122). All canals are in one single region except Trent and Mersey, Staffordshire and Worcester and Grand Union, which stretch across two regions.

LONDON AREA:
Grand Union Canal; Osterley Lock to Hayes leased by London AA. Hayes to West Drayton, Central Assc of London & Prov AC. West Drayton to Denham, London AA. Denham to Batchworth, Blenheim AS. Sabeys Pool and part of R Chess, West Hampstead AS. Batchworth to Lot Mead Lock, Sceptre AC. Lot Mead to Cassionbury, also R Gade stretch, Kings Langley AS. Hunton Bridge to Tring, London AA. Tring to Cheddington, Tring Anglers. Cheddington to Stoke Hammond. Luton AC. $\frac{1}{4}$m from Stoke Hammond, Milton Keynes AA. To Simpson, Coventry & Dist AA. Simpson to Great Linford, Milton Keynes AA. Great Linford to Wolverton Bridge, North Bucks Div of Working Mens C. Old Wolverton to R Ouse Aqueduct, Galleon AC. Aqueduct to Cosgrove, K C Bailey, Lock House, Cosgrove. Lock to Bridge, Cosgrove, Stony Straford WMC. Cosgrove to Castlethorpe, Deanshanger & Old Stratford AA. Castlethorpe to Yardley Gobion, Britannia AC. Yardley Gobion to Dodford, Northampton Nene AC. Brockhall to Buckby, Coventry & Dist AA, also Buckby to Calcutt Bottom Lock.
Grand Union: Arms and Branches: Paddington Arm; Bulls Bridge Junction to Lock

Bridge at Paddington, London AA.
Paddington Basin; Westminster AC.
Regents Canal; Little Venice to Islington, Raven AC. Islington to Mile End, London AA. Mile End to Commercial Road, Southgate & Dist AS. **Hertford Union Canal;** Junction near Victoria Park to Lee Navigation, London AA.
Slough Arm; BWF directly managed **Wendover Arm;** Main Line to Tringford, Tring Anglers. **Aylesbury Arm;** Main Line to Red House Lock, Tring A. To Aylesbury Wharf, Delco Sports & SC.
Northampton Arm; Main Line to Milton Malsor, Northampton Britannia AC. Milton Malsor, Northampton Castle AA. Milton Malsor to Hardingstone, Conservative WMC. Hardingstone to Cotton End, Cogenhoe WMC. Gayton Marina, Gayton AC.
River Lee; Cheshunt, Cadmore Lane Gravel Pit, Metrop Police AS. West bank Old R Lee, Kings Weir, W E Newton, Slipe Lane, Wormley. Carthegena Weir, Crown Fishery, A Harris, Carthegena Lock, Broxbourne. Dodds Weir Hoddesdon and above Kings Weir, London AA. Offside Bank between Hardemeade and Stanstead Locks, Ware AC.
Oxford Canal (South); R Thames at Oxford, John Radcliffe AC. Dukes Cut, Wolvercote Pool, Hythe Bridge Street to

169

Kidlington Green Lock, North Oxford AS. Kidlington Green to Lower Heyford, Coventry & Dist AA. Lower Heyford to Aynho, Banbury & Dist AA. Aynho to Banbury, Coventry & Dist AA. R Cherwell at Kirtlington, Coventry & Dist AA. Banbury to Cropredy, Banbury & Dist AA. Cropedy Lock to Claydon, Standard-Triumph Recreation C and Sphinx C. Claydon to Fenny Compton, Oxford Canal Alliance. Fenny Compton to Napton Junction, Coventry & Dist AA.

River Stort; Roydon, Bridges AS. To Hunsdon Mill Lock, Globe AS. Stort and Stort Navigation at Burnt Mill, Harlow FA. Spellbrook Backwater, O J Smith, Spellbrook Lane East, Bishops Stortford. Bishops Stortford and to Spellbrook Lock, Bishops Stortford & Dist AS.

GLOUCESTER AREA:

Bridgewater and Taunton Canal; Bridgewater to Durston, Bridgewater AA. Durston to Taunton, Taunton AA.

Gloucester and Sharpness & Stroudwater Canals; Stroudwater Canal; Walk Bridge to 'Feeders', Frampton & Dist AA, also from Ryalls Farm to 'Stone' near Frampton. Walk Bridge to Whitminster, Sphinx AC. Two Mile Bend, Gloucester, Gloucester UAA. Babcock AC also have stretch.

Kennet and Avon Canal; Eight stretches from Bear Wharf, Reading, to Aldermaston Lock, the junction with R Kennet, Reading & Dist AA, with the exception of beat near Sulhampstead Lock. Central Assc of London & Prov AC. Woolhampton Lock to Heales Lock and stretch near Oxlease Swing Bridge to Heales Lock, Glendale AC. Heales Lock to Midgham Bridge, Reading & Dist AA. Two stretches at Midgham Lock, Reed Thatcham AA. Thatcham to Widmead Lock, Thatcham AA. Bulls Lock to Ham Mills Lock, Newbury AA. Ham Mill (offside bank) I Fidler, Ham Mill, London Road, Newbury. Whitehouse Turnover Bridge to Greenham Lock, Twickenham PS. Greenham Lock to Greenham Island, Newbury, and Northcroft to Guyers Bridge, Newbury AA. Two sections at Kintbury (560 yds), Camden Raven AC. Ladies Bridge near Wilcote to Milkhouse Water Bridge, Pewsey and District AA. Ladies Bridge to Semington Bridge, Devizes AA.

Avoncliffe Aqueduct to Dundas Aqueduct, Bathampton AA.

Monmouthshire and Brecon Canal; from Pontypool to Brecon, BWF directly controlled fishery.

River Severn Navigation; Island bank at Upper Lode Lock, D G Jones, 2 Upper Lode Lock, Forthampton, Glos. Diglis (350 yds), BWF directly controlled. Belvere Lock, G H Drake, 30 Dunstans Close, Worcester. Holt Lock downstream, A S Portman, Holt Lock, Holt Heath, near Worcester. Holt Lock upstream, J King, 67 Sytch Lane, Wombourne. Salmon rights, Lincomb Lock, P Gough, Courtnay House, Feiashill Road, Trysull, WV5 7HT. Coarse rights, B Turner, Lincomb Lock, Stourport. West bank, Lincomb Lock, J E Austin, 11 New Street, Stourport (Severn Valley Sand & Gravel Ltd).

Swansea Canal; very little fishable. Pontardawne to Ynysmeudwy, Tawe & Tributaries AA. Clydachand section above Trebanos Bottom Lock, Tawe Disabled FA.

BIRMINGHAM AREA:

Ashby Canal; Ortons Bridge at Marston Junction to Dratleys Bridge, Coventry & Dist AA. Dratleys Bridge to Limekiln Bridge, Hinckley AC. The ten sections between Limekiln Bridge (Watling Street) and Snarestone Waterworks are leased by the following clubs, in correct order: Bagworth & Nailstone AC, Avondale AC, Manor AC, Ashby AC, B & D Morris AC, Avon Ho AC, 3M Health Care AC, Coventry & Dist AA, Shackerstone & Dist AC, Measham FC.

Birmingham and Fazeley Canal; Salford Bridge to Fazeley Junction, Birmingham AA. Fazeley Junction to Sutton Road Bridge, Fazeley Victory WMC AC. Sutton Road bridge to Huddlesford Junction, BWF directly managed.

Birmingham Canal Navigation (BCN), Wyreley and Essington Canal; Cannock Extension; Fishley Lane to Pelsall Road, Edward Street WMC. Lane Head Bridge to Castle Bridge, Swan AC. Castle Bridge to Wards Bridge, Wednesfield Social C, AS. Wards Bridge to Alma Street Bridge, Whitmore Reans CAA. Two beats, Yorks Bridge to Becks bridge, Star AC. **BCN Walsall Canal;** Scarborough Road to Walsall Locks, Pleck Community Assc. **BCN Tame Valley Canal;** Gorse Farm to Walsall Road, Red Admiral AC. **BCN Rushall and**

Daw End Branch Canal; Rushall Junction to Chasewater Reservoir, to be developed as BWF direct management scheme. **BCN Birmingham Canal Main Line;** Soho Loop, Soho Loop AA. Tipton Factory Bottom Lock to Owen Street, West Midlands Travel Social & Welfare AC. The rest of this canal BWF controlled. **Coventry Canal;** Coventry to Polesworth, Coventry & Dist AA. Bulls Head Bridge to Amington, Polesworth WMC. The remaining five sections leased by Elite AC, Gate Inn (Amington) AC, Shuttington & Alvecote AC, Weddington Social C, AS, Dordon AC. **Grand Union Canal, Main Line;** Buckby to Calcutt Bottom Lock, Coventry & Dist AA. Calcutt Bottom Lock to Junction Bridge, Warwick, Royal Leamington Spa AA. Junction Bridge to Ugly Bridge, Warwick & Dist AA. **Saltisford Arm;** Saltisford Trading Co. Shrewley Tunnel to Rowington, Charterhouse WMC. Rowington to Chessets Wood and small arm at Kingswood Junction, Massey Ferguson Recreation C. Knowle, Knowle Red Lion AC. Rowood Bridge. Seven Stars AC. **Grand Union Canal: Arms and Branches; Leicester branch;** Norton Junction to south end Crick Tunnel, Coventry & Dist AA. To end of Bosworth Tunnel, Rugby FA and Coventry Dist AA. **Welford Arm;** Coventry & Dist AA. Theddington to south end Sandington Tunnel BWF directly controlled. **Market Harborough Arm;** Foxton to Bowden Hall BWF directly controlled. Bowden Hall Bridge to Market Harborough Basin, Market Harborough & Dist AS. Kilby to Blaby, Wigston AS. Blaby to Aylestone, Leicester AS. Aylestone to North Lock, Leicester, BWF managed. **Oxford Canal (North);** Napton Junction to Willoughby Wharf, Coventry & Dist AA. Willoughby Wharf to Stretton, BWF managed. Nettle Hill Bridge, Jaguar Cars AC. Whitings Bridge to Hawkesbury Stop Lock, Hawkesbury Angling Society. **Staffordshire and Worcester Canal;** York Street Stourport to Botterham Lock, Birmingham AA. Botterham Lock to Giggetty Bridge and Dimmingsdale Lock to Wightwick Lock, Whitmore Reans CAA. **Stratofrd-upon-Avon Canal;** Kings Norton Junction to Kingswood Junction, BWF managed. **Worcester and Birming-**

ham Canal; Blackpole Bridge to Kings Norton Tunnel, Birmingham AA. **NOTTINGHAM AREA:** **Chesterfield Canal;** Stockwith to Drakeholes Low Wharf, Sheffield & Dist AA. Clayworth Church Lane Bridge to Retsford Bridge, Worksop & Dist. AAA. West Retford Bridge to Chequer House Bridge, Retford & Dist AA. Chequer House to Bracebridge Lock, Worksop United AA. Bracebridge Lock to High Grounds Farm Bridge, Grafton AA. **Erewash Canal;** Trent Lock to Long Eaton Lock, Long Eaton Victoria AS, also **Cranfleet Canal.** Long Eaton Lock to Sandiacre Lock, Long Eaton & Dist FA. Sandiacre Lock to B5010 Bridge, West End AC. B5010 to Pasture Lock, Lace Webb Spring Co Sports & SC. Pasture Lock to Stanton Lock, Draycott AC. Stanton Lock to Greens Lock, Middleton WMC. A6096 to Common Bottom Lock, Durham Ox FC. Common Bottom Lock to Shipley Lock, Cotmanhay AC. Shipley Lock to Langley Mill Lock, NCB No 5 Area FC. R Witham at Langrick, E A Drings (Farms) Ltd, Witham House, Langrick, Lincs PE22 7AJ. **Grantham Canal;** Lady Day Bridge to Gamston Bridge, Heathfield AC. Other sections, Nottingham AA. Very little of this canal is fishable. **River Stoar Navigation;** Aylestone to North Lock, Leicester, managed by BWF in conjunction with Leics AS. Sections at Thurmaston and Wreake Junction, Leicester & Dist ASA. Barrow Shallow to Kegworth Old Lock, Loughborough Soar AS. Kegworth Flood Lock to Ratcliffe Lock, Long Eaton & Dist AF. **River Trent;** Hazelford Island, British Rail Staff Assc AS (Eastern Region). Lenton, Raleigh FC. Beeston Canal, Nottingham AA. Trent at Gunthorpe, Nottingham & Dist FAS. These are small fisheries. **Trent and Mersey Canal;** Derwent Mouth to Weston-upon-Trent, Derby AC. Weston-upon-Trent, Derby Railway FC. Clay Mills Bridge to Wychnor Lock, Burton Mutual AA. **NORTHWICH AREA:** **Caldon Canal;** very good water quality. Etruria Lock to Bedford Lock No 3, Stoke City & Dist AA. Other sections leased by these clubs: North Staffs AA, North Staffs Gas Anglers, Abbey Hulton Suburban Club (AS), Aynsley China AC, Leek & Moorlands FC (Willow Cottage bridge to Oak Meadow Ford Lock),

Cross Keys FC (Hazelhurst Junction). **Coventry Canal; Northern Section;** Huddlesford Junction to Stepping Stones Bridge, Horse & Jockey (Lichfield) AC. Stepping Stones to Kings Orchard Bridge, Lamb AC. Kings Orchard to Streethay Bridge. Lichfield Marina AS. Streethay Bridge to Bearshay Bridge, Whittington Social Fishing Club. Bearshay to Brookhay Bridge, Walsall Education and Conservative AC. Next Stretch, Horse & Jockey AC, then to junction with Trent & Mersey Canal, Swadlictote & Dist AA **Llangollen Canal** has recently been offered to various clubs and associations by BWF. Frankton section is leased by Lower Frankton AC, R Dee at Berwyn, by Liverpool & Dist AA.

Macclesfield Canal; Hardingswood Junction to Hall Green Stop Lock, North Staffs AA. Four sections to Watery Lane Aqueduct, Burslem Suburban AC, Radway Green Sports & Social C, Royal Doulton AC, Victoria AC. To Astbury, Robin Hood AC. Astbury to Peel Lane Bridge, Victoria and Biddulph AS, also to Lamberts Lane Bridge. To Park Lane Bridge and on to Porters Farm Bridge, Congleton AS. Porters Farm Bridge to Buxton Road Bridge, Congleton, Macclesfield Waltonian AS. To Congleton Bridge, Stoke-on-Trent AS. To Macclesfield, Prince Albert AS. **Montgomery Branch;** Aston Lock to Berriew Wharf, Prince Albert AC. To Tan-y-From, Brynllwyn Farm, Garthmyl, Powys. Two further club waters are Montgomeryshire AA and Cammell Laird Sports & SCAS. R Severn at Penarth Weir, Potteries AS. **Peak Forest Canal (Lower),** BWF managed. **Peak Forest Canal (Upper)** to be leased to clubs.

Shropshire Union Canal; in Wolverhampton area Whitmore Reans CAA have section, then Tettenhall Club & Inst, George Carter Ltd AC. Further sections leased by Codsall Legionaires AC, Penkridge Anglers; section to Stretton Aqueduct, Swan AC. Stretton, Brewood AC. Next two sections are leased by Hazeldine AA and Royal Exchange AS. Section to Cowley Tunnel, Izaac Walton (Stafford) AA. To Gnossal, Hazeldine AA. The leased sections to Tyreley are held by the following clubs, Market Drayton AC, Eaton Lodge AC, Park AC, Stafford Hospital AC, Hodnet WMC AC, Palesthorpes AS, Crown AC. The last long 50m section to Ellesmere Port is BWF managed.

Staffordshire and Worcester Canal; Northwich Area sections held by The Dog Angling Club, Evode AC, Whitmore Reans CAA; Gailey Wharf to Penkridge Lock, Broomhills AS. Penkridge Lock to Roseford bridge, Whitmore Reans CAA; Roseford Bridge to Milford Aqueduct, Izaac Walton (Staffs) AA. Milford Aqueduct to Great Haywood Junction, Potteries AS.

Trent and Mersey Canal; Wychnor Lock-south west, Alrewas AC. Section to Woodend Turn, Woodside Caravan Park AC. Handsacre Bridge to Wolseley Bridge, Rugeley & Brereton AS. Wolseley Bridge to Colwich Lock, Norton Lido AC. Ingestre Bridge to Weston Lock, North Staffs AA. Section to Aston Lock, Stoke City & Dist AA. Aston Lock to Meaford Lock, Stone & Dist AS. Meaford Lock to Stoke Basin, Fenton & Dist AS. Eturia to Whieldon Road Bridge, Stoke, Stoke City & Dist AA. Section to SE end of Harecastle Tunnel, Middleport WMC. N end of Harecastle Tunnel to Rode Heath Bridge, North Staffs AA. Rode Heath to Rookery Bridge and Booth Lane Top Lock to Shrops Union Junction, Middlewich, Cheshire AA. Rookery Bridge to Booth Lane Top Lock, British Legion AC (Middlewich Branch). St Anne's Bridge, Middlewich to Preston Brook, Trent & Mersey Canal AA. **River Weaver;** various sections between Winsford and Newbridge, Winsford & Dist AA. Between Newbridge and Bostock Works, Meadow bank Social C AS. Three further sections leased by Northwich AA.

WIGAN AREA:

Ashton Canal; Manchester, Dulcie Street Junction to Dukinfield Junction, BWF managed (excluding one short length). Ashton New Road Bridge to Clayton Lane Bridge, Clayton Aniline AS.

Huddersfield Narrow Canal; water tends to acidity, but contains trout. Scout Tunnel to Mossley, Micklehurst Liberal Club Ltd. Oldham & Dist AAA have Greenfield to Saddleworth and Stonebottom offside bank, plus Diggle Brook. Saddleworth to Diggle, Saddleworth & Dist AS. Huddersfield to Marsden, Slaithwaite & Dist AC.

Lancaster Canal; whole of canal from a point 600 yds south of Stocks Bridge,

Preston, to M6 at Crooklands, also **Glasson Branch,** Northern AA.

Leeds and Liverpool Canal; Liverpool to New Lane, Burscough, Liverpool & Dist AA. Halsall Bridge to Top Lock Wigan, and to Moss Lane Bridge, Wigan & Dist AA. Barnoldswick Long Ing Bridge to Johnson's Hillock Bottom Lock, Northern AA. Banknewton Top Lock to Office Lock, Leeds, Leeds & Liverpool Canal AA. **Leigh Branch;** Dover Lock to Plank Lane Bridge, Ashton & Dist Centre Northern AA. To Leigh Wharf, Leigh & Dist AA.

Manchester, Bolton and Bury Canal; Mainly disused at present. Hall Lane to 'Blue Wall Length', Bolton & Dist AA.

St Helens Canal; the water is so warm that it has tropical fish in it. Two sections leased by St Helens AA; Blackbrook Branch, Carr Mill End to Old Double Locks, and Pocket Nook Branch, from Railway Swing Bridge to terminal at Pilkingtons.

CASTLEFORD AREA:

Huddersfield Broad Canal; section from Apsley Basin entrance, Holme Valley PA. Red Doles Lock to Deighton Mill, British Gas S & SC. **Pocklington Canal;** Pocklington to Derwent junction, East Cottingwith, BWF direct management. **Ripon Canal;** leases being negotiated. **Selby Canal;** wide commercial waterway. Selby Basin to Bawtry Road bridge, Wheatsheaf AC. Bawtry Bridge to Brayton Bridge, Knottingley Conservative Club AS. Brayton Bridge to Burn Bridge, Selby AA. Burn Bridge to Paperhouse Bridge, Goole & Dist AA. Paperhouse Bridge to Tankards bridge, Featherstone & Dist AA.

Sheffield and South Yorkshire Navigation (Stainforth and Keadby Canal); Keadby, off-side, Electricity SI (Humberside & Yorks) AAC. Keadby Lock to Mauds Bridge, Stainforth & Keadby Joint AC. Thorne Lock Bridge to M18 Bridge, plus off-side bank near Thorne, Taverners IFAC. M18 to Dunston Hill Bridge, Hatfield Colliery AC. Dunston Hill to Stainforth High Bridge, Stainforth Parish Council FA. Bramwith Lock to Barnby Dun Swing Bridge, Northfield Bridge to aqueduct on New Junction Canal, Doncaster & Dist AA.

Sheffield and South Yorkshire Navigation; wide commercial section. Barnby Dun to Kirk Sandal, Barnby Dun SAC. Kirk Sandal to Railway Bridge, Pilkington

(Kirk Sandal) Rec C. By-Pass Bridge to Ickles, Guest & Chrimes Ltd AS. Ickles to Holmes Lock, Laporte AC. Holmes Lock to Jordans Lock, Bacho Record Sports & SC.

Remainder Length; restocked some years ago by BWF, now a very good fishery. Tinsley & Dist ACA have two sections; Tinsley Canal junction with R Don, and R Don to Jordan Lock. Tinsley Wire Sports & SC have two basins, as do Firth-Derihon (Tinsley) FC. Broughton Lane to Tinsley, BSC (Tinsley) Sports & SC. To Coleridge Road, Tuffnells AC. Between bridges at Coleridge Road and Darnall Road, Fox House Social Club AS. Darnall Road to Shirland Road, Drawbridge AC. Staniforth Road to Bacon Lane, Horse & Jockey AC. Bacon Lane to Bernard Road, Woodbourne Hotel AC. Bernard Road to Cadman Street, Woodseats WMC. To Victoria Station Bridge, Woodbourne Hotel AC.

River Ure; Ure and Milby Cut at Boroughbridge, plus Milby Lock to Tinkers Lane; Harrogate & Claro Conservative AA. Also on Ure and Milby Cut at Boroughbridge, Unity AC.

RESERVOIRS AND LAKES in English Canal System:

Halton Reservoir, Wendover. Coarse fishery leased from BWF by Prestwood & Dist AC. Enquiries to hon sec.

Wormleighton Reservoir, near Banbury. Coarse fishery leased from BWF by Wormleighton FC. Enquiries to hon sec.

Gayton Pool, Gayton, near Northampton. Carp fishery; Gayton AC members only.

Welsh Harp Reservoir, Brent. Proposed BWF directly managed fishery with great potential, owing to abating pollution. At present its future is being debated with conservationists.

Tardebigge Reservoir, Bromsgrove, leased by Bourneville Atheltic Club. Selectively open to public membership at moderate charge.

Upper and Lower Bittell Reservoirs (near Bromsgrove). Rights owned by Barnt Green FC, who stock Lower Bittell and adjacent Arrow Pools with trout; other pools hold coarse fish, including pike and bream. Guest tickets for coarse fishing to members' personal friends only *(see also Arrow tributary of Warwickshire Avon).*

Lifford Reservoir. Birmingham Parks. DT from park keeper.

Earlswood Lakes. Three Lakes totalling 85

acres stocked with roach, perch, bream, pike; carp and tench in two. Large eels. Dt on bank from bailiff. Match booking enquiries to Mrs Palmer, The Bungalow, Valley Road, Earlswood, Birmingham. Tel: Earls (728) 2436.

Sneyd Pool, Walsall. Coarse fishing leased by Swan AC.

Harthill, near Worksop. Coarse fishing leased by Harthill AA.

Gailey Lower Reservoir, near Wolverhampton. 64 acre coarse fishery, with big pike. BWF managed, st £14.

Lodge Farm Reservoir, Dudley. Coarse fishery. Enquiries to Dudley Corporation.

Himley Hall Lake, Himley. Trout, coarse fish. Enquiries to Dudley Corporation.

Stanley Lake, Stoke-on-Trent. Coarse fishery leased by Stoke-on-Trent AS.

Huddersfield Narrow Canal Reservoirs. Brunclough, Saddleworth & Dist AS water; **Tunnel End, Slaithwaite, Red Brook, March Haigh, Black Moss, Swellands** and **Sparth,** Slaithwaite & Dist AS waters.

B.W.B. MATCH FISHING ARRANGEMENTS OPERATIVE FROM THE 1st JANUARY 1987

1. As and from 1st January 1987 all bookings in respect of matches scheduled to take place on waters controlled by British Waterways Board will be dealt with by the appropriate British Waterways Board booking office as indicated on the application form.

2. Applications, which will be dealt with in strict rotation, must be in writing and **should be accompanied by a self-addressed stamped envelope, in each case.**
Provisional reservations may be made by telephone but these will only be treated as firm bookings when the application has been confirmed in writing, and the appropriate reservation fee (see below) has been paid.

3. A non-returnable reservation fee of £3.00 per match (irrespective of the number of pegs booked), must accompany each match application. The booking fee is intended to cover any administrative charges arising from dealing with the application. This fee will be off-set against the total amount of the peg fees due for any particular match. **Where the number of pegs required is 30 or less, the whole fee is payable at the time of booking.**

4. Apart from "Open" matches (see 5 below), peg fees will be charged at the rate of 80p per peg booked. Persons booking matches will be responsible for ensuring that the previously agreed amount is paid to the appropriate booking office within two weeks of the date on which the match was held.

5. "Open" matches. Where matches are booked as "Open" events—and this is specifically stated when the application is made—**the subsequent payment** will be at the rate of 80p for each angler actually competing in the match.

6. No allowance will be made for cancellations, or for any reduction in the number of pegs previously booked, unless the appropriate booking office has been given at least fourteen clear days notice, in writing, to this effect, in advance, of the date on which the match is due to take place.

7. Clubs or organisations cancelling without due notice, or simply failing to turn up without any explanation, will be invoiced by the Board, at the appropriate rate, for the pegs previously booked, less the £3.00 booking fee.

8. Adjustments will only be allowed in those instances where, due to circumstances beyond the club's/organisation's control, (e.g. water levels or engineering works), the match can either not go ahead as planned, or the number of pegs, has to be reduced accordingly.

9. Special rates will apply in the cases of matches which are held for disabled anglers or junior competitors only. The Fisheries Officer, Mr T G Leatherland, British Waterways Board, Willow Grange, Church Road, Watford WD1 3QA, will be pleased to provide the relevant details on request.

10. All match bookings are accepted on the understanding that individual anglers competing in the matches will possess valid Regional Water Authority Rod Licences, their keep-nets will conform to the minimum requirement as laid down in the Water Authority bye-laws, and that all fish are returned to the water as carefully as possible, after being weighed at the anglers peg.

11. The length applied for should normally allow 15 yards of towing path/bank between pegs but MATCH ORGANISERS MUST NOT PLACE PEGS UNDER OR NEAR TO OVERHEAD POWER LINES. The length requested should make due allowance for this fact.

ENGLISH SEA FISHING STATIONS

IN the following list the principal stations are arranged in order from north-east to south-west and then to north-west. Sea fishing can, of course, be had at many other places, but most of those mentioned cater especially for the sea angler. Names and addresses of club secretaries will be found in the list of angling clubs; secretaries and tackleists are usually willing to help visiting anglers either personally or by post on receipt of a stamped and addressed envelope. Details of accommodation, etc, can generally be had from the local authority amenities officer or information bureau of the town concerned.

Seaham (Co Durham). Cod (Oct–April all beaches especially Blast), codling, whiting (all in winter), mackerel (June–Aug), coalfish, flounders, plaice (mainly from boats), skate (Seaham Hall beach, June–Sept, night fishing, early flood), pouting, gurnard, etc. Excellent fishing from two piers. Dt £1.50 from Harbour Gatehouse. Seaham SAC, Clifford House, is local sea angling club. details and boat information from J Franklin, 14 Conningham Terrace, Houghton-le-Spring (Tel 842271). Tackleists: R Wright, 20 Green Street; K B Fox, North Terrace. Further information from R M Shenton, 54 Fern Crescent, Parkside.

Sunderland (Co Durham). Cod and codling (best Oct–April), whiting (best Sept–Oct), mackerel (June–Aug), coalfish, flounders, dabs, plaice, throughout year. Roker Pier provides good sport with cod and flatfish. North Pier is free of charge to anglers. Several small-boat owners at North Dock will arrange fishing parties, but there are also good beaches. R Wear banks at entrance good for flounders throughout year. Bait can be dug in Whitburn Bay and bought from tackleists. Clubs: Sunderland Sea AA. Ryhope Sea AA (both affiliated to Assn of Wearside Angling Clubs). Tackleists: J H Tennick, 51 Dundas Street (bait supplier); Palmers, Market Square Arcade.

Saltburn (Cleveland). Flatfish, coalfish, codling, whiting, mackerel, gurnard, some bass in summer and haddock late autumn. Float-fishing from pier in summer gives good sport; good codling fishing Oct to March. Club: Saltburn and Dist SAA.

Redcar (Cleveland). Five miles of fishing off rock and sand. Principal fish caught: Jan–April, codling; April–June, flatfish; summer months, coalfish (billet), whiting, mackerel, gurnard. Larger codling arrive latter part of August and remain

all winter. South Gare breakwater (4m away); good fishing, but hard on tackle, spinning for mackerel successful. Good fishing from beach two hours before and after low tide. Competitions every month. Tackleists: Harry Brough, 20 West Terrace.

Whitby (N Yorks). Increasingly popular centre for boat, pier and beach fishing. Cod up to 42 lb taken from boats, as well as large catches of haddock, whiting, flatfish, black bream, wolf fish, ling, etc. From East and West Piers billet (coalfish), flounders, mackerel, whiting and eels can be caught during the holiday season. Good beach angling may be obtained between Whitby and Sandsend, at Upgang, and Newholme Beck; flounder, mackerel, billet, and (after October) codling. Basic bait here is mussel and in summer herring and mackerel pieces are ideal for flounders and mackerel from piers, or for larger fish from boats, but most successful large-fish bait for past few years has been heavy breaking-strain feathered cod jig. Boats: J Grayson, 42 Brook Park, Sleights (Tel 0947 81606) and from tackleist: E Wilson, 65 Haggersgate (Tel 0947 3885) who also hires rods.

Scarborough (N Yorks). Sea fishing good from boat or harbour piers most of year. Autumn whiting very good in bay. Codling most plentiful Aug onwards. Winter codling fishing from First or Second Points to south of Scarborough and the Marine Drive. Mackerel, June–Sept, float or spinning. Various boats take out parties; bags of 3–4,000 lbs of cod in 12 hr sessions at times taken. Many over 40 lb in 1987. Festival in Sept. Clubs: Scarborough Rock AC; South Cliff AC; Scarborough Boat AC. Tackleists: at 56 Eastborough, and Buckley's Angling Supplies; Leading Post Street (who issue dt for the Mere; coarse fish). Sixteen charter boats available, taking 8–12 anglers. Charge: approx £2.50 per person for 4 hrs but longer trips to fish reefs and wrecks now popular. Phone (0723) 890134, 72791, 362083, 374885 or 71775.

Filey (N Humberside). Famous Filey Brig, ridge of rocks from which baits can be cast into deep water, is best mark. From June to Sept very good float fishing with sliding float for mackerel, coalfish (billet) and pollack. Good flatfish from shore and boats in summer. Best mackerel mid-July to end of Sept; for cod Sept to March (fish of around 30 lb taken on Brig recently). Tackle and bait from R Lewis, 12 Hope St, Tel Filey 513732. Local bait digging now prohibited. Boats may be hired from beach from May to Sept. Advanced booking advisable in winter. Filey Brig AS (st £3) organises fishing festival every year (first week of Sept). Good flyfishing for coalfish (billet) from Brig. Hotels: White Lodge, Hylands.

Bridlington (N Humberside). South Pier may be fished free all year and North Pier from Oct 1 to March 31. Sport in summer only fair—small whiting, billet, flatfish mainly—but good codling from Dec–March. Good flatfish, thornback ray and codling (winter) from small boats in bay. Yorkshire "cobbles" fishing **Flamborough** marks take variety of fish, including cod, haddock, mackerel and plaice, with pollack and coalfish in rocky areas. Rock fishing from shore at Thornwick Bay. Bait: lugworm may be dug in South Bay and small sand-eels caught by raking and digging on edge of tide. Tackleists: Linford's, Hilderthorpe Road; and Buckley's, Harbour Road (also supply bait). Many boatmen.

Hornsea (N Humberside). Tope, skate, flounders, occasional bass from shore; cod, haddock, plaice, dabs, tope, skate from boats. May to Oct. Whiting, dabs, codling, Oct to May. *(For tackleists see Bridlington.)*

Grimsby (S Humberside). Sea fishing along Humber bank free, and along foreshore to Tetney Lock; plaice, codling, dabs, flounders, eels. West Pier: st from Dock Office. Good centre for fens and broads. Clubs: Humber SAC, Cromwell Social Club (SA section) st Tackleists: F W Lightwood, 172 Cleethorpes Road; Cromwell Pet Stores, Cromwell Road; Weelsby Angling Stores, 413 Weelsby Street; Pets Pantry, 245 Grimsby Road, Cleethorpes. Special warning: Great

Grimsby Borough Council requires that all boats and persons in charge of boats be licensed by Great Grimsby Council. This is a safety precaution. Enquiries to Municipal Officers, Town Hall Square; or Port Health Offices, Fish Dock Road.

Skegness (Lincs). Beach fishing for cod, whiting, dabs and flounders in winter; for silver eels, flounders and dabs in summer. Boat fishing for same winter fish, for thornback skate, tope, dogfish, flounders and dabs in summer. Chapel St Leonards, and Ingoldmills the best beaches in winter. Tackleists: Palmer Sports, High Street. Clubs: Skegness SAC, with beach and boat sections. Annual sub £3 and £10 respectively. HQ now Working Men's Club, Briar Way.

Mablethorpe (Lincs). Good sea fishing from Mablethorpe to Sutton-on-Sea. Beach all sand; mainly flatfish, but some bass, skate, mackerel, tope from boats. Cod in winter. Sept–Dec best. Boat fishing limited by surf and open beach. Good flounders in Saltfleet Haven; also sea trout in Sept. Local club: Mablethorpe, Sutton-on-Sea and Dist AC (water on Great Eau for members only). Tackleists: T Clarke & Co, 25 High Street; Bela's, Victoria Road. Hotels at Mablethorpe, Trusthorpe, Sutton-on-Sea.

Salthouse, near Sheringham (Norfolk). Sea here is deep quite close in shore, and fishing considered good. Good flatfish, Oct–Jan. Occasional bass and mackerel in summer. Guest house: Salthouse Hall.

Sheringham (Norfolk). Flatfish all year; cod autumn and winter, mackerel June–Sept. Beaches good all year, except April and May. Best sport west of lifeboat shed towards Weybourne or extreme east towards Cromer. Centre beaches too crowded in season. Bait can be ordered from tackleists. Boat fishing best well offshore. Tope to 40 lb and thornbacks to 20 lb; plenty of mackerel. Tackleists: Kingfisher Tackle, 28 Beeston Road. Club: Sheringham Sea AC.

Cromer (Norfolk). Good all-year fishing; mainly cod (Sept–April), whiting and dabs, with odd tope (summer); skate and bass (summer) from pier and beaches. Boat fishing in calm weather (beach-launching). Parking at owner's risk on W Prom. Clubs: Cromer Inshore Sea AC (membership £5 pa); Cromer Sea AC. Fresh lugworm available from Marine Sports (open Sundays), High St. Hotels: Cliftonville, Red Lion, Hotel de Paris,

Grange Court, Colne House, Cliff House.

Great Yarmouth (Norfolk). All styles of sea fishing catered for, including two piers, several miles of perfect shore line for beach angler, two miles of well-wharved river from harbour's mouth to Haven Bridge, and boat angling. To north are Caister, Hemsby, Winterton, Horsey, Palling, Weybourne etc, and to south, Gorleston-on-Sea and Corton. Sport very similar in all these places; ie Oct, Nov, Dec: cod, codling, whiting, dabs, flounders, dogfish. Jan, Feb, March: codling, dabs, flounders. April, May, June, July, Aug and Sept: dabs, flounders, eels, skate and tope; from boats and shore from the north end of Yarmouth and particularly from offshore boat angling at those places previously noted to the north. Most successful baits are lugworm, herring or mackerel, soft-back crab and ragworm. Sea-angling festival held annually. Further information from tackleists Pownall & Sons Ltd, Anglers' Depot, 74 Regent Road, who issue RD licences. Other tackleist: J Markham, 43 South Market Road. For charter-boats, contact F Moore, Nelson Rd South.

Gorleston-on-Sea (Norfolk). Whiting, cod, dabs and flounders from beaches and in estuary (best Oct to March); good skate Aug and Sept. Sport good in these periods from boats, pier or at Harbour Bend in river and on beaches. Baits: lugworm, crab and ragworm. Freshwater fishing (coarse fish) within easy reach on rivers and broads. Further information from Baker & O'Keefe Ltd, Anglers' Depot, 7 Pier Walk.

Lowestoft (Suffolk). Noted centre for cod, autumn–May. Also whiting, flatfish, pollack and coalfish, with bass, tope, ray from charter boats and mullet in warmer months. Lugworm best bait. Good sloping beaches to north and south. Hopton, Pakefield, Kessingland are best. North best on flood, south on ebb. Claremont Pier poor, compared to beaches; mullet up to 7 lb, from South Pier. Baits from S Hooks and other tackleists. Boats from Williams, 95 Waveney Crescent, tel: 518000; S Moxey (tel 3549); G Knights (tel 63704); J Unsworth (tel 60532) and J Woods (tel 518000). Open festivals in October. East Anglian beach championships; inquire hon sec, Assn of E Anglian Sea Anglers.

Tackleists: Ted Bean, 175 London Road N; Sam Hooks, 132 Bevan Street; Laurie Phillips, 189 London Road South; Arthur Collen, 17 Commodore Road, Oulton Broad. Other clubs: South Pier, Lowestoft SA. Further information from Publicity Officer, 7 The Esplanade.

Southwold (Suffolk); ns Halesworth. Good codling, whiting and sole fishing from beach, October to March. Bass main species in summer from harbour or shore; soles and silver eels also provide sport May to Sept. Tackleist: Southwold Angling Centre, 64 High Street (Tel 722085) who will supply information on freshwater and sea fishing in locality. Hotels: Swan, Crown, Red Lion, Pier Avenue, Craighurst, Lord Nelson.

Felixstowe (Suffolk). Best in autumn and winter, when cod are about. Good sport in summer with bass, garfish from the pier by day and sole at night, and with eels in the estuaries. Skate fishing good in May, June and July, especially in harbour. Best sport from boats and pier. Boat bookings, bait and tackle from Ron Hutchinson, 2a Bent Hill. Clubs: Felixstowe SAC and Felixstowe Dock.

Harwich and Dovercourt (Essex). Bass, mullet, eels, garfish, flatfish, sting-ray, thornback, skate, soles (all May to Sept), whiting, pouting, codling (Sept to March). Best fishing from boats, but Stone Breakwater, Dovercourt is good. several good boat marks in estuary of Stour and Orwell and in harbour approaches. Best baits: lug, king rag, soft and peeler crabs. Boats: H Garnett. Club: Harwich and Dovercourt AC. Tackleists: Messrs Barton Marine, West Street, Harwich. Copy of Borough Guide supplied by Town Clerk on request.

Walton (Essex). Bass, whiting, pouting, flatfish, codling, skate, tope, from boats, shore and pier. Cod fishing begins about second week in Sept and runs to end of March. Dt for pier 70p, st £11. Walton-on-Naze Sea Angling Club (joining fee £6.80, st £5.30), has a hut on the pier. HQ at Royal British Legion Club. Tackle (and bait): J Metcalfe, 15 Newgate Street. Boats: J Moore, 159 Hall Lane (Tel Frinton 5955) and S Murphy, 67 Woodberry Way (Tel Frinton 4274) and D Finch (Tel Frinton 3217). Hotels: Tudor Inn (HQ of Walton SAC); Frinton Lodge, Frinton.

Clacton (Essex). Mainly autumn and winter fishing for whiting and cod. Summer fishing confined to pier and boats—bass, thornback, dogfish, tope, flatfish. Annual festivals arranged by Clacton Sea AC. Tackleists: Brian Dean, 43 Pallister Road; bait supplied; boats from Deans.

Southend-on-Sea (Essex). Mullet, bass, mackerel, scad, garfish, plaice and flounders are the main catches from the pier during the summer, with cod, codling and large flounders in the winter. A fleet of registered charter boats operate daily from the Pierhead, but prior booking is recommended. Thornback, stingray, smoothhound, bass, tope, plaice and cod can be expected. Pier: st £14, dt 80p. Application form from Brent Walker, Pipps Hill Country Club, Basildon. Off season shore fishing available, with all year round facilities at the Thorpe Bay and Westcliff bastions, also the river Crouch. Numerous open, pier, shore and boat events organised, including the Borough two-day festival. Tackleists: (Southend) Goings, (A Report Station), 20 Market Place, Alexandra Street; Jetty Anglers. Essex Angling Centre (Westcliff).

Whitstable and Tankerton (Kent). Good sea fishing. Dabs, plaice, bass, skate, flounders, eels, etc. Cod in winter from Tankerton beach. Boats available. Freshwater fishing on Seasalter Marshes, near Whitstable; roach, rudd, tench, pike, eels. Rod licences and information on sea and coarse fishing from tackleist: Boulting's, 33 Harbour Street. Hotels: Duke of Cumberland, Marine. Illustrated guide from Clerk of the Council, The Castle, Whitstable.

Herne Bay (Kent). Skate, plaice, flounders, whiting, dabs, silver eels, mullet, dogfish, codling, stingray and garfish. Bass can be taken in numbers either spinning or bottom fishing from June to Sept. Short length of pier opened for fishing following fire. Facilities for anglers with their own dinghies to launch and recover from Neptune slipway for 6 hrs before and after high water. Clubs: Herne Bay AA (HQ 59 Central Parade). St £5.15 (permitting use of clubhouse). Heron AS (HQ West Beach). Tackle, bait and RA licences: R Edwards, 46 High Street. Hotels: Four Fathoms, High Street; The Royal Hotel, Central Parade.

Sandwich (Kent). Bass at the mouth of the haven; sea trout and mullet run up the river; flounders, grey mullet, plaice, dabs, codling and pouting more seaward.

Freshwater fishing at Reed Pond; dt. Local club: Sandwich and Dist AS. Tackleists: Mr Francis, The Butchery. Hotels: Bell, Haven Guest House. *For freshwater fishing, see Stour (Kent).*

Margate (Kent). Noted for mixed catches. Fine bass often taken fron shore on paternoster, and boat by spinning. Stone pier good for cod in winter. Bass and cod from rocks at low water. Spring and autumn cod plentiful; fish up to 20 lb. Flatfish taken on sand outside Nayland Rocks. Skate at Minnis Bay, Birchington. Tope fishing from boat from June on through summer. Also dogfish and conger. Clubs: Margate Fishing Club; Old Centrals AC (130 Grosvenor Place). Tackleists: Kingfisheries, 34 King Street; Geoff's, 36 Fort Hill.

Broadstairs (Kent). Bass, plaice, pouting, whiting, codling, tope, etc; shore and boats. Club: Broadstairs and St Peter's SAS (st £3.50; hon sec will provide further information on free launching facilities etc). Annual sea angling festival usually in October.

Ramsgate (Kent). Good sport along 2m of shore, harbour piers, and Eastern and Western Chines. No charges for fishing from piers. Beaches crowded in summer, so night fishing best. In spring and summer good bass fishing (from shore), also soles, flounders, dabs and thornbacks. In autumn and winter; cod (in large quantities), conger, dabs, flounders, soles, whiting, pouting, dogfish. Pegwell Bay (thornbacks, dogfish, dabs), The Rough (conger) and Dumpton Gap (flatfish) are good boat marks. Good boats always available and experienced boatmen, with excellent prospects of big catches of skate, cod, dabs, dogfish, whiting, pouting, conger eels and a few tope. Bait may be dug in Pegwell Bay or gathered from rocks. Boat and pier festivals held in October and November respectively. Tackleists: Fisherman's Corner, 6 Kent Place; Vic's Tackle & Bait, 86–88 King Street. Hotels, etc, from Information Bureau, 24 Kings Street (Thanet 51086).

Deal and Walmer (Kent). Excellent sea fishing throughout the year. Spring: skate, dogfish and codling. Summer: bass, mackerel, garfish, black bream, flatfish, occasional tope and john dory. Autumn and winter; cod and whiting. Pouting all year. Boats out of Deal and Walmer enjoy good wrecking sport in the summer with modern cabin boats now in use as well as traditional open boats. Boat and Pier Festivals run by local clubs and area council. Excellent facilities for visiting anglers. Boat, pier and beach fishing all available. Clubs: Deal and Walmer Angling Association. Deal Angling Club (1919). Tackleists: Channel Angling, Deal Pier; The Foc'sle opposite the pier; The Downs Tackle Centre, The Strand, Walmer. All supply bait and tackle. Hotels: Beachbrow, Clarendon, Royal, Pegasus Restaurant, Lobster Pot Café.

Dover (Kent). Excellent boat and beach fishing in the area; good fishing for bass, codling, whiting and flatfish from Admiralty Pier, breakwater and Prince of Wales Pier, and for mullet and pollack from the last named. Tackle and bait from Brazils of Dover, 162, Snargate Street.

Folkestone (Kent). Good boat, beach and pier fishing. Conger (one of 42 lb landed recently), cod, bass, bream, flatfish, whiting, pouting and pollack, with mackerel in midsummer. Cod caught from boats on the Varne Bank all through the year, but from the shore, Oct–Feb only. Beach fishing best dusk onwards for bass and conger. Good sport from pier (50p). Some good offshore marks. For boats and bait apply: Garry's Tackle Shop, Tontine Street. Boats also from Folkestone Sea AA (annual pier and boat festivals. Annual membership: £10. Hotels: Cavendish Court (club HQ), Barrelle, and others; details from Information Bureau, Civic Centre, Castle Hill Avenue.

Sandgate (Kent). Very good fishing from beach and boats. There is a ridge of rock extending for over a mile 20 yds out from low-water mark. Bass good July–October; codling, whiting, pouting, conger March–May, August–Nov; good plaice taken May–2June, especially from boats. Best months for boat fishing, Sept–Nov. The hon sec, Sandgate AS, will be glad to give information. Hotels: Wellington, Esplanade.

Hythe (Kent). Fishing from boat and shore for bass, codling, pouting, whiting, conger and flats. Princes Parade, **Seabrook,** is popular. Open storm beach, giving pouting, whiting, mackerel, sole, dab and flounder in summer and cod (up to 20 lb), whiting and pouting in winter. Few bass. Tackleists: J B Walker Ltd, 84

Stade Street, (tel: 0303 66228). Hotels: Imperial, Stade Court, White Hart, Swan. Clubs: Seabrook Sea AS; Sandgate Sea AS; Castaways Sea AS.

Dungeness (Kent). Boat and shore fishing, latter all year round. Whiting, pouting, codling, conger, dabs, plaice, mackerel. Good bass fishing in summer from shore and boat. Best months: May to Oct for boat fishing; Oct to Feb for shore fishing. Bait (lug) obtainable locally from diggers. Hotels: George, Railway, Dolphin; Jolly Fisherman at Greatstone. Club: Brett Marine AC.

Hastings (Sussex). Sea fishing from pier and boats. Tope, bass, conger, plaice, codling, whiting, etc. Boats available from local fishermen. Hastings and St Leonards SAA has its own boats on beach opposite headquarters. Association also has clubroom on Hastings Pier. East Hastings Sea AA has clubhouse and own boats on foreshore. Annual International Sea Angling Festival in October. Bait, tackle: Redfearn's, Castle. Street; George's, opposite pier. International boat and pier festivals held in the autumn.

St Leonards (Sussex). Good sea fishing all the year round from boats and beach for flatfish, bass, mackerel, conger, tope, whiting, cod, bull huss, turbot. Boats, bait and boatmen from Warrior Square slipway. St Leonards Sea Anglers' clubhouse at 16 Grand Parade. Competitions run throughout the year, boats and beach. Annual subscription £7 + £1 joining fee. Concessionary £4.

Bexhill (Sussex). Boat and shore fishing. Cod, conger, whiting (Sept to end Dec). Dabs, plaice, mackerel, tope (July–Sept). Bass, best months May, June and July. Tackleist: Renne's, 10 Buckhurst Place. Club: Bexhill AC (hon sec will help visitors, enclose sae). Freshwater fishing in Pevensey Sluice, Pevensey Haven and dykes; coarse fish. Hotel: Granville.

Eastbourne (Sussex). Boat, pier and shore fishing. Dabs, huss, pouting and conger (all year), cod in winter and skate (May to Dec). Best for place and bream from June to Nov. Also soles, whiting, flounders, mullet. Good bass and mullet in warmer months. Notable tope centre, many around 40 lb; June and July best. Some of the best beach fishing for bass around Beachy Head (up to 17 lb). Pollack from rocks. Flatfish off Langney Point and from pier. For boats inquire

Eastbourne AA, annual membership £20 (temp holiday membership £1, from boat steward). Good clubhouse and 18 boats for members' use. Other clubs: Nomads SAC. Bait mainly from Langney Point area and tackleists: Anglers kiosk on pier; Compleat Angler, Pevensey Road; Tony Kirrage, Seaside.

Seaford (Sussex). Beach and boat fishing. Bass, cod, codling, conger, flats, huss, mackerel and few ling and pollack. Good catches of tope few miles offshore. Club: Seaford AC (open to new members; inquiries hon sec).

Newhaven (Sussex). Variety of sport from beach and boat. Beach fishing for bass excellent May–Oct. Flounders from Tide Mills Beach. Good cod fishing from beaches between Seaford Head and Newhaven's East Pier, late Oct to early March. Breakwater gives good all-round sport, with bass, conger and cod all running large. Boat fishing excellent for cod in winter, large Channel whiting also give good sport. Monkfish off Beachy Head late August and Sept. Boats from Harbour Tackle Shop, Fort Road (tel 514441). Other tackleists: Dennis's, 107 Fort Road; Book & Bacca, 8 Bridge Street. Hotel: Sheffield.

Brighton and Hove (Sussex). Noted for black bream (June–Sept) from pier and boats. Bass from pier (12 lb biggest) and beaches. Mullet and mackerel from pier. Good tope from boats. Beach anglers take flatfish as well as bass. Good cod from pier and boats in winter. Shark sport growing. Boats mainly from Shoreham and Newhaven; a few at Brighton. Details from tackleists. Several beach, pier and boat festivals. Tackleists: Preston Aquarium, 44 Beaconsfield Road; Lagoon Bait and Tackle, 327 Kingsway, Hove. Most dealers supply bait. Clubs: at Kings Road Arches are three clubs—Brighton Deep Sea Anglers, Brighton Cruising Club and Sir Robert Peel AC (first two deep-sea fishing only). Queens Head AC specialises in beach fishing but membership limited (HQ Madeira Drive). Hove Deep Sea AC has boats for tope, conger, skate, turbot, plaice, dabs, etc. Friends of members can fish with members. Good trolling for bass, July–August, around Marina arms.

Shoreham and Southwick (Sussex). Boat and harbour fishing. Bass (July and August); grey mullet, skate and huss (June to Sept); cod and whiting (Sept to Dec); dabs, plaice, pouting, black bream, conger, mackerel and flounders (May onwards). Mullet fishing in River Adur near Lancing College very good July–August; light paternoster tackle and red ragworm recommended. Baits: white rag, red rag and lugworms may be dug from beach and mudbanks of river. Mussels and other baits can also be obtained.

Worthing (Sussex). Boat, beach and pier fishing. Codling, flounders, pollack, garefish, whiting, plaice, eels, bream, mullet (good). Excellent flounder fishing from beaches, spring and autumn. Bass has declined. Mixed catches from boats. River Adur, east of Worthing, noted for flounders, mullet and eels. Local association: Worthing Sea AA (HQ, Worthing Pier), annual membership £4 + £1 entrance fee. Tackleists: Ken Dunman Ltd, 2 Marine Place (opp Pier entrance). Boats from harbours at Shoreham and Littlehampton. Popular 2-day pier festival held in early September. Reduced fee to OAP.

Littlehampton (Sussex). Noted for black bream, but wide variety taken, including skate (all year), bass (June–Oct), cod (winter best) and plaice. Bait can be dug from beaches or ordered from David Jones, High Street. Boats through Littlehampton Skippers Assn, c/o Harbour View Cafe, Pier Road. Club: Licensed Victuallers Deep Sea AC (HQ Arun View Inn, The Bridge; membership open to publicans). Littlehampton and Dist AC, annual membership £4.50. Best sport from boats.

Bognor Regis (Sussex). Good sea fishing at several marks off Bognor. Tope, bass, pollack, mackerel, whiting, wrasse. From May to July bream are plentiful. The conger, skate and sole fishing is very good. Grey mullet abound in the shallow water between Felpham and Littlehampton Harbour. Good cod fishing between September and November. Bass weighing 5–10 lb and more caught from pier and shore. Also good pouting and pollack caught from coarse fishing in the Arun. The hon sec of Bognor Regis Amateur AS will supply information *(see also Sussex—lakes)*. Tackleist: Sports & Radio, 25–29 Aldwick Road; Fisherman's Den, Canada Grove. Boats can be had from local fishermen.

Hayling Island (Hants). From the South Beach of Hayling Island good fishing can be had with a rod and line for bass, plaice, flounders, dabs, whiting, etc, according to season. Fishing from boats in Hayling Bay for tope, skate, bass, mackerel, etc, is popular and a much favoured area is in the vicinity of the Church Rocks and in Chichester Harbour.

Southsea (Hants). Over 4m of beach from Eastney to Portsmouth Harbour provide good sport all year. Bass fishing especially good from spring to September. Flatfish and rays numerous, large mackerel shoals in mid-summer. Best sport from boats. Boom defence line from Southsea to IoW, although navigational hazard, is probably one of the best bass fishing marks on the South Coast. Vicinity of forts yields good bags of pollack, bass, black bream, skate, etc. Tope fishing good during summer. Portsmouth, Langstone and Chichester within easy reach and provide good sheltered water in rough weather. Boats can be hired from Portsmouth boatmen. Bait from harbours but not plentiful can be ordered from tackleists. Southsea Sports, 14 Highland Road; B Osborne, Bridgemary, Gosport; Paiges, 165 New Road, Portsmouth. Club: Southsea Sea AC, who have club boats. Tel 825508. Annual membership £11.50.

Southampton (Hants). Fishing in Southampton Water really estuary fishing; thus not so varied as at some coastal stations. However, flounders abound (float and/or baited spoon fishing recommended), and whiting, pouting, silver eels, conger, bass, grey mullet, soles, dogfish, thornback, skate, stingray, plaice, dabs, scad, shad, mackerel have all been caught. At the entrance to Southampton Water, in Stokes Bay and the Solent generally, excellent tope fishing may be had. Angling from Hythe Pier, and from Netley and Hamble shores, but best fishing from boats. Southampton Water is rarely unfishable. Good sport in power station outflow. Southampton Sea AC holds competitions throughout the season and an annual shore festival; information from hon sec. Tackleists Waterhouse & Connings, Woolston; Holt & Haskell, High Street, Shirley; Connor & Mitchell, St Marys; St Denys Sea Bait and Tackle, St Denys.

ISLE OF WIGHT

The Island provides a wealth of shore and boat fishing, and sheltered conditions can always be found. Bass are the main quarry for beach anglers, but pollack, conger, mackerel, pouting, thornback rays, flatfish and wrasse, with occasional tope, are also taken. Black bream, skate and shark are caught by boat anglers as well as the species already mentioned.

Alum Bay. This necessitates a steep descent from the car park down the steps provided. From March to October there is a chair lift in operation. Fishes well after dark for large conger, bass or rays. From the old pier remains to the white cliffs is the main area, although the rocks to the east, towards Totland, make a good station from which to spin for bass in the tide race, or to light leger with squid or mackerel.

Atherfield. A number of record fish have been taken from this stretch and although the cliff path is steep, it is not difficult. The beach is of shingle merging sharply with the rock of the ledge which extends for over a mile out to sea. Any of the previously mentioned baits are good with the addition of ragworm for bass or pout. A 50 lb monkfish was taken from here and conger to 45 lb, skate 30 lb, turbot 15 lb and tope of 40 lb. A bass of 10 lb was once taken only 15 yards out and the pout can run up to 3 lb.

Bembridge. The shore from Whitecliff to Bembridge is mainly rock formation with stretches of shingle and is good ground for bass and conger although not fished a great deal. Bass, mullet, conger and wrasse among the rocks. Here, the beach turns to fine flat sand and flatfish and bass are taken. Bembridge Harbour is a wide inlet with St Helens on the opposite bank. Boats may be chartered locally. A sand gully near the "Crab and Lobster" can be fished from the rocks. Fine bream may be taken from boats on Bembridge Ledge, early May to June. A good number of fish are taken in the harbour. Flounders, plaice, bass, silver eel with an occasional sole and bream. Many large mullet can be seen in the harbour but are seldom fished for. Kingrag and lugworm are good baits for ledgering and small mud ragworm on light float tackle is successful. Baited spoon or wander tackle works well for flounder and plaice. Tackleist: Bembridge Angling, Embankment Road. Club: Bembridge AC.

Bonchurch. Bass, conger, plaice, flounders, pout from beach.

Brooke. Bass off ledge and pouting on marks. Few good bass taken off shore at point in rough weather.

Chale. Bass from shore, pouting, mackerel and few conger, but difficult to arrange boat. Shore fishing after dark. Some tope. Hotel: Clarendon.

Colwell Bay. Mackerel, bass, pollack and wrasse off ledge. Boat obtainable. Hotel: Holmes Court.

Compton Bay. 1m west of Brooke. Good bass fishing from shore and near wreck.

Cowes. The River Medina runs from Newport to Cowes Harbour and offers flounder fishing throughout the year with the best sport from the late summer to autumn. The shoals move about the river with the tide and location is often a matter of local knowledge. As a general guide the fish may be expected further upstream on the stronger spring tides. Weights average up to a pound. Bass also move into the river and have been taken to 4 lbs, often on flounder tackle. Rowing boats may be launched from the Folly Inn on the East bank, reached by turning off the main Newport to East Cowes road. Kingston power station about a mile down from Folly is a good boat mark for school bass, plaice, sole and grey mullet.

Cowes Harbour. Bass, flounder, plaice and sole may be taken by the boat angler from either side of the fairway above and below the floating bridge and during the summer there are many large mullet within the harbour. Inside the break-water to the east, flounder and plaice are taken on the bottom from along the edge of the hovercraft channel to inshore towards the East Cowes Esplanade. Flounder and plaice are also taken from the mud-flats outside the East Cowes breakwater.

West Cowes Esplanade to Gurnard. Float fishing and spinning from the slipways and jetties. Along the Princes Green to Egypt Light, bass and conger can be found and in late summer bass often venture close in under the walls in search of prawns and may be taken by trailing a worm over the balustrade and walking it quietly along. At Egypt Light, the shingle slopes steeply so long casting is unnecessary, and tope have occasionally be landed here as well as bass to 8 lbs. The sandy patches among the rocks may yield plaice in season. Free car parking here. Hotels: Gloster; Fountain; Woodvale; Gantham, Holmwood; Waverley.

Freshwater Bay. Pouting, small pollack and few conger on marks. Few bass and occasional conger off shore in rough weather. Boats available. Hotels: Albion, Farringford, Osoborne Private. Tackleist: Evalyn's, Avenue Road, Freshwater.

Newport. Nearest sea fishing in River Medina; flounders, school bass, mullet.

Newtown. Bass and flounders in Newtown River. Clamerkin reach is best.

Niton. Pouting and conger. A few bass taken, fishing from the wall at Binnell Bay.

Osborne Bay. Small whiting and pouting in autumn. Boat from Cowes.

Ryde. Bass, small pollock, plaice, flounders, eels, bream and grey mullet from pier. Conger, dogfish, dabs, skate, mackerel from deep water marks, and plaice, flounder, bass and sole fishing inshore. Cod up to 24 lb taken in autumn. Sheltered resort giving ideal fishing conditions all year. All beaches fishable. King rag and lugworm plentiful. Vectis Boating and Fishing Club offers annual membership. Details from hon sec (enclose sae). Boats can be hired along shore. Bait and tackle: Sports & Model Shop, 9 Union Street, Don's Sports, 14 Cross Street; The Tackle Box, 73 High St. Inquiry office at Ryde Esplanade.

Sandown. Good beach and pier fishing. Bass all year, with largest in early autumn. Plaice, sole, dabs, pollack and grey mullet (doing very well of late), turbot, mackerel, garfish. Large skate, ray and conger from pierhead late summer and autumn, cod in winter. Best baits: ragworm, lugworm, herring, sandeels, slipper limpet. Local club: Sandown and Lake AS, organising frequent open competitions. Visitors welcome. Tackleist (and boats): Sea-Tac, 6–8 Wilkes Rd.

Seaview. From St Helens to Seaview the coast is a mixture of rocks and sand and shingle. Priory Bay is reached by boat and provides very good mackerel and bass fishing. Plaice may be taken to 3 lb from early April, with lugworm. During the summer months bream can also be taken from this spot. From June onwards, bass and mackerel are shoaling and large catches from boats are common. Cod are also taken late in the year. Boats from Mr Newell, High Street, and Seagrove Bay. Tackleists: Mr Dobson, Pier Road; Alvera's, High Street. Hotels: Seaview, North Bank.

Shanklin. Bass, conger and pollack from Luccombe and Horseshoe Ledges in boat. Pouting and flatfish from pier; bass and flatfish from beaches. Open competitions every Wednesday during the summer. Club: Shanklin AS. Tackleist: 2 Piers Tackle, Sports Shop, Regent Street.

Totland. Bass off shingle bank from boat. Bass, conger from shore. Fishing also from pier 20p. Boats from Fair Deal Amusements, The Pier. Hotels: Totland Bay, Chalet, Sentry Mead.

Ventnor. The western end of the beach is good for bass, skate, pout and conger and the sea wall in front of the canoe lake is a good bass spot. The pier has produced good fish including pollack, mullet, pout, skate, conger, plaice and sole with the occasional bream and brill. Access to the pier is through the amusement premises which are closed in winter, with a loss of good potential fishing. Boat (from Blakes) for pollack and mackerel. Club: Ventnor AC (associate members welcome). Tackleist and bait: Bates & Son, 5 Spring Hill. Beach fishing *(see also Bonchurch).*

Wootton. School bass and flounders.

Yarmouth. Bass, small pollack; pier fishing suspended pending repairs.

Mainland continued

Lymington (Hants). Tope, sting-ray (May–July), conger (May–Nov), cod (Oct–March) from boats and beach. Hurst Castle area good beach spot for cod and large bass. Flounders (Oct–Feb) Hurst and Pennington–Lymington Marshes, boat and shore. Pouting (March–Nov), whiting (Oct–March), bass, flatfish (April–Nov). All beaches from Hurst Castle westwards to Mudeford. Tackleists: Smiths Sports, 25 Queen Street, Lymington; Boats from Lymington and Keyhaven. Hotel: Angel, Club: Lymington & Dist Sea FC (HQ: The Railway Hotel) annual memb £5.

Mudeford (Dorset). At entrance to Christchurch Harbour. Good all-round sea fishing in Christchurch and Poole Bay, the vicinity of the Ledge Rocks and farther afield on the Dolphin Banks. Tope, dogfish, conger, bream, pout, pollack, whiting and good sport spinning for mackerel and bass. Plaice off Southborne; flounders, dabs, skate and sole off beaches at Highcliffe, Barton and Southbourne; flatfish, bass, whiting, etc, from quay, beach, groyne or shore at Hengistbury Head; large tope, stingray, skate and occasional thresher shark off The Dolphins. Fairly good cod fishing in winter, Needles–Christchurch Ledge, Pout Hole and Avon Beach (off Hengistbury Head). Whole squid favourite bait, but large baited spoons and jigs also successful. Good sole from Taddiford and Highcliffe Castle (best after dark). Groyne at Hengistbury good for bass in summer; sand eels by day and squid by night. Best months for general sport, mid-June to mid- or late Sept. Most local fishermen now take parties out mackerel fishing in summer. Flounders, eels, bass and mullet taken inside the harbour. Boats from R A Stride, The Watch House, Coastguards Way, Mudeford, and R Keynes, The Quay, Christchurch. Hotels: Avonmouth, Waterford Lodge, The Pines Guest House. *For other tackleists and freshwater fishing, see Christchurch under Avon (Hampshire) and Stour (Dorset).*

Bournemouth (Dorset). Fishing good at times from the pier yielding bass, grey mullet, plaice, dabs, etc. Excellent catches of plaice, dabs, codling, silver whiting, mackerel (spinning), tope up to 40 lb, conger, skate, from boats. Shore fishing, when sea is suitable, for bass and other usual sea fish. Bait supplies fairly good. Clubs: Boscombe and Southbourne SFC; Bay AS; Christchurch AA; Christchurch Sea FC. Tackleists: The

Triangle Sports Shop, 111 Commercial Road, who will advise visitors, arrange trips from pier. Good accommodation for anglers at Edelweiss Guest House, 32 Drummon Rd, and Malvern Guest House, 7 Hamilton Rd, Boscombe (angling proprietor). For freshwater fishing, *(see Avon (Hampshire) and Stour (Dorset))*.

Poole (Dorset). Boat, beach and quay fishing in vast natural harbour. Great variety of fish, but now noted for deep-sea boat angling and bass fishing. Conger, tope, bream, etc, are caught within three miles of the shore. Bass, plaice, flounders, etc, caught inside the harbour at Sandbanks and Hamworthy Park in their seasons. Local tackle shops should be consulted for up-to-the-minute information. Boat fishing facilities largely controlled by Derek Case Angling Agency, 5 High St, Poole (tel 676597), who has over thirty boats available. Sea Fishing (Poole) Ltd also cater for bass and deep-sea angling (tel 679666). Baits favoured locally: mackerel, squid, sand eel and ragworm. Tackleist: Derek Case Angling Agency.

Swanage (Dorset). Four tides a day in area. Many species taken from pier incl bass, mullet, pollack, mackerel, flounder and pouting. Beach here and at **Studland Bay** produces good bass, flounder and dabs at night; too crowded for daytime fishing. Tope, skate, conger, black bream and brill taken from boats outside bay. Boats available daily from Swanage. Around Peveril Ledge and Durlston Head there is good pollack fishing to St Alban's Head; also bass and mackerel. Chapman's Pool: pollack, codling, bass, pout. Old Harry Rocks: bass, prawns. Durlston Bay good for mullet. Local association: Swanage and Dist AC (annual membership: £4) from clubhouse, next to lifeboat slipway. Details

of accommodation from information bureau and Swanage Angling Centre, 6 High St.

Weymouth (Dorset). Centre for the famous Chesil Beach, Shambles Bank, Portland and Lulworth Ledges. The steeply sloping Chesil Beach provides year-round sport for many species, but autumn and winter best for mackerel, codling, whiting, bream and dogfish; beach fishes best at night; fairly heavy tackle required. Good conger fishing at the Chesil Cove end, Ringstead Bay, Redcliffe and round the piers. Piers yield good sport with grey mullet. Good bass from Greenhill beach in heavy surf, with variety of flatfish at most times. Ferrybridge and the Fleet noted for bass, mullet and flounders. Boat fishing: In the area around Portland Bill some big skate and stingray give good sport, while the notable Shambles Bank continues to yield turbot and skate, etc. Lulworth Ledges have a large variety of fish including tope, blue shark, conger, skate, dogfish, black bream, pollack, whiting, etc. Best baits are lugworm, ragworm, soft crab, mackerel and squid. No boats from Chesil Bank, but 16 boatmen operate from Weymouth throughout year. Angling Society booklet from Weymouth Publicity Office, Weymouth Corporation and hon sec. Tackleists: Anglers' Tackle Store, 64 Park Street; S Hayman, 13 Trinity Road; Gilbert Sports, 4 St Alban Street; J M Hockaday, Portland Road, Wyke Regis.

Portland (Dorset). Good bass fishing in harbour; live prawns for bait. Mullet, mackerel, whiting and conger are plentiful. Boats from fishermen at Castletown (for the harbour), Church Ope, The Bill and on the beach. Near the breakwater is a good spot, where refuse from the warships drifts up.

Check before you go

While every effort has been made to ensure that the information given in "Where to Fish" is correct, the position is continually changing and anglers are urged, in their own interests, to make preliminary inquiries before travelling to selected venues. This is especially important with reference to prices quoted. Inevitably, the rate of inflation is affecting stability in this quarter. Anglers' attention is also drawn to the fact that the hotels mentioned under the various fishing stations do not necessarily have water of their own. Any amendments or further data for inclusion in subsequent editions, and any criticism, will be welcome.

CHANNEL ISLANDS

Wide variety of sport from beaches, rocky headlands and boats. Many specimen fish landed from deep-sea marks. Shark fishing growing in popularity. Boats often difficult to come by.

Guernsey. No fewer than 52 different species recorded in Bailiwick of Guernsey rod-caught record list. Many headlands offer first-class spinning for pollack, mackerel, garfish and scad; grey mullet everywhere. Other species are red and black bream, red mullet, wrasse, whiting, pouting and conger. A flat, sandy, west coast gives good surf-casting for bass and a few flatfish. Several Guernsey fish accepted as new British records. Boat fishing for shark, turbot, etc, but organised fishing trips are few, due to difficulties in obtaining licensed boats. There is, however, one boat which makes two trips a day for general fishing from St Peter Port; details from Ron Taylor, Le Baugy Estate, Jerbourg, St Martin. Occasional vacancies for visitors interested in shark and tope with Guernsey 30 Fathom Club; inquire at Baker's 43, The Pollet, St Peter Port. D H Langnois of St Peter Port takes out parties (equipped with their own tackle) from 10 am to 5 pm. £11 per person per day. Tel 0481 26307 for bookings. Other boat operators are D Lane, tel: 27161, from St Peter Port; M Ryan, tel: 44712, G Hamel, tel: 57947, from St Sampson. Fresh sand-eel is best bait; available at very nominal price in local fish market. Ragworm widely used but fairly difficult to obtain. Clubs: Guernsey Sea AC; 30 Fathom Club. Tackleists: Marquand Bros, North Quay; Baker's, 43 The Pollet (**St Peter Port**); T Henry, The Hermitage,

Vale; G Domaille, The Bridge, St Sampson. Brochure and accommodation guide from States Tourist Committee, St Peter Port.

Jersey. The island offers a great variety of first-class sea fishing from beaches and harbours for a wide variety of fish. Several records have been broken here in recent years. Species caught at various stations around the island include pollack, wrasse, conger, plaice, scad, bass, garfish, mackerel, mullet, pouting, flounder, black bream, sole and ray. Fishing is particularly good at the following venues: St Helier's harbour heads; St Aubin's Bay, harbour, and fort; Noirmont Point; St Brelade's Bay; La Corbiere; L'Etacq; Plemont; Greve de Lecq; Bonne Nuit Bay harbour; Bouley Bay harbour; Rozel Bay harbour; St Catherine's breakwater; Gorey harbour; Grouville Bay; St· Aubin's Bay. Jersey SFC (HQ 16 Broad Street, St Helier) will help visitors. Coarse fishing in St Ouens Canal, wt £3 and permits for reservoir trout fishing (dt £8) from tackle shop in vegetable market. Five sea angling clubs hold competitions. For boat charters, £15, Angling Charters Ltd, tel: 63679. Tackleists: Wheways, 16 Broad St; Hunt, 71 King St; The Fishing Centre, and P J N Fishing Tackle, 7 Beresford Market. Tel: 0534 74875. All St Helier. For further details, P Gosserin, Nouages Neavaine, Golf Lane, Grouville.

Mainland continued

Bridport (Dorset). Beach fishing yields bass, pouting, flatfish, thornback rays and conger, with whiting and cod in winter and large numbers of mackerel in summer. From boats: black bream, conger, pollock, whiting, pout, dogfish, bull huss, rays, cod and wrasse. West Bay (1½m distant) the angling centre. Burton Bradstock, West Bexington and Abbotsbury are popular venues on Chesil Beach. Eype and Seatown favoured to west. Bait: ragworm, squid, mackerel favoured. Tackleists: L A Rathbone, The Tackle Shop, West Bay

Road, West Bay, who arranges boat-fishing (Tel 0308-23475). Lyme Bay Marine, Old Customs House, West Bay. Club: West Bay Sea AC. Hotel: The George, W Bay.

Lyme Regis (Dorset). Bass may be caught from the shore (bait with fresh mackerel obtained from motorboats in harbour or lugworm dug in harbour at low tide). Mackerel may be caught from May to October. Conger fishing from the high wall of harbour. Pollack plentiful in spring months. Conger and skate can be caught from boats about 2m from shore.

Motor and rowing boats can be hired at harbour. Tackleists: R J Stratton Ltd, 15 Broad Street.

Seaton (Devon). Boat fishing. Pollack, pouting, conger, wrasse (March to Sept), bass (virtually all year, but best Sept–Nov), bream, mackerel, dabs, skate, plaice, dogfish. Axe estuary good for bass, mullet and sea trout. Hotels: Pole Arms, Bay. Tackleists: F Ackerman & Co Ltd, Fore Street.

Sidmouth (Devon). Sea fishing in Sidmouth Bay. Mackerel (May to Oct), pollack (excellent sport spring and summer east and west of town), bass (to $13\frac{1}{4}$ lb in surf at Jacob's Ladder beach during summer), large winter whiting (July–Oct on rocky bottom), skate to $105\frac{1}{2}$ lb and conger to 44 lb have been taken; bull huss to $19\frac{1}{2}$ lb, and tope. Also plaice, dabs, flounders and occasional turbot. Hon sec, Sidmouth Sea Angling Club, can give information about baits and tempororary membership. *For freshwater fishing see Axe, Otter, Sid (trout) and Exe and Exeter Canal (coarse)*. Information, bait and tackle from Sidmouth Sports Shop, Market Place. Boats from S French and S Bagwell. Details of accommodation from Publicity Officer, Council Offices. Budleigh Salterton: a few bass at Otter mouth; beach best for flat-fish night fishing. Some mackerel from boat. No tackleist or hotel.

Exmouth (Devon). Bass are caught here all the year round, from the $3\frac{1}{2}$ miles of sandy beach, or with live sand-eel from a boat at anchor or drifting. Mackerel fishing popular in summer. Flounders, eels, plaice and dabs may be taken with soft crab, lug or ragworm; pollack with sand-eel, ragworm or artificial lure off Straight Point and pier, where pout, mullet, conger and bass are also taken. Reef fishing from boats excellent, for a wide variety of species. Interest in shark fishing now growing. Tackleist: Fred Statham, (qualified NFSA instructor) Pier Head; Exmouth Tackle Shop, 20 The Strand. Boat-bookings from both.

Dawlish (Devon). Dabs and whiting in bay off Parson and Clerk Rock and between Smugglers' Gap and Sprey Point. Mackerel good in summer. Conger eels and dogfish about $\frac{3}{4}$m from shore between Parson and Clerk Rock and Shell Cove. Good fishing sometimes off breakwater by station and from wall of Boat Cove. Boats from Boat Cove. Good trout

fishing at Chagford and Moretonhampstead.

Teignmouth (Devon). Sea fishing ideal (especially for light spool casting with sand-eels for bass). Bass, pollack, flounders in estuary. Mackerel, dabs and whiting in the bay. Good flounder fishing from the shore. Deep sea, wreck and offshore trips available. The town has an annual sea fishing festival. Club: Teignmouth SAS (HQ, River Beach). Tackleists: Doel Sports, 12/13 Bank Street and The Sea Chest, 8 Northumberland Place (for RD licences, permits for Newton Abbot waters, coarse fishing; bait for sea angling; information). Boats and bait from John Perry, Sid Back, John Harvey and Bob Hussey. Details of accommodation from Town Enquiry Bureau, The Den.

Torcross; nr Kingsbridge (Devon). Hotel: Torcross Apartment Hotel, offering both self-catering facilities and high-class catering. Right beside the Slapton Ley nature reserve and coarse fishery. Slapton Sands; ns Kingsbridge. The sea fishing is very good, especially the bass fishing. Hotel can make arrangements. *For coarse fishing see "Slapton Ley".*

Torquay (Devon). Base for famous Skerries Bank and Torbay wrecks; conger, cod, pollack, turbot, flatfish, whiting, etc. Hope's Nose peninsula provides best venue for shore angler, with bass and plaice mainly sought. Other species caught are dabs, wrasse, mullet, flounder, gurnard. Babbacombe Pier good for mackerel. Bass and pollack off the rocks. Natural bait hard to come by except for mussels from harbour walls, but tackleists can supply. Tackleists: Tuckerman's Angling Centre, 141 St Marychurch Road, Plainmoor, tel: 36216; Fletcher's Sports, 9 Fleet Street (tel: 27035). Local associations: Sea AA, Torbay ASA, Babbacombe SA (HQ, Babbacombe Beach Café). Details of accommodation from Local Authority Publicity Dept, 9 Vaughan Parade. *For freshwater fishing, including Torquay Corporation reservoirs, see Teign and Dart.*

Paignton (Devon). Summer and autumn best. Bass, mackerel and garfish can be taken from beaches between Preston and Broadsands and from harbour, promenade and pier respectively. Mullet also present, but very shy. Fishing from rockmarks, too. Small boats to be hired by the hour, mackerel trips, and a charter-boat, "Tuonela", takes parties to fish Torbay. Good catches recorded. Tackleists: H Cove Clark, 45–47 Torbay Road; The Sportsman, 7 Dartmouth Road. Venture Sports, 371 Torquay Road. Club: Paignton Sea AA, who have information service and social centre for anglers at HQ at Ravenswood, 26 Cliff Road, The Harbour (open 7.30 pm onwards); annual membership £4 (temporary: 50p). Details of accommodation from Publicity Officer, Old Town Hall, or hon sec (advice and information).

Brixham (Devon). Boat fishing in bay for plaice, dabs, mackerel. Good pollack off East and West Cod rocks of Berry Head (neap tides best; worms for prawn). Farther out is Mudstone Ridge, a deep area, strong tide run, but good general fishing with big conger. Local boats take visitors out to deep water marks (wreck fishing) or to Skerries Bank, off Dartmouth, for turbot, plaice, etc; advance bookings (at harbour) advisable. Shore fishing: Bass, pollack, wrasse, conger, mackerel from Fishcombe Point, Shoalstone and the long Breakwater. Grey mullet abound in the harbour area (bait, bread or whiting flesh). Bass from St Mary's Beach (best after dark) and south side of Berry Head (bottom of cliffs) for flat fishing. Sharkham Point good for mackerel and bass (float with mackerel, strip bait or prawn for bass). Mansands Point good for bass and pollack (float). Night fishing from Elbury or Broadsands beach for bass, flatfish or conger (use thigh boots). Club: Brixham SAA. Annual membership: £9. Tackleist: Yacht Supplies, 72 Middle Street. Quayside hotel has boats.

Dartmouth (Devon). Boat and rock fishing for pollack, mackerel, garfish, dabs, pouting, conger, whiting, bass and wrasse. Skerries Bank excellent; turbot, plaice, etc. Bass, plaice, dabs, flounders, mullet and mackerel in Dart estuary. Tackleists: Sportsman's Rendezvous, 16 Fairfax Place (RD licences); Sea Haven, Newcomen Road, Bosun's Locker, Bayard's Cove (also boats). Boatmen include J Atkins, E R Curl, R Leech, B Lineham, J Goddard (c/o Dartmouth & Dist AA HQ at 5 Oxford St). Hotels: Castle, Victoria, Dart Marina. *For freshwater fishing, see Dart.*

Salcombe (Devon). Good bass fishing in estuary, and bass, pollack, etc, from nearby coves. Best April to Oct. Mackerel June to Sept and turbot, dabs, flounders, plaice, skate and rays rest of year. Plenty of natural bait. Beaches crowded in summer, but bass can be taken in winter. Wreck fishing for conger, bream, etc. June–Oct. Turbot numerous. Boats: Taylor Marine, White Strand; H Cook, White Strand (live sand-eels). Club: Salcombe and Dist SAA (HQ: Mid Folly, Folly Lane); annual membership £4 (jun £2); annual festival seven days from first Sunday in October; special prizes and trophies for visitors throughout season. Bait and tackle from The Tackle Shop. Hotel: Fortescue.

Newton Ferrers (Devon). Noted station on Yealm Estuary. All-year bottom fishing; bass, flounders, pollack (from rocks), with mullet, conger, mackerel and flatfish from boats; shark June–Oct. Good base for trips to Eddystone. Boats from D Hockaday (Tel: 359); L Carter (Tel: 210). Abundant bait in estuary. Hotels: River Yealm, Family, Anglers, Yachtsmen.

Plymouth (Devon). One of finest stations in country for off-shore deep water fishing at such marks as East & West Rutts, Hands Deep and, of course, famous Eddystone Reef. Specimen pollack, conger, ling, whiting, pouting, cod, bream and mackerel plentiful. Fishing vessels available for charter are Decca and Sounder equipped—fast exploring numerous wrecks within easy steaming of port; outstanding specimens taken. Inshore fishing for same species off Stoke Point, The Mewstone, Penlee, Rame and The Ledges. Sheltered boat and shore fishing in deep water harbour and extensive estuary network—at its best in autumn for bass, pollack, flounders, thornback and mullet. Shore fishing from rocks at Hilsea, Stoke, Gara Point, Rame Head, Penlee and Queeners for bass, pollack and wrasse, etc. Beach (surf) fishing at Whitsands and sand bar estuaries of Yealm, Erme and Avon rivers for bass, flounder and ray. All angling associations in city—British Conger Club, Plymouth Federation Sea AC and Plymouth SAC—now under one roof, on waterfront, at Plymouth Sea Angling Centre, Vauxhall Quay. Visiting anglers cordially welcomed. Tackleists: D K Sports Ltd, 88 Vauxhall Street; Osborne & Cragg, 37 Bretonside; The

Tackle Box, 85 Exeter Street; Clive's Tackle and Bait, 13 Beaumont Street, St Judes. Charter boats are all moored on Sea Angling Centre Marina, Vauxhall Quay, and ownership is as follows: J Folland, tel: 668322; R Williamson, 405975; D Pearn, 880413; H Hayler, 401370; R Street, 075538 666; T Reed, 367787; D Brett, 551548; F Goudge, 338545; G Hannaford, 500531; B Hoskins, 404603.

Looe (Cornwall). Excellent centre for all-round sport. Bass, pollack and mullet from "Banjo Pier" breakwater from mid-September to May 1. Good rock fishing from White Rock, Hannafore, westwards to Talland Bay and Llansallos, where pollack, bass, conger and wrasse can be taken. Eastwards, flatfish and bass from beaches at Millendreath, Downderry and Whitsand Bay. Bass, flounders, eels, pollack and mullet from river at quayside and upriver. Excellent sport from boats on deep-sea marks; porbeagle, mako, blue and some thresher shark taken, and wide variety of other fish. Deep sea boats from the tackle shop, Quay, East Looe (Tel: 2189). Shark tackle for hire. Tackleists: Jack Bray, The Quay, East Looe; Sams Camping and Fishing, Buller Street. Bait from tackleists or may be dug in river estuary. Clubs: HQ of Shark AC of Gt Britain is at The Quay, East Looe; Looe is official weighing-in station for British Conger Club; Looe Sea AA (information from hon sec, Vic Sneed). Temporary membership gives access to club boat at slightly less than commercial rates. Information also from Looe Information Bureau. Useful bookets from tackleists.

Polperro (Cornwall). Boat, shore and pier fishing. Cod, ling, conger, bass, bream, whiting, skate, pollack, mackerel, gurnard, turbot, brill (best months July to October). Hotels: Claremont, Noughts & Crosses, Ship, Three Pilchards; also farm accommodation.

Fowey (Cornwall). Excellent sport with bass (June to Oct) in estuary and local bays from Udder to Cannis. Pollack numerous and heavy (20 lb and more). Good bream, cod, conger, dogfish, ling, mullet, mackerel, wrasse, whiting and flatfish (big flounders and turbot). Bass, mullet and flounders taken from river. Par Beach to west also good for bass. Rock fishing at Polruan. Sand-eel, rag and lugworm obtainable. Boats: Globe

Inn, Fore Street; Hazelton Bros, Golant; Tabb, 2 Fore Street, Golant. Self-drive boats from Town Quay. Tackleists: Sports Shop, 10 Esplanade. Local club: Fowey AC (HQ, Safe Harbour).

Mevagissey (Cornwall). Excellent sea fishing, boat and shore, especially in summer. Six shark boats are based here (local club affiliated to the Shark AC of Great Britain). Shark Centre & Quay Tackle Shop will make arrangements for shark and deep-sea trips. £12 per day, £6 $\frac{1}{2}$ day. Limited scope for shore fishing, but results excellent, especially bass from beach. Good pollack off Dodman Point and from marks out to sea. Bass in large numbers were at one time taken at the Gwinges, but few have been caught in recent years. Excellent sport with large mackerel at Gwinges and close to Dodman from late Aug. Sport from the pier can be very good at times, especially with mullet. Boatmen can be contacted through Shark Centre, and The Tackle Box, 4 Market Square, who hires out tackle, has bait always in stock and carries out rod and reel repairs on the premises. Other tackle shop: P Johns, The Quay. Club: Mevagissey SAC (HQ, The Ship Inn, Pentewan; visitors welcome). Annual sub £3.

Gorran Haven (Cornwall). Same marks fished as at Mevagissey. Rock fishing available. Bass from sand beach. The Gorran Haven fishermen offer some facilities for visitors wishing a day's fishing. Excellent pollack fishing from boat with rubber sand-eel off Dodman Point. Limited accommodation at the Barley Sheaf ($1\frac{1}{2}$m); also Llawnroc Country Club and houses.

Falmouth (Cornwall). Excellent estuary, harbour (pier, shore and boat) and off-shore fishing, especially over Manacles Rocks. Noted for big bass and pollack, latter taken off wreck and rock marks. Most other species present in numbers. Bait in estuary or from tackleists. Boats from Customs House Quay on Prince of Wales Pier. Club Falmouth and Penryn AA (festival each autumn). Tackleists: A B Harvey, Market Strand; Goodwins, Church Street. Shark fishing and other deep-water fishing from various MVs. Apply: Frank Vinnicombe, West Winds, Mylor Bridge, near Falmouth (Penryn 72775), or Berks and Langdon (as above). Charter-rates per rod (shark) £12, (wreck fishing) £15. Per boat £100 and £120 approx. Details of hotel accommodation from Town Information Bureau, Prince of Wales Pier. *For freshwater fishing, see River Fal.*

Porthleven (Cornwall). Bass are to be taken from the rocks in Mount's Bay. Best bass fishing from Loe Bar, $1\frac{1}{2}$m E. Good pollack and mackerel fishing outside the rocks. Nearly all fishing is done from the Mount's Bay type of boat in deep water. Small boats for fishing parties; some for private hire. Hotel: Tye Rock.

Penzance (Cornwall). Excellent boat, pier, rock and shore fishing for pollack, mackerel, mullet and bass. Shark fishing also available. Best months: June–Nov. Club: Mount's Bay AS (headquarters: Dolphin Inn, Newlyn). Annual fishing festival, five weeks, Aug–Sept. Tackleists: The Quay Shop, Quay Street; F Westren, Newlyn Bridge, Newlyn; Lanxon Bros, Causewayhead; Sports Centre, Union Street; Dunns Sports, Market Place; Ken's Tackle, 26 Causeway Head; The Tackle Shop, Newton Germoe. Live and preserved bait supplied during summer months. Coarse fishing available. Phone W Knott, 0736 710249.

Mousehole, via Penzance (Cornwall). Good station for fishing Mount's Bay. Excellent mackerel, bream, pollack, conger, whiting, bass close to harbour according to season. Sheltered from west. Rock fishing available in rough weather. Some boats and boatmen; inquire of harbour master. Best grounds: Longships and Runnel Stone. Good results with sharks. Hotels: The Ship; Old Coastguards; The Lobster Pot.

Isles of Scilly. From shores and small boats around islands, wrasse, pollack, mackerel, conger and plaice; farther off in deep sea, particularly on The Powl, south-west of St Agnes, big catches made of cod, ling, conger, pollack, etc. Mullet pay periodical visits inshore, but usually caught by net; bass rare in these waters. Some shark fishing, but visitors advised to take own tackle. Peninnis Head and Deep Point on St Mary's are good rock marks for pollack, wrasse and mackerel; Pelistry Bay likely beach venue. Boating can be dangerous, so experience essential. Accommodation limited, early bookings advisable between May and Sept. Full information from Clerk of Council, Town Hall, St Mary's. For boats inquire of St Mary's Boating Assn,

Hugh Street, St Mary's. Several shops stock tackle.

St Ives (Cornwall). Surf fishing for bass principal sport. Mullet, mackerel, pollack, flatfish (plaice, flounders, occasional turbot) can all be caught from shore, especially from island, Man's Head, Clodgy Point and Godrevy Point. Boat fishing gives sport with mackerel (summer months) and large pollack (off reef from Godrevy Island). Bass, tope, mullet, flatfish and occasional sea trout taken in Hayle river estuary. Trout fishing on Drift Reservoir, Penzance and St Erth Stream (4m). Tackleist: Digey Corner Gift Shop, 52 Fore Street.

Newquay (Cornwall). Boat, beach; rock and estuary fishing. Mackerel (April to Oct); school bass (June–Sept); larger fish July onwards, including winter; pollack (May–Nov); flatfish, wrasse (May–Sept); whiting in winter. Mullet good from June–Sept. Shark and deep sea fishing possible (two or more boats). Trout fishing in Porth Reservoir. Sea trout and brown trout in Gannel estuary. Numerous hotels; details from town guide.

Padstow (Cornwall). Mackerel, plaice, whiting (winter only), bass, pollack, rays, turbot, grey mullet, conger. Sport with tope can be good at times. Several boatmen. Tackleist: H Radford Ltd, Duke Street. Hotels: Dinas, Metropole.

Bude (Cornwall). Bass and ray main quarry. Northcott Mouth and Sandymouth good for bass. Rays may be taken from shore in late summer and autumn. Very little boat fishing and bait difficult to obtain, except from tackleists, N Cornwall Pet Supplies, Princes Street. Club: Bude and Dist SAC.

Hartland (Devon); nr Barnstaple, 24m. Good all-round sea fishing, especially for bass at times with india-rubber sand-eel, prawn or limpet from beach or rocks according to tide (bass up to $11\frac{1}{2}$ lb have been caught); whiting, mullet, conger and pouting also taken. Hotels: Hartland Quay, New Inn, King's Arms.

Lundy (Bristol Channel). Good mackerel, conger, pollack and wrasse inshore. Ray, plaice, dabs, tope and bass at East Bank. $1\frac{1}{4}$ to $2\frac{1}{2}$m E. Good anchorage at Lundy, but no harbour. No boats for hire. For accommodation write to The Agent, Lundy, via Ilfracombe, N Devon.

Clovelly (Devon); W of Bideford. Whiting, cod, conger, bull huss, dogfish and the occasional plaice caught all the year round; ray in spring, bass and mackerel in summer. Few inshore boats; fishing from the breakwater forbidden from 9 am to 6 pm in summer. Tackleists: see Bideford. Hotels: New Inn; Red Lion.

Appledore. N of Bideford in Torridge estuary. In summer, good bass fishing from rocks. Greysands and boats. Cod, some over 20 lbs, and whiting in winter. Lugworm beds at Appledore and Instow. Few boats. Tackleist: B & K Angling Supplies, 14 The Quay.

Bideford (Devon). Bass (from the bridge, in summer) flounders, mullet higher up the river. 2m miles away at Westward Ho, extensive beach and rocks from which bass, dogfish, smoothhounds, bull huss, tope and mackerel may be taken in summer; cod in winter. Tackleists: Gales Sports, Mill Street. Local club: Bideford and District AC. Hotels: Royal; New Inn; Tantons; Ring o' Bells; Market. Yeoldon House nr Bideford. *(For freshwater fishing see Taw and Torridge.)*

Ilfracombe (Devon). Good sea fishing from rocks, pier, boats. Bass, pollack, mackerel, tope, skate, conger, mullet, etc. Best July–Oct. Shark fishing Aug and Sept depending on mackerel shoals. Boats from harbour reliable, boatmen being available and essential. Club: Ilfracombe and District AA. Reservoir trout fishing available *(see Freshwater Section)*. Hotel: Longwood, Montpelier Terrace, Royal Britannia. Details of other accommodation from Publicity Officer, Tourist Information Centre, The Promenade. Tackle and bait from Labbets, 61–2, High St, who act as secretary to the angling club.

Lynmouth (Devon). Good harbour and boat fishing. Grey mullet and bass from harbour arm. Trolling for pollack and mackerel. Tope, skate and conger in Lynmouth Bay and off Sand Ridge, 1m. Motor boats with skipper available. Best months: June to Oct. Several hotels in Lynton and Lynmouth; details from Information Office, The Esplanade, Lynmouth. *(For freshwater fishing see Lyn.)*

Minehead (Som). Beach, boat and rock fishing, principally for tope, skate, ling, thornback ray, conger, cod, bass and flatfish (Dunster to Porlock good for bass from beaches). Dogfish in bay. Mackerel in summer. Harbour and promenade walls provide sport with mullet, codling and some bass. Boats:

through the tackleist named below, all year round. Bait from sands at low water. Club: Minehead and Dist SAC. Tackleist: Minehead Sports (A J Hartgen), 18 The Parade. For further information and for boats contact Information Centre, Market House, The Parade.

Watchet (Som). Watchet and Dist Sea Angling Society fishes all the year round, covering coast from St Audries Bay to Porlock Wier. Monthly competitions from piers and shore. Codling, bass, whiting, conger and skate, according to season. Good boat fishing. New members welcomed by AS.

Weston-super-Mare (Avon). Flounders, sole, bass, skate, conger and silver eels taken during summer, and whiting, pout and cod in autumn and winter. Shore fishing from Berrow Sands, Brean Down, Black Rock, Axe estuary, Town beach, Old Pier, Kewstoke Rocks and Sand Point. Best Baits: local-dug lugworm, and herring. Best times: low water at Brean Down and two hours before and one hour after high tide on inshore rocks and beaches. Tackleists: Maroli, 19 Orchard Street; Jotchams Sports, 10 High St, Burnham.

Southport (Merseyside). Dabs and flounders with whiting and codling in winter, are the chief fish caught here; also skate, mullet, dogfish, sole, plaice, conger, gurnard and some bass. Shore flat and sandy, and fishing mainly from pier. Local clubs: Southport SAS. Good coarse fishing on River Crossens; dt. Tackleists: Robinsons, 71 Sussex Road.

Blackpool (Lancs). Fishing from North Pier for codling, whiting and dabs. Oct to March best, night fishing allowed Nov–May. Tackle and bait obtainable at both piers and S Waterhouse & Son, Cookson Street; Anglers Den, 41 Warley Road (near Derby Baths); B Ogden, 254 Church Street; Sports Shop, 63 Whitegate Drive. No boat fishing. Club: Blackpool and Layton AS. Coarse fishing in Stanley Park Lake. Dt.

Morecambe and Heysham (Lancs). Beach and pier fishing throughout year. Beaches yield plaice, flounders, dabs, bass and eels from June to October, and dabs, whiting and flounders in winter. Estuary catches up to 100 flounders to 2 lb weight at Arnside. Central Pier open for angling; plaice, bass, flounder, eels. From Stone Jetty angling free; good catches of plaice, flounders, whiting. At Heysham Harbour day permits. Flounders, dabs, pouting, conger and mullet can be taken. Tackle and bait from Charlton and Bagnall, 15 Yorkshire St; Club: Morecambe Bay AC (annual open contest).

Fleetwood (Lancs). Plaice, whiting, skate, codling, tope, etc, from boats and shore. Club: Fleetwood and District AC. Tackleists: D Langhorne, 80 Poulton Road. Boats: C B Bird, 25 Upper Lune Street.

Barrow-in-Furness (Cumbria). Tope, bass, cod, plaice, whiting, skate. Good marks include Foulney Island, Roa Island, Piel Island, Scarth Hole and Black Tower (Walney Island) and Roanhead. Full-time charter-boat arranged by Hannays Tackle Shop, Tel 0229 22571. Plenty of rag, lug and mussel bait. Tacklelists: Hannay's, 50 Crellin Street, J V Quigley, Forshaw Street.

ISLE OF MAN

The Island's coastline is extremely varied. The long, flat, surf-beaches of the North contrast sharply with the sheer faces of the South. Similarly, its fishing methods and species of fish are equally diverse. Despite the Island's location, coastline and clean waters, saltwater angling from both shore and boat remains unexploited and largely undiscovered. Information from Isle of Man Board of Agriculture and Fisheries.

Castletown. Conger, pollack, cod, wrasse, tope, flatfish from beach and boat; best months, June to Oct. Big skate from boats 600 yds off Langness; best Aug–Sept. Boats available locally.

Douglas. Cod, plaice, sole, dogfish, coalfish, conger, from Victoria Pier; best months, May to Oct, coalfish, wrasse, cod, plaice, dabs, sole from boats in Douglas Bay. Rock fishing off Douglas Head; float or spinner (good for pollack). Cod, wrasse, red gurnard, plaice, Little Ness Head to Douglas Head; skate from boats 2m out, and large tope, conger, cod, etc. Club: Douglas (IOM) and District AC, annual membership fee £6, juv £2, apply by post to G M Curtis, 22 Sunningdale Drive, Onchan (membership includes trout fishing rights in **R Glass**).

Kirk Michael. Beach fishing from here to Point of Ayre is excellent for bass, flatfish, dogfish.

Laxey. Plaice, dabs and bass from March to Oct from beach. Cod, mackerel, flatfish, offshore from boats at Garwick Bay. Clubs: Garwick Sailing and Fishing Club.

Peel. Breakwater: cod, coalfish, l s dogfish (Dec to June); mackerel, dogfish, coalfish, plaice, flounder, dabs (July to Oct). Beach: similar. Rock fishing: from Castle rocks and headlands plenty of pollack. Sand eel best bait all season. Plenty of lugworm on beach. Boat fishing: cod and haddock in winter. In spring and summer spur dogfish common. Rock fishing off St Patrick's Isle for mackerel, wrasse, coalfish; float and spinner. Information from P Chatel, 17 Kerroo Coar, Peel. Tel: 2865. Local club; Peel Angling Club.

Port Erin. Good sport from pier and breakwater for pollack, mackerel, wrasse, grey mullet, coalfish, angler fish and conger. The bay yields flatfish and mackerel, with cod in the colder months. The Sea Fish Hatchery & Aquarium here is worth a visit. Tackleist: Henry Crellin, IOM Sea Sports Ltd, Strand Road.

Port St Mary. Probably best centre on island. Pollack, coalfish, wrasse from rocks, pier, boats (most of year). Flatfish and mackerel offshore and pier during herring season. Tope, skate, cod, conger, ling from boats. Boats from J Williams, c/o Albert Hotel and W Halsall, Lime Street PSM. Several competitions. Inquiries to hon sec, Southern AC. Visitors welcome. Hotels: Station, Albert and Bay.

Ramsey. Plaice and cod from pier. Dogfish, flatfish, conger and (in Sept) bass from Ramsey beach to Point of Ayre. Coalfish, pollack and wrasse may be caught float fishing from rocks, using lugworm for bait. Pollack also taken by spinning with artificial sand-eel. For help with bait and boats, contact officials of Ramsey SAC, M Davison (Tel 0624 814791) or W Hall (Tel 0624 814134). Annual membership fee: £2.50. Tackleist: J Mead, Parliament Street.

FISHING CLUBS & ASSOCIATIONS IN ENGLAND

THESE lists have once again been expanded and now total well over 1,000, covering freshwater and sea angling. Further information can be had from the secretaries. A stamped addressed envelope should be enclosed with postal enquiries. Some clubs have had to be omitted because of lack of space. Note: *Where information has been supplied, waters held by club are usually noted, and availability of tickets, at end of each entry. Further details under individual centres.*

NATIONAL BODIES

Anglers' Co-operative Association
Allen Edwards, Director
Midland Bank Chambers,
Westgate, Grantham, Lincs NG3 6LE
Tel: 0476 61008

Angling Foundation
Prudential House, 10th Floor
Wellesley Road
Croydon CRO 9XY

Angling Trade Association
Prudential House, 10th Floor
Wellesley Road
Croydon CRO 9XY

Atlantic Salmon Trust
Moulin, Pitlochry
Perthshire PH16 5JQ
Director: Rear Admiral D J Mackenzie

Association of Professional Game Angling Instructors
D Downs
The Mead, Hosey
Westerham, Kent

British Casting Association
Mrs M Morgan
Swyn Teifi
Pontrhydfendigaid
Ystrad Meurig
Dyfed SY25 6EF

British Conger Club
Tom Matchett
5 St Michael Avenue
Keyham Barton
Plymouth, Devon PL2 1LN
Tel: 0752 562434
HQ: Sea Angling Centre, Vauxhall Quay
Sutton Harbour, Plymouth, Devon

British Field Sports' Society
John Hopkinson
59 Kennington Road
London SE1 7PZ
Tel: 01-928 4742

British Record (rod-caught) Fish Committee
Peter H Tombleson, Secretary
National Anglers' Council
11 Cowgate,
Peterborough PE1 1LZ
Tel: 0733 54084

British Waterways Fisheries
Melbury House, Melbury Terrace
London NW1
Tel: 01-262 6711
All Fishery enquiries to
Fisheries Officer: T G Leatherland
Willow Grange, Church Road,
Watford, Herts WD1 3QA
Tel: Watford 226422

European Federation of Sea Anglers
(British Section)
D S Dallas, Secretary
11 Park Circus
Ayr, Strathclyde

Flyfishers' Club
Commander N T Fuller RN
24a Old Burlington Street
London W1
Private members club, no fishery.
Publishers of The Flyfishers Journal—
editor Timothy Benn
Tel: 01-734 9229

Freshwater Biological Association
The Director
The Ferry House
Far Sawrey, Ambleside
Cumbria LA22 0LP
Tel: Windermere 2468

Grayling Society
Derek Froome,
3 Broom Road
Altrincham
Cheshire WA15 9AR

Marine Biological Association of the United Kingdom
The Secretary
The Laboratory, Citadel Hill
Plymouth PL1 2PB
Tel: 21761
National Anglers' Council
Peter H Tombleson, Executive Director
11 Cowgate
Peterborough PE1 1LZ
Tel: 0733 54084
Representative body for all anglers
National Association of Specialist Anglers
Dr B Broughton
27 Ashworth Avenue
Ruddington, Nottingham NG11 6GD
Tel: 0602 841703
National Federation of Anglers
Chief Administration Officer
Halliday House
2 Wilson Street
Derby DE1 1PG
Tel: Derby 362000

National Federation of Sea Anglers
R W Page
26 Downsview Crescent
Uckfield, Sussex TN22 1UB
Tel: 0825 3589
Salmon and Trout Association
James H Ferguson, Director
Fishmongers' Hall
London Bridge
London EC4R 9EL
(full list of local organisers on pages (000–000)
Tel: 01-283 5838
Shark Angling Club of Great Britain
Brian Tudor
The Quay, East Looe
Cornwall PL13 1DX
Tel: Looe 2642
Sports Council
16 Upper Woburn Place
London WC1H 0QP
Tel: 01-388 1277

CLUBS

Abbey Cross Angling Society
P Jordan
37 Dawley,
Welwyn, Hertfordshire
Rib, pits. Private
Abingdon and Oxford Alliance Trout Section
R H Williams
2 Holyoake Road
Oxford OX3 8AE
Members and guests only
Abingdon and District Angling and Restocking Association
R Bateman
16 The Gap
Marcham
Abingdon, Berkshire
Thames. Guest tickets only
Accrington and District Fishing Club
A Balderstone
42 Towneley Avenue
Huncoat, Lancashire
Greta. Tickets
Addingham Angling Association
Fleece Inn
Addingham
West Yorkshire
Addlestone Angling Society
Mrs Sharp

24 Heathervale Road
New Haw, Addlestone
Weybridge, Surrey
Wey. Members only
Adult Schools Angling Association
T Davis
22 Meg Thatchers Green
St George
Bristol BS5 Avon, Boyd, Silverland Lake
Aln Angling Association
John Gibson
45 Chapel Lands
Alnwick, Northumberland
Aln. Tickets
Alrewas Angling Club
J Young
3 School Close
Norton Canes
Nr Cannock, Staffs
Alston and District Angling Association
G Hagon
10 The Firs
Alston, Cumbria
S Tyne. Tickets
Altrincham Angling Society
A Lea
37 Crossgates Avenue
Sharston, Manchester

Ampthill and District Angling and Fishing Preservation Society
S Gadsden
16 Larkway
Monthill Estate
Flitwick, Bedfordshire MK45 1RE
Amwell Magna Fishery
Colonel N Blair
41 Bolton Gardens
London SW5
R Lee. No tickets
Anchor Angling Association
F James
54 Hilliat Fields
Drayton,
near Abingdon, Berkshire
Andover Angling Club
B Carter
54 Galahad Close
King Arthurs Way
Andover
Appleby Angling Association
J A Henderson
c/o Barclays Bank,
Appleby, Westmorland
Eden. Tickets
Appletreewick Barden and Burnsall Angling Club
J G H Mackrell
Mouldgreave
Oxenhope
N Keighley, West Yorks BD22 9RT
Wharfe. Tickets
Arrowsmiths Angling Club
R Swanborough
42 Primrose Lane
Kingswood, Bristol
River Avon
Arundel Victoria AC
Mrs V Jeffery
'Arosa', 3c Fitzalan Road
Arundel BN18 9JP
Asfordby Society of Anglers
Mr & Mrs H Birch
Riverside Cottage, Mill Lane
Asfordby, Melton Mowbray
Leicestershire
Ashbourne Fly-Fishers' Club
C Woolliscroft
10 Hillside Avenue
Ashbourne, Derbyshire
Dove. Members only
Ashby Angling Club
A S Lyndon
45 Station Road
Woodville
Burton-on-Trent, Staffs DE11 7DX
Ashford and District Angling and Preservation Society

C J Hyder
37 Northumberland Avenue
Kennington
Ashford, Kent
Royal Military Canal. Tickets
Ashmere Fisheries
Mr and Mrs K Howman
Felix Lane
Shepperton, Middlesex
Trout lake. Season tickets only
Ashton and District Centre Northern Anglers Association
A Brown
10 Dale Road, Golbourne
Warrington, Lancs WA3 3PN
Aspatria Angling Club
R Baxter
25 Outgang Road,
Aspatria, Cumberland
Ellen. Members only
Association of East Anglian Sea Anglers
F Culshaw
84 Westwood Avenue
Lowestoft, Suffolk
Association of Teesside and District Angling Clubs
A Allan
1 Scalby Grove, Fairfield
Stockton-on-Tees, Teesside
Reservoir. Tickets
Association of Wearside Angling Clubs
Address unknown
Avon Fishing Association (Devon)
J E Coombes
19 Stella Road, Preston
Paignton, South Devon
Devonshire Avon. Tickets
Avon Fly Fishers Club
S Fitton
39 Fouracres Close
Withywood, Bristol
Avon Ho Angling Club
G D Abbot
88 Ashby Road
Hinckley, Leicestershire LE10 1SN
Avon and Tributaries Angling Association
J G L Lewis
Chapel Cottage
Clarendon Road
Widcombe, Bath
Avon, Frome
Avon Preservation and Restocking Society
I H Mock
6 Fenton Close
Saltford, near Bristol
Avondale Angling Club
M Clark
71 Lister Road
Atherstone, Warwickshire CV9 BX

Axminster Sea Angling Club
Miss K Hawkes
208 Henson Park
Chard, Somerset
Aylesbury District and Izaak Walton Angling Association
W Cheney
14 Yardley Green, Elmhurst Estate
Aylesbury, Buckinghamshire
Aylsham and District Angling Club
K Sutton
17 Town Lane
Aylsham, Norfolk
Babbacombe Sea Angling Association
W J Hern
29 Westhill Road
Torquay
Babcock Angling Club
R G Evans
5 Andrew's Close
Brookthorpe, Gloucester GL4 0UR
Banbury and District Angling Association
D Brewer
42 Stanwell Lea
Middleton, Cheney
Banbury, Oxon
Cherwell and Oxford Canal. Tickets
Barking Angling Society
A J Sperden
27 Cambell Road,
East Ham, London E6
Water for members only
Barkingside and District Angling Society
D J French
64 Khartoum Road
Ilford, Essex
Roding and Blackwater. Tickets
Barnard Castle Angling Society
G Richardson (Chairman)
17 Galgate
Barnard Castle, Co Durham
Tees
Barnard Castle Fly-Fishing Club
J C Walker
3 Vane Road
Barnard Castle, Co Durham
Private
Barnes and Mortlake Angling Society
K Dellard
23 Cleveland Gardens
Barnes SW13 0AE
Barnsley and District Amalgamated Anglers' Society
A Noble
9 Coronation Drive
Birdwell, Barnsley
Yorkshire
Barnstaple and District Angling Association
Martin Turner

67 Taw View
Freminton
Barnstaple, North Devon
Taw. Visitors' Tickets only from local tackleists
Barnt Green Fishing Club
Reservoir Cottage
Upper Bittell
Barnt Green
Birmingham B45 8BH
Barrow Angling Association
J R Jones
69 Prince Street
Dalton-in-Furness, Lancashire
Reservoirs. No Tickets
Basingstoke Angling Club
M C Elie
10 Verdi Close, Brighton Hill
Basingstoke, Hampshire
Bath Anglers' Association
A J Smith
68 Bloomfield Rise
Odd Down, Bath
Avon, brooks. Tickets
Bathampton Angling Association
D Crookes
25 Otago Terrace
Larkhall
Bath, Avon
Trout and coarse fishing
Avon, canal, brooks. Tickets
Beachcasters (Brighton) Angling Club
D H Shead
53 Scotland Street
Brighton
Beccles Angling Club
W D Holmes
21 Glenwood Drive
Worlingham,
Beccles, Suffolk
Bedford Angling Club (1)
Mrs M E Appleton
18 Moriston Road
Bedford
Bedford Angling Club (2)
A S Brown
80 Lincroft
Darkley, Beds
Great Ouse. Limited dt
Bedlington and Blagdon Angling Association
S Symons
8 Moorland Drive
Bedlington, Northumberland NE22 7HB
Blyth. Tickets
Bellingham Angling Club
B P Tilley
25 Hillside, Bellingham
Hexham, Northumberland
Tyne. Some tickets

Belper and District Angling Club
J Nelson
4 Wilmot Road
Belper, Derbyshire

Bembridge (IOW) Angling Club
W Staplehurst
71 Gt Preston Road
Ryde, IOW

Benson and District Angling Club
E Bond
5 Sands Way
Benson, Oxford OX9 6NS

Bentham Angling Association
A R Green
The Post Office
Main Street, Bentham
via Lancaster LA2 7HL
Wenning. Tickets

**Berkhamsted and District
Angling Society**
L Hartwell
140 Chaulden Lane
Hemel Hempstead
Hertfordshire HP1 2BT

**Betteshanger Colliery Welfare Angling
Society**
A Herbert
22 St James Hall Gardens
Walmer, Kent
Medway. Tickets

Bexhill Sea Angling Club
J Boston
17 St James Street
Bexhill-on-Sea, Sussex

Bicester Angling Society
B Truby
91 Bucknell Road
Bicester, Oxfordshire
Lake. No tickets

Bideford and District Angling Club
V B Eveleigh
21 Capern Road
Bideford
Sea and coarse fishing

Bideford and District Sea Angling Club
Harry Bottomley
Glen View, Raleigh Hill
Bideford, Devon

**Biggleswade, Hitchin and District Angling
Association**
H Taylor
14 Broadmead
Biggleswade, Bedfordshire SG4 0PD
Ivel and Ouse. No tickets

Billericay and District Angling Society
E A Dyer
159 Wood Street
Chelmsford, Essex

Bingley Angling Club
P Exley
5 Highfield Road
Frizinghall, Bradford BD9 4HY
Yorkshire
Aire, lakes. Members only

Birmingham Anglers' Association Ltd
F A Jennings
100 Icknield Port Road
Rotton Park, Birmingham B16 0AP
Severn and tributaries,
Avon, and tributaries,
Wye and tributaries, canals and lakes.
Members only

Birstwith Private Angling Club
P W Lowndes
Prospect House
Kirkby Overblow
Near Harrogate, N Yorks HG3 1HQ
Nidd. Members only

Bishop Auckland and District Angling Club
J Winter
7 Royal Grove
Crook, Co Durham DL15 9ER
Wear. Tickets

**Bishop's Stortford and District Angling
Society**
C Costema
31 Thornbera Road
Bishop's Stortford, Hertfordshire
Stort. Tickets

**Blackburn and District Sea Anglers'
Association**
Harold Walton
55 Redlam
Blackburn, Lancashire

Black Ox Angling Club
R M Wright
5 Lascelles Lane
Northallerton, N Yorks
Bedale Beck and Swale. No tickets

Blackfords Progressive Angling Society
T W Ponder
4 Long Croft
Huntingdon
Cannock, Staffs

Blackpool and Layton Angling Society
E Wadeson
24 Elgin Place
Blackpool, Lancashire

Blandford and District Angling Club
M Leslie
20 Salisbury Road
Blandford, Dorset
Dorset Stour. Tickets

Blenheim Angling Society
F W Lancaster
2 Peony Gardens
Shepherds Bush, London W12

Blunham Angling Club
Hon Sec
c/o Horse Shoes Inn
Blunham, Bedfordshire
Ivel. No tickets
Bodmin Anglers' Association
R Burrows
26 Meadow Place
Bodmin, Cornwall
Camel. Tickets
Bognor Regis and District Freshwater Angling Club
R Huskisson
5 Orchard Way, Fontwell
Arundel, W Sussex
Rother, canal, lakes. Tickets
Bolton and District Angling Club
T McKee
1 Lever Edge Lane
Great Lever
Bolton, Lancs
Bolton Fishing Association
J H Siddall
Fairfields
The Shawl
Leyburn, Yorkshire
Ure. Restricted tickets
Boroughbridge and District Angling Club
G Whitaker
9 Manor Drive
Kirby Hill
Boroughbridge, Yorkshire
Ure. Tickets
Boscombe and Southbourne Sea-Fishing Club
E White
14 Clifton Road
Boscombe, Bournemouth
Boston and District Angling Association
J D McGuire
6 Churchill Drive
Boston, Lincolnshire
Witham. Membership book needed
Boston Spa Angling Club
A Waddington
The Cottage, Main Street
Thorp Arch
Wetherby, Yorkshire
Wharfe. Tickets
Bottesford and District Angling Association
G C Baker
8 Meadow End
Gotham, Notts
Grantham Canal (dated)
River Devon (summer time only)
Bowland Game Fishing Association
B Hoggarth
1 Moorfield Road
Leyland, PR5 3AR

Boxmoor and District Angling Society
K Charge
11 Catsdell
Hemel Hempstead
Bradford City Angling Association
H Briggs
4 Brown Hill Close
Birkinshaw
Bradford, Yorkshire
Ure, Wharfe, Aire, Swale, canals, lakes
Tickets
Bradford No 1 Angling Association
C W Smith
44 Fleet Lane
Queenbury
Bradford, West Yorks
Wharfe, Ure, canal, lake. Tickets
Bradford-on-Avon and District Angling Association
J H W Davis
30 Marsh Mead
Hilperton, Trowbridge
Wiltshire
Avon, Biss, Frome, canal, brook.
Tickets
Bradford Waltonians' Angling Club
H J B Swarbrick
43 Hawksworth Drive
Manston, Ilkley
West Yrokshire LS29 6HP
Braintree and Bocking Angling Society
S Giovanni
32 Drake Gardens
Braintree, Essex
Brampton Angling Society
T Donockley
1 Denton Crescent
Low Row
Brampton, Cumberland
Irthing and tributaries, Gelt, King,
Cambeck. Tickets
Brandon and District Angling Club
P Cooper
16 High Street
Feltwell, Thetford
Norfolk
Little Ouse. Tickets
Brett Marine Angling Club
Galloways Road
Lydd, Kent
Brewood Angling Club
F W Hodgkins
290 Wolverhampton Road
Sedgley
Dudley, Staffs
Bridges Angling Society
B G Beckwith
2 Ducketts Mead
Roydon, Essex CM19 5EG

Bridgnorth Angling Society
R J Ball
23 Haughton Close
Tasley
Bridgnorth, Shropshire
Bridgwater Angling Association
P Summerhayes
4 Raleigh Close
Bridgwater, Somerset TA6 4NL
Bridgwater and Taunton Canal,
Dunwear Ponds, King's Sedgemoor
Drain and Huntspill River. Tickets
Bridlington Angling Association
W Farr
53 Milner Road
Bridlington, Yorkshire
Brighouse Angling Association
M Riley
30 Ravenstone Drive
West Vale
Greetland, Halifax
Calder and canal. No tickets
Brighton Cruising Club Angling Section
J G Pennell
79 King's Road Arches
Brighton, Sussex
Brighton Deep Sea Anglers
F Bean
139 King's Road Arches
Brighton, Sussex
Brighton Palace Pier Angling Association
L R Lawrence
1 Hamblin House, Broadway
Southall, Middlesex
Bristol and District Amalgamated Anglers
J Parker
16 Lansdown View
Kingswood, Bristol BS15 4AW
Trout and coarse fishing on Avon, Brue,
Chew, Yeo, etc. Tickets for coarse
fishing only
Bristol and West of England Federation
B Williams
157 Whiteway Road
St Georges, Bristol BS5 7RH
Avon, Kennet and Avon Canal, Frome,
lake. Affiliated clubs share rights
**Bristol Avon and District Anglers
Consultative Association**
J S Parker
16 Lansdown View
Kingswood, Bristol BS15 4AW
Bristol Channel Federation of Sea Anglers
R Rogers
1 Willow Cottage
East Bower, Bridgwater
Bristol City Docks Angling Club
R Sims
65 Sandy Lane

Brislington, Bristol 4
Bristol Golden Carp Angling Association
C Golding
24 Queens Street
Two Mile Hill
Kingswood, Bristol BS15 2AZ
Bristol Omnibus Angling Assocation
M Pople
5 Dunster Gardens
Ventura Park, Willsbridge
Bristol
Bristol Post Office (Angling Section)
O A Edwards
4 Friezewood Road
Ashton Gate, Bristol
Bristol Reservoir Flyfishers' Association
C Ogborne
c/o Glebe Cottage
Rectory Close, Farmborough
Near Bath
**British Rail Staff Association
(Angling Section)**
G Harcom
8 Upper Belmont Road
St Andrews, Bristol
Brixham Sea Anglers' Association
G Walton
85 New Road
Brixham, Devon
Clubhouse at 16a Castor Road, Brixham
**Broadstairs and St Peters Sea Angling
Society**
L Withey
31 Cumberland Avenue
Broadstairs, Kent
Brockenhurst Manor Fly-Fishing Club
Mrs Chessell
The Laurels,
Dibden Purlieu
near Southampton, Hampshire
**Bromsgrove and District Association of
Angling Clubs**
D Pennells
5 Burcot Lane
Bromsgrove, Worcestershire
Brotherhoods Sport Club
Honorary Secretary
c/o Peter Brotherhoods Ltd
Lincoln Road
Peterborough
Nene. Tickets
**Broughton Working Men's Angling
Association**
T H Large
23 Knowefield Avenue
Stanwix, Carlisle
Derwent. Restricted permits
Buchan Park Angling Association
D W Newnham

The Bungalow
Coombe House Lane
Bolney, Sussex
Lakes. Permits

Buckingham and District Angling Association
W Kensett
Sunnyside, Upper Street
Tingewick. Bucks
Hyde Lane Pits, Great Ouse
Tickets (limited) from local
tackleist only

Bude Angling Association
Lt-Cdr S F W Blackall RN
5 Ward Close
Stratton, Bude, Cornwall EX23 9BB
Tamar. Tickets

Bude and District Sea Angling Club
Mrs Ward, Hon Sec
Woodfield Road
Bude, Cornwall EX23 8RJ

Bude Canal Angling Association
P Braund
Wesley House
Leven Terrace
Bude, Cornwall

Burford Angling Club
K Wilkes
1 South Mere
Brize Norton
Oxford OX8 3PX

Burgess Hill Angling Society
R Shakeshaft
23 Holmesdale Road
Burgess Hill, Sussex
Arun. Tickets

Burnham-on-Crouch Angling Club
W Cole
35 Station Road
Burnham-on-Crouch, Essex

Burnley Angling Society
J H Walton
23 St James Row
Burnley, Lancashire
Reservoir. Tickets to local residents only

Burneside Angling Association
R Tallon
28 Beck Nook
Staveley, Kendal
Cumbria
Kent. Tickets

Burnt Mill and Nettlewell Angling Society
S A Sullivan
162 Felmongers
Harlow, Essex

Burslem Suburban Angling Club
F W Newbold
115 Bank Hall Road
Burslem, Stoke-on-Trent

Burton-on-Trent Mutual Angling Association
D J Clark
7 Denton Rise
Burton-on-Trent,
Staffordshire DE13 0QB

Bury Angling Association
A Little
Woodbine Cottage
Summerseat
Bury, Lancs

Bury District Angling Society
F Booth
142 Bury Road
Tottington, Bury
Lancashire
Ponds, reservoirs. Tickets

Bury St Edmunds Angling Association
N J Bruton
'Sarafand'
Tut Hill
Farnham All Saints
Bury St Edmunds, Suffolk

Buxton Fly-Fishers' Club
M Plimmer
8 Glenmoor Road
Buxton, Derbyshire

By Brook Fly-Fishers' Club
M V M Clube
Hilton Lodge
20 Downleaze
Bristol 9
Trout. Members only

Byfleet Angling Association
L Chapman
43 Eden Grove Road
Byfleet
Weybridge, Surrey
Wey. Dt.

Calder Angling Association
W N Nixon
10 The Knoll
Thornhill, Egremont
Cumbria CA22 2SN

Calne Angling Association
R J Reeves
16 Wessex Close
Calne, Wiltshire SN11 8NY
Marden. Tickets

Cambridge Albion Angling Society
R G Turpin
79 Kings Hedges Road
Cambridge

Cambridge Fish Preservation and Angling Society
G W Tweed
85 Hereward Close
Impington Camb

Cambridge Trout Club
J Dillon-Robinson

Sammy's, Widdington
near Saffron Walden, Essex
**Cambridgeshire and Isle of Ely Federation
of Anglers**
H R Page
35 Old School Lane
Milton, Cambridgeshire
24 affiliated clubs
Canterbury and District Angling Association
The Secretary
14 Mill Road
Sturry, near Canterbury
Kent CT2 0AF
Carlisle Angling Association
T Graham
23 Orton Road
Carlisle, Cumbria CA2 7HA
Eden. Tickets
Carnforth and District Anglers' Association
A McCartney
3 Ullswater Crescent
Carnforth, Lancashire LA5 9AY
Keer. Tickets
Carshalton and District Angling Society
J Fiddimore
17 Prestbury Crescent
Woodmansterne, Banstead
Surrey
Mole. Season permits
Castle and Sible Hedingham Angling Club
G F Ruffle
New England
Sible Hedingham, Essex
**Castleford and District of Society of
Anglers Clubs**
R Holmes
1 Hope Street East
Castleford, West Yorks
Nidd, Ouse, Wharfe, Rye, Derwent,
Pickering Beck, etc. Some tickets
**Central Association of London and
Provincial Angling Clubs**
J B Killick
22 Shawley Crescent
Epson Downs
Surrey KT18 5PH
Chard Angling Association
D Lemon
38 Glanville Avenue
Chard, Somerset
River Isle, Otter
Charing and District Angling Club
E R Bennet
Rosary, Warren Street Road
Charing, Kent
Chatton Angling Association
A Jarvis
New Road, Chatton
Alnwick

Northumberland
Till. Members and associates only
Cheadle Angling Club
R F Heakin
Police House, Barnfields Lane
Kingsley, near Cheadle, Staffordshire
Cheddar Angling Association
A T Lane
1 Orchard Close
Cheddar, Somerset
Chelmsford Angling Association
D Christopher
8 Glebeland Road
Hatfield Peverel
Essex CM3 24X
Chelmer. Tickets
(Membership Secretary at
60 Delamere Road.)
Cheltenham Angling Club
A Cox
4 Ewens Road
Cheltenham, Gloucestershire GL52 6JP
Avon. Tickets
Chepstow and District Angling Club
A J Black
51 Severn Avenue
Tutshill, Chepstow, Gwent
Cherry Tree Angling Club
I Gosling
37 St Mary's Terrace
Flixton Road
Bungay, Suffolk
Waveney. Members only
Cheshire Anglers' Association
George Brassington
12 Highfield Drive
Nantwich, Cheshire
Severn, Dane, canal. Members only
Cheshunt Angling Club
R Carpenter
37 Spencer Avenue
Hammond Street
Cheshunt, Hertfordshire
Lake. Members only
Cheshunt Carp Club
A T Davies
28 Pollards Close
Waltham Cross
Hertfordshire
Chester-le-Street and District Angling Club
T Wright
156 Sedgeletch Road
Houghton-le-Spring, Tyne and Wear
Wear. Day ticket
Chew Fly-Fishing Club
Dr R R Fells
17 Mortimer Road
Clifton, Bristol 8
Chew. Members and guests only

Chichester and District Angling Society
G Booker
56 Bishop Luffa Close
Chichester, Sussex PO19 3LS
Pits. Weekly tickets

Chichester Canal Angling Association
D S Richardson
117-121 Rose Green Road
Rose Green
Bognor Regis, Sussex
Tickets

Chippenham Angling Club
Mrs M Steel
21 Braemor Road
Calne, Avon, Bristol.
Avon. Tickets

Christchurch Angling Club
K Hall
32 Wycliffe Road
Winton, Bournemouth
Avon. Fleet Pond.
Some tickets

Christchurch and District Sea Fishing Club
A Palmer
18 Hengistbury Road
Southbourne, Dorset

Churchfield Tavern Angling Club
J A Dangerfield
29 Westminster Road
Stone Cross
West Bromwich B71 2JJ

Cinque Ports Angling Society
R MacGregor
31 Burmarsh Road
Hythe, Kent

Cinque Ports, Sea Angling Society
G Colley
8 Wingate Road
Folkestone, Kent

City of Bristol Angling Association
M G Haskins
27 Hill Lawn
Brislington, Bristol BS4 4LF

Civil Service Angling Society
N J Day
74a Honor Oak Road
London SE23 3RR
Thames, Medway, Kennet, lakes, reservoirs.
No tickets

Civil Service Flyfishers' Society
J Ford
304 Knightsfield
Welwyn Garden City
Hertfordshire AL8 7NQ

Clanfield Angling Club
I Macdonald
The Tavern, Clanfield

Clitheroe Angling Association
E Hodgkinson
288 Whalley Road
Accrington, Lancashire
Ribble, Hodder and Lune
Limited tickets through members only

Clive Vale Angling Club
J Greenhalf
Broadlands
33 Hollington Park Road
St Leonards-on-Sea
Sussex TN38 0SE
Reservoirs. Period tickets

Cockermouth and District Angling Association
K Davison
43 Oaktree Crescent
Cockermouth, Cumbria
Cocker. Season tickets only

Colchester Angling Preservation Society
D K Upsher
36 Winsley Road
Colchester, Essex CO1 2DG
Colne, Stour and gravel pits. No tickets

Colchester Piscatorial Society
N Browning
3 Greenstead Court
Colchester, Essex
Colne. No tickets

Collier Row Angling Society
A Chopping
16 Rush Green Road
Romford, Essex
Roding. Members only

Collingham Angling Association
Mrs J Wilson
93 Braemar Road
Collingham
Nottinghamshire NG23 7PN

Colne (Lancs) Angling Association
B Dean
282 Gisburn Road
Blacko, Nelson, Lancashire
Brownhills Reservoir. Members only

Colnes' Angling Society
K Murrells
1 Hillie Bunnies
Earls Colne, Colchester, Essex
Suffolk Stour

Colt Crag Angling Association
F L Brogdon
The Bungalow
Hexham, Northumberland

Compleat Angler Fishing Club
V W Honeyball
12 Bodmin Close, Longlands Road
Eastbourne, E Sussex BN20 8HZ
Cuckmere and Pevensey Levels
Tickets

Comrades Angling Club
L J Wickham
1 Hollands Lane
Henfield, Sussex
Congleton Angling Society
N J Bours
8 Norfolk Road
Congleton, Cheshire
Coniston and Torver Anglers' Association
D E Lancaster
Wetherlam, Mount Pleasant
Greenodd, Nr Ulverston
Cumbria LA12 7RF
Cookham and District Angling Club
K R Beards
10 Fulton Close
Downley
High Wycombe, Buckinghamshire
Thames. No tickets
Coquet Angling Club
J Eagles
5 Fontburn Crescent
Ashington, Northumberland
Fish waters of Northumbrian Federation
Corbridge Riverside Sports Club
Neville Tortice
4 Crofts Close
Corbridge
Northumberland NE4 55ND
Tyne. Tickets for members' guests
Cotmanhay Angling Club
E Statham
26 Oak Drive
Eastwood, Notts
Cotswold Flyfishers
A W Smith
95 Islip Road
Oxford
Windrush. No tickets
Cotterstock Angling Association
Mrs Joan E Popplewell
40 North Street
Oundle, Peterborough PE8 4AL
Nene. Tickets
Countess Wear Salmon FA
Address unkown.
Cove Angling Society
M Mills
4 Chestnut Close
Blackwater
Camberley, Surrey
Loddon, Hart, Whitewater, Fleet Pond
No tickets
Coventry and District Angling Association
P O'Connor
48 Donacaster Close, Manor Farm
Wyken, Coventry CV2 1HX
Avon, Anker, Vyrnwy, Nene, Cherwell
canals, reservoirs, etc

Crawley Angling Society
Mr Kichols
24 Rillside
Furness Green
Crawley, Sussex
Lakes, streams. Some tickets
Crawley and District Sea Anglers
C R Woolger
70 Wakehurst Drive
Southgate, Crawley, Sussex
Crayford Kingfishers Angling Preservation Society
E G Costen
4 Ravensbourne Road
Crayford, Kent
Cray and lake. Season tickets
Crediton Fly Fishing Club
G Eccles
James Combe
Alexandra Close
Crediton, Devon
5m of trout fishing on Yeo and Creedy; tickets
Crewe Amalgamated Anglers
T Kelly
9 Beech Street
Crewe, Cheshire
Crew Pioneers
W J Hart
83 Underwood Lane
Crew
Croft Angling Club
L H Dent
11 High Street
Skegness, Lincolnshire
Steeping. Permits
Cromer Sea Angling Club
T Riches
Lynewood Road
Cromer, Norfolk
Cromer Inshore Sea Angling Club
J Kimp
High Street, Overstrand
Norfolk NR7 OAB
Cromford Fly-Fishers Club
F W Cooper
Wishingstone Cottage
Bull Lane, Matlock
Derbyshire DE4 5LX
Cromwell Sea Angling Club
B Fukes
39 Daubney Street
Cleethorpes, S Humberside DN35 7BB
Cross Keys Fishing Club
P S Holloway
12 Oxford Avenue
Sneyd Green
Stoke-on-Trent,
Staffs ST1 6DJ

Crown Angling Club
K Fox
23 High Street
Eccleshall, Staffs ST21 6BW
Croydon Angling Society
G Hobbs
69 Woodmere Avenue
Shirley, Croydon, Surrey
Use of water on Arun, Mole and
Medway
**Croydon and District Sea Angling
Association**
H J Summers
358 Purley Way
Croydon, Surrey
**Cumberland and Westmorland
Angling Alliance**
T Cousin
28 Mayburgh Avenue
Penrith, Cumbria
An advisory body
Danby Angling Club
The Secretary
2 Greenbank
Danby, Whitby, Yorkshire
Yorkshire Esk. Tickets
Darent Valley Trout Fishers
R F Cobbett
15 Birchwood Drive
Wilmington, Kent DA2 7NE
Darent. No tickets
Darley Dale Fly-Fishing Club
A L Carter
Holly Mead
Kempton
Craven Arms, Salop
Darlington Anglers' Club
Address unknown
Tees. Tickets
Darlington Fly Fishers' Club
R Healey
14 Oakdene Avenue
Darlington
Tees. Members only
**Dartford and District Angling and
Preservation Society**
D E Reeve
29 Berkeley Crescent
Dartford, Kent
Dart Angling Association
S J F Lovegrove
Moorlands House
Churscombe Road
Marldon Cross, Paignton, Devon
Dart. Some tickets
Dartmouth and District Angling Association
E R Curl, c/o Club HQ
5 Oxford Street
Dartmouth, Devon

Darwen Anglers' Association
J Priestley
24 Knowlesly Road
Darwen, Lancashire
Reservoirs. Limited day tickets
Dawlish Sea Angling Club
L Loram
82 Churchill Avenue
Dawlish, Devon
Deal Angling Club
Mrs Hilary Green
c/o The Marina, Deal, Kent
Deal and Walmer Angling Association
R L Emmins
29 The Strand
Walmer, Kent
Deanshanger Angling Association
Eric Longhurst
Puxley, Potterspury,
Towcester, Northamptonshire
Great Ouse. Members only
**Deanshanger and Old Stratford
Angling Association**
J Pearson
20 Goran Avenue
Stony Stratford
Milton Keynes MK11 1HQ
Debden Angling Society
Hon Secretary
15 Cleland Road
Loughton, Essex
Roding. Tickets
Deeping St James Angling Club
J Cran
53 Castle Drive
Northborough, Peterborough
Market Deeping Several Fishery. Tickets
Derby Angling Association
J Callaghan
3 Calvin Close
Alvaston
Derby DE2 0HX
Derby Joint Anglers' Council
H Amos
78 Morley Road
Chaddesden, Derbyshire
Trent and canals. Dt
Derbyshire Angling Federation
P Fox
16 Ecclesbourne Avenue
Duffield, Derbys
Dereham and District Angling Club
A F Youngman
Stranton Avenue
Yaxham, near Dereham, Norfolk
Wensum. Tickets
Derwent (Durham) Angling Association
H Walton
13 Woodlands Road

Shotley Bridge, Co Durham
Derwent (Tyne). Members only
Derwent (Yorks) Anglers' Club
I V Brett, F.R.I.C.S
North House
Wykeham YO12 0BR
Derwent. Tickets
Derwent Flyfishing Club
F H Colley
Heywood House
Grindleford, Nr. Sheffield S30 IHN
Devizes Angling Association
T W Fell
21 Cornwall Crescent
Devizes, Wiltshire SN10 5HG
Kennet and Avon Canal. Tickets
Ditherington Angling Society
G Moss
4 Morville Road
Heath Farm Estate, Shrewsbury
The Dog Angling Club
E D Roberts
The Cottage
Oak Lane
Calf Heath, Nr Wolverhampton
Doncaster and District Angling Association
H W Calder
205 Shadyside
Hexthorpe, Doncaster DN4 0HE
Idle. Tickets
Dorchester (Oxon) Angling Association
Address unknown
Thame, Thames. Tickets
Dorchester (Dorset) Angling Society
T J Clarke
4 Alington Road
Dorchester, Dorset DT1 1NT
Stour, Frome, ponds; coarse fishing
Members and friends only
Dorchester (Dorset) Fishing Club
J Fisher
Rew Hollow, Godmanston
Nr Dorchester, Dorset DT2 7AH
Frome (Dorset). No tickets
Dordon Angling Club
C Lavery
59 Coppice Drive, Dordon
Tamworth, Staffordshire
Dorking and District Angling Society
P Knight
28 Falkland Road
Dorking, Surrey
Mole. Tickets
Douglas (IOM) and District Angling Club
G H Hull, ACIS AAAI
1 Hillcrest Grove
Birch Hill Park, Onchan, IOM
Dover Sea Angling Association
R G Brittenden

129 Canterbury Road
Folkestone, Kent
Downtown Angling Association
B Hayward
37 Bridge Street
Fordingbridge
Hampshire
Avon, lakes
Dreadnought Sea Angling Society
E F Joslin
61 Sherrick Green Road
Willesden, London NW10
Drawbridge Angling Club
D J Leesing
5 Webster Close
Kimberworth
Rotherham, South Yorks
Draycott Angling Club
D Pollard
44 Fairfield Crescent
Old Sawley
Long Eaton, Nottinghamshire NG10
AH
Droitwich and District (Talbot) Angling Society
c/o Talbot Hotel, High Street
Droitwich, Worcestershire
Severn. Tickets
Dudley Angling Society
Address unknown.
Duke of Gloucester Angling Society
Barry Neville
21 Lincoln Close
Woodside Green, London SE25
Medway. Members only
Dunmow and District Piscatorial Society
E G Gilbey
11 Market Place
Dunmow, Essex
Durham City Angling Club
G Hedley
3 Hawthorn Crescent
Durham
Wear, ponds. Dt for members' guests
Durweston Angling Society
J H Thatchell
Methody, Durweston
Near Blandford, Dorset
Stour
Earl of Harrington Angling Club
Address unknown.
East Anglian Piscatorial Society
J March
Clarence Harbour
Clarence Road, Norwich
Eastbourne Angling Association
The Club House,
Royal Parade
Eastbourne, Sussex

East Cowes AS
R Gustar
2 Fairmount Drive
Staplers
Newport, IoW
East Grinstead Angling Society
W Ford
20 Greenstede Avenue
East Grinstead, Sussex
East Hastings Sea Anglers' Association
C F Thomas
17 Rymill Road
St Leonards-on-Sea, Sussex
Ecclesbourne Flyfishers' Club
W Smith
"Wayside", Longfield Lane
Ilkeston, Derbyshire
Ecclesbourne. Strictly private
Egremont Angling Association
C Fisher
69 North Road
Egremont, Cumbria
Ehen. wt.
Elan Valley Angling Association
Honorary Secretary
2 Glangrafon, Elan Valley
Rhayader, Powys
Elite Angling Club
B Fitzpatrick
13 Goodere Drive
Polesworth
Tamworth, Staffordshire B78 1BY
Ellen Angling Association
G Howard
36 Main Street, Ellenborough
Maryport, Cumbria
Ellen. Permits
**Elm Park, Hornchurch and District
Angling Society**
W Holton
4 Fairford Way
Harold Hill, Romford, Essex
Roding and lakes. Tickets
Ellesmere Angling Club
Mrs B Roger
Newton Cottages
Ellesmere, Shropshire
Vyrnwy, lake and canal. Some tickets
Elmore (Sea) Angling Club
L A Woods
12 Beacon Way
Park Gate, Southampton
Ely Highflyers Angling Club
Address unknown
Great Ouse. Tickets
Enton Fly-Fishers' Club
Address unknown
Trout lakes at Witley. No tickets

Epsom Angling Society
J C J Wood
19 West Hill Avenue
Epsom, Surrey KT19 8LE
Mole. No tickets
Esk and Liddle Fisheries Association
R J B Hill
Solicitor
Bank of Scotland Buildings
Langholm, Dumfriesshire DG13 OAD
Border Esk and Liddle. Tickets
Esk Fishery Association
H B Thomas
Angrove House, Great Ayton
Teesside
Yorkshire Esk. Tickets
Essex Fly-Fishers' Club
D A L Birrell (Chairman)
High Hedges, Little Waltham
Chelmsford, Essex
Reservoir. Trout. Members only
Exeter and District Angling Association
D Beaven
46 Hatherleigh Road
Exeter
Exe. Culm, canals, ponds, etc.
Tickets
Exmouth Sea Anglers' Association
Mrs P Moffat
13 Lawn Road
Exmouth, Devon, EX8 1QJ
Exmouth Deep Sea Fishing Club
J H R Lethbridge
6 Lower King's Avenue
Exeter
Falmouth and Penrhyn Angling Association
David Johns
32 Old Hill Crescent
Falmouth, Cornwall
(Sea only)
**Falmouth Shark and Big-Game Angling
Club**
W Lane
4 Railway Cottages
Falmouth, Cornwall
Farmoor Fly Fishing Club
R Foreman
27 Manor Road
Ducklington
Near Witney
Oxfordshire OX8 7YD
Farnborough Angling Society
J Raisin
2 Park Road
Farnborough, Hampshire
Trout and coarse fish
Farnham Angling Society
The Secretary
70 Prince Charles Crescent

Farnborough
Hampshire GU14 8DL
Faversham Angling Club
A P Baldock
5 Kennedy Close
Faversham, Kent
Pits. Tickets
**Featherstone and District Angling
Association**
B Betteridge
24 Wentbridge Road
Featherstone
Pontefract, West Yorks WF7 5DZ
Federated Anglers (Preston Centre)
R Mayor
258 Brownedge Road
Bamber Bridge
Preston, Lancs
Ribble & tributaries. Canals. Tickets
Felixstowe Sea Angling Association
P G Borley
2 Oak Close
Felixstowe, Suffolk
Felling Fly Fishing Club
J Irving
25 Sherwood Close
Washington
Tyne and Wear NE38 7RJ
Fenton and District Angling Society
C Yates
The Puzzels
5 Gatley Grove
Meir Park
Stoke-on-Trent, Staffs
Ferryhill and District Angling Club
A Roxley
60 Linden Road
West Cornforth, Co Durham
Wear, Tyne, Swale, Ure, ponds
Members only
Filey Brigg Angling Society
K C Carpenter
18 Ash Grove
Filey YO14 9LZ, N Yorks
Flower Pot Angling Association
G Simmonds
7 Lambridge, Bath
River Avon
Folkestone Sea Angling Association
H King
Little Mead, Brewers Hill
Sandgate, Kent
Fordingbridge Angling Club
A Lynn
10 Penny's Crescent
Fordingbridge, Hampshire
Avon, Stour. Members only
Foston Fishing Club
A T Unwin

Treetops, Upper Poppleton
Yorkshire
Foston Beck. Members only
Fowey Angling Club
D Johnson
c/o Club Headquarters
Safe Harbour, Fowey, Cornwall
Frampton and District Angling Association
K R Kilmister
5 Bybrook Road
Tuffley
Gloucester
Frome and District Angling Association
R J Lee
Marvil, Keyford Terrace
Frome, Somerset
Frome. Tickets conditional
Frome Vale Angling Club
C Baker
7 Salem Road
Winterbourne, Avon
Frosterley Angling Club
T Gannon
Mill House
Frosterley, County Durham
Wear. No tickets
Fry's Angling Club
M Parslow
32 Aldwick Avenue
Hartcliffe, Bristol
River Avon
Galgate Angling Association
Inquire R Johnson
5 Main Road, Galgate, Lancashire
Condor. No tickets
Galleon Angling Club
M Starkey
25 Brownfield Road
Yardley Gobion
Northants NN12 7TY
Game Fishers' Club
F W Peaker
24 Linden Road
Bournville, Birmingham B30 1JU
Fly-fishing on streams in Worcestershire
and Welsh border.
Guest permits only
Garstang and District Angling Association
D E Irvin
Windsor Road
Garstang, Preston
Lancashire
Wyre. Some wt for resident holiday
visitors
Gate Inn (Amington) Angling Club
V R Garbett
c/o 75 Collett
Glascote
Tamworth, Staffordshire

Gayton Angling Club
 S D Barker
 91 Buttmead
 Blisworth, Northants
Gillingham and District Angling Association
 J R K Stone
 Ferndale
 Ham
 Gillingham, Dorset SP8 4LL
 Stour. Tickets
Gipping Angling Preservation Society
 George Alderson
 19 Clover Close
 Chantry, Ipswich, Suffolk
 Gipping. Tickets
Glaston Manor Angling Association
 M Spencer
 21 Berkeley Road
 Street, Somerset
 Brue, South Drain
Glendale Angling Club
 R P Lane
 33 Ridley Road
 London NW10
Globe Angling Society
 R Eaton
 80 Caversham Avenue
 Palmers Green, London N13 4LN
Gloucester United Anglers' Association
 J Gibby
 70 Robert Raikes Ave
 Tuffley, Gloucester GL4 OHJ
 Severn. Tickets
Glyme Valley Fly Fishers
 Derek Weston
 Crown Cottage
 Wootton
 Woodstock, Oxon
Goathland Angling Club
 P H Skelton
 Darnholme, Goathland
 Whitby, Yorkshire
Godalming Angling Society
 M Richardson
 87 Summers Road
 Farncombe, Godalming, Surrey
Godalming and District Angling Society
 A G Johnson
 86 Peper Harow Road
 Godalming, Surrey
 Wey and lake. Tickets
Godmanchester Angling and Fish Preservation Society
 B P Doherty
 5 Kisby Avenue
 Godmanchester, Huntingdonshire
 Great Ouse
Golden Hill Club
 A O Harland

61 Main Street
 Skidby, Cottingham
 N Humberside HU16 5TZ
 No tickets
Golden Valley Fishing Club
 S Hooper
 155a High Street
 Bitton, Near Bristol
 Boyd Brook, Frome, Avon, Axe, ponds
 Tickets to members' friends only
Goole and District Angling Association
 L Rogers
 29 Westfield Square
 Goole
 North Humberside DN15 6QR
 Derwent. Some tickets
Gorleston Sea Anglers
 G Baker
 7 Pier Walk, Gorleston
 Great Yarmouth, Norfolk
Gosforth Anglers' Club
 A Gealden
 12 Meadowfield, Gosforth
 Seascale, Cumbria CA20 1HX
 Irt. Members only
Grafton Angling Association
 K Hill
 102 Cavendish Road
 Worksop, Notts
Grantham Angling Association
 W J C Hutchins
 28 Cottesmore Close
 Grantham, Lincolnshire NG31 9JL
Great Yarmouth Gorleston and District Amalgamated Angling Association
 W Platten
 1 Audley Street
 Great Yarmouth, Norfolk
Greenwich Angling Society
 A Cole
 1 Bexhill Road
 London SE4
Gretna Angling Association
 G Graham
 126 Currock Park Avenue
 Carlisle, Cumbria
 Esk, Kirtle. Tickets
Grimsby and District Society of Anglers
 J M Marshall
 62 Caistor Drive
 Nunsthorpe, Grimsby
 Lincolnshire
 Pond at Cleethorpes.
 Tickets
Grizedale Angling Association
 W E Coates
 Grizedale, Hawkshead
 Ambleside, Cumbria
 Grizedale Beck. Tickets

Groe Park and Irfon Angling Club
H G Lloyd Dolrhedyn
Irfon Road
Bulith Wells, Powys LD2 3DE
Irfon. Tickets
Guernsey Sea Anglers' Club
J Oakley
"Ridgeway"
Point's Lane, St Andrews
Guernsey, Channel Islands
Guernsey 30-Fathom Club
T W Rowe
Carantec, Rue du Marnis
Vale, Guernsey, Channel Islands
Guildford Angling Society
G Pank,
72 St Phillips Avenue
Worcester Park, Surrey
Wey
Hadleigh and District Angling Society
J S Hill
18 Highlands Road
Hadleigh, Ipswich, Suffolk
Brett. No tickets
Hailsham Angling Association
A Dean
5 Garfield Road
Hailsham, Sussex
Cuckmere. Tickets
Halifax Fly-Fishers' Club
L Stott
6 Craven Court
Hopwood Lane
Halifax, Yorkshire
No water
Halstead-Hedingham Angling Club
M Hardy
13 Tryon Court
Halstead CO9 3NZ, Colne
Some tickets only
Haltwhistle and District Angling Association
J Mason
27 Woodhead Park
Haltwhistle, Northumberland NE49 9DD
Tyne. Some tickets
Hants and Sussex Alliance (inc Portsmouth, Bognor Regis, Petworth and Petersfield clubs)
L G French
27 Locarno Road, Copnor
Portsmouth PO3 5DG
Rivers, canal, lakes. Weekly ticket and some daily tickets
Harleston, Wortwell and District Angling Club
J C Adamson
Yew Villa, Roydon
Diss, Norfolk
Pits. Tickets

Harlow Angling Society
W J Pegram
Burnside, 5 The Hill
Harlow, Essex
Stort. Tickets
Harlow Fishing Association
Recreation & Entertainment Manager
Harlow Council
1 Adams House, The High
Harlow, Essex CM20 1BE
Harrogate and Claro Conservative Angling Association
C Whittington
107 Dragon Parade
Harrogate, Yorkshire
Ure. Tickets
Harrogate Flyfishers' Club
J Darby Tredger
18 St Catherine's Road
Harrogate
Water on Nidd. No Tickets
Harthill Angling Association
H R King
8 Carver Close
Harthill, Sheffield S31 8XA
Hartlepool and District Sea Angling Club
W Colling
6 Wilson Street
West Hartlepool, Co Durham
Hastings and St Leonards Sea Angling Society
G Wall
3 Marine Parade
Hastings, Sussex
Hastings, Bexhill and District Freshwater Angling Association
P K Jury
5 Old Church Road
St Leonards, Sussex
Trout and coarse fisheries (good carp)
Members only
Hastings Flyfishers' Club Ltd
D E Tack
23 Wealden Way
Little Common
Nr Bexhill-on-Sea
E Sussex TN39 4NY
Trout fishing in reservoirs. Waiting list for membership. Daily ticket at reservoirs
Hatfield and District Angling Society
E F Denchfield
44 Stockbreach Road
Hatfield, Hertfordshire
Hawes and High Abbotside Angling Association
A H Barnes
Manidew
Gayel, Hawes

North Yorkshire DL8 3RZ
Yore. Tickets
Hawkesbury Angling Society
K Bull
138 Aldermans Green Road
Coventry, West Midlands CV2 1PP
Haywards Heath and District Angling Society
S F Whetstone
2 West View Cottages
Lindfield, Sussex
Ouse
Hazeldine Anglers Association
J W Hazeldine
8 Dudley Road
Sedgley
Dudley, Staffs DY3 1SX
Heathfield Angling Club
A P Hopkinson
23 Arkwright Walk
The Meadows
Nottingham NG2 2HW
Henfield and District Angling Society
Mrs Jean Crawford
5 Myrtle Terrace
Weavers Lane
Henfield, West Sussex
Hereford and District Angling Association
J Astley
The Lindens
Bishopstone, Hereford
Wye and Lugg. Tickets
Herne Bay Angling Association
Honorary Secretary
c/o HQ, 59 Central Parade
Herne Bay, Kent
Heron Angling Society of St Albans
J Pugh
38 Hopgreen
Woodside Estate
Watford WD2 7HQ
Hertfordshire Anglers' Consultative
Association
E F Banfield
14 Catham Close
St Albans, Hertfordshire
Herts-Chiltern Anglers
Peter Frost
28 Garden Road
Dunstable, Bedfordshire
Hexham Anglers' Association
H Watson
25 Beaufront Avenue
Hexham, Northumberland
Tyne. No tickets
Higham Ferrers Angling Club
M Haynes
Elmhurst, Roland Way
Higham Ferrers
Northamptonshire

Highflyer Fishing Club
H R Page
35 Old School Lane
Milton, Cambridgeshire
Hinckley and District Angling Association
L J Ashton
75 Forest Road
Hinckley, Leicestershire
Soar, Sence, Thames and Avon, canals,
lakes and reservoirs. Permits
Histon and District Angling Society
R Cooper
236 Histon Road
Cottenham, Cambridgeshire
Old West River, Members only
Hitchin and District Angling Association
L G Day
14 Thatcher's End
Hitchin, Hertfordshire
Ouse, Arlesey Lake. Members only
Holbeach and District Angling Club
S H Bowell
67 Battlefields Lane
Holbeach, Lincolnshire
Holland Anglers' Society
G S Mankelow
51 Warren Lane
Holland, Oxted, Surrey
Eden (Kent). Members only
Holmesdale Angling Society
Mrs V Wright
59 High Street
Chipstead
Sevenoaks, Kent TN13 LRW
Lake at Sevenoaks
Holme Valley Piscatorial Association
P J Budd
39 Derwent Road
Honley
Huddersfield HD7 2EL
Holt Fleet Fishing Club
J King
"Rookery Nook"
67 Sytch Lane
Wombourn, West Midlands
Horncastle Angling Club
Address unknown
Horse and Jockey Angling Club
A Frith
The Stocks
Stock Hill
Ecclesfield, Sheffield
Horse and Jockey (Lichfield)
Angling Club
M R Bennett
38 Ponesfield Road
Lichfield, Staffs WS13 7NL
Horsham and District Angling Association
G R and L T Kempson

11 Clarence Road
Horsham, Sussex
Houghton and Wyton and Hemingfords Angling Society
A Rout
The Haven, Fenstanton
Huntingdonshire
Great Ouse. Daily ticket
Houghton Bridge and District Angling Society
W G Charman
27 South Lane
Houghton, Sussex
Houghton Fishing Club
P K George
The Old Parsonage
Shorne, Gravesend, Kent
Test. No tickets
Hounslow Piscatorials
P Bowden
7 Denbigh Drive
Hayes, Middlesex
Wyrardisbury and Colne
Hove Deep Sea Anglers
J Greenfield
Club House, Western Esplanade
Hove, Sussex
Huddersfield Angling Association
C A Clough
38 Holly Bank Avenue
Upper Cumberworth
Huddersfield, Yorkshire
Water on reservoirs
Hull and District Amalgamated Angling Association
J Holdenby
1 Grebe Road
Thimblehall Lane
Newport
N Humberside, Yorkshire HU15 2PJ
Hull Rock Angling Club
S Medcalf
237 Portobello Street
Holderness Road
Hull, Yorkshire
Humber Sea Angling Club
A S Burman
134 Penshurst Road
Cleethorpes, S Humberside DN35 9EN
Hungerford Canal Angling Association
A A Chandler
27 Bockhampton Road
Lambourn, Newbury
Berkshire
Hungerford and K and A Canals. Tickets
Huntingdon Angling Society
T W S Biram
56 Desborough Road

Hartford, Huntingdon,
Cambs
Great Ouse. Tickets
Hutton Rudby Angling Association
B Milburn
11 South Side
Hutton Rudby,
Yarm-on-Tees, Yorkshire
Tees, Leven Limited st.
Ilchester and District Angling Association
R Tate
14 Great Orchard Way
Ilchester
Yeo, Somerset
Ilford and Wanstead Angling Society
H Mead
6 Windsor Road
Ilford, Essex
Ilford Piscatorial Society
R S Oughton
31 Fowey Avenue
Roding Lane South, Redbridge
Ilford, Essex
Ilfracombe and District Anglers' Association
Messrs Labbetts
61-2 High Street
Ilfracombe
Ilkley and District Angling Association
J A Cockerill
31 Grange Estate
Valley Drive
Ilkley, Yorkshire
Wharfe. Tickets
Ilminster and District Angling Association
A Green
1 Heme Rise
Ilminster, Somerset
Isle. Tickets
Ingatestone and Fryerning Angling Club
E B Quale
45 Willow Green
Ingatestone, Essex
Ingleton Angling Association
N W Capstick
Bower Cottage,
Uppergate, Ingleton
via Carnforth, Lancashire
Greta (Lune). Tickets
Ipswich Sea Angling Association
H D Ellwood
105 Wallace Road
Ipswich, Suffolk
Irthlingborough, Raunds and District Angling Club
C E Crawley
20 Palmer Avenue
Irthlingborough, Northamptonshire
Isfield and District Angling Club
M A Wickman

33 Stonedene Close
Forest Row, Sussex
Uck, Ouse and lakes
Isis Angling Club
K D Sykes
53 Arnolds Way
Cirencester, Glos
Avon, Marden, Thames, lakes.
No tickets
Isle of Man Angling Association
G H Hull
1 Hillcrest Grove
Birch Hill Park
Onchan, Isle of Man
Isle of Wight (Freshwater) Angling Society
G Peacey
76 Long Lane
Newport, Isle of Wight
Isle of Wight Angling Society
Mrs S Jackson
70 Hunnyhill
Newport, IoW
Ivel Protection Association
R Hitchcock
10 The Crescent, Beeston,
Sandy, Bedfordshire
Ivel. No tickets
Izaak Walton (Stafford) Anglers' Association
T H Babbs
4 Fieldside
Wildwood, Stafford
Sowe. Penk and canal
Jersey Sea Fishing Club
HQ, 16 Broad Street
St Helier, Jersey, CI
Jolly Anglers
R Dell OBE
Brookside, Winterbrook
Wallingford, Berkshire
Thames. Tickets
Keighley Angling Club
L Brocklesby
11 Eelholme View Street
Keighley, Yorks
Aire and reservoir. Tickets for reservoir
only
Kelvedon and District Angling Association
M Murton
189 High Street
Kelvedon, Essex
Blackwater, pits. Dt for pits only
**Kent, Bela, Winster, Leven and Duddon
Fisheries Association**
O R Bagot
Levens Hall, nr Kendal
Cumbria
Advisory body
Kent (Westmorland) Angling Association
P D Bayliss

The Hyena
9 Fountain Brow
Kendal, Cumbria
Kent, Mint, Sprint and reservoir. Tickets
Keswick Angling Association
W Ashcroft
Spring Haven, How Lane
Portinscale, Keswick, Cumbria
Greta (Cumberland) and Derwentwater
Tickets
**Kettering, Thrapston and District Angling
Association**
L R Garrett
10 Naseby Road
Kettering, Northamptonshire
Nene. Tickets
Keynsham Angling Association
G A Edwards
10 Clyde Avenue
Keynsham, Bristol
Avon BS18 1PZ
Chew, Avon. Tickets
Kibworth and District Angling Society
H Taberer
11 Weir Road,
Kibworth-Beauchamp, Leicestershire
Canal. Tickets
**Kidderminster and District Angling
Association**
M Millinchip
246 Marpol Lane,
Kidderminster, Worcestershire
Severn. Members and associates only
Kilnsey Angling Club
J S Nesbitt
The Old Hall
Kettlewell, Skipton
N Yorks
Wharfe and Skirfare. Members only
Kingfisher Angling and Preservation Society
P D Stewart
Heathfield House
Bourne Road, Crayford, Kent
King of French Angling Club
W E West
31 Listowel Crescent
Clifton, Nottingham
Trent. No tickets
Kings Arms Angling Club
R D Barber
43 Stoneleigh Avenue
Enfield, Middlesex
Kings Langley Anglers
B Harris
16 Torridge Walk
Grove Hill, Hemel Hempstead
King's Lynn Angling Association
G T Bear
1 Cock Drove

Downham Market, Norfolk
Great Ouse. Tickets
Kingswood Disabled Angling Club
G Thompson
1 Honey Hill Road
Kingswood, Bristol
King William IV Angling Association
(refer to Bristol and Dist AA)
Kintbury Angling Association
Brian Culley
Bray Cottage
Kintbury, Berkshire
No tickets
Kirkby Fleetham Angling Club
S Schofield
1 Colstan Road
Northallerton
Yorkshire
**Kirkby Lonsdale and District Angling
Association**
G Clough
Keepers Cottage, Burrow
via Carnforth LA6 2RN
Lune. Tickets
**Kirkby Stephen and District Angling
Association**
J B Owen
Shire Hall
Appleby, Cumbria CA16 6XN
Eden. Members only
Kirkham and District Fly Fishers' Club
A Hinchcliffe
11 Ulverston Avenue
St Annes-on-Sea, Lancashire
Reservoir. Tickets
Knaresborough Anglers' Club
M G James
2 Hurstleigh Terrace
Harrogate, Yorkshire
Nidd. Tickets for members' friends only
Knaresborough Piscatorials
R B Gray
26 St Margarets Gardens
Knaresborough, Yorkshire
Nidd. Tickets
Knowle (Bristol) Angling Association
A R J Riddell
43 Highworth Crescent
Yate, Bristol
Chew, brooks. Tickets
Knowle Red Lion Angling Club
J Kelly
2 Chelmar Close
Castle Bromwich
Birmingham B36 0SX
Ladykirk and Norham AA
J Blythe
14 St Cuthbert's Square
Norham, Berwick-upon-Tweed

Lakenham Angling Club
C F Wickham
2 Robin Hood Road
Norwich
Lamb Angling Club
D Skudder
52 Glascote Road
Tamworth, Staffs B77 2AD
Lancashire Fly-Fishing Association
J Winnard
Manor House
Tosside, nr Skipton
N Yorks
Ribble, Hodder, Lune, Wenning, Dean
Clough Reservoir. Day ticket for
members' friends only
Lancaster and District Angling Association
C T Preston
Greenacre, High Biggins
Kirkby Lonsdale, Cumbria LA6 2NP
Lune. Tickets
Lancing Anglers
Gilbert A Ramsey
Elinor Lodge, East Street
Lancing, Sussex
Langley Park Angling Association
A Brown
8 Oak Street
Langley Park
County Durham DM7 9ST
Water on Browney
Langport and District Angling Association
Mrs I Barlow
Florissant
Northfield
Somerset TA1 16SJ
Lanhydrock Angling Association
The National Trust
Estate Office
Lanhydrock Park
Bodmin, Cornwall. Fowey
Lansil Angling Association
J E N Barnes
88 West End Road
Morecambe, Lancashire
Water on Lune. Tickets
Launceston Anglers' Association
J Fraser
11 Duke Street
St Stephens
Launceston
Cornwall
Tamar, Ottery, Kensey, Permits
Lavington Angling Club
M Gilbert
Gable Cottage
24 High Street
Erlestoke, nr Devizes, Wilts
Semington Brook

Lawford Angling Society
R W Nunn
Mistley Hall Cottage
Clacton Road, Mistley
Manningtree, Essex

Leamington Spa Angling Association
E G Archer
9 Southway
Leamington Spa, Warwickshire
Avon and canal. Some tickets

Leatherhead and District Angling Society
R J Boychuk
22 Poplar Avenue
Leatherhead, Surrey
Mole, ponds. Private

Ledbury and District Angling Association
C F Davies
The Wren, Banit Crescent
Ledbury, Herefordshire

Leeds Angling Association
H Wigglesworth
84 Westfield Road
Wrose, Shipley, Yorks
Private club. Swale. Members and guests only

Leeds and District Amalgamated Society of Anglers
G Copley
Anglers Club
Becket Street, Leeds 9
Ouse and tributaries Tickets

Leeds and Liverpool Canal Angling Association
W M Toman
7 Hall Royd
Shipley, West Yorks BD18 3ED

Leek and Morlands Fishing Club
D White
20 Campbell Avenue
Leek, Staffordshire
Churnet, canal

Leicester Angling Club
V D Coles
60 Chadwell Road, Leicester
Grand Union Canal. Tickets

Leicester Angling Society
M Forrest
23 Needham Avenue
Glen Parva
Leicester LE2 9JL
Soar, Grand Union Canal. Tickets

Leicester and District Amalgamated Society of Anglers
L H Barnsley
25 West Avenue
Clarendon Park
Leicester LE2 1TS
Wreake, Nene, Eye, Soar, Grantham and Grand Union Canals. Tickets

Leigh and District Association of Anglers
T Kelly
70 Diamond Street
Leigh, Lancs WN7 4JG

Leighton Buzzard Angling Club
W J Moore
9 Cotswold Drive
Leighton Buzzard
Bedforshire LU7 7UQ
Great Ouse, Ouzel, Claydon Lakes, pits, etc. Tickets for members' friends only

Letchworth Angling Club
F Young
224 Rushby Mead
Letchworth,
Hertfordshire

Leven Angling Association
Bare Syke
Backbarrow
Newby Bridge
Near Ulveston
Cumbria LA12 8NB

Lewisham Piscatorials
D Bresnahan
30 Charldane Road
New Eltham, London SE9
Beault. No tickets

Licensed Victuallers' Deep Sea Angling Club (South-Eastern)
E D Goodwin
15 Greenhill Bridge Road
Herne Bay, Kent
London and South: E E Doree
1 Norfolk Court, Rustington, Sussex

Lichfield Marina Angling Society
C H Turner
Streethsay Basin
Burton Road
Lichfield, Staffs

Lincoln and District Angling Association
I F Morris
55 Grantham Road
Waddington, Lincoln LN5 9LS
Lake. Tickets

Lincolnshire Anglers' Federation
J D McGuire
6 Churchill Drive
Boston, Lincolnshire

Lincolnshire Rivers Anglers' Consultative Association
J D McGuire
6 Churchill Drive
Boston, Lincolnshire

Linesmen Angling Club
Andrew Wilson
30 Baker Street
London W1
Fisheries in eight counties

Linton, Threshfield and Grassington Angling Club
H T Astley
Shiel, Raines Meadows
Grassington, Skipton
Yorkshire
Wharfe. Tickets

Liskeard and District Angling Club
D G Gilbert
11 Richmond Road
Pelynt
Nr Looe, Cornwall
Fowey, Camel, Lynher, Seaton, Looe, Inny. Tickets

Littleborough Angling Society
H Ingham
86 Whalley Avenue, Littleborough
nr Rochdale, Lancashire
Canal. No tickets

Littlehampton and District Angling Club
Fisherman's Quay
Littlehampton

Littleport Angling Club
J W Shelsher
8 Victoria Street
Littleport, Cambridgeshire
Great Ouse and Lark

Liverpool and District Anglers' Association
J Johnson
97 Liverpool Road North
Maghull, nr Liverpool
Lancashire
River Dee. Tickets

Llandrindod Wells Angling Association
B D Price
The Cedars
Llanyre
Llandrindod Wells, Powys
Ithon. Tickets

Llanfair Fishing Club
Honorary Secretary
Llanfair-Caereinion
Powys
Banwy. Some tickets

Llanidloes Angling Society
1 Glyn Tilsley
Foundry House
Llanidloes, Powys
Severn, Clywedog, Dulus. Tickets

London Anglers' Association
Forest Road Hall
Hervey Park Road
Walthamstow,
London E17 6LJ
(LAA offices)
Thames, Lee and tributaries; Hampshire Avon, Arun, Gt Ouse, Suffolk Stour, canals, lakes, etc. Day ticket for some waters

London Brick Co (Angling Section)
R Peake
Phorpres Club
London Road, Fetton
Peterborough
Brick pits; members only

London Catchers Club
Dave Lawrence
57 Knightsbridge, SW1
Offers service to anglers. Tickets for many waters

Long Eaton and District Angling Federation
W Parker
75 College Street
Long Eaton, Nottinghamshire
Trent. Tickets

Long Eaton Victoria Angling Society
D L Kent
18 Collingwood Road
Long Eaton, Notts NG10 1DR
Soar, Trent, Erewash and Cranfleet canals, ponds. Tickets

Long Preston Angling Club
J Bowker
Pendle View, Long Preston
Skipton, N Yorks
Ribble. Tickets

Looe and District Sea Angling Association
V Sneed
c/o Cotton's Tackle Shop
The Quay, E Looe, Cornwall PL13 1AQ

Lostwithiel Fishing Association
J H Hooper
4 Reeds Park
Lostwithiel, Cornwall
Water on Fowey. Tickets

Loughborough Soar Angling Society
M Downs
16 Durham Road
Loughborough, Leicestershire
Soar and canal. Tickets

Louth Cawacs Angling Association
G Allison
15 Florence Wright Avenue
Louth, Lincolnshire

Lower Frankton Angling Club
C Ellis
Bridge Cottage
Lower Frankton
Nr Oswestry, Shropshire

Lower Teign Fishing Association
P M Knibbs
1 Lower Brook Street
Teignmouth, Devon
Teign. Tickets

Lowestoft Freshwater Angling Club
David Shreeve
52 Highland Way
Lowestoft, Suffolk

Our water supply reservoirs hold some remarkable fish. Dave Wood, Chairman of the "Queen Mother Fly Fishers", is shown here with a $14\frac{1}{2}$ lb. brown trout which is currently the reservoir record for the species in Britain. *Photo: Mike Peters.*

Lowestoft Sea Anglers
E Weaver
Waterloo Road
Lowestoft, Suffolk

Lowestoft (South Pier) Angling Club
S G Hok
132 Bevan Street
Lowestoft, Suffolk

Ludlow Angling Club
A J Carter
26 Housman Crescent
Ludlow, Shropshire
Teme. Tickets

Luton and District Anglers' Association
S R Branch
3 Holmbrook Ave
Luton, Bedfordshire
Upper Ouse, Linford Lakes. Members only

Luton Angling Club
D Bacon
18 The Hedgerows
Parkside
Furzton, Milton Keynes MK4 1BD

Lychnobite Angling Society
P D White
13 Margaret Avenue
St Albans, Herts

Lydney and District Angling Club
M G Nash
42 Templeway West
Lydney, Gloucestershire

Lymington and District Sea Fishing Club
B Greenwood
2 Boldre Lane
Lymington, Hampshire

Lymm Angling Club
S Griffiths
18 Manor Way
Lymm WA13 0AY
Lake. Tickets

Lyttelton Angling Association
F M Rowley
2A Red House Road
Astley Cross
Stourport, Worcestershire DY13 0NW
Severn. Tickets

Mablethorpe, Sutton-on-Sea and District Angling Club
V A Hardy
33 Alford Road
Sutton-on-Sea, Mablethorpe
Lincolnshire
Great Eau

Macclesfield and District Amalgamated Society of Anglers
C Sparkes
High Lodge, Upton
Macclesfield, Cheshire

Macclesfield Flyfishers' Club
A H Ashness
School House, Langley
nr Macclesfield, Cheshire
Dane and Clough, lakes. No tickets

Macclesfield Victoria Angling Society
A Jackson
8 Barton Street
Macclesfield, Cheshire
Canal. Tickets

Macclesfield Waltonian Angling Society
P O'Reilly
4 The Green
Cookshill
Caverswall, Stoke-on-Trent

Maidenhead Angling Society and District Association
T Pemberton
26 Kidswell Close
Maidenhead, Berks SL1 5PH
Thames. Members only

Maidstone Victory Angling and Medway Preservation Society
P Makin
174 Brompton Farm Road
Strood, Kent
Medway. Tickets

Maldon Angling Society
P Revill
Langford Limes
94 Crescent Road, Heybridge
Maldon, Essex CM9 7SN
Blackwater. No tickets

Malton and Norton Angling Club
M Foggin
Westwood, 123 Welham Road
Norton, Malton, Yorkshire
Derwent. Tickets

Manchester Anglers' Association
F Fletcher
7 Alderbank Close
Kearsley, Bolton
Lancs, BL4 8JQ
Ribble and Lune. No tickets

Manchester Federation of Anglers
C McDonough
38 Solway Road
Crossacres
Wythenshawe, Manchester

Mansfield and District Angling Association
A Quick
158 Huthwaite Road
Sutton-in-Ashfield
Nottinghamshire NG17 2GX
River Devon, pits. Members only

Mannin Angling Club
A Pennington
10 Lhag Beg
Port Erin, I.O.M.

Manor Angling Club
  D Cartwright
  18 Dorset Close
  Nuneaton, Warwickshire CV10 8EN
Manx Game Fishing Club
  Honorary Secretary
  5th Floor, Victory House
  Douglas, I.O.M.
Marazion Angling Club
  B Trevitt
  6 Chyandaunce Close
  Gulval, Penzance
March and District Federation of Anglers
  J Abbott
  17 North Street
  March, Cambridgeshire
  Fen waters. Tickets
March Working Men's Angling Club
  H Davis
  North Drive, March
  Cambridgeshire
  Twenty Foot. Permits
Marconi Angling Society
  Honorary Secretary
  Marconi Athletic Social Club
  Beehive Lane, Chelmsford, Essex
  Canal. Tickets
Mardon Angling Club
  C G Austin
  70 Whiteway Road
  St George, Bristol
  River Avon
Margate Fishing Club
  F Lamberton
  2 Chilham Avenue
  Westgate-on-Sea, Kent
Market Drayton Angling Club
  C Booth
  The Willows
  Ashbourne Drive
  Prospect Road
  Market Drayton, Shropshire TF9 3EA
Market Harborough and District Society of Anglers
  R Haycock
  16 Maurice Road
  Market Harborough
  Leicestershire
  Canal. Tickets
Marlborough and District Angling Association
  M Ellis
  "Failte", Elcot Close
  Marlborough, Wiltshire
  Kennet and Avon Canal. Tickets limited
Marlow and District Angling Association
  F Warwick
  2 Elizabeth Road
  Marlow, Buckinghamshire
  Thames. No tickets

Marsden Star Angling Society
  D Brown
  36 Western Avenue
  Riddlesden
  Keighley, Yorks
Masham Angling Club
  W P Todd
  Greenways, Fearby Road
  Masham, Yorkshire
Mawgan Angling Club
  T J Trevenna
  Lanvean House
  St Mawgan, Newquay
  Cornwall
Measham Fishing Club
  J Wainwright
  6 The Square
  Oakthorpe
  Burton-on-Trent DE12 7QS
Melksham and District Angling Association
  D Branton
  16 Ingram Road
  Melksham
  River Avon
Melton Mowbray Society of Anglers
  R W Benskin
  24 Chetwynd Drive
  Melton Mowbray, Leicestershire
  Eye and Wreake (Trent). Tickets
Mere Angling Club (Derwent Sector)
  W H Smith
  1 Cecil Court, Ryndleside
  Scarborough, Yorkshire
  No tickets
Middlewich Angling Society
  C Bratt
  13 Elm Road
  Middlewich, Cheshire
Midland Angling Society
  W Oldham
  57 Albury Drive
  Aspley Estate
  Nottingham
  Trent
Midland Flyfishers
  A D Clark
  5 Deansway
  Worcester WR1 2JG
  Onny, Welsh Dee. Tickets
Mid-Northants Trout Fishers' Association
  T Broughton
  52 Bush Hill
  Northampton
Millhouse Beck Fishing Club
  D J Broady
  Ings Lane, Dunswell
  Hull, Yorkshire
  Beck. Members only

Millom and District Angling Association
D Dixon
1 Churchill Drive
Millom, Cumbria
Members only
Milnthorpe Angling Association
A R Park
Hawkshead House, Priest Hutton
Carnforth, Cumbria LA6 1JP
Bela. No tickets
Milton Keynes Angling Association
T A Jeans
6 Bolton Close
Bletchley
Milton Keynes MK3 6LJ
Minehead Sea Angling Club
R Tudball
The Beacon, Beacon Road
Minehead, Somerset
Monsal Dale Fishery
C A Roose
Estate Office, Edensor
Bakewell, Derbyshire
Wye (Trent). No tickets
Monmouth and District Angling Society
A Doolan
2 Elm Drive
Monmouth
Monnow
Montgomeryshire Angling Association
T J Evans
48 Gungrog Road
Welshpool, Powys
Severn and tributaries, canal,
lakes. Tickets
Moor Hall and Belhus Angling Society
M Tilbrook
46 Mill Road
Aveley, Essex
Stour, Ham River, pits. No tickets
Morecambe Bay Angling Club
J Smith
17 Barnes Road
Morecambe, Lancashire
Moss Side Social AS
A Jones
10 Purley Avenue
Northenden, Manchester 22
Dee. Members only. Bosley Reservoir
Tickets
Mounts Bay Angling Society
D Cains
29 Treassowe Road
Penzance, Cornwall
Myddelton Angling Club
J B Harland
Barradene, 57 Grove Road
Ilkley, Yorkshire
Wharfe. Tickets

Nantwich Angling Society
J Haighton
The Bungalow, Worleston Road
Reaseheath, Nantwich, Cheshire
Weaver. No dt
NETA Angling Society
F Rye
42 Northfield Road
Laleham, Middlesex
Newark and District Piscatorial Federation
J N Garland
58 Riverside Road
Newark, Nottinghamshire
Newark Dyke. Tickets
Newbrough and Fourstones Angling Association
C Telford
Howlett Hurst
Fourstones
Hexham, Northumberland. S Tyne
Newbury and District Angling Association
D Buckwell
37 Pegasus Road
Oxford OX4 5DS
Kennet, canal. No tickets
Newhaven Deep Sea, Anglers' Club
D F Wood
Lakri, 56 Slindon Avenue
Peacehaven, Sussex
Newport (Gwent) Angling Association
P Climo
2 Darwin Drive
Newport, Gwent
Newport Pagnell Fishing Association
F J Read
19 Chicheley Street
Newport Pagnell
Buckinghamshire
Great Ouse, gravel pits. Tickets
New Studio Angling Society
W Dexter
62 Battersby Road
London SE6
Medway. Members only
Newton Abbot Fishing Association
D Horder
22 Mount Pleasant Road
Newton Abbot, Devon
Lakes. St only
Nidderdale Angling Club
Mrs J Dalton
Bracken House, Princess Road
Ripon, N Yorks
Nidd. Tickets
Northallerton and District Angling Club
G Easby
24 Quaker Lane
Northallerton, Yorkshire
Swale. Tickets

Northampton Britannia Angling Club
C W Gray
61 Bouverie Walk
Northampton NN1 5SN

Northampton Castle Angling Association
C Howe
137 Lutterworth Road
Northampton

Northampton Nene Angling Club
M Eaton
12 Thorne Hill
Briar Hill
Northampton NN4 9SN
Ouse, Nene. Tickets

North Buckinghamshire Angling Association
N Clutton
95 Lakes Lane
Newport Pagnel
Buckinghamshire

North Country Anglers
I G Whale
17 Watling Terrace
Willington
Crook, County Durham DL15 0HL

Northern Anglers' Association
B Davies
51 Brennand Street
Burnley, Lancashire
Ribble, Dee, canals, etc. Tickets

North Oxford Angling Society
J Humm
11 Summerfield
New Hinksey
Oxford
Water north of Oxford. No tickets

North Somerset and West Wilts Federation of Anglers
I H Mock
28 Somerset Terrace
Bedminster, Bristol

North Somerset Association of Anglers (Embracing old Highbridge, Clevedon and Weston-super-Mare clubs)
R Newton
64 Clevedon Road
Tickenham
Cleveden, Avon
Axe, Brue, drains and ponds. Tickets

North Staffordshire Association of Anglers
C Moore
38 Debenham Crescent
Stoke-on-Trent
Staffs

North Walsham Kingfishers
P Hooker
21 Fairview Road
North Walsham
Lake. Dt.

Northumbrian Anglers' Federation
P A Hall
3 Ridley Place
Newcastle-upon-Tyne
Northumberland NEI 8JG
Salmon and trout water on Coquet, Tyne
Tickets

North-West Durham Angling Association
J W Geddes
Snook Acres Farm
Witton Gilbert, Durham DH7 6TQ
Tyne & Wear. Trout reservoirs. Tickets

Northwich and District Angling Association
R Hankey
P O Box 18
Northwich, Cheshire
Weaver. Tickets

Norwich and District Angling Association
C E Wigg
3 Coppice Avenue
Norwich NR6 5RB
Thurne, Bure, Broads. Tickets

Norwich Sea Anglers
D Mundford
68 Heath Road, Norwich

Norwich City Supporters' Angling Club
R Stolworthy
595 Earlham Road, Earlham
Norwich, Norfolk
Broads. Members only

Nottingham Anglers' Association
E J Collin
224 Radford Boulevard
Nottingham NG7 5QG
Trent. Tickets

Nottingham and District Anglers' Joint Council
N A Cade
82 Broxtowe Lane
Nottingham NG8 5NJ

Nottingham and District Federation of Angling Societies
W Belshaw
17 Spring Green
Clifton Estate, Nottingham
For matches contact Mrs M Whitmore
47 Criftin Road, Nottingham
Trent. Tickets

Nottingham Fly Fishers' Club
P J Ardwinckle
34 Renal Way
Calverton, Nottingham
Lakes and river. No tickets

Oakham Angling Society
R Taylor
8 Beech Road
Oakham, Rutland
Welland, Glen canal and ponds.
No tickets

Offord and Buckden Fishing Society
A Plumb
75 High Street
Gt Paxton
Huntingdon, Cambs
Great Ouse, Limited tickets
Oldham and District Amalgamated Anglers'
Association
H Garside
60 Queensway
Greenfield
Nr Oldham, Lancs
Oldham United Anglers' Society
J K Lees
22 Epping Close
Chadderton, Lancs
Reservoirs. Tickets
Old Windsor Angling Club
D A Meakes
51 Bulkeley Avenue
Windsor, Berks
Thames. Tickets
Olton Mere Club
J E Cox
Mere Cottages
Warwick Road
Olton, Solihull
Orpington and District Angling Association
R Bright
133 The Drive
Bexley, Kent
Lakes. No tickets
Oswestry Angling Society
R A Griffiths
22 Cambrian Drive
Oswestry, Salop
Tickets for holiday visitors
Otley Angling Club (Trout Preserves)
D M Lane
Braeburn, Cherin Avenue
Menston, Ilkley,
W Yorks, LS29 6PR
Wharfe. Members only
Ottermouth Trout Association
W K H Coxe
Council Chambers
Budleigh Salterton, Devon
Oulton Broad Piscatorial Society
O Lay
205 Victoria Road
Oulton Broad
near Lowestoft, Suffolk
Oundle Angling Association
G Colver
48 Springfield Road
Oundle, Northamptonshire
Nene. Members only
Ouse Angling Preservation Society
Dr J L Cotton

Down End, Kingston Road
Lewes, Sussex
Sussex Ouse. Limited season tickets
Over and Swavesey Angling Society
M D Cook
13 Cromwell Park
Over, Cambridgeshire
Great Ouse. Members only
Oxford and District Anglers' Association
P Weston
18 Linden Road
Bicester, Oxon
Paignton Sea Anglers' Association
C Holman
50 Hayes Road
Paignton, Devon TQ4 5PL
Palmers Green Angling Society
B Bailey
7 College Court
Cheshunt, Herts, EN8 9NJ
New River, Mimram, Avon, lake
Pangbourne and Whitchurch District
Fishing Club
Mrs Lusted
74 Radstock Road
Reading, Berkshire
Peak Forest Angling Club (Derbyshire)
W H Blewitt
Top Farm, The Lane
Spinkhill, Sheffield S31 9YF
Members only
Peel Angling Club
P Chatel
17 Kerroo Coar
Peel, Isle of Man
Penkridge Anglers
W J Robins
Tight Lines
Market Street
Penkridge
Staffs ST19 5DH
Penrith Angling Association
R F Allinson
7 Scaws Drive
Penrith, Cumbria
Eden, Eamont, Petterill (Eden) and
Lowther. Tickets
Penshurst Angling Society
M Mills
3 Montgomery Road
Tunbridge Wells, Kent
Medway and Eden (Kent). No tickets
Peper Harow Flyfishers' Club
Miss M E Hide
Tanglewood, Moushill Lane
Milford, Nr Godalming, Surrey
Private club with trout water on Wey
and
two ponds; rods limited

Peterborough and District Angling Association
 W Yates
 75 Lawn Avenue
 Dogsthorpe, Peterborough
 Nene
Peterborough Jolly Anglers' Society
 C Graves
 8 Saxon Road
 Peterborough
Petersfield and District Angling Club
 D G Quinton
 12 Heather Road
 Petersfield
 Hampshire
 Rother. No tickets
Petworth, Bognor and Chichester Amalgamated Anglers
 A W Pascoe
 53 Wesley Lane
 Copnor, Portsmouth
 Western Rother. Tickets
Pewsey and District Angling Club
 Mrs M Draper
 14 Haines Terrace
 Pewsey, Wiltshire SN9 5DX
 K & A Canal. Tickets
Pickering Fishery Association
 C Hardy
 3 Westbourne Grove
 Pickering, Yorkshire
 Pickering Beck, Costa Beck, Oxfolds Beck
 and trout lake; members only, but
 Honorary Secretary will help visitors
Piscatorial Society
 J H S Hunt
 76 High Street
 Market Lavington
 Devizes, Wilts
 Itchen, Lambourn, Kennet and Wylye
 No tickets
Plowden Club
 R H P Kidson
 Westgate, 1 Westland Avenue
 Wolverhampton
 Onny. Private
Plymouth and District Freshwater Angling Association
 D L Owen
 39 Burnett Road
 Crownhill
 Plymouth PL6 5BH
 Plym. Members only
Plymouth Federation Sea Angling Club
 Roy Drew
 Sea Angling Centre
 Vauxhall Quay, Plymouth
Plymouth Sea Angling Club
 Sea Angling Centre
 Vauxhall Quay, Plymouth, Devon

Portcullis Angling Association
 J S Parker
 16 Lansdown View
 Kingswood, Bristol
Poole Dolphin Sea Angling Club
 Mrs I Wright
 9 Buckland Grove, Highcliffe
 Christchurch, Dorset
Portsmouth and District Angling Society
 R G Snook
 86 Carnarvon Road
 Copnor, Portsmouth
 Hants PO2 7NL
Portsmouth Services Fly Fishing Association
 R Snook
 86 Carnarvon Road
 Copnor
 Portsmouth
Potter Heigham and District Angling Club
 W Platten
 1 Audley Street
 Great Yarmouth, Norfolk
Potteries Angling Club
 D Heath
 180 Broadway
 Meir, Stoke-on-Trent
Preesall Angling Club
 C Rowe
 24 Sandy Lane
 Preesall, Lancashire
 Wyre. Members only
Prestwood and District Angling Club
 B D Putt
 72 Frances Street
 Chesham, Buckinghamshire
Pride of Derby Angling Association
 A Miller
 16 Mercia Drive
 Willington, Derby
 Trent. Members only. Waiting list
Prince Albert Angling Society
 C Clarke
 2 Avon Close
 Upton, Macclesfield
 Cheshire SKII 3DB
 Rivers, streams, lakes, pools
Pulborough Angling Society
 M Booth
 5 South Lane
 Houghton
 Arundel, W Sussex
 Arun
Purnells Fishing Club
 M Hancock
 Sunnyside, Tilley Lane
 Farmborough
 Near Bath
Quorn Angling Society
 W Boyd

28 Beaumont Road
Barrow-on-Soar, Leicestershire
Soar, canal. Tickets

Radcot Angling and Preservation Club
C R Neville
Clanville House, Bampton Road
Clanfield, Oxfordshire
Thames. Tickets

Ramsey Angling Club
G Corkish
44 Waterloo Road
Ramsay, Isle of Man

Raven Angling Club
E G Mears
16 Broomshouse Road
Fulham, London SW6 3QX

Reading and District Angling Association
D Capon
61 Thame Road
Haddenham
Bucks HP17 8EP
Kennet. No tickets

The Red Admiral Angling Club
G Thorne
15 Yately Avenue
Great Barr, Birmingham B42 1JW

Redditch Angling Club
G W Blundell
99 The Meadway
Redditch, Worcestershire B97 5AE
Avon. Tickets

Redditch and District Anglers' Federation
C Wright
16 Cyprus Avenue
Ashwood Bank
Redditch, Worcestershire

Red Spinner Angling Society
L J Halliday
28 Cranfield Crescent
Cuffley
Hertfordshire EN6 4EH
Evenlode, Stour (Dorset)
Ebble, Hampshire
Avon
Cheshunt Reservoir
Bearwood Lake. Members only

Remenham Angling Society
W A Hickman
Bell Cottage
Beverlay Gardens
Wargrave
Reading, Berks
Thames. Tickets

Retford and District Angling Association
H Oxby
6 Orchard Leigh
Ordsall, Retford
Nottinghamshire
Chesterfield Canal. Tickets

Rhayader Angling Association
Mrs B Jones
Ty Gwyrth
South Street
Rhayader, Powys
Wye, Marteg and lake

Richmond (Yorks) and District Angling Society
D Hutchinson
28 Cross Lanes
Richmond, N Yorkshire
Swale. Tickets

Ridgeway Angling Association
R Walker
Westholme, Stone
Berkeley, Gloucestershire

Ringwood and District Anglers' Association
R Smith
1 Avon Castle Drive
Matchams Lane
Ringwood, Hampshire

Ripley and District Angling Club
R Turner
2a Argyll Road
Ripley, Derbyshire
Amber, reservoirs. Tickets

Ripon Angling Club
S Looney
12 St Agnesgate
Ripon, Yorkshire
Yore, Laver, Skell, reservoir. Tickets

Ripon Piscatorials
P Godden
3 Oak Road
Ripon, Yorkshire
Yore. Tickets

Ripponden Fly-Fishers
H Hamer
The Hollies, Greetland
Halifax, Yorkshire
Reservoir

River Glaven Fishery Association
T G Bird
Newgate Green
Cley, Holt, Norfolk
Trout fishing in Glaven

Robin Hood Angling Club
G Smith
Robin Hood Inn
High Street, Rookery
Kidsgrove, Stoke-on-Trent ST7 4RL

Rochdale Walton Angling Society
Address unknown

Ross-on-Wye Angling Club
V R Hepburn
30 Claytons Bridstow
Ross-on-Wye, Wye
Tickets

Rother Angling Club
Mrs V Smithers
"North Bank"
June Lane
Midhurst, Sussex
Western Rother. Tickets
Rotherham and District Limited Anglers'
Federation
H Howarth
4 Scarborough Road
Wickersley
Rotherham, Yorkshire
Rowley and District Angling Society
S R Woodhouse
52 St Brades Close
Landsdowne Heights
Trividale, Warley
W Midlands B69 1NX
Severn. No tickets
Royal Leamington Spa Angling Association
E G Archer
9 Southway
Leamington Spa, Warwickshire
Royal Ramsgate Invicta Angling Association
B A Kirkaldie
67 Boundary Road
Ramsgate, Kent
Royal Tunbridge Wells Angling Society
Clifford C Lupini
25 The Drive
Hedge Barton, Fordcombe, Kent
Rother, Teise, Medway.
No tickets except to members
Rugby Federation of Anglers
P Felton
23 Malvern Avenue
Rugby CV22 5JN
Avon, canals. Permits
Rugeley and Brereton Angling Society
J T Connolly
36 Ravenslea Road
Brerton, Staffs WS15 1AF
Rushden and Higham Ferrers & Irchester
Angling Association
Enquiries to J Leach
Anglers Depot
Rushden, Northants
Ryburn Angling Society
L Kitching
44 Sellerdale Avenue
Wyke, Bradford, Yorkshire
Ouse. Tickets
Rye and District Angling Society
A V Curd 34 The Maltings
Peasmarsh, Sussex
Rother. Tickets
Ryedale Anglers' Club
J A W Leech
Northfield House

Hovingham, Yorks YO6 4LG
Rye. Members only
Sabrina Angling Club
P Liversage
43 Lansdowne Road
Shrewsbury
Severn and Roden. Members only
Saddington Angling Society
J Mason
8 Honiton Close
Wigston, Leicestershire
Saddleworth and District Angling Club
C T Johnson
3 Birch Road
Uppermill
Nr Oldham, Lancs OL3 6JN
St George Angling Club
R Rudd
29 Kingsdown Road
Trowbridge
Semington Brook
St Helens Angling Association
J Corkish
65 Laffak Road
Carr Hill
St Helens, Lancashire WAII 9EH
Welsh Dee, canal, lakes. Limited weekly
tickets
St Ives and District Fish Preservation and
Angling Society
P Keepin
2 New Road, St Ives
Huntingdon, Cambs
Great Ouse. Tickets
St Leonards Sea Anglers
HQ, 16 Grand Parade
St Leonards, Sussex
St Mawgan Angling Club
G Booker
St John's Lanherne
St Mawgan, Newquay, Cornwall
River Menalhyl
St Michael's Angling Association
A J Moss
West Bungalow, St Michael's
Preston, Lancashire
Wyre
St Neots and District Angling Society
A G Watling
43 Shakespeare Road
Eaton Socon
Huntingdon, Cambs PE19 3HG
Great Ouse. Tickets
Salcombe and District Sea Anglers'
Association
Headquarters
Victoria Inn
Fore Street
Salcombe, Devon TQ8 8BT

Salisbury and District Angling Club
R W Hillier
"Inverleith"
29 N Zealand Avenue
Salisbury, Wiltshire SP2 7JX
Avon, Bourne, Nadder, pits.
Some tickets
Salopian Fly Fishing Association
Donald Jones
56 Wrekin View
Madley, Shropshire
Saltaire Angling Association
W Troman
7 Hall Road
Shipley, Yorkshire
Wharfe and Aire. Tickets
Saltburn and District Sea Anglers' Association
Mrs E M Vickery
3 Wardsman Crescent
Redcar, Yorkshire
Sandgate Sea Angling Society
R J Piddock
"Kerry Vale"
West Street
New Romney, Kent
Sandown and Lake Angling Society
F Clarke
37 Culver Way
Yaverland
Sandown, Isle of Wight
Sandwich and District Angling Association
D W R Daniels
48 Hazelwood Meadow
Sandwich, Kent CT13 0AR
Sawbridgeworth Angling Society
R Edwards
41 Lawrence Avenue
Sawbridgeworth, Hertfordshire
Stort. Tickets
Scarborough Boat Angling Club
J A Martin
26 Ling Hill
Newby, Scarborough
Scarborough Mere Angling Club
G A Colley
The Bungalow
Cayton School
Mill Lane, Cayton
Scarborough, Yorkshire YOII 3TE
Scarborough Rock Anglers
H Dobson
1 Uplands Avenue
East Ayton, near Scarborough
Yorkshire
Sceptre Angling Club
D T Hobbs
77 The Gossamers
Garston
Watford, Herts

Scunthorpe and District Angling Association
I A Robertson
35 Merton Road
Bottesford
Scunthorpe, Yorks
Seabrook Sea Anglers' Association
R Perrin
74 Horn Street
Hythe, Kent
Seaham Sea Angling Club
K B Fox
41 Burnhall Drive
Seaham, Co Durham
Sedbergh and District Angling Association
G Bainbridge
El Kantara
Sedbergh, Cumbria
Trout water on Lune. Tickets
Selby Angling Association
C Ward
3 Ferndale Road
Selby, North Yorks YO8 9DQ
Selsey Tope Fishers Specimen Club
R G Horrod
28 Beach Road
Selsey, Sussex
Services Dry Fly Fishing Association
(Salisbury Plain)
Brigadier C A Landale
Quartering Branch
HQ South West District
Wyvern Road, Bulford Camp
Salisbury SP4 9PA
Avon. Private
Settle Anglers' Association
M G Riley
Stockdale Cottage
Austwick
via Lancaster FE1 20R
Ribble. Tickets
Seven Angling Club
Mrs Betty J Stansfield
Sun Seven
Sinnington, Yorkshire
Seven. Members only
Seven Stars Angling Club
B Chambers
12 Mason Close
Headless Cross, Redditch B97 5DF
Shanklin Angling Society
M Kingswell
52 North Road
Shanklin, Isle of Wight
Sheffield Amalgamated Anglers' Society
A D Baynes
H/Q Lord Nelson
166/8 Arundel Street
Sheffield S1 4RE
Trent and tributaries, canals, etc. Permits

Sheffield and District Anglers' Association
F E Turner
PO Box 218
Sheffield S1 1BU
Trent and tributaries, canals, etc. Permits
Shefford and District Angling Association
J Anderson
44 Ampthill Road
Shefford, Bedfordshire
Sheringham Sea Angling Club
R Sitters
Holway Road
Sheringham, Norfolk
Shiplake and Binfield Heath Fishing Club
R Fisher
88 Buckingham Drive
Emmer Green
Reading, Berks
Thames. Members only
Shipston-on-Stour and District Angling Club
E Draper
37 Station Road
Shipston-on-Stour, Warwickshire
Shrewsbury Angling Society
D Clarke
5 Albert Street, Castlefields
Shrewsbury, Salop
Shuttington and Alvecote Angling Club
M H Taylor
39 Alveote Cottages
Alvecote
Nr Tamworth, Staffordshire B79 0DJ
Sidmouth Sea Angling Club
A C Thorne
25 Coleridge Road
Ottery St Mary, Devon
Silver Dace Angling Association
J Bedford
12 Henbury Court, Station Road
Henbury, Bristol
Avon, Frome, Chew
Sinnington Angling Club
J D Hattersley
2 Willow Rise
Kirkby Moorside, N Yorks
Seven. Occasional tickets
Sittingbourne Angling Club
C Brown
5 Sunnybanks, Murston
Sittingbourne, Kent
Pits. Dt (restricted).
Skegness Angling Association
L H Dent
11 High Street
Skegness, Lincolnshire
Skegness Sea Angling Club
S Kinning
20 West End
Burgh-le-Marsh, Skegness, Lincs

Skerton and Morecambe Angling Society
C Boswell
16 Slyne Road
Skerton, Lancashire
Skipton Angling Association
J W Preston
Hill Crest, Beech Hill Road
Carleton, Skipton
Yorkshire BD23 3EN
Aire. Tickets
Slaithwaite and District Angling Club
A Bamforth
43 Binn Road
Marsden, near Huddersfield
Yorkshire
Trent, Rye, canals and reservoirs, etc.
Tickets
Soho Loop Anglers Association
M T Holt
26 Worcester Road
Oldbury
Warley, West Midlands
Somerfords Fishing Association
D Hitchings
88 Cleeve Wood Road
Downend, Bristol
Frome, Loddon. Tickets to members'
friends only
South Coast Sea Angling Association
R G Horrod
28 Beach Road
Selsey, Sussex
South Molton Angling Club
Inquire Thompson's (tackleist),
The Square, South Molton, Devon
Tickets for Taw, Mole.
Southampton Piscatorial Society
P J Dowse
35 Arnheim Road
Lordswood, Southampton
Stour, Avon, Blackwater
Southampton Sea Angling Club
P Thomas
28 Laundry Road, Shirley
Southampton SO1 6AN
Southend Amateur Angling Society
G Kirby
25 The Meads, Vange
Pitsea, Essex
Southern (IOM) Angling Club
A A Kelly
Dunvegan
Bay View Road
Port St Mary, IOM
Southern Counties Angling Federation
(31 member clubs)
Douglas Richardson
117-121 Rose Green Road, Rose Green
Bognor Regis, Sussex

Southgate and District Angling Society
D G Hodgkins
18 Cedar House
Winkfield Road
Wood Green, London N22
Southsea Sea Angling Club
42 Granada Road
Southsea, Hampshire
South Tyne Angling Association
G Liddle
North Bank
Haydon Bridge, Hexham
Northumberland
S Tyne. Tickets to local residents only
Spalding Angling Association
H E Parkinson
76 St Thomas Road
Spalding, Lincolnshire
Glen (Welland). Tickets
Spilsby Angling Association
G Matthews
57 Ancaster Avenue
Spilsby, Lincolnshire
Sphinx Angling Club
W J Jenkins
284 Stroud Road
Tuffley, Gloucester
Staines Angling Society
G H Brown
134 Page Road
Bedfont, Middlesex
Stainford and Keadby Joint Angling Committee
J Cunliffe
13 Wesley Road
Kiveton Park
Sheffield
Stalbridge Angling Association
P Sansom
19 Waterlake
Stalbridge, Dorset
Stamford Welland AAA
G E Bates
16a Austin Street
Stamford
Lincs PE9 22P
Stanhope Angling Association
J J Lee
1 Eastcroft, Stanhope
Co Durham
Wear. Tickets
Stapleton Angling Association
A Harrison
18 The Chippings
Southside
Stapleton, Bristol
Avon, Chew, Frome
Star Angling Club
A G Jones

6 Blandford Gardens
Burntwood
Nr Walsall, Staffordshire
Staveley and District Angling Association
D A Taylor
18 Rawes Garth, Staveley
Cumbria, Kent
Gowan, lake. Tickets
Stevenage Angling Society
W J Lewis
54 Stonycroft
Stevenage, Hertfordshire
No water
Stockport and District Anglers' Federation
C Holland
121 Northgate Road
Edgeley
Stockport, Cheshire
Stockton Angling Association
R Corner
120 Station Road
Billingham, Cleveland
Tees. No tickets
Stoke City and District Anglers' Association
P Johansen
31 East Crescent, Sneyd Green
Stoke-on-Trent, Staffordshire
Canal
Stoke-on-Trent Angling Society
S F Broadgate
5 Kingsfield Oval
Basford
Stoke-on-trent, Staffs ST4 6HN
Stokesley Angling Club
F Farrow
11 Dale End, Danby
Whitby, N Yorkshire YO21 2JF
Stoke-sub-Hamdon Angling Association
D Goad
2 Windsor Lane
Stoke-sub-Hamdon, Somerset
Parrot. Members only
Stone and District Angling Society
F Worsdale
45 Church Street
Stone, Staffs ST15 1AF
Stony Stratford Angling Club
T R Valentine
34 Mallets Close
Stony Stratford
Wolverton, Buckinghamshire
Stour Fishery Association
L G Holtom
Barton Mill
Canterbury
Kentish Stour. No tickets
Stowe Angling Club
J Freedstone
2 Hazel Close

Brackley
Northamptonshire
Stowmarket and District Angling Association
J Eade
37 Windermere Road
Stowmarket, Suffolk
Sturminster and Hinton Angling Association
T J Caines
Coombe Gate, The Bridge
Sturminster Newton, Dorset
Stour. Restricted permits
Sudbury and District Angling Society
T R Fairless
39 Pot Kiln Road
Gt Cornard
Sudbury, Suffolk
Stour. Tickets
Suffolk Fly Fishers' Club
J Bird
27 Norbury Road
Ipswich, Suffolk
Sussex County Angling Association
Miss S Colquhorn
38 Limes Avenue
Horley, Sussex
Sussex Piscatorial Society
C J Eydmann
10 Greenleas
Hove, Sussex
Ponds and lakes. Tickets for members'
friends only
Sutton Coldfield Angling Society
Address unknown
Lakes. No tickets
Swadlincote and District Anglers'
Association
P Woolrich
27 Chapel Street
Smisby
Nr Ashby-de-la-Zouch
Leis LE6 5TJ
Swaffham Angling Club
Honorary Secretary
30 Kings Street
Swaffham, Norfolk
Trout lake. St.
Swan Angling Club
J Stanhope
4 High Road
Lane Head
Willenhall, West Midlands
Swanage and District Angling Club
R Chellingworth
12 Osborne Road
Swanage, Dorset
SWEB (Angling Section)
D Hurst
26 Abbots Avenue
Hanham, Bristol

Swindon Golden Carp Angling Association
K Hale
11 Elmina Road
Swindon, Wiltshire
K and A Canal. Tickets
Tadcaster Angling and Preservation
Association
S Barker
4 Westfield Square
Tadcaster, N Yorks
Wharfe. Tickets
Talbot Angling Society
R W Griffin
11 St Richards Gardens
Droitwich Spa, Worcestershire
Severn. Tickets
Tamworth Working Men's Club
M Stokeheld
14 Bridge Street
Amington, near Tamworth
Staffordshire
Tickets
Tanfield Angling Club
J Whitfield
7 King Street, Mirfield
W Yorks WF14 8AP
Tickets to guests of members only
Tarporley Angling Club
R W Cross
25 Burton Avenue
Tarporley, Cheshire
Oulton Mill Pool. Tickets
Taunton Angling Association
H King
145 Henson Park
Chard, Somerset
Tone, Taunton Canal, Drains
Taunton Fly-Fishing Club
J S Hill
21 Manor Road
Taunton, Somerset
Tavy, Walkham and Plym Fishing Club
Mrs J P Smalley
Haytown
Sampford Spinney
Yelverton, Devon
Tickets
Taw Fishing Club
J C C Jourdan
Bush House
Spreyton
Crediton, Devon
Taw. Restricted tickets
Tawe Disabled Fishers Association
R G Waters
23 Verig Street
Manselton, Swansea SA5 9NQ
Tawe & Tributaries Angling Association
M Matthews

32 Farm Road
Cwrt Sart, Briton Ferry
Neath, West Glamorgan
Tebay and District Angling Club
H Riley
White Cross House
Tebay, via Penrith, Cumbria
Lune. Tickets
Teignmouth Sea Angling Society
D J Lawer
Triscombe
19 Inverteign Drive
Teignmouth, Devon TQ14 9AF
Teise Anglers' and Owners' Association
Dr N Goddard
Chickenden Farmhouse
Staplehurst
Kent
Teise. Tickets
Tenbury Fishing Association
J Weston
Berrington Mill
Tenbury, Worcestershire
Teme. Limited tickets
Tenterden and District Angling Preservation Association
N E Sharp
123 High Street,
Tenterden, Kent
Rother. No day or period tickets.
Membership covers Rother Fishing
Association waters
Test and Itchen Fishing Association
Mrs M F Baring
Well House, Malshanger Green
Basingstoke, Hampshire
Register compiled of rods to let; apply
Honorary Secretary
Tewin Fly-Fishing Club
K F Atkins
9 Warren Way, Digswell
Welwyn, Hertfordshire
Mimram. Members only
Tewkesbury Angling Association
M K Higginbotham
36 Tirlebank Way
Newtown, Tewkesbury
Goucestershire
Severn. Tickets
Thames Angling Preservation Society
A E Hodges
The Pines
32 Tile Kiln Lane
Bexley, Kent
(Crayford 25575). Voluntary body
concerned with fishery improvement
Thameside Angling Society
D Hammond
62 Thong Lane

Gravesend, Kent
River Cray and lake. No dt.
Thatcham Angling Association
K G Roberts
12 Malham Road
Thatcham Farm
Thatcham, Berkshire
Kennet. No tickets
Thirsk Angling Club
R W Stephenson
76 New Estate, Norby
Thirsk, Yorkshire
Cod Beck, Thirsk and Swale. Tickets
Thornaby Angling Association
D Speight
10 Stainsby Gate
Thornaby
Cleveland
Tees, Eden, Swale, Ure. Members only
Thurrock Angling Club
D Nutt
94 Eriff Drive
South Ockendon, Essex
Lakes. No tickets
Tinsley and District Angling Clubs Association
D M Dearman
2 Trentham Close
Brinsworth
Rotherham, South Yorks S60 5LS
Tisbury Angling Club
P Lever
1 Maypole Bungalow
Ansty, Tisbury, Wiltshire
Nadder. Tickets to members' friends only.
Tiverton and District Angling Club
R Retallick
21 Allstone Road
Canal Hill, Tiverton
Devon
Exe
Tiverton Fly Fishing Club
M J Ford
9 William Street
Tiverton, Devon
Exe. Limited tickets
Todmorden Angling Society
R Barber
12 Grisedale Drive
Manor Park Farm
Burnley BB12 8AR
Tonbridge Angling and Fish Preservation Society
A S Wolfe
59 Hunt Road
Tonbridge
Kent
Medway. Day tickets (limited)

Torbay Association of Sea Anglers
J M R Easton
Risca
23 Hatfield Road
Ellacombe
Torquay TQ1 3BW
Torquay Sea Anglers' Association
C F Finch
14 Clifton Road
Paignton
Torridge Fly Fishing Club
K L Parker
4 Merryfield Road
Bideford E, Devon
Reservoirs
Towcester and District Angling Association
P Kimbell
53 Newcombe Road
Northampton
Tove. No tickets
Trent and Mersey Canal Angling Society
F Egerton
19 Bowden Drive
Northwich, Cheshire
Trimpley Angling Association
10 College Road
Kidderminster
Worcestershire DY10 1LU
Tring Anglers
B Boucher
2 Hivings Park
Chesham, Bucks
Grand Union Canal. Tickets
Tunbridge Wells Angling Association
A R Woodhams
19 Park Street
Tunbridge Wells
Kent.
Twickenham Piscatorial Society
L C Pallett
37 Stuart Way
Windsor,Berks
Kennet, Thame, pits. Tickets
Two Mills Flyfishers' Club
J V Borthwick
Mills Platt, Box Hill
Chippenham
Wiltshire SN14 9EZ
By Brook. No tickets
Twyford Angling Club
G L Addy
16a Woods Road
Caversham, Reading, Berkshire
·Thames. No tickets
Ulverston Angling Association
H B Whittam
29 Lyndhurst Road
Ulverston, Cumbria
Lakes, becks and canal. Tickets

Unity Angling Club
E K Mann
19 Busfield Street
Bradford, Yorks BD4 7QX
Upper Alde and Ore Angling Club
R C Foster
Maltings Farm, Aldham
Ipswich, Suffolk
Alde. Trout tickets
Upper Coquet Angling Club
A C Dixon
7 Douro Terrace
Sunderland
Coquet. No tickets
Upper Culm Fishing Association
T A Blackhore
"Sunset", Clayhidon
Cullompton, Devon
Culm. Tickets
Upper Tamar Fishing Club
M Summers
Carey View, Tower Hill
St Giles on the Heath
Devon
Upper Tanat Fishing Club
George Lewis
c/o Crampton Pym and Lewis
The Poplars, Willow Street
Oswestry, Shropshire
Tanat. No tickets
Upper Teign Fishing Association
A J Price
Gibbons Meadow, Chagford
Newton Abbot, Devon TQ13 8DS
Teign. Tickets
Upper Weardale Angling Association
G Hughes
"Hi Ghyll"
Ireshopeburn
Weardale, Co Durham
Wear. Tickets
Upton-on-Severn Angling Association
R Tainton
136 Poolbrook Road
Malvern, Worcs
Uttoxeter Angling Association
I E Davies
The Coppice, Sunnyside Road
Uttoxeter, Staffordshire
Dove
Vectis Boating and Fishing Club
M T Sawyer
27 Salters Road
Ryde, Isle of Wight
Ventnor Angling Club
R Gibbons
43 Dudley Road
Ventnor
Isle of Wight

Victoria Angling Club
B G Simpson
9 Lansdowne Road
Harthill, Stoke-on-Trent ST4 6EY
Victoria and Biddulph Angling Society
P Moston
73 Mayfield Road
Biddulph, Staffs
Wadebridge Angling Association
E J Renals
Coppins, Whiterock Close
Wadebridge, Cornwall
Walton-on-the-Naze Sea Angling Club
R Hawes
c/o Metcalfes
15 Newgate Street
Walton-on-the-Naze, Essex CO14 8TD
Walton-on-Thames Angling Society
A Finalyson
14 Harrow Road
West Belfont
Feltham
Middlesex
Mole, lake. No tickets
Wangye Angling Society
N Smith
7 Sherwood Road
Barkingside, Ilford, Essex
Wansbeck Angling Association
D J Bell
9 Bilton's Court, off Newgate Street
Morpeth, Northumberland
Wansbeck. Members only
**Wansford, Yarwell, Nassington and District
Angling Club**
C W J Howes
43 Elton Road, Stibbington
Wansford, Peterborough
Ware Angling Club
D Bridgeman
30 Musley Lane
Ware, Herts SG12 7EW
Wareham and District Angling Society
P J Dominy
94 Heights Road
Upton, Poole
Dorset
Frome, Piddle. No tickets
Warmington Angling Club
I G W Brudenell
10 Church Street
Warmington
Peterborough PE8 1TE
No tickets.
Warminster and District Angling Club
D M Vickers
113 Westleigh
Warminster, Wilts
Wylye, lakes. No tickets

Warrington Anglers' Association
J S Jackson
23 Nora Street
Warrington, Cheshire
Dee, Severn and tributaries, Ribble,
Dane, canal, lakes, etc. Members only
Warwick and District Angling Association
L Sargent
218 Warwick Road
Kenilworth
Warwickshire CV8 1FD
Watchet FC
c/o The Gardeners Arms
Bishops Lydeard
Taunton, Somerset
Waterside Angling Association
A Chivers
57 Specklemead, Paulton
Near Bristol
Cam Brook
**Wath Brow and Ennerdale Angling
Association**
D F Whelan
11 Crossing Close
Cleator Moor, Cumberland
Ehen. Tickets
Watford Piscators
N F Brandon
25 Leaford Crescent
Watford, Hertfordshire
Gade, canal, lakes
**Wellingborough and District Nene Angling
Club**
S H Battison
36 Church Way
Weston Favell, Northampton
Nene, Great Ouse. No tickets
Wellington (Somerset) Angling Association
J Hayes
1 Tonegate
Wellington, Somerset
Tone. Tickets
Wellworthy Angling Club
I H Dibble
28 Longstone Avenue
Bridgwater
Welshpool Angling Association
F Eakins
Westwood Park Hotel
Salop Road
Welshpool, Powys
Severn, Mule, Rhiew and Banwy. Some
permits
Wem Angling Club
D Trow
40 Eskdale Road
Telford Estate
Shrewsbury, Shropshire
Lake. Tickets

Wensleydale Angling Association
Mrs P A Thorpe
Rose and Crown Hotel
Bainbridge
Leyburn, N Yorks
Yore. Tickets

Wessex Federation of Angling Clubs
J J Mathrick
25 Ashwell Lane
Glastonbury, Somerset BA6 8BG
Parret, Isle; affiliated clubs share rights

West Bay Sea Angling Club
Mrs H Pettet
Home Farm View
Bothenhampton
Bridport, Dorset

West Beck Preservation Society
C W G Derrick
3 Link Road
Cottingham, E Yorkshire
West Beck. Members only

West Country Fly Fishers
J W Hamilton Roberts
64 Hampton Park
Redland, Bristol BS6 6LJ

West End Angling Association
R A Richardson
68 Raby Street, Byker
Newcastle upon Tyne

The West End Angling Club
M E Gundy
77 Travers Road
Saniacre, Notts

Western Wight Angling Club
Mrs R A Pearson
The Quarn
Moortown Lane
Brighstone, IoW

West Ham Angling Society
A E Mileham
43 Avenue Road
Forest Gate
London E7
Lee. Some tickets

West Hampstead Angling Society
E Baker
38 Townholme Crescent
Hanwell
London W7 2NA

Westminster Angling Society
N Patterson
118 Hall Place
London W2
Club fishes Calpac Waters

Weston-super-Mare and District Angling Association
K Tucker
26 Coniston Crescent
Weston-super-Mare, Avon

Weston-super-Mare Sea Angling Association
W Letts
21a Brean Down Avenue
Weston-super-Mare, Avon

Weswater Angling Club
The Clubhouse
Hallington Reservoirs
Colwell, Hexham
Northumberland

Wetherby and District Angling Club
F H Atkinson
Quarry Farm
Kirk Deighton
Wetherby, Yorkshire
Wharfe. Tickets

Weybridge Angling Club
P Daymon
61 Byron Road, Addlestone
Weybridge, Surrey
Wey. Members only

Wey Navigation Angling Amalgamation
I V Fraser
43 Kingston Rise
New Haw, Weybridge
Surrey KT15 3EX
Wey. Tickets

Weymouth Angling Society
L Thomas
Angling HQ
Commercial Road
Weymouth, Dorset

Wheatsheaf Angling Club
C Best
27 Bassett Close
Selby
North Yorks

Wheelock Angling Society
A Darlington
Overland House, Moss Lane
Elsworth, Sandbach, Cheshire

Whitby Sea Anglers' Association
T G R Sleightholme
2 Crescent Avenue
West Cliff, Whitby
Yorkshire

White Hart Dagenham Angling Society
D Brown
100 Crescent Road
Dagenham, Essex

White Swan Piscatorial Society
C E Clarke
186 Walford Road
Birmingham B11 1GE

Whitmore Reans Angling Association
R H Hughes
6 Tettenhall Road
Wolverhampton WV1 4SA
Severn, Roden, Tern, Penk, Sowe and local canals. Tickets

Whitstable and District Angling Society
Mr Foyle
48 Albert Street Whitstable, Kent
Whitstable Sea Fishing Association
H S Noel
34 Grimshill Road
Whitstable, Kent
Whittlesey Angling Association
J Canham
12 Aliwal Road
Whittlesey
Peterborough PE7 2AY
Nene, Twenty Foot, Cock Bank, pits
Tickets
Wigan and District Angling Association
W Gratton
66 Balcarres Road
Aspull
Wigan, Lancashire
Ribble, Wyre, Winster, Lake Winder-
mere,
reservoirs, flashes, ponds. Tickets
Wigston Angling Society
P A Hebborn
10 Sandringham Road
Glen Parva, Leics
Canal tickets
Willington and District Angling Club
R Lumb
18 Shipley Terrace
West View Estate
Crook, County Durham
Wear; dt
Wilmslow and District Angling Association
P H Curbishley
16 Alderdale Grove
Wilmslow, Cheshire
No tickets
Wilton Fly-Fishing Club
C B White
The Old Vicarage
Morgans Vale Road
Redlynch, Salisbury
Wylye. Limited membership
Winkworth Fly Fishers
M Richardson
87 Summers Road
Farncombe
Godalming, Surrey
Wimborne and District Angling Club
S P Piper
38 Chetnole Close
Canford Heath
Poole, Dorset BH17 8BE
Members only
Windermere, Ambleside and District Angling
Association
C J Sodo
1 Cragwood Cottages

Windermere
Cumbria
Rothay, Troutbeck and Rydal Water
Tickets
Windmill Angling Association
N Gooding
11 Chilkwell Street
Glastonbury
Somerset
Butleigh Wootton Lake
Windsor Angling Society
G E Johncey
2 Bradshaw Close
Windsor, Berkshire
Thames
Winsford and District Angling Association
J S Bailey
22 Plover Avenue
Winsford
Wisbech and District Angling Association
B Lakey
The Cot
Leverington Common
Wisbech, Cambridgeshire
Witham and Dist Joint Anglers Federation
R Hobley
30 Gunby Avenue, Lincoln LN6 OAW
Witham Sea Anglers Club
Leonard Harding
65 Chelmer Road
Witham, Essex
Witney Angling Society
W V S Mann
86 Early Road
Witney OX8 6EU
Members only
Woking and District Angling Association
D Powell
Maymont
Guildford Road, Knaphill
Woking, Surrey
Wey. Tickets
Wolsingham Angling Association
J L Peart
37 West End
Wolsingham, Co Durham
Wear. St
Woodbridge and District Angling Club
T Pryke
12 Bredfield Road
Woodbridge, Suffolk
Woodford Angling Society
Honorary Secretary
22 Evanrigg Terrace
Woodford Green, Essex
Roding. Members only
Wootton Bassett Angling Club
T Strange
15 Shakespeare Road

Wootton Bassett
Swindon, Wiltshire
Lake, Brinkworth Brook. Members only
Worcester Angling Society
H L Cull
49 The Hill Avenue
Worcester
Teme. No permits
Worcester and District United Anglers'
Association
The Association Secretary
Centre Course Building
Pitchcroft
Worcester
Avon, Severn, Teme, Canal.
Some tickets
Workington Angling Association
G E Craswell
26 Calva Brow, Seaton
Workington, Cumbria
Worksop and District United Angling
Association
G D Rollinson
31 Lincoln Street
Worksop, Notts
Canals and Trent. Tickets
Wormleighton Fishing Club
J Roe
47 Northumberland Road
Coventry CV1 3AP
Worthing and District Piscatorial Society
(Freshwater)
R P Tunnicliffe
79 North Lane
Portslade BN4 2NF, Sussex
Worthing Sea Anglers' Association
G Riley
39 Greystone Avenue
Worthing, Sussex
Headquarters. Worthing Pier, Worthing,
Sussex
Wybunbury Angling Association
J Harding
234 Newcastle Road
Shavington

Wylye Fly-Fishing Club
Commander P D Hoare, RN (Retd)
Monks Farm House
Corsham, Wiltshire
Members and guests only
Yarm Angling Association
A W Allen
4 Blenavon Court
Yarm
Stockton-on-Tees, Cleveland
Tees. Tickets
Yeovil-Sherborne Angling Association
N Garrett
18 Springfield Road
Yeovil, Somerset
Trout and coarse fish on Yeo and
tributaries; two ponds
York and District Amalgamation of Anglers
John M Lane
39 Lowfields Drive
Acomb, York YO2 3DQ
Ouse, Foss, Derwent, Nidd, becks and
ponds. Tickets
York Angling Association
H White
(Chairman)
21 Linton Street
Poppleton Road, York
Derwent, Pocklington Canal. Tickets
and match bookings
York Flyfishers' Club
Major L M Stansfield, MBE
Miles Croft
Thornton-le-Clay, Yorkshire
Trout lakes. No tickets
York Tradesmen's Angling Association
J R May
1 Neville Drive
Bishopthorpe, York
Various becks. Members only
Yorkshire Flyfishers' Club
Honorary Secretary
2 Devonshire Crescent
Leeds LS8 1EP, Yorkshire
Eden, Eamont, Lyvennet, Ribble and
Yore. No tickets

**Fishing Clubs: When you appoint a new secretary, do not forget to give us
details of the change. Write to Thomas Harmsworth Publishing, 13 Nicosia
Road, London SW18 3RN.**

WELSH FISHING STATIONS

IN the pages that follow, the catchment areas of Wales, are given in alphabetical order, being interspersed with the streams and the lakes of the Principality under headings such as "Powys (streams)"; "Gwynedd (lakes)," etc. The rivers of each catchment area are arranged in the manner described under the heading "English Fishing Stations", on p 21 and the other notes given there apply equally to Wales. The whole of the Wye and the Severn, it should be remembered, are included in the section on England, while the whole of the Dee is listed among the Welsh rivers.

Note: *Sea trout are commonly referred to as "sewin" in Wales, although some associations define sewin as immature sea trout returning to the river for the first time.*

AERON

(For close seasons, licences, etc, see Welsh Water Authority, p 17–18)

Rises in Llyn Eiddwen, 7m north-west of Tregaron, and flows about 17m to sea at Aberaeron. Excellent run of sewin from June onwards with smaller salmon run. Brown trout plentiful but small.

Aberaeron (Dyfed). Salmon, sewin and trout. Permits, which also enable anglers to fish **Arth** and **Teifi,** available from Aberaeron Town AC. St £52.50, wt £30, dt £7.50. Tel: 0545 570579. **Wyre** and **Arth,** two streams to north, hold brown trout and have small runs of sewin. Fishing mostly held by farmers, who often give permission.

ANGLESEY (streams)

(For close seasons, licences, etc, see Welsh Water Authority, p 17–18)

ALAW: Rises above Cors y Bol bog and flows some 7m to sea beyond **Llanfachraeth,** opposite Holyhead. Fishes well (trout) for first three months of season and again in September when good run of small sea trout expected; usually too low in summer. Permission of farmers.

BRAINT: Small stream which flows almost whole width of the island, parallel with Menai Straits, to sea at Aber Menai, beyond **Llangeinwen.** Trout, some sea trout, but usually fishable only first three months of season. Permission of farmers.

CEFNI: Rises above Llangwyllog, flows through Llŷn Frogwy, on to **Llangefni** and Cefni Reservoir *(see Anglesey Lakes),* and then to sea in 6m. Lower reaches canalised. Only fair-sized river in island. Brown trout and chance of late salmon or sea trout. Permission of farmers. Hotel: The Bull.

CEINT: Small stream entering sea at Red Wharf Bay; some trout; permission of farmers; summer conditions difficult. Fishing station: **Pentraeth.**

FFRAW or GWNA: Under the name of Gwna rises 4m above Bodorgan and waters Llyn Coron *(see Anglesey Lakes)* just below village. Stream then takes name of Ffraw and runs to sea at **Aberffraw** in 2m. Little more than brook. One or two pools fishable early on, but overgrown June onwards. Trout, some sea trout. Hotels: Prince Llewellyn, Crown, both Aberffraw; Merrick Arms, Bodorgan Arms, **Bodorgan.**

WYGYR: Small stream falling into sea at **Cemaes Bay.** Trout; restocked. Wygyr AA has about 2m (both banks); st, wt and. dt. Tickets from Cefn Glas Inn, Llanfechell; or Gwynfa Stores; fly only. Good sea fishing in bay.

Note: *Many hotels issue visitors' permits, but where numbers are limited, guests naturally have prior claim.*

ANGLESEY (lakes)

Cefni Reservoir. Llangefni. 173 acres. Brown and rainbow trout; fly only; good wading; boats. Leased by WWA to Cefni AA. Dt £5, wt £14, st £35, (limits), from Treasurer (season); Look Around Sports, Llangefni; K Johnson, Trigger Tackle, Menai Bridge and bailiff on site. Concessions jun & OAP.

Coron Lake, Bodorgan. Trout, sea trout; fly only. St £75, wt £15, dt £4 and evening tickets £3 from Bodorgan Estate. Hotels: Meyrick Arms; Bodorgan Arms. RD licence from Bodorgan Estate Office.

Dinas Lake, Valley. Mainly roach; permission of farmers. **Penrhyn Lake:** mainly perch; permission of farmers; **Traffwll Reservoir;** roach, perch, trout; inquire locally.

Fodol Lake, Rhosgoch. Fishery ruined by damage to dam. Future uncertain.

Hendre Lake. Gwalchmai. No fishing at present, due to WAA drainage scheme works. Rights owned by Mrs. E Hughes, Hendre Farm.

Llyn Alaw. Llanerchymedd. Tel. 0407 730762.

Situated in open lowland countryside this productive 777 acre reservoir offers fly fishing, spinning and worming for brown and rainbow trout. Dt £5.50 on site, evening £4, wt £27, st £134 from visitor centre at reservoir. Concessions to OAP & jun. Boat for disabled available at no extra charge. Season March 20 – Oct 17 for brown. March 20 – Oct 31 for rainbow.

Llyn Euronwy, Rhosneigr. $1\frac{1}{2}$ acre lake; carp, tench, rudd and roach. Dt £2 from Mr Summerfield, Ty-hen Farm.

Maelog Lake. Rhosneigr. Roach, perch, rudd, bream, brown trout; Holyhead FWAS control part only; dt £2. Hotel: Maelog Lake and Glan Neigr. Tackle, tickets, licences from K D Highfield, 7 Marine Terrace, Rhosneigr (Tel: 810598).

Mynydd Badafon Lake. Roach and perch; free. No licence required for coarse fishing.

Hotels in Anglesey: Dinorben Arms, Amwlch; Faraway, Cemaes Bay; Bull, Valley; Tysilio Guest House, Rhosgoch.

CLEDDAU (Eastern and Western)

(For close seasons, licences, etc, see Welsh Water Authority, p 17–18)

East Cleddau rises on the east side of Mynydd Prescelly and flows 15m south-west, partly along old Carmarthenshire border, to north branch of Milford Haven. West Cleddau rises on west side of mountain and flows about 20m south-east to same creek of Haven. Rivers hold salmon, sewin and trout. Sewin fishing good in June, July and August.

WESTERN CLEDDAU: Salmon, trout.
Haverfordwest (Dyfed). Pembrokeshire AA has water; st £25, wt £23, dt £8 from County Sports, Old Bridge. Further information from hon sec. Riparian owners may give permission elsewhere. Sewin fishing good June to August. At **Llysyfran** (8m NE) is 187 acre reservoir with good trout fishing; Rb and B trout. Season March 20–Oct 17. St £134, wt £22, dt £5.50, evening £4 from reservoir; boats extra. Concessions to OAP, juniors

and disabled. Estates & Recreation Officer, SW Division, WWA, Hawthorn Rise, Haverfordwest SA61 2BH. Fly and worming. Hotels: Mariners, County, Red House, Llawhaden, Nr Haverfordwest, Dyfed.

EASTERN CLEDDAU: Salmon, trout. Fishing station **Clynderwen** (Dyfed).
Clarbeston (Dyfed). Eastern Cleddau, 3m off. Farmers may give permission *(see Haverfordwest)*. Sewin good, May to August.

POLLUTION

Anglers are united in deploring pollution. To combat it, urgent action may be called for at any time from any one of us. If numbers of fish are found dead, dying, or seriously distressed, take samples of both fish and water and contact the office of the Director of Scientific Services at the appropriate Regional Water Authority.

CLWYD

(For close seasons, licences, etc, see p 17–18)

Salmon runs in summer and autumn, but mainly sea trout river with some heavy fish; June to August. Good below Ruthin and Llanfair on tributary Elwy. Trout numerous (average 9 in) but better in Wheeler and Elwy.

Rhyl (Clwyd). Tidal; fishing free to RD licence-holders from sea up to Rhuddlan, 3m away; salmon and sea trout, but fish tend to run straight through; no holding pools. Also flounders, bass and eels (no licence required). Rhyll AA has water on Clwyd, **Elwy** and **Prion Reservoirs.** Members only. Permits for **Brenig** (*see below*), **Alwen Reservoir** and **Llyn Aled,** the former containing perch but stocked with trout, the latter containing a variety of coarse fish species. For Alwen, st £34.50, dt £2.50; for Aled, dt £1.50, from Fish & Conservation office, WWA, Shire Hall, Mold, Clwyd. Concessions on both for OAP, juniors, etc. **Dolwen** and **Plas Uchaf Reservoirs** well stocked with brown and rainbow trout; fly, spinning and worming; 6 fish limit. Dt only, available from D & J Davies, Newsagents, 2 Church View, Bodelwyddan, Nr Rhyl. **Llyn Aled Isaf** now a club water (Chester AS). Sea fishing from river mouth, foreshore and boats. Tope, skate, plaice, mackerel, etc. Tackleists: Wm Roberts (Rhyl) Ltd, 131 High St; The Anglers Den, 29 Queen St.

Llyn Brenig. Cerrig-y-Drudion. 919-acre reservoir amid heather moorland and forest. Fly only, brown and rainbow trout. St £134, dt £5.50, evening £3.80, motor boats £12/£10 according to day of week. Season: April 1 to Oct 17. Concessions for OAP, juniors and

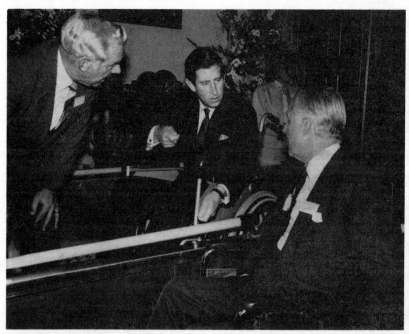

Angling makes special provision for the disabled. Here we see HRH The Prince of Wales at a ceremony to mark the completion of a specially equipped boat. With His Royal Highness are Mr Len Warren, co-designer of the boat, and Mr B Buchanan of the Country Landowners' Association, the body which raised the money to finance it.

disabled; block bookings offered. Tickets from Information Centre at reservoir.

Rhuddlan (Clwyd). Salmon, sea trout, brown trout. Bodrhyddan Estate owns fishing on both banks of Clwyd from Rhuddlan Bridge upstream to St Asaph and also **River Elwy** upstream from junction with Clwyd (1m above Rhuddlan) to old Pentre railway bridge. Season permits to local anglers only, but dt £10 sometimes available from Lord Langford's secretary.

St Asaph (Clwyd). St Asaph AA has water on Clwyd, **Elwy** and **Aled.** St £28 + £30 joining fee; limited dt for two beats on Elwy available from Faxons Tackle, Penrhwl, St Asaph and Black Lion, Llanfair TH. Waiting list. Rhyl and Dist AA has water on Elwy.

Denbigh (Clwyd). Clwyd, 2m E; salmon, sea trout, brown trout. Denbigh AC has extensive water on Clwyd, Ystrad, Elwy,

Wheeler, also small stocked trout lake; members only, but membership open (£40) to non-residents. St £48 + joining fee, dt £6 (limited to 2 per day). Tickets from hon sec or Treasurer, Barclays Bank. **Brenig** and **Alwen Reservoirs,** 11m SW; trout. **Llyn Aled,** 11m SW; coarse. St and dt from Welsh WA Office at Llyn Brenig. Hotel: Bull, Bryn Morfydd.

Ruthin (Clwyd). Trout, salmon, sea trout. Ruthin Castle Hotel has ½m free to guests. Clwyd AC has about 5m from Ruthin to junction of Clwyd and **Clywedog** below Llandrynog. Members only. Salmon and sea trout only late in season and very few; more run up Clywedog. Clywedog practically all private, and where not private very overgrown. Both rivers shrink to low levels in mid-summer. Other hotels: Bridge Inn, Bontuchel, near Ruthin, which has short stretch at back of hotel.

Tributaries of the Clwyd

ELWY: Sea trout (June onwards), some salmon, small brown trout.

Llanfair-Talhaiarn (Clwyd); ns Abergele, 6m. Trout, sea trout, salmon; preserved by Llangernyw A; members only. Other water strictly preserved and no permits obtainable. **Melan** 2m SW. **Aled,** 2m E. Llansannan SC has 3m on Aled; st £5, wt £3 and dt £1. Hotels: Tarhodes, The Black Lion (LL22 8RY), which has 1½m of water, wt £10, dt £2.50, but hotel

guests given preference. Early and late water.

CLYWEDOG: Trout, preserved. Salmon and sea trout (very late), trout. All water strictly preserved. Clwyd AC and Denbigh & Dist AC have water.

WHEELER: Trout. Denbigh and Dist AC has 2m; some fly only. Mold Trout A has ¼m. Mold Kingfishers AC has fishing on Wheeler and on lake at Afonwen.

CONWAY

(For close seasons, licences, etc, see Welsh Water Authority, p 17–18)

Rises on Migneint, in Gwynedd and flows between the old Caernarvonshire and Denbighshire boundaries for much of its course, emptying into the Irish Sea near Conway. The upper part of its valley is noted for its beauty. Spate river with salmon runs throughout season (May and June usually best); grilse early July; sea trout late June to September.

Conway (Gwynedd). Tidal; sea fishing only. Codling, dabs, plaice, bass and mullet above and below suspension bridge. Boats available. Tackleists: Cambrian Supplies, Castle St. Hotels: Castle, Erskine Arms.

Dolgarrog (Gwynedd). Salmon, sea trout; deep tidal pools. Dolgarrog FC has 2½m

of tidal water. Dt, salmon and sea trout are issued. St £20, wt £10, dt £5. Brown trout on upland watershed, including **Llyn Eigiau** (boats) and **Llyn Coedty** and connecting rivers.

Tal-y-Cafn (Gwynedd). Salmon, sea trout; deep tidal water. Ferry Hotel has short length. Dolgarrog FC has 2½m tidal

Conway; visitors welcomed. Guests can obtain other fishing on Llanrwst AC waters.

Llanrwst (Gwynedd). Salmon and good sea trout; brown trout poor. Llanrwst AC has 1¼m, both banks. Limited st £36 and wt £20 (to Sept 12 only) from Secretary, The Old Library, 36 Station Road (who stock some tackle). Sunday fishing allowed. At **Glangorse**, in the Conway valley near the town, a stillwater fishery stocked with salmon and rainbow' trout. Dt £27: limit two salmon; rainbow trout unlimited. Tel. Llanrwst 641584. Permits from Forestry Commission, Gwydyr Uchaf, for left bank of **Machno** from junction with Conway and portion of right bank. Tickets also from Mrs Jones, Pandy Mill and Post Office, both **Penmachno**. Hotels: Maenan Abbey, Victoria (both have salmon and trout fishing).

Bettws-y-Coed (Gwynedd). Conway; Lledr; Llugwy; trout, salmon, sewin. Gwydyr Hotel has about 15m on **Rivers Conway, Lledr** and **Llugwy**, from near semi-tidal Trefriw Quay upstream to Plantation Pool near Pontypant on Lledr and to Mymbyr Lake at Capel Curig on Llugwy; 55 pools, some semi-tidal, flats, and well-known "The Rocks" stretch of Lledr are included. Hotel waters also include Elsi Lake (stocked with Loch Levens), another trout lake (Siabod) and semi-tidal stretch called Belmont, about 1m down river from Trefriw Quay. Charges: Residents only. Sunday fishing. Tickets and details from hotel. Bettws-y-Coed AC has 1m of Conway (left bank only) and 3m of Llugwy (both banks). Wt only. Swallow Falls Hotel, via Bettws-y-Coed, has trout lake *(see Capel Curig)*. Other hotel: Plas Hall, Pont-y-Pant.

Ysbyty Ifan (Gwynedd). Trout (half-pounder, good fish). About 11m of National Trust water. Conway river in Ysbyty Ifan area, st £10, from Conway Falls Bridge to Rhydlanfair Bridge, £4. Parts of **Machno** and **Glasgwm** rivers owned by National Trust, £5. Tickets from The National Trust, Dinas, Bettws-y-Coed and Caradog Evans, 3 Trem Afon, Ysbyty Ifan.

Tributaries of the Conway

ROE: Trout.

Roe-Wen (Gwynedd) ns Talycafn. Fly fishing impossible on lower reaches. Accommodation at Ty Gwyn Hotel.

DDU: Trout.

Pont Dolgarrog (Gwynedd). Trout. Ddu enters Conway ½m below village; drains Llyn Cowlyd. River Dolgarrog FC water; st £12, wt £10, dt £3. Lake free to licence holders by permission of Conway Valley Water Supply Unit, 50 Mostyn Street, Llandudno; no boats.

CRAFNANT: Trout.

Trefriw (Gwynedd). A 60 acre lake stocked with rainbow trout, also wild brown trout; dt £5 and RD licences from Lakeside Cafe.

LLEDR: Trout, sewin, salmon.

Dolwyddelan (Gwynedd). Gwydyr Hotel has water *(see Conway)*, but Dolwyddelan FA has most of both banks from village to Pont-y-Pant. Resident visitors, not campers or caravanners, st £40, wt for salmon and sewin (late summer and early autumn best) March–June £2, July–Oct (m to f) £16 from post office or hon sec. Prince Albert AS has stretch here; enquire hon sec. Lakes: Diwaunedd (two) 3m W; trout; preserved. Hotels: Gwydyr, Elen's Castle, Plas Hall. *(For Conway water below Dolwyddelan see Bettws-y-Coed and Llanrwst.)*

LLUGWY: Trout.

Capel Curig (Gwynedd). Trout; right bank preserved from Bettws-y-Coed to Capel Curig (Llynau Mymbyr) and left bank to Miners' Bridge by Conway FA which issues tickets *(see Bettws-y-Coed)*. Gwydyr Hotel has water *(see under Conway)*. Hotels: Tyn-y-Coed and Cobden's Snowdonia (joint fishing on 2m of river and numerous lakes in neighbourhood; boats can be had on several; dt issued). Tickets and tackle available locally. *(See also under Dolwyddelan for FC waters.)*

GWRYD (trib of Llugwy): Trout.

Pen-y-Gwryd (Gwynedd) ns Llanberis or Bettws-y-Coed. Trout. Gwryd runs to Llynau Mymbyr, near Capel Curig. Fishing on river has improved with re-stocking and 3m are available to guests at Pen-y-Gwryd Hotel (left bank only). Wt £5, dt £1, no charge to residents.

Llynau Mymbyr belongs to Sports Council, Plas-y-Brenin, Capel Curig. Llyn-y-Cwm Ffynnon; trout. Llynau Diwaunedd, 2m SE; trout; Free. Gwynant 3m S; boats. Edno, 7m S; large trout; free.

HWCH: Trout.
Gwynedd RD issues tickets for this river and **Arddu.**

MACHNO: Trout.
Penmachno (Gwynedd). Tickets (60p day) from Mrs Jones, Pandy Mill, and Post Office for one stretch. Good free trout fishing for RD licence-holders. National Trust has fishing on Machno and **Glasgwm.** Tickets from NT Office, Trinity Square, Llandudno, Gwynedd.

NUG: Trout.
Pentre Voelas (Gwynedd). Now private, advance applictions may be considered, apply to Cooke Wood & Caird, 154 High Street, Bangor. **Alwen Reservoir:** trout; permits from Superintendent's office on site.

DEE (Welsh)

(For close seasons, licences, etc, see Welsh Water Authority, p 17–18)

Usually has a spring run of fish up to 30 lb. Grilse enter in June and there is a run of grilse and summer fish until the end of the season as a rule. In spring most fish are taken from Bangor to Corwen. Trout from Bangor upstream and grayling above Llangollen. Coarse fish predominate downstream of Bangor. River holds good bream, roach, dace, perch and pike.

Chester (Cheshire). Coarse fish. Little permit-free fishing. No licence for coarse fishing in tidal waters. Most fishing controlled by Chester AA; st £5 for trout and coarse fishing only from hon sec. Assn also has fishing on **R Llafar, R Vyrnwy, Llyn Aled Isaf** and **River Severn** at Shrewsbury and Welshpool. Dee AA issues salmon permits (limited) for **Sutton Green** stretch; separate trout and coarse fish permits. St Helens AA also has water at Sutton Green; members only. Other clubs with fishing on lower river: Lavister AC, Warrington AA, Northern AA, Liverpool AA; all members only. **River Gowy,** which runs into Mersey, passing by Mickle Trafford about 3m from Chester: Warrington AA has water. St £8 + £8 entrance. Concessions ladies and juniors. Trout and coarse fish. **Meadow Fishery,** Mickle Trafford, trout; 5 acres; st and dt. Tel: 024 300 236. Tackleists: E P Martin, The Tackle Box, 53 Lower Bridge Street; H Monk, 8 Queen Street; D Gibson, Upper Northgate St; Mrs I M Williams, 316 High Street, Connah's Quay; G Boddy, Westminster Road, Hoole, Chester. Hotels: Grosvenor, Queen, Blossoms.

Holt (Clwyd). Salmon, pike, bream. Alyn, 2m NW; trout. Dee AA, Chester, rents a number of stretches in the Holt, Farndon, Sutton Green area. St for salmon or trout. Northern AA and Warrington AA rent stretches at **Shocklach, Berwyn, Lower Hall** and **Churton.**

Bangor-on-Dee (Clwyd). Salmon, trout, coarse fish. Bangor-on-Dee AA rents long stretch downstream. St £50 (S) and £4.50, dt £4 (S) and £1 from S Adams, The Stores, High Street. Hotel: Buck.

Overton Bridge (Clwyd). Salmon, sea trout, trout, coarse fish; Bryn-y-Pys AA has approx 7m between Overton Bridge and Bangor-on-Dee, well stocked annually with b and rb trout. St £6 from hon sec; dt £2.50 from Deggy's Fishing Tackle, 2 Ruabon Road, Wrexham or Town and Country Supplies, Bangor-on-Dee. Boat Inn, Erbistock, has salmon and trout beat.

Trevor (Clwyd). Trout, salmon, coarse fish (including pike and grayling). Maelor AA has water. Limited st (S) £50, (T) £10, wt £5, dt £1 for trout and coarse fish only on 1½m (both banks). Coarse fishing good September onwards. Tickets from hon sec. Newbridge AA has trout, grayling and coarse fishing; members only; st £12 (£14 for new members); members to reside within local radius of 5m.

Llangollen (Clwyd). Trout, grayling, salmon, pike. Llangollen AA preserves about 6m below bridge to village of Rhewl. Trout and coarse fish; st, wt and dt for salmon and trout. Wading necessary. March to end of June best. No coarse fishing allowed in close season for salmon and trout. Tickets from W N & H A Elbourn (tackleist), Chapel Street.

St (S) £52, waiting list. Wt (S) £33, dt (S) £8. Wt (T) £11, dt (T) £3. Concessions to juniors. No dt fishing Oct 17—March 3. Dt for coarse fishing in canal, 50p. Maelor AC has water from here to Pontcysyllte; members only. Liverpool & Dist AA has salmon fishing at Chain Bridge; also waters on Dee at Churton, Farndon, Holt and Lower Hall. St £7 + £10 salmon licence, apply to hon sec. Warrington AA had good stretch. Ceiriog, 3m S. Alyn, 7m N, at Llandegla; trout. Hotels: Golden Pheasant, Llwynmawr (salmon beats on Dee and Severn, and trout and grayling fishing on rivers and lakes; several miles free to guests), Hand, Ponsonby, Bryn Howel (all have fishing for guests), West Arms, Llanarmon.

Glyndyfrdwy (Clwyd). Glyndyfrdwy Preserves, salmon; fly only; dt £7. Apply to D & E P Thomas, Berwyn Arms Hotel (tel: 049 083 210). Midland Flyfishers has 4m on Dee; trout and grayling (salmon fishing for full members only); dt £2 from Berwyn Arms Hotel and Mrs R Jones-Roberts, Coedial Farm.

Corwen (Clwyd). Corwen and Dist AC controls most of trout and grayling fishing on Rhug Estate (about 4m), Dee and **Alwen**. Association also has fishing on **Cynwyd Reservoir** (trout). St £20. Capenhurst AC has stretch down stream of Carrog Bridge; members only. Tackleist: Williams and Hope, Waterloo House.

Cynwyd (Clwyd). Trout, grayling, salmon. Corwen and Dist AC has $\frac{1}{2}$m above Cynwyd; members only. Inns: The Blue Lion and Prince of Wales.

Llandrillo (Clwyd). Salmon, trout, grayling, perch and pike. Strictly preserved by executors of Duke of Westminster's Palé Estate. Hotel: Dudley Arms.

Llandderfel (Gwynedd). Salmon, trout, grayling, perch and pike. Permits for water on Palé Estate (1m L bank, $\frac{3}{4}$m R) for trout and grayling, fly only, from W E Pugh, Bala. (*See following entry*). Lakes: Caereini (3½m); also Mynyllod and Maesclawdd, strictly preserved by private landowners. No permits. Hotels: Bryntirion Inn (which has two rods for guests on 1¼m; trout and grayling, fly only).

Bala (Gwynedd). Salmon, trout, perch, pike and grayling. From confluence with Tryweryn to Bala Lake it is Bala AA water. Members (non-residents admitted) may fish another stretch of Dee and lake itself. Assn also has water on **Tryweryn, Lliw, Llafar,** (dt), **Cwm Prysor Lake** (trout; fly only; dt) *(see also Llanuwchllyn)*; Sunday fishing allowed; visitor's wt and dt issued, inquire hon sec or tackleists. Block permits for small clubs for Bala AA waters. **Lake Bala** itself (trout early on, coarse fish) owned by County Council; st £20, wt £10, dt £3 from tackleists and Lake Warden. **Llyn Celyn:** (4m); brown trout; tickets from tackleists. Tackleists: W E Pugh, 74 High Street; E W Evans, Yr Eryr Sports & Tackle, 33 High Street. Hotels: White Lion, Royal, Plas Coch, Goat, Ye Olde Bulls Head, Ship. *(See Gwynedd Lakes.)*

Llanuwchllyn (Gwynedd). Trout and grayling. No Sunday fishing or ground baiting. Clubs: Bala AA; Prince Albert AS (trout and grayling fishing on Little Dee, Twrch and Lliw; members only).

Tributaries of the Dee

ALYN: Trout.

Rossett (Clwyd). Trout and dace, Rossett and Gresford FC restock 2½m annually; membership limited. Warrington AA have water lower down and 2m on Dee, at Almere Farm.

Gresford (Clwyd). Trout *(see Rossett).* Llay AS has The Flash; tench, carp, pike, rudd; members only *(see Llay).* Griffin AC has three stretches; members only.

Wrexham (Clwyd). Wrexham and Dist AA has water on Alyn. Other clubs: Caergwrle AC; Llay Hall AA; Bradley AC (members only); Llay AS; Rossett and Gresford FC; Cerrig-y-Drudion AA; Bryn y Pys AA. Warrington AA fishes on 600 yds of **Worthenbury Brook.** Permits from 21 Egerton Street (Wrexham 291777) for upper and lower **Penycae Reservoirs** (trout). Tackleists: H Jones, 2 Ruabon Road.

Llay (Clwyd). Llay AS has trout water on Alyn and **Clywedog** and good coarse fishing in **The Flash, Gresford** (tench, carp, pike, rudd;) **Llay Reservoir** (tench, carp, rudd, perch, pike;) **Vyrnwy, Dee** and **Cain.** All waters members only. £6 pa. Concessions to jun & OAP. Apply Membership sec J Henshaw, 2 Queens

Terrace, Mold Road, Cefn-y-bedd, Wrexham.

Hope (Clwyd). Wrexham and Dist AA has trout fishing from Llong railway bridge to Pont y Delyn; fly only; permits issued to members' guests only. Caergwrle AC has 3m; stocked regularly with brown trout; wet and dry fly and worming. St £12 from hon sec. Dt from June 1 only.

Mold (Clwyd). Clwyd County Council hold fishing rights in **Loggerheads** area, leased to local clubs. Mold TA has 3m on Alyn and $\frac{1}{2}$m on **R Wheeler**; st £12 and £17 (£6 jun) from Grosvenor Pet Shop. Mold Kingfishers AC has stretch on R Wheeler and lake at Afonwen; also coarse fishing at quarry pools; members only; st £4 (£2 jun, £1 OAP). Cilcain FFA has five trout reservoirs nearby. Dt (four only) from hon sec (enclose s/a envelope); fly only. Tackleists: Blundells, 1-2 The Cross.

SARN:
Whitchurch (Salop). No stream fishing. Coarse fishing in lakes: **Brown Moss Lakes** $1\frac{1}{2}$m SE; pike, bream, roach, tench; apply N Shropshire RDC for permits. Quoisley Big and Little Meres, 3m N; boats. Marbury Mere, 3m NE; dt. Blakemere, 1m NE; pike, perch, bream, roach; dt; boat from A W Hiles, Yockingsgate. Osmere, 2m NE; good bream, tench, pike, rudd, roach; dt (bank only) from J E Windsor, Black Park. Tackleist: Speeds, Watergate Street. St £5 issued for local lake stocked carp and other coarse fish.

CEIRIOG: Trout.

Chirk (Clwyd). Good coarse fishing on **Shropshire Union Canal.** Chirk Fishery Co. Ltd. has hatchery here. Chirk AA has 24m on Ceirog (dt £3.50, fly only) and water on **Dee** (dt £10 S and £3 NT). Advance bookings to hon sec for Ceirog; tickets for Dee from N Elbourn, Newsagent, Chapel Street, Llangollen.

Llwynmawr (Clwyd). Some public fishing for trout and coarse fish in the district.

Glyn Ceiriog (Clwyd). Farmers sometimes give permission. Golden Pheasant Hotel, Glyn Ceirog LL20 7BB, has water in this area.

Llanarmon DC (Clwyd). Ceiriog, $2\frac{1}{2}$m, brown trout. Hotels: West Arms, which has free fishing on $1\frac{1}{2}$m (both banks) for hotel guests; Hand Hotel, which has trout and coarse fishing for guests (both hotels issue RD licences).

ALWEN: Flows out of large reservoir (trout, perch) on Denbigh Moors and enters Dee near Corwen. Very good trout fishing and some salmon. For **Alwen Reservoir** permits apply Dee and Clwyd Division of WWA. Dt from office at Brenig Reservoir. Cerrig-y-Drudion AA has river fishing; members only. St £15 from hon sec; and dt £2 from Ken Parry, Pen-y-Bont Fishery, Llanfihangel GM, nr Corwen. Trout fishing permits from Crown Inn, Llanfihangel GM; dt £1.50 (free to hotel residents). Tel: 049 082 209.

TRYWERYN: Joins Dee below Lake Bala. Good trout fishing. Bala AA has 4-5m and mountain lake **Cwm Prysor.** Tickets from Bala tackleist. *(See Bala.)*

DOVEY

(For close seasons, licences, etc, see Welsh Water Authority, p 17–18)

Rises on east side of Aran Fawddwy and flows 30m south and south-west to Cardigan Bay at Aberdovey. Has long estuary and provides splendid sport with sewin (sea trout) and salmon. Many large sea trout taken. Salmon run in small numbers from May to October; sea trout from May on. Best months: July, August, September. Small tributaries hold many little trout, and leave can generally be obtained from owners.

Aberdovey (Gwynedd). At estuary mouth; surf and estuary fishing. Free trout fishing in Happy Valley on permission of farmers; stream; trout small.

Machynlleth (Powys). Salmon, sea trout. New Dovey Fishery Association controls 15m (both banks) of river between Llyfnant stream and Nant Ty-Mawr and L

bank, from opposite Llyfnant mouth to Abergwybedyn brook. Permits cost £36, entitling the holder to fish four days in one week, once in a season. There is an allocation of dt £7 to fish a portion of the Association water marked by notice boards. These are available from D G Evans, Garage, Cemmaes Road and Mrs E

Jones, PO, Cemmaes. Other enq to Hon Sec, D Morgan Jones, Plas, Machynlleth, Powys. Tel Machynlleth 2721. Hotels: Wynnstay (Trust House), Glyndwr and Lion Hotel, Machynlleth; Ynyshir Hall, Eglwysfach, Penrhos Arms, Cemmaes; and Riverside Hotel, Pennal. Permission from farmers for **Pennal Stream;** rapid water; trout small but plentiful. Corris AC controls 3m of **N Dulas.** Llugwy Hotel, Pennal has half-mile on **S Dulas** free to guests.

Cemmaes (Powys). Trout, sea trout, salmon. For details of permits *(see Machynlleth).*

Llanbrynmair (Powys). 5m from Cemmaes Road. On **Twymyn;** sewin, salmon, fair trouting. 3m of **Twymyn** controlled by Prince Albert AS; inquiries to hon sec. Llanbrynmair and Dist AC has water from village to confluence with Dovey apart from one stretch held by Prince

Albert AS; good trouting; st £50, wt £15, dt £5 from hon sec at Evans Garage, Cemmaes Road and Mrs Lewis, Cegin Dyfi.

Dinas Mawddwy (Gwynedd). Sewin, salmon, trout; fishing good. Brigands Inn, **Mallwyd,** has some of the best pools on upper reaches and stretch of **Cleifion;** sea trout taken to $12\frac{3}{4}$ lb in 1986; dt £8.50 for guests only. Buckley Arms hotel has water from the **Cowarch** down to hotel, for residents only. New Dovey AA has water on **Cleifion;** inquire hon sec. Sea trout runs (water permitting) May, July, Sept; best July to October. **Twrch,** 8m E; good trouting. Prince Albert AS has $2\frac{1}{2}$m stretch of Dovey at Gwastad Coed, **Gwerhefin.** Inquire hon sec for details of society's rights, which include **Llyn-y-Foel** (south half) and stretch of **Lledr** *(see Conway).* Other hotel: Dolbrawmaeth Hall ($\frac{1}{2}$m on Dovey; dt issued).

DWYRYD

(For close seasons, licences, etc, see Welsh Water Authority, p 17–18)

Rises in small, nameless pool 3m above Tan-y-Grisiau and flows into Cardigan Bay through estuary north of Harlech. Holds trout, sewin and salmon. Salmon and sea trout run up as far as the falls on the main river and its tributaries, Teigl and Cynfal. Late June to Oct best months for sea trout and salmon.

Tan-y-Bwlch (Gwynedd). Sewin, salmon. For local possibilities, consult tackleist in High Street, Portmadoc.

Maentwrog (Gwynedd). Grapes Hotel has about 3m of River Dwyryd; trout, sewin and salmon (June to Sept best). Tickets issued. Other stream and lake fishing for trout available **Tecwynuchaf** and **Tecwynisaf Lakes,** 2m SW Talsarnau AA; st from hon sec. Trawsfynydd. Licences and tickets for Talsarnau AA and Cambrian AA waters can be obtained at Grapes Hotel.

Ffestiniog (Gwynedd). Principal trout

lakes controlled by Cambrian AA as follows: **Dubach** (3m N), **Manod** (2m NE), **Morwynion** (2m E), **Cwmorthin** (3m NW). Full information from hon sec. Visitors' tickets: st £15, wt £9, dt £4. Cambrian AA has also some trout fishing on tributaries of Dwyryd. **Tan-y-Grisau Reservoir** (2m NW), 95 acres, stocked with brown and rainbow trout. Dt from Post Office and local tackleist. Spinning and bait fishing allowed. Tackleist: F Roberts, 32 Church Street, Blaenau Ffestiniog. Hotels: Pengwern Arms, Ffestiniog.

Tributaries of the Dwyryd

PRYSOR (and Trawsfynydd):

Trawsfynydd (Gwynedd). **Prysor** and **Trawsfynydd Lake** controlled by Prysor AA. Trout, perch and rudd. St £55, wt £14, dt £4. Assn also has 3m on **Eden** (salmon, sewin). Permits for lake and river from M P Atherton, Newsagent,

Manchester House, Trawsfynydd. Hotels: Cross Foxes and White Lion, Trawsfynydd; Oakley Arms and Grapes, Maentwrog; Abbey Arms and Pengwern Arms, Ffestiniog *(see also Gwynedd Lakes).* Tackleists: M P Atherton, Trawsfynydd; C Davies, Porthmadog.

DYFED (streams)

(For close seasons, licences, etc, see Welsh Water Authority, p 17–18)

ALLAN. Fishing station: **St David's;** ns Haverfordwest, 18m. Allan (6m long); 4m suitable for fishing, mostly on private property on owners permission; trout good quality but small.

BRAWDY BROOK. Fishing station: **Brawdy;** ns Haverfordwest, 10m. Brook is 7m long. Small trout.

CARN. Fishing station: **Loveston;** ns Templeton, 3m. Carn rises $1\frac{1}{2}$m W from Templeton station, runs 3m to Loveston, and 1m down, 3m from Begelly, is joined on left bank by Langden Brook, 3m long. Carn runs $2\frac{1}{2}$m to Milford Haven. Small trout.

CAREW BROOK. Fishing station: **Carew;** ns Pembroke, 4m. This brook, which rises by Redberth, is 4m long, joining sea water at Carew which is an inlet from Milford Haven. Small trout.

CLARACH. Enters sea 1m N of **Aberystwyth.** Holds trout, sewin and occasional salmon; preserved; permission from farmers.

COWIN. Fishing station: **Sarnau.** Sea trout, occasional salmon. Only worth fishing June onwards. Permission from farmers.

DISSILIO. Fishing station: **Llandissili-Gogo;** ns Lampeter, 20m. Dissilio is 6m long. 1m W runs Tydi, 6m long. Small trout.

GARNAS BROOK. Fishing station: **Cronware;** ns Whitland, 5m. This brook rises 1m above here, and joins the sea 3m down. Small trout.

GWAUN. Fishing station: **Fishguard.** This 8–9m trout stream rises on lower slopes of Prescelly Mountains, and runs through a beautiful wooded valley. Trout not large but provide excellent sport with fly, and sewin also caught in season. A few salmon. Permission freely given by landowners and tenants. Dt. Further information from hon sec, Fishguard AA (enclose sae). Tackleists: Hughes (chemist), **High Street** and **Evans** (saddler), West Street, Fishguard. Hotel: New Inn at Rose Bush. Guest houses: Glyn-y-Mel, Fishguard, and Pentower, Tower Hill, Fishguard.

GWENDRAETH FACH. Fishing station: **Kidwelly.** Carmarthen and Dist AC has 5m; very good trout fishing; occasional sea trout in lower reaches. St £15, dt £3.

(See also Towy–Carmarthen.) **Gwendraeth Fawr** runs 1m E from Kidwelly; trouting fair. Hotel: White Lion. Tackleist: F M and H E Davies, Bridge St.

KILRELGY BROOK. Fishing station: **Begelly.** This stream, 5m long, runs 1m E. Carn, 3m. Langdon Brook, 3m. Small trout.

LLANDILO BROOK. Fishing station: **Maenclochog.** Gilfach Brook, 1m. Syfynfy, 2m. Corwyn, 4m. Crynanich, 4m. Small trout.

LLETHI. Fishing station: **Llanarth;** ns Lampeter, 13m. Llethi Gido rises 3m above Llanarth, and 2m down is joined on left bank by brook 4m long. Llethi runs to Llanina and sea, 1m. One mile NE runs Drowy to sea, 4m long. Small trout.

MARLAIS. Fishing station: **Narberth.** Gwaithnoak, 2m. Eastern Cleddau, 2m. Taf, 5m. Small trout. Hotel: Red House, Llanhaden.

MULLOCK BROOK. Fishing station: **St Ishmael's;** ns Milford, 5m (small trout), 6m long, joining the sea at Dale Road.

NEVERN (Dyfed): Rises near Crymmych and flows to sea at **Newport:** ns Fishguard and Goodwick, 7m. Cardigan, 10m. Fast-flowing, densely wooded, deep holding pools. Nevern AA has water (ft £20, wt £12). Permits from B Williams, tackleist, Newport. Membership details from hon sec. Other tackleists: H T Birch and M Evans, both Fishguard; A W Williams, Cardigan.

PERIS. Fishing station: **Llanon;** Peris is 6m long. Llanon, 4m long, runs $\frac{1}{2}$m. Small trout.

RHEIDOL. Fishing stations: **Aberystwyth** and **Devil's Bridge.** Salmon, sea trout. Hydro-electric scheme governs flow. River almost entirely Aberystwyth AA water. Assn also has stretch of **Ystwyth** and several lakes: *(See under Dyfed, lakes).* Non-residents' permits for whole fishery from Sports Centre, North Parade, Aberystwyth. St (whole fishery) £70, wt £30, dt £7.50. Dt £2.50 for Penrhyncoch Lakes. Llanilar AA has 14m of trout and sewin fishing on Ystwyth; tickets from Sports Centre (as above) and E H Evans, Erwyd Garage, Ponterwyd, Dyfed.

WYRE. Fishing station: **Llanrhystyd;** Aberystwyth, 9m. Trout (small), some salmon and sometimes good for sewin.

Hotel: Black Lion. WWDA permits from PO.

DYFED (lakes)

Devil's Bridge. Aberystwyth AA has the Penrhyncoch lakes in the hills between Devil's Bridge and Nant-y-Moch Reservoir; (**Llyn Craig-y-Pistyll, Llyn Syfydrin, Llyn Rhosgoch, Llyn Blaenmelindwr** and **Llyn Pendam**), **Llyn yr Oerfa** and **Llyn Llywernog** 2m SW of Ponterwyd, and the Trisant lakes (**Llyn Frongoch, Llyn Rhosrhydd** and **Llyn Glandwgan**) 2m SW of Devil's Bridge. Some are stocked, others self-stocking. Several contain trout up to 2 lbs. Some are fly only; spinning and restricted bait fishing on others. The Assn also has water on **Rheidol.** St (full) £70, (lakes and part of Rheidol fishery) £50. Wt £30. Dt £7.50. Dt for Penrhyncoch Lakes only, £2.50. Concessions for OAP and juvs. Boats extra. Tickets from Aberystwyth tackleists and Erwyd Garage, Ponterwyd. Full details of fishings from hon sec. Hotel: Hafod Arms.

Llys-y-fran Reservoir. (8m NE Haverfordwest). Trout. St £134, dt £5.50, boat extra. Permits from Reservoir Superintendent.

Nant-y-moch and Dinas Reservoirs. CEGB waters in hills about 12m E of Aberystwyth. Dinas, 38 acres, stocked frequently with brown and rainbow trout; fly, spinning and worming. Dt £4.40 and £2.80 (OAP & jun), evening £3.10. Nant-y-Moch, 500 acres, native brown trout and perch. Trout fishing only 1 April–30 June; fly only. Trout and perch fishing 1 July–17 Oct. St £15 and dt £1.50. Permits from E H Evans, Birch Villa, Ponterwyd, and Mr Hubbard, Compton Tackle Shop, Borth.

Pembroke. Pembroke Town Mill Pool; mullet, bass, flatfish; also trout and sewin higher up. **West Orielton Lake,** 3m; coarse fish, no pike; permission sometimes obtainable; inquire at West Orielton Farm. **Bosherston Lily Ponds,** Stackpole (6m). Pike, perch, tench, roach. Pembroke and Dist AC. Wt £4, dt £1 (concessions for OAP & jun), tackle, and licences from Frank Donovan, 61 Bush Street, Pembroke Dock (sports outfitters). Hotels: King's Arms, Royal, George, Lion, Castle Inn. *(For sea fishing, see Pembroke Dock.)*

TROUT FISHING
— MID WALES

Enjoy superb trout fishing in the beautiful, secluded Plynlimon hills.

Dinas and Nant-y-Moch lakes are twelve miles from Aberystwyth off the A44 at Ponterwyd in Dyfed.

DINAS — 38 acres, well stocked with browns and rainbows; fly, spin and ledgered worm; bag limit 6 fish. Season: 1 April-mid October.

NANT-Y-MOCH — 500 acres, native, hard fighting browns; fly only. Season: 1 April-30 September.

LOCAL AGENTS:
Aber Sports, Aberystwyth; Suede and Leather Shop, Aberystwyth; Compton Tackle, Borth and Evan's, Birch Villa, Ponterwyd.

For information phone
CEGB, Rheidol Fishery.
Tel: Capel Bangor 667

Pontrhydfendigaid. Nearby are **Teifi Lakes,** at headwaters of Teifi. Dt £3 from Post Office, Pontrhydfendigiad; apply PO for boat-booking. **Llyn Egnant** (3m). **Llyn Gorlan** and **Llyn Fyddron Fawr** in the vicinity; much deterioration here due to effects of acid rain; access difficult; no permits required.

Rosebush Reservoir. 11m NE of Haverfordwest on B4329. 39 acres. Wild brown and stocked rainbow trout. Free use of boats for fly fishing; 200yds of bank for worm fishing. Permits: Season £45. Day £3.50. Evening (after 1600) £3. Concessions for OAPs, juveniles and disabled. Permits, WWA licences and access from Mr S Askew, Blaenpant, Rosebush, Clynderwen, Dyfed, SA66 7RA (TEL: 09913 507).

Talybont. Trout. Talybont AA issues st £20 and dt £5 for four lakes and various rivers; **Lerry** and **Einion.** Concession prices to OAP, juniors, disabled.

Tregaron. Lake Berwyn, 5m. Liming has taken place and as a result it holds excellent brown trout up to $1\frac{1}{2}$ to 2 lbs. Stocked periodically. Tregaron AA hold fishing rights. *(For river fishing in neighbourhood see Rivers Teifi and Aeron.)*

DYSYNNI

(For close seasons, licences, etc, see Welsh Water Authority, p 17–18)

Rises in Llyn Cau, on steep southern side of Cader Idris, then falls rather rapidly via Dol-y-Cau. Falls into Tal-y-Ilyn Valley about half a mile above well-known Tal-y-Ilyn Lake. Emerging from lake, flows westwards as typcial upland stream to Abergynolwyn where, joined by the Gwernol, it turns north through narrow valley until it enters upper end of broad Dysynni Valley. At Peniarth it becomes deep and sluggish and finally enters Cardigan Bay $1\frac{1}{2}$m north of Towyn. Trout along whole length and tributaries, and sea trout (sewin) and salmon travel beyond Tal-y-Ilyn Lake and up to Dolgoch on Fathew. In lower reaches good sport may be had, early and late in season, with trout and sewin; August generally best. Also excellent grey mullet and bass in estuary.

Towyn (Gwynedd). Dysynni; salmon, sewin, trout, with grey mullet in tidal parts and excellent bass fishing at mouth and from adjacent beaches. Some free fishing to licence-holders and three main stretches for which permits may be had. Later are: **Peniarth,** st £15, wt £8, dt £2. **Peniarth Uchaf:** $2\frac{1}{2}$m both banks held by Prince Albert AS; details from hon sec. **Estimaner** (Estimaner AA has 8m and restocks annually); st £12, wt £5, dt £2.50 (concessions for OAP & jun). Tickets from The Sports Shop, 6 College Green; and from Mrs Rowlands, Post Office,

Abergynolwyn: Nr Abergywolwyn. **Bodilan Fawr** stocked trout lakes. Dt £4. Phone 232. Permission from farmers for **Afon Fathew.** **Tal-y-llyn** (Gwynedd). Good trout fishing in **Tal-y-llyn Lake;** owned by Tyn-y-Cornel Hotel and reserved for guests but few dt available £6; fly only. For river fishing *see Towyn.* Fishing also available at Llanfihangel-y-Pennant; fast stream, trout; fly or worm; permits from cottages in Llanfihangel *(see also Gwynedd Lakes).*

GLAMORGAN (West, Mid and South)

(For close seasons, licences, etc, see Welsh Water Authority, p 17–18, unless otherwise stated)

AFAN. Fishing station: **Aberavon.** Small trout stream (with sewin on lower reaches) on which Afan Valley AC has water from Aberavon to Cymmer; wt £12, dt £3. Association has improved sport; tremendous runs of sewin in last few years; regular stocking. Fly only in March; worming allowed rest of season; spinning July–Sep at certain water levels. Permits, RD licences and tackle from Selwyn Jenkins Sports, 45 Station Road, Port Talbot. River Nedd 4m away; trout, sewin. Ogmore easily accessible. Hotels: The Twelve Knights; Berni Inn, Beach. **CADOXTON STREAM.** Fishing station: **Cadoxton.** Cadoxton Stream rises $6\frac{1}{2}$m

from Cardiff and enters the sea 2m below Cadoxton. Small trout; permission from farmers (Glamorgan RD). **Eglwys Nunydd** near Margam, British Steel Corporation (Port Talbot) reservoir. Excellent trout fishing, brown and rainbow; fish run large. Season: March 3–Sep 30. St £45.50, and dt £5, special terms for working and retired employees, and families. No boats. Fishing Lodge available for anglers. Apply company Sports Club, Groes, Margam, Port Talbot. (Port Talbot 871111 Ext 3368 during day). **KENFIG.** Small stream entering sea between Port Talbot and Porthcawl. Trout (av ¾ lb). Fishing station: **Kenfig Hill.** Club: Kenfig Hill and Dist AA. Kenfig Pool (90 acres) holds pike, carp, bream, tench, roach, rudd; rainbow and brown trout and perch successfully introduced. St £15, dt £3, concessions for OAP and jun.

NEATH. Rises in the Brecon Beacons and flows 27m to sea. Salmon, sewin, brown trout. Fishing station: **Neath.** Neath Canal, which holds a head of coarse fish, stocked with trout by Neath and Dulais AA, which also has water on both Neath and **R Dulais.** St, wt and dt. Regular re-stocking with 8–10 in trout. Tributaries of the Neath are **Dulais** and **Pyrddin.** Glynneath and Dist AA has 17m on Neath and tributaries and two stillwaters. Trout, and some coarse fishing. Pontneathvaughan; good fly-fishing. Wt £4 and dt £2 from hon sec; water restocked. Pyrddin AS (10m from Neath) has water; dt and wt (also RD licences) from hon sec; water restocked. In headwaters of the Neath is Ystradfellte Reservoir. Tackleist: 'Fishing Tackle', 63 Old Road.

OGMORE. Fishing station: **Bridgend.** Rivers Ogmore, **Ewenny** and tributaries; trout, sewin, salmon. Licences, information and tackle from W E Watts, 1 Adare Street, Bridgend. Hotels: Wyndham, York, Dunraven, all Wyndham Street. Another tributary is **Llynfi.** Fishing station: **Maesteg.** Club: Llynfi Valley AA, which has 8m excellent trout fishing and coarse fish pond; wt £8 and dt £3 from hon sec. Tackleist (and licence distributor): C Gow, Sports Shop. 19 Commercial Street, Maesteg.

RHYMNEY. About 30m long, rises above town of **Rhymney,** Gwent. Polluted in lower reaches, but some trout fishing higher up. Fishing free to licence-holders from Rhymney Bridge to New Tredegar. Caerphilly AA has stretch from Llanbradach to Bedwas; wt, dt. Rhymney and Dist AS has rights on two reservoirs: **Butetown** and **Rhos-las.** Both well stocked with coarse fish of all usual species; pike in Rhos-las. St £5, dt £1 (concessions for jun) for both reservoirs

from PO, Middle Row, Butetown, or Ward, Tackle Dealer, Tanfan Square, New Tredegar. For details of fishing on **Pontsticill, Dolygaeer** and **Upper Reservoir,** apply to Taff Division, WWA, Crwys House, Crwys Road, Cardiff. Tel 399961. Llangorse Lake *(see Brecon, on Usk)* and Talybont Reservoir *(see Talybont and Newport, on Usk)* are accessible. Caerphilly and Dist AA has coarse fishing in three large lakes at **Caerphilly:** mirror carp, bream, tench, roach, perch, pike (restocked). Dt issued. Association also has stretch on **Taff** at Taffswell. Members only.

TAWE. Centres: **Swansea, Pontardawe** and **Ystradgynlais.** River is pollution-free from Clydach to Moriston and from Pontadawe to the Source. Salmon and sewin more numerous than ever; Upper reaches noted for scenery. Tawe and Tributaries AA has 25m on Tawe and tributary **Twrch;** headquarters at Ystradgynlais; st and wt from Linnards Sports, High Street, Swansea; Rowlands, Sports Shop, Ystalyfera; W Wales Gun Co, 6 James Street, Pontardawe, and J G Davies, The Pharmacy, Abercrave and Ystradgynlais. Sunday fishing allowed. From Pontardawe to Morriston about 6m, is largely Pontardawe AS water; good trout fishing. Trout fishing on **Cray Reservoir,** near Trecastle, Powys. Apply Glamorgan RD, 86 Kingsway, Swansea SA1 5JL, or reservoir keeper. Llangyfelach and Dist AA has water on **River Llan** (sewin, brown trout). St £8 and wt £2, from T Day, 27 Vicarage Road, Morrison, Swansea. Sunday fishing permitted. Swansea Amateur AA has water on **Cothi;** (visitors to be accompanied by member). Good sea fishing (especially bass) from **Swansea** at **Mumbles** and all along Gower Coast. Advice and tackle from Capstan House, Beach Street, P E Mainwaring, 9 Dillwyn Road, Sketty, and Keith Pryer & Co, 31 Kings Road, Mumbles. Rowlands Sports, Ystalyfera. Hotels: Gwyn Arms (above Craig-y-nos) (permits); Ancient Briton (Penycae); Dynevor Arms (Pontardawe); and Gough Arms and Yniscedwyn Arms (Ystradgynlais).

Keep the banks clean

Several clubs have stopped issuing tickets to visitors because of the state of the banks after they have left. Spend a few moments clearing up.

GLASLYN

(For close seasons, licences, etc, see Welsh Water Authority, p 17–18)

Rises in Llyn Glaslyn, 3m south-west of Pen-y-Gwyrd, and flows through three lakes to Beddgelert then along Pass of Aberglaslyn to lower reaches and Portmadoc, where it enters the sea. Noted sea trout river and efforts are being made to increase salmon run. Best trout fishing in upper reaches, mountain lakes and tributaries. Best spots for salmon and sewin are: Glaslyn Hotel Bridge; Verlas; and above the pass.

Portmadoc (Gwynedd). Salmon, sewin, brown trout, Glaslyn AA water, Portmadoc to Beddgelert except two private stretches; st £25, dt £5 (Mon to Fri) from Mr Jones, 27 High Street, and Coffee Bar, Beddgelert. Lake; **Cwm Ystradllyn,** 4m N; trout, good fly fishing: $\frac{3}{4}$ lb to 4 lb. Tackleist: Angling and Gun Centre, High Street. Hotels: Queen's, Royal Sportsman. Brynallydan at Llanfrothen.

Beddgelert (Gwynedd); ns Portmadoc, $7\frac{1}{2}$m. Trout, sewin, salmon, Glaslyn AA has river from Beddgelert to Portmadoc (both banks, except two private stretches). Best months are: April and May for trout; April to Oct for salmon; May to Oct for sewin. Association tickets available *(see Portmadoc)*. Fishing rights on left bank from Beddgelert to and including **Dinas Lake** and stretch above lake belong to R H Williams, Breddgelert; wt, dt and boats. Permits (salmon, sewin, trout) for part of **Gwynant Lake** (boats only) also available from Beddgelert and Nantgwynant Post Offices. Sunday fishing on river and lakes. Hotels: Royal Goat and Saracen's Head (both can provide fishing on several miles of river).

GWYNEDD (streams)

(For close seasons, licences, etc, see Welsh Water Authority, p 17–18)

ABER. Fishing station: **Aber.** Aber rises in Llyn-Anafon, runs to Aber and sea in 2m. Trout (average 7–8 in). Now a Nature Reserve. No fishing. Hotel: Aber.

ARTRO. Rises in Llyn Cwmbychan, 6m E of Harlech, and enters sea 1m below Llanbedr. In tidal waters is good bass fishing. Noted for night fishing for sea trout. Good fly pools below village and above Dol-y-Bebin. Fishing station: **Llanbedr.** Sewin, occasional salmon. 4m (both banks) leased by Artro FA; tickets at Newsagent opposite Victoria Hotel, Llanbedr. St £12, wt £6, dt £4. Concessions for OAP and junior. Good free trout fishing in tributary **Nantcol.** This has been dammed to form lake in which stocked trout up to 3 lb taken (mostly on minnows). Several lakes also free (trout), while permission can be had for others. Lakes include: **Eiddewbach** (trout); **Fedw** (trout); **Eiddewmawr** (trout); **Graigddrwg** (trout); **Cwmbychan** (sewin, trout; preserved); **Gloywlyn** (good trout); **Pryfell** (trout); **Twrglas** (trout); **Hywell** (trout). Hotel: Victoria *(see also Gwynedd—lakes).*

DARON. Fishing station: **Aberdaron:** ns Pwlhelli, 17m. Daron and Cyll-y-Felin run down two valleys and join at Aberdaron; restocked and hold good-sized trout. Sea fishing for mackerel, pollack, lobsters, crab, etc, from rocks or boat. Tackle and licences from Jones, Spar Stores, Aberdaron.

DWYFAWR and DWYFACH. Fishing station: **Criccieth.** Best part of river lies in 1m W of Criccieth, where there is length of 12m unobstructed and good for fly fishing. Salmon fishing has greatly improved owing to restrictions on netting. Sewin very good; late June to Oct; night fishing best. Criccieth, Llanystumdwy and Dist AA controls about 10m both banks; st £51, wt £19. $\frac{3}{4}$m available on dt £2 (£3 Sundays). Association also has about 2m on Dwyfach; shorter river than Dwyfawr (about 10m) and rather heavily wooded but good for brown trout and sewin (mid-July onwards). RD licences and assn permits from R T Pritchard, Sheffield House, High Street. Good sea fishing in this area. Hotels: Lion; Ranch Hotel, Llanystumdwy.

ERCH. Fishing station: **Pwllheli.** Trout, sewin. Some good fishing here and on **Soch, Rhydhir** and tributary (11m) in hands of Pwllheli and Dist AA; Association also has good trout fishing on Rhydhir and **Cwymstradlyn Lake,** approx 10m NW; 95 acre lake holding wild and stocked brown trout. Tickets for lake and for Pwllheli Association water on rivers from D Hughes, Walsall Stores, Penlan Street Pwllheli. St £16. Ft £10, wt £6, dt £2. Hotels: Rhyllech Mansion (1m on Rhydhir), Tower, West End, Crown.

GEIRCH. Fishing station: **Nevin,** ns Pwllheli, 8m. Geirch, 2m W, 5m long; good sea fishing at Morfa Nevin. RD licences and tackle from D Chapman, High Street, Pwllheli.

GWYRFAI. Issues from Llyn Cwellyn, near Snowdon, and flows into Menai Strait through **Bettws Garmon** and **Llanwnda.** Salmon, sea trout, trout. Seiont, Gwyrfai and Llyfni AS controls much of river; st £50, wt £20, dt £6. Llyfni 1m NW of Rhyd-ddu; trout.

LLYFNI. Rises in Llyn-y-Dywarchen, 1m NW of Rhyd-ddu and runs through Nantlle Lake; salmon, sea trout (good), trout. Seiont, Gwyrfai and Llyfni AS controls both banks downstream of Llyfni Bridge to sea (4m) *(see Seiont).* *Tickets as in previous entry.*

SOCH. Fishing station: **Llangian** ns Pwllheli, 7m. Trout and rudd; an early stream; dry fly useful; weeds troublesome later; some sewin, late; plenty of sea fishing, bass, pollack, whiting, flatfish, at Abersoch (ns Pwllehi, 7m), from which this stream can be fished. Licences at Abersoch and Llangian post offices.

WEN. Fishing station: **Afon-wen.** Wen rises 4m above Llangybi station, runs 1m to Chwilog, and sea at Afon-wen, 1m; sea trout and brown trout; permission from farmers.

YSGETHIN. Fishing station: **Talybont.** Small trout. River rises in Llyn Bodlyn (trout, char, free). **Llyn Irddyn** and **Llyn Dulyn** also provide free trout fishing (3 or 4 to lb).

GWYNEDD (lakes)

(For close seasons, licences, etc, see Welsh Water Authority, p 17–18)

Bala (Llyn Tegid). Owned by Gwynedd County Council, Caernarvon. Permits from Lake Warden, Warden's Office on foreshore and Bala tackleists. Charges for visitors as follows: st £11, wt £4, dt £1.50 with concessions to clubs and parties. Salmon may sometimes be taken and trout early in season. Pike, perch, roach, grayling, eels. Bala is largest natural lake in Wales 4m long, 1m wide. Here, too, is found that rare and interesting fish called gwyniad. Coarse fishermen will find all their wants more than provided for; pike up to 25 lb; perch and good roach. RD licence required. Hotels quite close to fishing in Bala town. Llanuwchilyn AC issues tickets for Lower Lliw and Twrch; wt and dt from Post Office at Llanuwchilyn. Bala AA has stretch upstream of Bala New Bridge (dt) and winter fishing for members only on another stretch, both banks. Assn also has water on **Tryweryn** (members only), **Lliw, Llafar** (dt) and **Cwm Prysor Lake** (dt). St, wt and dt from Bala tackleists.

Bethesda. Ogwen Valley FA has four trout lakes: **Ogwen,** 5m; **Idwal,** 7m SE, a large lake, well known for rugged scenery; **Ffynnon Lloer,** fly only; **Bochlwyd,** 6m SE. Assn also has fishing on River Ogwen. Permits from David McCarter Sports, 36 High Street. Other lakes: **Melynllyn,** 5m E; **Dulyn,** 6m E; **Cowlyd** (5m W Llanwrst); all trout reservoirs belonging to Water Authority; free to licence holders.

Beddgelert. Dinas, 2m NE; abundant sea trout and salmon; permits for fishing including **Dinas Lake** from Aberglaslyn Bridge Café, Beddgelert. Best for sea trout mid-May to early Sept; salmon May–Oct; st £25, dt £5 (Mon to Fri). Llagi, 4½m E; trout numerous good size. Yr Adar, 5m E; trout; fishing sometimes good. Edno, 6m NE near Llagi; trout large but difficult.

Llyn Celyn near **Bala.** Reservoir managed by WWA, Shire Hall, Mold, Clwydd. Trout. April 1–Sept 30. Visitors' permits: st £81, dt £4 from Bala tackleists. Concessions for juvs. and OAP. Sunday fishing *(see Bala under Dee).*

Llyn Crafnant, Trefriw; 3m W of Llanrwst. One of the most beautiful lakes in Wales. Trout only (av 2 lbs) tickets from lakeside café. St £40, wt £12, dt £2.50. Boats, rod licences and information from café. Sunday fishing. Tel: 0492 640818.

Llyn Cwellyn, nr Caernarvon. Salmon, sewin, brown trout. St, wt and dt from Mrs Davies, Castell Cidwm Hotel, Betws Garmon.

Dolgellau. Tal-y-llyn, 8m S; a well-known trout lake with hotel accommodation *(see River Dysynni).* Gwernan, 2m SW; brown and rainbow trout. Cynwch, 2m N; brown and rainbow trout; fishing generally leased. Aran, 3m S; trout, fishing free. Cregennan, 4m SE; trout; dt £5. Gader, 4m SW; trout, free fishing, but rather poor. Y-Gafr, 4m SW; trout; near Gader, free, not very good. Bryndu Fishery, Llanelltyd, 2m NW; trout; dt £4. *For stream fishing see River Mawddach.* Permits and tackle from Celfi Diddan, Eldon Square LL40 1PS *(advt below).*

Dolwyddelan. Llyn-y-Foel, 3m NE. Diwaunedd, 3m W. Free trout fishing. **Llyn Bychan** and **Llyn Goddionduon** nr

Capel Curig, are leased by Bettwys-y-Coed AA. Dt from Tan Lan Café.

Y Dywarchen, Rhyd Ddu, ½m S of Llyn Cwellyn; Seiont, Gwyrfrai and Llyfni AS water. Fly only. *See Seiont.*

Y-Gader, 4m on main road to Caernarvon; trout; reputed good fly lake; boats obtainable at village *(see Gwyrfai— streams).*

Llyn Gwynant, 3m S; salmon, trout, sea trout; part private, part Glaslyn AA water *(see Glaslyn).* Lockwood's Llyn; trout; dt at petrol station, boat available.

Harlech. Good centre for Llanbedr and Talsarnau Lakes, and Artro and Glyn rivers. **Hafod-y-llyn Lake,** coarse fish, is private. 2m SE. **Craigddrwg,** 5m NE. **Dywarshen,** 8, NE. Du, 8m NE. **Eiddewfach,** 8m NE. **Eiddew-mawr,** 8m NE. These last-named lakes are free.

Llanberis. Llyn Peris no longer a fishery; **Llyn Padarn** stocked with wild brown trout and arctic char. Spinning and worm permitted. St £50 and dt £3 from Seiont, Gwyrfai and Llyfai AS.

Llanbedr, Cwm Bychan Lake. Trout and sewin; good fishing. Apply Cwm Bychan Farm, Cwn Bychan (dt £1.50). For

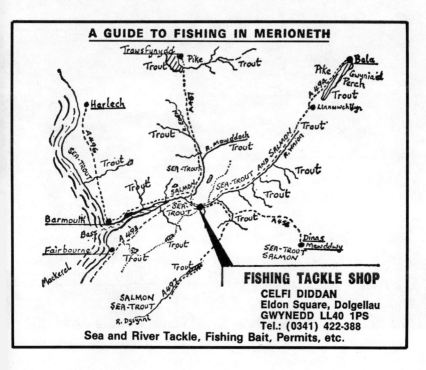

A GUIDE TO FISHING IN MERIONETH

FISHING TACKLE SHOP
CELFI DIDDAN
Eldon Square, Dolgellau
GWYNEDD LL40 1PS
Tel: (0341) 422-388
Sea and River Tackle, Fishing Bait, Permits, etc.

Gloywlyn Lake apply Cwmrafon Farm. Apply Artro FA, Llanbedr, for **Llyn Hywel;** trout; good fishing. **Llyn Perfeddau,** trout, good fishing; free. For stream fishing, *see River Artro.* Apply Artro FA.

Maentwrog: ns Tany-y-Bwlch. **Y-Garnedd,** 1m N (trout) and **Hafod-y-llyn** 1m NW (pike, coarse fish) are both private. **Tecwyn-Uchaf,** 2m SW and **Tecwyn-Isaf,** 2m SW, are under Talsarnau AA; trout; st issued. Other lakes under Cambrian AA are: **Morwynion, Cwmorthin, Manod, Barlwyd, Dubach, Dubach-y-bont.** St £15, wt £9, dt £4. **Trawsfynydd** is accessible. For stream fishing, *see River Dwyryd.*

Manod. Manod, 1m E; trout fishing often good; tickets from Cambrian AA, who have a number of mountain lakes around Blaenau Ffestiniog, some producing large fish. *(See above.)* Tickets from Blaenau Ffestiniog tackleists: F W Roberts, 82 Church Street. *For stream fishing, see River Dwyryd.*

Penmaenpool. Trout, sewin, and salmon; **Mynach Gadr,** 1m S Llechan, 2m W. Lake: **Cwmmynach,** 4m N (preserved).

Pen-y-Gwryd. Llyn Cwm Ffynnon. Excellent fly lake, trout plentiful but very small; free: **Teyrn,** $\frac{1}{2}$m SW; RD experimental lake; strictly preserved. **Diwaunnedd,** 2m SE; good trout on occasion; free *(see Dolwyddelan).* Llydaw, 2m SW.

Talsarnau. Glyn Group Lakes: Fedw (good-sized trout numerous), **Caerwych** (small trout, private), **Eiddew Bach** (numerous free-rising trout, 4 to 1 lb), **Eiddew Mawr** (small trout). Tecwyn group lakes: **Tecwyn-Isaf** (coarse fish), **Tecwyn-Uchaf** now stocked annually with 12–14 in rainbows, some larger native fish. Glyn river and tributary hold numerous small trout. Talsarnau AA issues st £4 and wt £2. Licences and tickets at Post Office, Talsarnau; The Pharmacy, Harlech; Mr

Fishing the fly for sea trout in one of Snowdonia's lovely streams. *Photo: Moc Morgan.*

Pierce (ironmonger), Penrhyndeudraeth; and The Grapes Hotel, Maentwrog.

Tal-y-llyn. Tal-y-llyn; trout, reserved for guests at Tynycornel Hotel but few dt available. £6 fly only. For river and stream fishing, *see Dysynni*.

Trawsfynydd Lake. 1200 acres. Managed by the Prysor Angling Association, brown and rainbow trout (average $1\frac{1}{2}$ lbs), also perch and rudd. Season: Rainbow trout 1 February–31 December; brown, trout 1 March–30 September; coarse fish 1 February–31 December. Fly fishing, bottom fishing and spinning. St £50, wt £14, dt £3.50, extra for boats. Concessions for OAP and junior. Fly only from boats. Regular weekly trout stocking from Association's own hatchery. Association also control 5 miles Prysor River; provides good trout fishing especially towards the end of the season when the lake brownies run up. Also 3 miles upper Eden: salmon and sea trout July onwards. Membership and permit enquiries to hon sec, Prysor Hatchery, Trawsfyndd, or to Permit Agent, M P Atherton, Newsagent, Manchester House, Trawsfynydd. Hotels: Cross Foxes and White Lion, Trawsfynydd; Grapes and Oakely Arms, Maentwrog; Abbey Arms and Pengwern Arms, Ffestiniog. Self-catering accommodation available at Bronaber Holiday Chalets, Trawsfynydd.

LLWCHWR (or LOUGHOR)

(For close seasons, licences, etc, see Welsh Water Authority, p 17–18)

Rises some 3m east of Llandybie on Taircarn Mountain and flows 15m south-west through Ammanford and Pontardulais to Burry Inlet, north of Gower Peninsula. Fishing very good for sewin, and some brown trout and salmon (April–July; August–October best). Salmon and sewin runs reported to be increasing. Most fishing controlled by clubs, from whom tickets are available.

Pontardulais (Glamorgan). Trout and a run of sea trout; some salmon. Pontardulais and Dist AA has 6m good fishing; st £20 + £5 joining fee, wt £10, dt £5 from Bridge Café. Concessions for OAP and jun. Ammanford AA has water on middle and upper reaches and tributaries; st issued. No dt or wt, but visitors' permit for 14 days issued. Swansea AAA and Llangyfelach AA also have water. Hotels: Gwyn; Penrhiw Guest House, Ammanford; Wernolau Hotel, Pontamman.

Tributaries of the Llwchwr

AMMAN. Trout, sewin, few salmon. Very fast running; fishes well in spate. Fishing stations: **Garnant, Bryn-Amman, Ammanford, Pantyffynon** (all Dyfed). Ammanford & Dist AA has water on **Llwchwr,** 5m; **Amman,** 3m; **Lash,** 3m; **Marlais,** 3m; **Cennen,** $\frac{1}{2}$m; **Gwili,** $1\frac{1}{2}$m. Sea trout run from May onwards. St £16 + £5 entrance, dt £3, according to conditions; tel: 0554 820477. Accommodation: West End Guest House, Pen-Rhiw Guest House.

MARLAIS BROOK. Sewin. July onwards. Fishing stations: **Llandybie** (Dyfed). Llwchwr, 3m. Gwendraeth Fawr, 5m W. Lake: Llyn Lechowen, 5m W.

MAWDDACH

(For close seasons, licences, etc, see Welsh Water Authority, p 17–18)

Rises in hills between Bala and Trawsfynydd Lakes and flows 10m south to confluence with Wnion, 2m below Dolgellau, and thence through long estuary to sea at Barmouth. River holds salmon, sea trout and brown trout and is all preserved, although permits can be had for some stretches. Successful stocking with locally hatched salmon fry. Salmon and sea trout may be taken up to Pistyll Mawddach.

Barmouth (Gwynedd). Within radius of 10m from Barmouth angler can have every variety of fishing. Rivers: Mawddach and **Wnion;** trout, sea trout and salmon. Run of sea trout and salmon is from beginning of June to end of season *(see Penmaenpool).* Other nearby streams are Arthog, Gwril, Bontddu, Glandwr, Artro, Scethin, Afon Cwm Mynach and Ardudwy; permission can usually be obtained from landowners; trout, not large, but plentiful. Lakes: Dilyn, Bodlyn, Urddyn, Cwmbychan, Glawlyn, Llyn Howell, Llyn Cwmmynach and Ubi. Trout; also some char.

Penmaenpool (Gwynedd). Sewin, salmon, few trout; tidal. Hengwrt Estate water, which extends 2m down and 1m up from

Llanelltyd Bridge now owned by Macclesfield Prince Albert AS. Mynach Gadr, 1m S, Llechan, 2m W. Lake: Cwm-mynach, 4m N (preserved). Hotel: George. *For licences and tackle, see Dolgellau.*

Llanelltyd and Ganllwyd (Gwynedd). Salmon, sewin, trout (small); preserved. Best months for salmon, June onwards; for sea trout, June to Sept. Hengwrt Estate water now rented by Prince Albert AS, Macclesfield. Various small streams and lakes holding trout for which permission may be given. Hotels: Tyn-y-Groes *(advt below)* ($1\frac{1}{2}$m salmon and sea trout fishing on river); Dolmelynllyn Hall ($1\frac{1}{4}$m on Mawddach; dt).

Tributary of Mawddach

WNION: Salmon, sewin, brown trout.
Dolgellau (Gwynedd). Wnion and Mawddach rivers. Wnion runs by Dolgellau and joins Mawddach 2m below town. Mawddach, 1m NW. Dolgellau AA owns rights on Wnion, also Mawddach and

Clywedog at Dolserau Hall, 1m from town. Dt £5, wt £12, st £32 from Country Life, Eldon Square and Siop y Bont, Bridge Street. Assn also has trout fishing on **Llyn Cynwych** (£4 day). **Tal-y-llyn** 8m S; good trouting for residents of

TYN-Y-GROES HOTEL

GANLLWYD — NR. DOLGELLAU — N. WALES
TELEPHONE; GANLLWYD (034-140-275)

SALMON AND SEA-TROUT
ON THE MAWDDACH
AND GLASLYN

*10 Bedrooms.
Fully licensed
Dining Room
and Bar.*

Tynycornel Hotel. Free lakes nearly all containing trout, some of them coarse fish also, are: Arran, 3m S; Gafr 4m SW; Cyri; Cader; Cau. Best months for salmon: April, Sept and Oct; for sea trout, June to Sept, for brown trout, April, May, late August, Sept. Tackle and licences from Celfi Diddan, The Square *(advt p 249).*

Bont Newydd (Gwynedd). Wnion; trout, sewin. Permits, wt and dt, from Celfi Diddan, Dolgellau. Hotels: Dolmelynl-lyn Hall, Ganllwyd (salmon, sea trout fishing on Mawddach), Tyn-y-Groes *(see Llanelltyd)*; Cross Foxes (mountain streams and fishing by arrangement at Trawsfynydd).

Drws-y-Nant (Gwynedd). Wnion; trout, sewin; preserved by owners. Hallog, Cwm-ochr, Ciddow, 1m W Fiddow, $1\frac{1}{2}$m W Dovey, 3m. Mawddach, 4m N; trout, sewin, salmon. Lakes: Dyfi, 3m W. Crych-y-wayen, 4m N.

OGWEN

(For close seasons, licences, etc, see Welsh Water Authority, p 17–18)

Rises in Ogwen Lake, half way between Bethesda and Capel Curig, with tributaries running in from Ffynnon Lloer and Bochlwyd Lakes, and runs from lake to outlet at Menai Straits, near Bangor, about 10m in all. Excellent trout fishing; leased by Ogwen Valley AA from Penrhyn Estate. Extensive restocking programme, with trout, sea trout (sewin) and salmon. Catches improving. Autumn good for salmon.

Bangor (Gwynedd). Ogwen, 2m E; salmon, sewin, trout. Parts of river leased by Ogwen Valley AA, which also has lake fishing *(see Bethesda).* Sea trout run starts about mid-June. Salmon best Aug–Oct. Sea fishing very good in the Menai Straits, near suspension and tubular bridges; bass whiting, pollack, etc. Hotels: Waverley, British Castle, Railway.

Bethesda (Gwynedd). Ogwen Valley AA has water. Tackleist T Jones, Windsor House, High Street.

POWYS (lakes)

Llyn Clywedog. Llanidloes (3m); 615 acres; Llanidloes and Dist AA. Reservoir shared with sailing club; western half is fishery area, but fishing permitted in much of eastern half also by arrangement with sailing club. Well stocked with brown and rainbow trout averaging $1\frac{3}{4}$ lb. Fly only. Dt £4 (evening £3), st £50 (concession rate for residents) from hon sec and Traveller Rest Restaurant, Longbridge Street, Llanidloes. RD licence required. *See also Llanidloes.*

Lake Vyrnwy, nr **Llanfyllin,** 1,100 acre lake stocked with rainbow, brown and American brook trout. Annual catch 3,000 to 3,500 averaging 1 lb. Fly only. Dt £5.75 (high season), £4.25 (low season); boats £6, or £8 with electric engine. Ghillies and instructors can be arranged together with hire of rods. Apply to Lake Vyrnwy Hotel, Llanwddyn, via Oswestry, Shropshire SY1O OLY. (Tel: 069 173 692).

Llangorse Lake. Brecon 6m. Holds good pike, good bream, perch, roach, eels, etc. Boats from Mr R P B Davies at lake side caravan park. Fishing free but WWA rod licences required. Llynfi runs from lake to Wye at Glasbury and holds a few trout; overgrown in places; requires short rod. Hotel at Llangorse: Red Lion.

Blaentawe. Fan Fawr, 1m. Fan Fach, 3m; many small trout; small charge made.

Talybont. 6m SW of Brecon. WWA reservoir, stocked with brown and rainbow trout. Season Ticket £81, day ticket £4. Day ticket by self issue permit vending machines on site.

SEIONT

(For close seasons, licences, etc, see Welsh Water Authority, p 17–18)

Rises in two tarns in Cwm-glas, under crest of Snowdon, and runs to Llanberis, 3m, where it enters the Llanberis Lakes, Llyn Peris and Llyn Padarn. Flows thence to Menai Straits to Caernarvon. Attractive river with long flats, nice runs and excellent pools holding salmon (May onwards), sea trout (June onwards), and brown trout. Trout rather small, but in faster water can give good account of themselves.

Caernarvon (Gwynedd). Salmon, sea trout, trout. Seiont, Gwyrfai and Llyfni AS control the following: bank fishing on **Llyn Gadair,** with boat-fishing rights; **Llyn Padarn** and 40 miles of salmon and sea trout fishing on **Seiont, Gwyrfai** and **Llyfni.** St £50, wt £20, dt £6 and £3 for lake. Permits from hon sec. Tackleists: Mrs D Huxley-Jones, 1 and 3 South Penrallt. Hotels: Eagles, Prince of Wales,

Castle, Royal, Black Boy.
Llanberis (Gwynedd). Trout, salmon, sewin; preserved (as Caernarvon). Hwch, 2m NW; trout. Mar, 3m NE. **Llanberis Lakes:** L Peris no longer fished: L Padarn leased to Seiont, Gwyrfai & Llyfni AA *(see previous entry).* Tickets for lake from Caernarvon tackleist and Eirw Fawr Hotel. Other hotels: Victoria, Dolbadarn, Padarn Lake, Castle.

TAF

(For close seasons, licences, etc, see Welsh Water Authority, p 17–18)

Rises on Mynydd Prescelly and flows about 25m south-west and south-east to Carmarthen Bay at mouth of Towy. Has reputation for sea trout (sewin) and also holds salmon and brown trout. Sewin run from June onwards.

St Clears (Dyfed). Salmon, sewin (brown trout poor). April, May, Sept best for salmon, sewin July onwards. Some open waters. Camarthen and Dist AC have water on Taf and stretch on **Dewi Fawr** (for charges *see Towy).* St Clears and District AA has good water; st £22, wt £10, dt £5, from hon sec. Glynin; trout, sewin. Cowin, 3m; trout, sewin. Permission of farmers. Hotels: Railway, Yelverton, Fisher's Arms. RD licences

from Post Offices at St Clears and Meidrim.

Whitland (Dyfed). Salmon, sea trout, brown trout. Whitland AA has 6m of fishing. St £35, wt £20 and dt £5 from A Wilson (tackleist), Llyshowell; R M Jones, Ivyhouse; and Post Office. Waungren Mansion and Farm has ¾m. Hotels: Waungren, Farmers Arms, Yelverton, Taf.

TAFF and ELY

(For close seasons, licences, etc, see Welsh Water Authority, p 17–18)

Taff has its source in two headstreams on the Brecon Beacons and flows about 40m south-east to the Bristol Channel at Cardiff. Trout and sea trout, but river hard-hit by pollution and clubs fighting uphill battle; one club dissolved. Ely joins mouth of Taff at Penarth.

Cardiff (Glamorgan). Brown trout (stocked) and run of sea trout and salmon. Glamorgan AC (membership 500) has about 6m on **Trothy** at Dingestow and Mitchel Troy (trout); 5m on Ely, at Llantrisant (trout); 8m on Taff (salmon, trout, coarse), stretches from Canton Bridge, Cardiff, to Radyr station. Club also holds rights on

freshwater reservoir at Barry Docks *(see Barry, under Sea Fishing Stations)* and on the St-y-Nyll ponds at St Brides. Tickets from hon sec, but no dt for trout issued from May 1 to Aug 1 inclusive. Trout season March 1 to Oct 1. Bute AA has fishing at **Marshfield Reens;** good carp, tench, etc. St from hon sec. Also coarse fishing on Wye and Usk. **Monmouthshire** and **Brecon Canal** (roach and perch), controlled by BWF. Centres: **Cwmbran, Pontypool, Newport.** Roath Park Lake (Cardiff Corporation) holds rudd, roach, carp, tench. Many good sea fishing stations are within reach. Tackle and advice from Bale's *(see below).* Local sea-angling organisation is Cardiff Sea AA. **Cardiff Reservoirs.** WWA waters managed by the Fisheries & Conservation Officer, South East Division, Pentwyn Road, Nelson, Nr Treharris, mid-Glamorgan (tel: 0443 450577). Taf Fawr Group, **Beacons Reservoir** (52 acres) brown trout, fly only; **Cantref Reservoir** (42 acres) rainbow trout, fly only; **Llwynon Reservoir** (150 acres) rainbow trout and brown trout, fly, worm and spinner. All located in Brecon Beacons National Park adjacent to A470 (T) road, 3 miles North of Merthyr Tydfil and 15 miles South of Brecon. Taf Fechan Group, **Pontsticill Reservoir** (253 acres) and **Dolygaer Reservoir** (96 acres), roach, pike, perch and brown trout; fly, spinner, worm, maggot, cereal baits and sea fish deadbaits; **Upper Neuadd Reservoir** (57 acres) managed as wilderness brown trout fishery, fly only, located in Brecon Beacons National Park 4m N of Merthyr Tydfil; **Lower Neuadd** has been drained to allow repair work to dam. Day permits from Pontsticill Depot, Old Filter Works, Pontsticill. Cardiff Group, **Llanishen** (59 acres) and **Lisvane** (19 acres) reservoirs, rainbow trout and brown trout, fly fishing only. Located within Cardiff City boundary, approach via B4562 road. Day permits available from self-service vending machines. Charges: the reservoirs are graded and season tickets conferring the

right to fish more than one, range from £34.50 to £134. These are obtained from South Eastern Division of the WWA. Season and day tickets obtainable on site, range similarly from £2 to £5.50. Fishing season all reservoirs—20th March to 17th October inclusive. Extension to 28th February for winter rainbow trout fishing on day permit only basis at Llwynon, Cantref, Llanishen, Pontsticill and Dolygaer reservoirs. Tackleists: A Bale, 3 Frederick Street (information, bait, licences); W Powell, Grangetown; Luxton's, Custom House Street; Norrie's, Arcade, Newport Road; Anglers Supplies, 172 Penarth Road. Cardiff hotels: Alexandra, Angel, Central, Grand, Park, Queen's, Royal.

Llandaff (Glamorgan). Taff: river unfishable due to pollution.

Pontypridd (Glamorgan). At junction of Taff and Rhondda. Club: Pontypridd and Dist AA, which has water here holding trout (av $\frac{1}{2}$ lb); which includes 4m on **Honddu** (Powys) and small lake.

Treharris (Glamorgan). At junction of Taff and **Taff Bargoed.** Clubs: Treharris AA and Bedlinog AA, which has 7m of **Taff Bargoed,** mountain stream holding brown trout. Also two ponds; coarse fishing. Inquire hon sec for details.

Merthyr Tydfil (Glamorgan). Merthyr Tydfil AA has rights on Taff, Taff Fechan and Taff Fawr from reservoirs to Quakers Yard about 15m in all; also a stretch on the **Tarrell** at Libanus, 4m from Brecon. Assn has coarse fishing in Penywern Ponds and lake in Cyfarthfa Park. Tickets from hon sec. *(For details of reservoirs in vicinity, see Cardiff entry on this page.)*

Tributaries of Taff

RHONDDA FAWR and FACH:
Pontypridd (Glamorgan). At Junction of Rhonddas Fawr and Fach and Taff. Club: Pontypridd and Dist AC.
Treorchy (Glamorgan). Rhondda; trout; Upper Rhondda AA control river from Blaencwm to Treorchy and **Llyn Fawr Reservoir.** Annual stocking with 10/13 in fish. St for river, but no vacancies except for local people. Dt for reservoir.
Tonypandy (Glamorgan). Glyncornel AA has 6m of Rhondda between Porth and Treochy; restocked annually with brown

trout. St £30 from local tackle dealers. Club holds rights on Rhymney Bridge Reservoir, fly only, and coarse fishing at **Darran Park Lake.** Inquiries to hon sec. Dt for coarse fishing at **Darran Park Lake** from local sports shops.
CYNON:
Aberdare (Glamorgan). Cynon joins Taff between Treharris and Pontypridd. Aberdare and Dist AA has trout fishing on Cynon, **Aman, Dare, Lliw** at **Ystradfellte, Cilenni** at **Pentrebach,** near Sennybridge, **Yscir,** near Brecon, and **Taff** at

Cefn Coed-y-Cymmer. Dt and wt from local tackleist, Leather Stores, Cannon Street.

ELY:

Peterson (Glamorgan). Trout, Glamorgan AC has coarse fishing in St-y-Nyll ponds at St Brides. *(Tickets, see Cardiff.)*

Llantrisant (Glamorgan). Trout. Glamorgan AC has 5m (not continuous), beginning at Miskin Weir (upstream limit of Taff and Ely water) and total length of **Clun Brook.** *(For tickets see Cardiff.)* Local club: Llantrisant and Dist AC, which has about 5m trout fishing upstream of Miskin Weir on Ely.

TEIFI

(For close seasons, licences, etc, see Welsh Water Authority, p 17–18)

Rises in Lyn Teifi, near Strata Florida, in NE Dyfed, flows south-west and then west, entering Cardigan Bay below Cardigan Town. Association water provides salmon, sea trout (sewin) and brown trout fishing. April and May are the best months of spring salmon; summer salmon fishing depends on floods. Sea trout run from July onwards. Coracle and draft nets come off September 1.

Cardigan (Dyfed). Salmon, sewin, trout. Bass, mullet and flounders below bridge to sea, 2m; boats available. Tackleists: M & A Williams, 10a Pendre, who supplies information about district. Hotels: Black Lion, Angel, Grosvenor.

Llechryd (Dyfed). Castle Malgwyn Hotel has 1m free to guests. Llwyndyris Mansion Hotel has 650 yards; st issued. Teifi Trout Assn water *(see Newcastle Emlyn).*

Cenarth (Dyfed). Salmon, sewin, trout. Famous falls; last site of historical coracle fishing for salmon. Teifi Trout Assn water *(see Newcastle Emlyn).*

Newcastle Emlyn (Dyfed). Salmon, sewin. Good centre for Teifi, Teifi Trout A has 12m of water in and around Newcastle Emlyn and including Cenarth. St £50, ft £40, wt £25, dt £7.50 from tackleists. Concessions to OAP. Tackleists: Cliff Jones, Emlyn Boot Stores. Hotels: Emlyn Arms (AA), Cawdor.

Llandyssul (Dyfed). Salmon, sewin, brown trout. Popular centre; fishing good. Best April–May and Aug–Sept for salmon; sewin July onwards. Llandyssul AA has about 27m of fishing in all. St £45, wt (March–August) £20 (Sep to end of season) £30, dt for members' guests only. Permits from G Jones, The Alma. Cerdin Twelli; trout (good). Clettwr, 2m; trout (good). Bargoed, 5m. Hotels: Porth and County Gate, Llanfihangel-ar-Arth, Pencader (on river bank, several miles of private water; dt issued; other fishing by arrangement).

Llanybydder (Dyfed). Salmon, sewin, brown trout. Llanybydder AA has salmon and trout water. St and dt from hon sec. Black Lion Hotel has four excellent beats totalling about 3m. Highmead Arms has 1¼m including eight pools; st £35, mt £15, wt £10, dt £5. Other hotel: Cross Hands.

Lampeter (Dyfed). Salmon (April onwards), some sewin, brown trout (3 to lb, good for dry fly). Dulas: trout. Grannell, 3m trout. Aeron, 6m W, salmon, sewin, trout. Cothi, 8m E; salmon, sewin trout. Llandyssul and Llanybydder clubs have water. St £26.80, st (T) £7.65, ft £12.50, dt £4.60. Tickets from tackleist, Roddy Rees, 56 Bridge Street. Cwmann AA has 6m starting within five minutes' walk of town. Portardulais & Dist AA has a stretch on Teifi downstream from town. Hotels: Black Lion, Falcondale, Royal Oak, Castle.

Tregaron (Dyfed). Good fly fishing for brown trout. Salmon fishing also good when conditions right. Tregaron AA has 14m of Teifi from Lampeter to Pontrhydfendigaid. St £32.50, wt £12, dt £3. Permits from Barclays Bank, Tregaron; Roddy Rees, 56 Bridge Street, Lampeter and W Rees, London Shop, Lllandewi Brefi. Permits for **Teifi Pools,** 8m; £2 dt, from M Morgan, Post Office, Pontrhydfendigaid *(see also Strata Florida).* Other good fishing on Aeron, 6m. Hotels: Talbot (1m on Teifi); Sunny Hill; Red Lion, Brynawel and Aberdwr Guest Houses. Licences from Caron Stores.

Strata Florida (Dyfed). Strata Florida AA has 6m stretch of Teifi in the vicinity of the village. Near Strata Florida are **Teifi Lakes,** on headwaters of river. *(See* details under *Tregaron*. **Llyn Gorlan** and **Llyn Bach** belongs to Earl of Lisburne, who also owns 3m of double bank fishing and $1\frac{2}{3}$m of single bank fishing on Teifi. Inquire at Talbot Hotel, Tregaron and Hafod Arms Hotel, Devils Bridge; also Belle Vue Royal, Aberystwyth. **Llyn Gynon,** 7m; difficulty of access, but is well stocked with trout. Permits from Post Office, Pontrhydfendigaid. Hotels: Red Lion, Black Lion, Llysteg.

TOWY (or TYWI)

(For close seasons, licences, etc, see Welsh Water Authority, p 17–18)

Rises in the Cambrians, near source of **Teifi**, and enters seaward end of Bristol Channel by small estuary. Lower reaches near Carmarthen are tidal holding trout, salmon and sewin in season (June and July best); association waters. Above this Towy mostly preserved, but some fishing by leave, ticket or from hotels. Salmon average 12 lb and sea trout up to 8 lb are taken; brown trout generally small.

Carmarthen (Dyfed). Salmon, sewin, trout. April and May usually good for large sewin. Tidal up to Carmarthen and 3m above. Carmarthen Amateur AA has three stretches on Towy (one tidal) and other good water on **Gwili, Cothi** and **Gwendraeth Fach** (15m in all); salmon, sea trout, wt £35 and £48 issued for all or part of fishings; all fishing within about 6m *(see Nantgaredig Gwili)*. Permits from Lyric Sports, King Street. Carmarthen and Dist AC has useful waters within 2 or 3m of town and extending for 2m of Towy. These cover tidal reaches, which give sport with salmon, sewin and trout. Club has water also on **Cothi, Gwili;** sea trout, trout, some salmon; **Gwendraeth Fach** (6m to 8m away; sea trout lower, trout only upper); **Taf** (10m away) and **Dewi Fawr.**

Importance is attached by Welsh sea trout fishers to the fly having "life". This one appears to have possessed that attribute. *Photo: Moc Morgan.*

St and wt issued. Trout only (average $\frac{1}{4}$ lb) in Gwendraeth Fach and Dewi Fawr. Permits and RD licences from Jones-Davies, King St, Carmarthen; Towy Sport, 9 King St, Llandeilo; R Thomas, Stepney St, Llanelli; and PO, Nantgaredig. Broadsheet giving full details of all waters issued by hon sec. Hotels: Falcon, Boar's Head, Golden Lion, Ivy Bush, Park. Hon secs of Carmarthen associations will be pleased to give information.

Nantgaredig (Dyfed). Salmon, trout, sewin; fishing private. Cothi; salmon, sewin. Carmarthen AAA has water on **Cothi** and **Gwili**, wt £22.50. Assn also has lower reaches of Cothi; inquire of hon sec. For middle reaches inquire of Forest Arms, Brechfa, and Black Lion Hotel, Abergorlech. *(See also Pumpsaint and Carmarthen.)*

Llanarthey (Dyfed). Hotel: Golden Grove Arms. Salmon, sewin, trout; mostly preserved.

Golden Grove (Dyfed). Preserved by Millbank Dyfed Estates and well keepered. Upper Water: Runs from Llandeilo Bridge to Myddfai Brook (Cilsane); 1m single bank, $1\frac{2}{3}$m double bank; fly only. Middle water runs from the old footbridge at Glantowy to Rofawr boundary post (about $4\frac{1}{4}$m, both banks); fly whenever conditions permit. Lower Water: from Bremenda-Isaf Boundary to old footbridge at Glantowy (about $1\frac{2}{3}$m, single bank). St £253 (upper and middle beats), £195.50 (lower beat), wt £45, dt (week-days) £15. Full details from

Bidwells, The Estate Office, Llangathen, Nr Carmarthen, Dyfed, SA32 8QE. (Tel: 05584 271).

Llandeilo (Dyfed). Salmon, sewin; Llandeilo AA preserves 8m on Towy, about 1m on Lower **Dulais** and about 1m on Lower **Cennen**; st £60, wt £30, dt £9 from hon sec. Juniors half-price. Fishing good when water in condition. Black Lion Inn, Llansawel, has $2\frac{1}{2}$m on Towy; rods also available on **Teifi** and **Cothi** *(see under Brechfa)*. **Cennen** good trout stream. Hotels: Morfa King's Head, Cawdor Arms, Castle, Edwinsford Arms.

Llangadog (Dyfed). Salmon, sewin, trout. Swansea Piscatorials and Llangadog AA have water. Wt, dt and limited night-fishing tickets issued. **Bran, Marlais, Sefin, Sawdde;** salmon, sewin, brown trout; mostly preserved by landowners. Hotel: Red Lion, which issues dt for 2m.

Llandovery (Dyfed). Salmon, sewin (best June-Sept), trout. Day and weekly tickets for visitors on Llandovery AA waters; 2m on **Gwydderig**, 3m on **Bran** and $10\frac{1}{2}$m on Towy. Tickets and licences from tackleist: C Bancroft, 11 Stone Street. St on application to hon sec only; wt (Towy) £16.50 and £5.50; (tributaries) £5.50, £1.65, juniors $\frac{1}{2}$ price. **Usk Reservoir** (11m), trout tickets from keeper. Swansea Amateur AA has water at Tonn Farm, above Llandovery Bridge, both banks; dt and wt (8 days) from hon sec (visitors must be accompanied by member). Hotels: Castle, King's Head, North Western, Royston, Picton Court and Llwyncelyn (last three private).

Tributaries of the Towy

GWILI. Small river of 12 ft to 16 ft in width which joins Towy 1m north of Carmarthen. Sea trout (sewin), fish running from early June onwards, averaging 2 lb and attaining 6 lb. Brown trout fishing poor. Occasional salmon caught. Carmarthen Amateur AA has about 6m; Carmarthen & Dist AC, a shorter stretch; wt £25 *(see Carmarthen).*

Bronwydd Arms (Dyfed). Sewin, trout, occasional salmon; Carmarthen Amateur AA has about 6m of water *(see Towy— Nantgaredig)*; accessible by bus. Car-

marthen and Dist AC has 6m *(see Carmarthen).*

Conwil (Dyfed). Trout, sewin mostly preserved by Conwil AA; mt, wt and dt available for **Conwil;** best June onwards. **Duad** and its tributary, Cochen, give good trouting. Cowin, 7m; trout, sewin.

COTHI. Larger stream than Gwili, but rocky and difficult to fish. Excellent sport with sewin (June onwards); salmon quite good. Some fly water middle and upper reaches. Spinning most popular, but worm also much used.

Carmarthen (Cothi, 6m). Swansea Amateur AA has two stretches of about 1m each; dt for members' guests only. Hotel: Cothi Bridge.

Llanfynydd (Dyfed). Penybont Inn has 2m; Cresselly Arms, Cothi Bridge, has short stretch for residents. Tickets from hotel for Assn water.

Brechfa (Dyfed). Salmon, sea trout. Mrs Beaulieu, Brechfa Fishing Lodge, has 3m of excellent water with many holding pools. Tel: 0267 89212. Accommodation at the Old Vicarage, Gwernogle. Tel: 0267 89258. Black Lion Inn has short stretch at **Abergorlech;** and a longer stretch lower down the river; dt issued *(see Llandeilo).*

Pumpsaint (Dyfed). Cothi and **Twrch.** Trout, sea trout (June onwards); salmon from early July. Dolaucothi Arms has $4\frac{1}{2}$m stretch running through National Trust property; fishing reserved for guests; limited wt £18, dt £3.50 if guests not fishing.

SAWDDE: ns Llangadock (Dyfed). Small trout; free. Inn: Cross, Llandeusant.

BRAN. Fishing station: **Cynghordy.** Towy, 3m; trout; fishing preserved. Rhaiadr, 3m. Crychan, 3m. Gwenffwrd 6m.

USK

(For close seasons, licences, etc, see Welsh Water Authority, p 17–18)

Good salmon river and first rate for trout. Geological formation is red sandstone, merging into limestone in lower reaches. Trout average from about $\frac{3}{4}$ lb in the lower reaches to $\frac{1}{4}$ lb towards the source. Some tributaries also afford good trout fishing; Ebbw, Afon Llwyd and Sirhowy are recovering from pollution and providing good sport in places. Salmon fishing mostly private, but several opportunities for trout.

Newport (Gwent). Newport AA has stretch of **Monmouthshire and Brecon Canal, Woodstock Pool, Morgans Pool** and **Liswerry Pond**; all providing good coarse fishing, including carp and tench. Assn also has $\frac{1}{2}$m (left bank) trout and coarse fishing on R Ebbw; and $1\frac{1}{2}$m salmon and coarse fishing on **R Wye** between Goodrich and Symonds Yat (members only and no day tickets for Wye). St £12 + £4 joining fee. Dt £1.50, concessions for juniors. From Newport tackle shops, bailiff on bank or membership sec D Lewis, 299 Claremont, Newport, Gwent. **Llandegfedd Reservoir** (430 acres) recently developed by WWA as a major boat fishery; well stocked with brown and rainbow trout; season March 20 to Oct 30. St £134, dt £5.50, morning £3.80 and evening £4; all available on site (day permits from machine). Boats £7 (£10 with engine). **Wentwood Reservoir** now leased to Wentwood Reservoir FFA. **Pantyreos** and **Ynysyfro Reservoirs,** trout; st and dt. Tel: 0633 59886. **Tredegar House Lake** in Country Park open for fishing. Good tench, carp and roach. St £25, dt £1 from Tredegar House & Country Park, Newport, NP1 9YW. Concessions for OAP, junior etc. Personal callers only. Islwyn & Dist AC have trout fishing on Ebbw, **Sirhowy** and

Penyfan Pond. St £33 (£16.50 junior) from membership secretary Mrs J Meller, 7 Penllwyn Street, Cwmfelinfach. Dt £3.50 and £5 from Pontllanfraith Leisure Centre. Tackleists: ARC Tackle, 8 Caerleon Road; Greens Tackle Shop, Pontllanfraith; Pill Angling Supplies; Dave Richards, 73 Church Road. Hotels: King's Head, Queen's, Westgate, Tredegar Arms.

Pontypool (Gwent). Usk private. Tributary **Afon Llwyd,** good trout fishing and regularly stocked by local clubs. Subject to periodic pollution but soon recovers due to exceptionally fast flow. Pontypool AA and Cwmbran AA have stretches. Pontypool AA also has **Olway Brook,** nr Usk, trout, dace and chub: Pontypool Park Lake, not yet fully developed: and restricted fishing on Llandetty stretch of River Usk (1 Oct–16 Jan). St £12.50 (£8.50 OAP, jun and disabled), dt £3 (trout, limit 3 fish) and £1 (coarse); available from Larcombe Sports. Cwmbran AA has coarse fishing on **Monmouthshire & Brecon Canal** and at Llantarnam Industrial Estates Ponds (2 ponds opened as fisheries in 1986 and stocked with roach, perch and dace): and excellent mixed fishing on **River Monnow,** trout, grayling, roach, perch, dace, chub and carp. St £10.50 (£5 jun) and dt 50p and £1.50; available from D H Powell (ironmongers), Chapel St, Pontnewydd, and Pet Stores, Cwmbran.

Usk (Gwent). Usk Town Water FA holds about 2m mostly above Usk Bridge, Trout tickets only are issued. Usk RD licences required. Wading advisable. Merthyr Tydfil AA has water at Kemeys Commander. Permits, tackle and licences from Sweet's Fishing Tackle, Porthycarne Street. Hotels: Three Salmons, Castle, Cross Keys, The Olway Inn, Glen-yr-Avon and Bridge Inn, Kemys.

Abergavenny (Gwent). Salmon, trout. Monmouth D C holds both banks from Llanfoist Bridge to below Sewer Bridge. St (S) £43.50, st (T) £18.25, wt (S) £18.25, wt (T) £8.45, dt (S) £6.50, dt (T) £4. Concessions to juniors. Tickets from Bridge Inn, Llanfoist. Crucorney Trout Farm, on **River Honddu**; stocked with rainbow and brown trout; fly only. Tel: 0873 890545. Merthyr Tydfil AA has recently puchased Mardy Fishery $1\frac{1}{4}$m above town. Tickets for various waters from PM Fishing Tackle. **Gavenny;** trout. **Mynachdy Brook,** 3m. **Trothy,** 4m; trout. **Full Brook,** 5m. **Honddu,** 5m; trout.

Monnow, 6m; trout. Hotels: Angel (Trust House); Great Western, Clytha Arms (salmon and trout fishing); and Bell, Glangrwyney (salmon and trout fishing). Tackleists: PM Tackle, 12 Monk Street; Fussells Sports, 53 Cross Street, both Abergavenny; Brutens, Market Street, **Ebbw Vale.**

Crickhowell (Powys); ns Abergavenny, 10m. Salmon, sea trout, brown trout. Gliffaes Country House Hotel (Tel 0874 730371) has water ($2\frac{1}{2}$m); first-class brown trout and salmon fishing, some sea trout; dt (S) £10 (T) £7.50 available *(advt below)*. Bridge End Inn has short length below bridge. For stretch of about $\frac{1}{2}$m upstream of Llangynidr Bridge (south bank). Major Llewelyn, Hill Crest, Llangynidr, issues tickets, £10 day. Trecastle and Talybont Reservoirs are within reach. Crickhowell AC has water. Dt for salmon and trout from Vine Tree Inn, Llangattock. Tackleist: Kirkland's, High Street.

Glangrwyney (Powys). Salmon, sea trout, brown trout. Bell Hotel has water here and issues tickets to residents and non-

GLIFFAES
Country House Hotel
near CRICKHOWELL, POWYS
NP8 1RH

Tel: 0874 730371

GLIFFAES invites you to relax and enjoy:
* Wild Brown Trout and Salmon fishing on $2\frac{1}{2}$ miles of the River Usk.
* Beautiful trees and shrubs in 29 acres of grounds.
* Good country cooking.
* Wonderful walks and views with abundant bird life.
* Tennis, putting, croquet and billiards.
* Golf, riding, swimming and hang-gliding nearby.

We have 19 bedrooms, all with bathrooms, comfortable sitting rooms with log fires. You will find us 1 mile off the A40, $2\frac{1}{2}$ miles west of Crickhowell.

Write or telephone for brochure and tariff
London via M4 3hrs. Birmingham via M5/M50 2hrs. Bristol via M4 $1\frac{1}{2}$hrs.

residents (dt £3.50) for salmon and trout fishing. Hotel stocks Usk flies.

Talybont (Powys). River privately preserved. Trout fishing in **Talybont Reservoir** (318 acres) well stocked with browns and rainbows; st £81, dt £4. From reservoir or Div Office, Usk Division, WWA, Station Buildings, Queensway, Newport, Gwent. Hotel: Usk (trout and coarse fishing arranged).

Brecon (Powys). Usk: salmon, trout av $\frac{3}{4}$ lb. Tributaries: **Honddu, Tarell, Bran.** Brecon AC has L bank from boathouse on river promenade to Llanfaes Bridge. Fly and worming only, dt £1.50. Brecon FA has 1m both banks below Llanfaes Bridge. Trout (fly only) dt £3.50; salmon £7.50; baits as per WWA regulations. Permits and rod licences, also coarse fishing permits for pools at Darew Farm, Llyswen, from D Spilsbury, Tackleist, Watergate, Brecon. Anglers visiting the farm pools are advised to bring their bait with them. 5m from Brecon, **Llangorse Lake**; pike, perch, roach and bream. Boats and caravans from Mr Davies at Waterside. Hotels: Castle of Brecon, Nythfa, Uskview GH.

Sennybridge (Powys). Trout, salmon. Permits for about $2\frac{1}{4}$m just below Sennybridge on one bank of the Usk (site of capture of Usk record brown trout—$9\frac{1}{4}$ lb) and another $1\frac{1}{2}$m stretch upstream; st (S) £26.80, st (T) £7.65, ft (S) £12.50, ft (T) £1.85, dt (S) £4. Concessions OAP, jun. Tickets and licences for this and other trout water on Usk from W J Davies (tackleist), Drug Stores, Sennybridge. Details of other Usk fishings between Sennybridge and Brecon from Woosnam & Tyler, Dolgarrog, North Road, Builth Wells. Permits for Usk tributaries from farmers. At **Trecastle** is **Usk Reservoir;** (280 acres) rainbow and brown trout. Fly fishing, spinning and worming. Located in Brecon Beacons National Park near Trecastle (Brecon). Season ticket £90. Day ticket £4.00 available on site. Rods also available on **Crai Reservoir.** Owned by Cnewr Estate Ltd, Sennybridge, Brecon LD3 8SP. Wild trout; flyfishing from bank only. Dt £5 from reservoir keeper (£3 OAP & jun). Hotels: Usk, Railway, and White House ($1\frac{1}{2}$m on river), all Sennybridge and Castle, Trecastle.

Trout fishing on Usk Reservoir. *Photograph by Eric J Chalker.*

WELSH SEA FISHING STATIONS

Those given in the following list are arranged from south to north. Sea fishing is available at other places also, but those mentioned are included because they cater specially for the sea angler. Further information may be had from the tackleists and club secretaries (whose addresses will be found in the club list). When writing, please enclose stamped addressed envelope for reply. Local authorities will help with accommodation.

Swansea and Gower. Bass, flatfish from beaches and rocks (Worm's Head). Fish baits cast from Llanmadoc take conger, tope, thornbacks and monkfish. Mackerel caught in warmer months. Bass, mullet and flounders in estuary at Loughor Bridge. Excellent boat fishing in Carmarthen Bay and off Worm's Head, but boats difficult to obtain. Welsh Tope, Skate and Conger Club charters boats leaving Swansea riverside quays and fishing the bay and Pwlldu. Bookings through clubs and skippers. Club membership made through qualifying fish. HQ: Rock and Fountain Inn, Skewen. Small bass, mullet, flatfish and mackerel off Mumbles Pier; no night fishing. Docks permit required for Queens Dock breakwater; good for cod in winter. Bait can be dug in Swansea Bay and estuary; squid, herring, sprats and mackerel from Swansea Market. For details of charter-boats, apply to Derek Jones, 24 Cilonen Road, Three Crosses. Tackleists: Capstan House Pro-Angling Centre, Beach Street; Mainwarings, Dilwyn Road, Sketty. Other clubs: Swansea Sea AC; Mumbles Motor Boat and Fishing Club,

Fishguard (Dyfed). Main captures from shore and breakwaters are flatfish, codling, conger, pouting, mackerel, bass, pollack, whiting and some tope. Sea trout and mullet near mouth of Gwaun. Tope, mackerel, conger, skate, etc. from boats. Boats from Fishguard Yacht & Boat Co, Main Street, Goodwick. Tel Fishguard 873377 and Brooks, Lower Town. Club: Fishguard & Goodwick SA, annual membership: £1. Tackleists: Collins, 46 West Street; Thomas, Dyfed Sports, 21 West Street; Johns, The Square, Goodwick. Hotel: Fishguard Bay.

Tenby (Dyfed). Good sport from Old Pier; whiting, pollack, bass, codling and grey mullet; good bass fishing from south and north sandy beaches, and spinning from rocks. Fine mackerel fishing most seasons, and tope off Caldey Island. For boats inquire Morris Bros (*see below*) and D Bowler, 1 Lexdem Terrace. Shark trips also arranged; Tackleist: Morris Bros, St Julian Street.

Milford Haven and Pembroke (Dyfed). Fine surf-fishing and spinning from rocks for bass from Freshwater West and Broad Haven (Bosherton); best late summer and autumn. Kilpaison good for bass, flatfish early on; also codling and coalfish. Stone piers and jetties inside Haven provide deepwater sport for pollack, skate, rays, whiting, codling, dogfish and coalfish. Hobbs Point (Pembroke Dock) excellent for conger and skate. Mackerel from rocks and boats (Stackpole Quay good). Tope from boats in Barafundle Bay and mackerel and bass from rocks. Other useful venues are Nab Head, Martins Haven and Angle Bay, Thorn, Rat and Sheep Islands and Harbour Rock. Mackerel from boats at harbour entrance. Lugworm and razor fish may be dug in several places, esp mudflats at Kilpaison and Angle Bay. Pennar Gut and Pembroke River. Tackleists: Sports and Leisure, Main Street and F Donovan, Bush Street, Pembroke; Humbers, Diamond St, Pembroke Dock; F Powell, 84 Charles St, Milford Haven. Boats (for tope fishing) from Sinclair Bros and D V Howells at Hakin Point. Clubs: Pembroke and Dist AC and Milford Haven Sea AC.

Aberystwyth (Dyfed). From the shore, May to November, bass (especially on soft crab bait), pollack, painted ray, mullet, huss, conger, wrasse. From October to January, whiting; July to September, mackerel. Dogfish, dabs and flounder throughout the year. Fish caught off the rocks off storm beaches, from the harbour and stone jetty. Borth beach and Leri estuary specially good for flounders; Tan-y-bwlch beach particularly good for whiting. Bull huss and thornback ray form the backbone of the boat fishing, but dogfish, dabs, gurnard, pollack, tope, bream, turbot, monkfish and porbeagle shark are taken in their seasons. Boat trips are run from the harbour ranging from 2 hour sessions for mackerel to 12 hours out at sea. There are many well-equipped boats commanded by highly experienced skippers. Mr D Taylor, Cwmmeurig, Cwmsymlog (tel: 0970 828815) will be pleased to help visitors with more detailed information, and advice. Tackleists: Aber Guns & Tackle, 13 Terrace Road; J Rosser, 3 Queen's Street and E & L Reddington, 23 Chalybeate St. Club: Aberystwyth SAC.

Barmouth (Gwynedd). Bass (large), flatfish, mullet in Mawddach estuary and from nearby beaches; also codling, mackerel, flatfish, and even tope and skate from boats. Ynys y Brawd island good for bass and flounders from shore and boats. Tackle, bait and boats (6-hour trip £7): All Sports, Beach Road. (Tel 280240.)

Pwllheli-Criccieth (Gwynedd). Excellent bass fishing April–October; dogfish, dabs, plaice, skate, pollack and a few sole the year round; mackerel, tope and monkfish from June to September. October to January; whiting and coalfish. Also salmon, sea trout and brown trout on lake; st £51, wt £19 from R T Pritchard *(see below)*. Boats and bait available. Tackleists: Walsall Stores, 24 Penlan Street, Pwllheli; R T Pritchard, Sheffield House, High Street, Criccieth

LL52 0EY.

Bangor (Gwynedd). Centre for Menai Straits and Anglesey. Excellent bass and plaice in Menai Straits, but thornbacks and tope more often taken by boat anglers. Good beaches between Bangor Pier and Menai Bridge; bass, flatfish, conger, etc. Boats: inquire piermaster. For parties and clubs apply A J Regan, 106 Orme Road, or J Evans (Bangor 3854). Tackleists: Edwards, 6 Dean Street; Davies, High Street.

Deganwy (Gwynedd). Wide variety of fish taken from boats in Gt Orme, Menai Straits and Puffin Island areas. Bass in estuary and off Benarth, Bodlondeb and Deganwy Points and Beacon Light. Bait from shore and estuary. Many boats.

Llandudno (Gwynedd). Skate, codling, pollack, bass, mackerel, plaice, whiting, conger, coalfish, etc. Rocky beach at corner of Little Orme good for bass; so is west shore, especially Black Rocks area. Bait plentiful. Fishing from pier, beach, rocks and boats. Tope and mackerel taken by boat fishers. Boats from M Davies, Pentywyn Road, Deganwy LL31 9TL (tel: 0492 81983).

Colwyn Bay (Clwyd). Bass off Rhos Point and Penmaenhead. Whiting, codling in winter from beach. Dabs, whiting, some plaice from pier (dt available all year). Tope and skate from boats. Tackleists: Duttons, 52 Sea View Road (bait); R D Pickering, 60 Abergele Road; Pet Stores, Market Hall.

Rhyl (Clwyd). Bass, flatfish from shore. Tope, dabs, plaice, whiting, turbot, skate, cod, bass, etc from boats. Boats (in season) from Blue Shark, Quay Street; Marina Service Station, Wellington Road. Tackle and bait: Wm Roberts (Rhyl) Ltd, 131 High Street.

ANGLESEY

Holyhead and Holy Island. Fishing off Holyhead Breakwater, $1\frac{1}{4}$ long, good on any tide; summer and winter fishing, many species caught. Very good fishing also on Stanley Embankment, at Cymran, Rhoscolyn, Trearddur Bay, Porthdafarch and Holyhead Mountain. Bull huss, dogfish, pollack, wrasse, mullet, cod, plaice, dab, flounder, conger, whiting, codling, thornback ray and bass all taken in season from the various

shore-marks. Boat-fishing, possible in all but the worst of weather, yields also shark, tope, ling and smoothhound. Bait readily available. Excellent boat fishing; thornbacks, tope, etc. Bait in harbour or from tackleists: Dorset Stores, Kingsland; R P Owen; Thos Owen, 19/20 Cybi Street; Holyhead (J's) Sports, 2 Boston Street, which acts as an agency for charter-boat hire. Sells fresh and frozen sea-bait, provides instruction, and repairs rods and reels on the premises. Hotels: County, Holborn, Scimitar, Queen's.

Amlwch. Tope taken to 40 lb, skate, conger, herring, mackerel, etc, from boats; obtainable at Amlwch and at Bull Bay ($1\frac{1}{2}$m). Hotel: Dinorban Arms.

Beaumaris. Big bass, tope, pollack, mullet and mackerel opposite Beaumaris and along the Straits. Between Menai and The Tubular Bridge fair-sized bass and conger are caught. For boat fishing, contact Starida Boats, Beaumaris. Tackleist: Odds & Rods, Church Street, Beaumaris, and K Johnson, Water Street, Menai Bridge.

FISHING CLUBS & ASSOCIATIONS IN WALES

INCLUDED in this list of fishing clubs and associations in Wales are some organisations which have their water on the upper reaches of the Wye or Severn, details of which are contained in the English section of *Where to Fish*. The secretaries of the clubs are usually pleased to supply further information, but they appreciate the inclusion of a stamped addressed envelope with postal inquiries.

NATIONAL BODIES

Wales Tourist Board
Brunel House
2 Fitzalan Road
Cardiff, South Glamorgan

Welsh Anglers' Council
Hubert T Gwynne
87 Shirley Drive
Heolgerrig,
Merthyr Tydfil,
Mid Glam

Welsh Federation of Coarse Anglers
J Mayer
6 Biddulph Rise
Tupsley
Hereford

Welsh Federation of Sea Anglers
G H Jones
8 Moreton Road
Holyhead
Gwynedd

Welsh Salmon and Trout Association
MocMorgan
Swyn Teifi
Pontrhydfendigaid
Ystrad
Meurig, Dyfed

Welsh Tope, Skate and Conger Club
Colin Delfosse
16 Moorside Road
West Cross
Swansea SA3 5EY

CLUBS

Aberaeron Town Angling Club
D Rees
10 North Road
Aberaeron, Dyfed SA46 0JF
Aeron. Tickets

Aberdare and District Angling Association
J Bebb
40 Ynyscynon St, Cwmbach
Aberdare, Glamorgan
Cynon and Usk tributaries. Tickets

Aberystwyth Angling Association Ltd
PO Box 15, Aberystwyth

Dyfed SY23 1AA
Rheidol, Ystwyth and lakes. Tickets

Afan Valley Angling Club
R Hope
1 Wellington Place
Port Talbot
W Glamorgan

Amlwch and District Angling Club
J Davies
Ty'n Giat Garage
Amlwch, Anglesey

Ammanford and District Angling Association
R Woodland
2 Pontarddulais Road
Llangennech
Llanelli, Dyfed
Llwchwr, Amman, Cennen, Marlais and
Lash. Members only
Artro Fishing Association
P G Cozens
Awelfryn
Llanbedr, Gwynedd LL45 2HL
Bala and District Angling Association
D M Rees
12 Tegid Street
Bala, Gwynedd
Dee and tributaries and Lake Bala
Tickets
Bangor City Angling Club
M Partridge
1 Lon Isaf
Menai Bridge, Anglesey
Bangor-on-Dee Salmon Angling Association
S Adams
Hendy
High Street
Bangor-on-Dee, Wrexham
Clwyd
Dee. Tickets
Barry Angling Society
J Slatter
3 Vere Street
Cadoxton, Barry
Glamorgan
Bedlinog Angling Association
E Jones
52 Hylton Terrace
Bedlinog, Treharris
Glamorgan
Betwys-y-Coed Angling Club
Ernest Jones
7 Bro Gethin
Betwys-y-Coed, Gwynedd
Birchgrove (Cardiff) Angling Association
E Parry
13 Westmoreland Street
Canton, Cardiff
Bishopston Angling Club
E C Roberts
"Croydon"
10 Heal Lane
Pennard, Gower
Blackwood Angling Club
D B W Lewis
4 Brynglas Avenue
Pontllanfraith, Gwent.
Bradley Angling Club
Keith Jones
17 Heol Camlas
Gwersyllt

Nr Wrexham, Clwyd
Alyn. Members only
Brecon Angling Society
W L Peters
53 Ffynnon Dewi
Llanfaes, Brecon, Powys
Bryn-y-Pys Angling Association
Mrs A Phillips
2 Ruabon Road
Wrexham, Clwyd LL13 7BB
Dee. Tickets
Buckley Angling Association
R W Jones
Cresta
35 Bryn Awelon
Mold, Clwyd
Lake permits
Bute Angling Association
L V Powell
176 Clare Road
Grangetown
Cardiff, Glam
Caergwrle Angling Club
Mrs E Lewis
Bronwlfa
Hawarden Road, Caergwrle
Nr Wrexham, Clwyd
Alyn; st only
Caerphilly and District Angling Association
J E Lintern
74 Station Terrace
Nelson, Treharris, Glam
Lakes. Tickets
Cambrian Angling Association
G Williams
Y Gilfach
Pantllwyd
Blaenau Ffestiniog LL41 4PW
Gwynedd
Lakes. Tickets only
Cambrian Fly Fisheries
S Diggory
Pontcysyllte
Clwyd
Dee. Tickets
Capenhurst Angling Club
A T Howdon
24 Saughall Hey
Saughell
Chester, Cheshire
Cardiff Sea Anglers' Association
H Allen
10 Clareston Road
Cardiff
Cardigan and District Angling Club
W H McManus
Cheriton, Aberporth
Dyfed
Teify. Tickets

Carmarthen Amateur Angling Association
G Evans
Brwyn, 118 Llanstephan Road
Johnstown, Carmarthen
Towy. Tickets
Carmarthen and District Angling Club
H Evans
25 Maple Crescent
Carmarthen
Towy, Gwili, Taf, Gwendraeth Fach
Cowin and Cennen. Tickets
Cefndeuddwr Fishing Syndicate
c/o Post Office
Ganllwyd
Dolgellau
Mawddach and Eden. Tickets
Cefni Angling Association
G R Williams
Tyn Lon, Gaerwen
Pentre Berw
Anglesey
Ceri Angling Association
J E Morgans
Gwynfryn Beulah
Newcastle Emlyn
Dyfed
Cerrig-y-Drudion Angling Association
W M Roberts
4 Cae Lwydd
Cerrig-y-Drudion
Clwyd
Alwen. Members only
Chester Association of Anglers
P Massey
40 Timberfield Road
Saughall
Chester, Cheshire
Chirk Angling Association
J L Davies
76 Longfield, Chirk
nr Wrexham
Clwyd
Cilcain Fly Fishing Association
A E Williams
Gwynfryn
Caerwys Hill
Caerwys
Mold, Clwyd
Trout reservoirs. Permits
Clwyd Angling Club
B J B Roberts
17 Mwrog Street
Ruthin, Clwyd LL15 1LB
Clwyd; limited membership
Connah's Quay and District Angling Club
P Ryan
5 New Brighton Road
Sychdyn
Mold, Clwyd

Conway Fishing Association
Miss Connell Smith
Gwydyr Hotel, Betws-y-Coed
Gwynedd
Conway. Tickets
Conwil Angling Association
Honorary Secretary
c/o Rock and Fountain
Conwil Road
Carmarthen
Gwili. Tickets
Corwen and District Angling Club
M J Green
69 Clawdd Poncen
Corwen, Clwyd
Dee and Alwen; members only
Criccieth, Llanystumdwy and District Angling Association
G Hamilton
Morawell, Llanystumdwy
Criccieth, Gwynedd
Dwyfawr. Tickets
Crickhowel Angling Club
V H Hesketh
Brick House
Church Lane
Crickhowell, Powys.
Usk. Tickets
Cwmbran Angling Association
P M Gulliford
16 The Circle
Cwmbran, Gwent
Afon Lwyd. Tickets
Dee Anglers. Association
E E Owen
2 Snowdon Crescent
Lache Lane
Chester, Cheshire
Dee Tickets
Denbigh and District Angling Club
J D Gambles
38 Crud y Castell,
Denbigh, Clwyd
Clwyd. St only
Dolgarrog Fishing Club
P Jones
12 Hillside Cottages
Dolgarrog
Conway Gwynedd LL32
Conway and Roe. Tickets
Dolgellau Angling Association
E M Davies
Maescaled, Dolgellau
Gwynedd LL40 1UF
Dolwyddelan Fishing Association
E Roberts
Pen-y-Cafnau, Dolweyddelan
Gwynedd LL25 0EQ
Lledr. Tickets

Estimaner Angling Association
W G Humphrys
2 Pandy Square
Abergynolwyn
near Towyn, Gwynedd
Drysynni. Permits
Glamorgan Anglers' Club
Paul Mason
8 Denys Close,
Dinas Powis, S Glamorgan
Taff, Ely, and Trothy. Tickets
Glaslyn Angling Association
O W Jones
5 Britannia Terrace
Portmadoc, Gwynedd
Glaslyn. Tickets
Glyncornel Angling Association
J M Evans
126 Ystrad Road
Ystrad, Pentre, Glamorgan
Glynneath and District Angling Association
R Cole
24 Woodlands Park Drive
Cadoxton, Glamorgan
Gowerton Angling Association
G Thomas
10 Elba Street
Gowerton, nr Swansea
Griffin Angling Club
E D Hughes
19 Greenway View
Gresford, Clwyd
Alyn. Members only
Grosvenor Angling Association
D E Whitehouse
Stretton
School Lane
Guilden Sutton
Chester, Cheshire
Dee. St only
Gwent Angling Society
W Watkins
Deristone
76 Monk street
Abergavenny Gwent
Gwent Federation of Angling Societies
G Gurmin
26 Railway Terrace
Hollybush, Blackwood, Gwent
Holyhead and District Angling Club
Kings Road,
Holyhead
Anglesey, Gwynedd LL65 2BG
Holywell Anglers
S J Burns
Hazeldine
Holway Road
Holywell
Clwyd

Isca Angling Club
B Evans
22 Eton Road
Newport, Gwent
Islwyn and District Anglers
Mrs J Meller
7 Penllwyn Street
Cwmfelinfach, Gwent NP1 7HE
Kenfig Hill and District Angling Association
A Waite
16 Marlas Road
Pyle, Glamorgan
Kirkdale Angling Association
A C Hoer
61 Baythorne Road
Liverpool
Dee. St only
Lavister Angling Club
G Watkins
Rathgillan
Lache Hall Crescent
Lache Lane
Chester, Cheshire
Dee. Members only
Liverpool and District AA
Water on Dee
(See English list)
Llanbedr Fishing Association
H Warburton
Ty Mawr
Llanbedr
Gwynedd
Llanbrynmair and District Angling Club
Tony Marsh
Plas Llysyn
Carno, Powys
Llanybydder Trout Fishing Association
Mr Thomas
Lloyds Bank Ltd
Llanybydder, Dyfed
Llandegfedd Fly Fishers
M Williams
Wellfield Farm
Coedypaen, Usk
Llandeilo Angling Association
Regd. Office
Llystewydd, Ffairfach
Llandeilo, Dyfed
Towy. Tickets.
Llandovery Angling Association
M Davies
Cwmrhuddan Lodge
Llandovery, Dyfed
Towy. Tickets
Llandrindod Wells Angling Association
A H Selwyn
4 Park Crescent
Llandrindod Wells, Powys
Ithon. Tickets

Llandudno and District Sea Angling Club
Miss C C Jones
7 Gogarth Avenue
Penmaenmawr, Gwynedd
Llandyssul Angling Association
A Jones
Glas-y-Dorlan
Llynyfran Road
Llandyssul, Dyfed
Teify. Tickets
Llanfair-p-g and District Sea Angling Club
S R Walburn
97 Tan-y-Bryn Road
Rhos-on-Sea, Colwyn Bay
Clwyd
Llangadog Angling Association
J O Slaymaker
Brynamelon
Llangadog Dyfed
Llangernyw Anglers
I W Clayton
Cefn-y-Groes
Fawr
Llansannan, Clwyd
Elwy. Members only
Llangollen Angling Association
W N Elbourn
12 Chapel Street
Llangollen, Clwyd
Dee. Tickets
Llangyfelach Angling Association
M L Griffiths
3 Aldwyn Road
Cockett, Swansea
W Glamorgan
Llanidloes and District Angling Association
I J Dallas Davies
Dresden House
Great Oak Street
Llanidloes, Powys
Llanilar Angling Association
W M Jones
Bryn Ystwyth, Llanilar
Aberystwyth SY23 4PJ
Llanrwst Angler's Club
D W P Hughes
36 Station Road
Llanrwst, Gwynedd
Conway Tickets
Llansannan Anglers
G W Owen
Glasfryn Stores
Llansannan
Tickets
Llantrisant and Pontyclun Anglers
G H Davies
2 Lanelay Road
Talbot Green
Llantrisant, Glamorgan

Llanuwchllyn Angling Club
H E Morris
Plas Newydd
Llanuwchllyn
Gwynedd
Dee Tickets
Llay Angling Society
J Preston
20 Mold Road Estate
Gwersyllt, Clwyd LL11 4AA
Alyn. Tickets
Llay Hall Angling Association
M Tilley
Daisy Bank
Fellows Lane
Caergwrle
Nr Wrexham, Clwyd
Alyn. St only
Llynfi Valley Angling Association
G Ball
2 Heol-y-Bryn
Llangynwyd, near Bridgend
Glamorgan
Maelor Angling Association
K Bathers
Sunnyside, Hill Street
Cefn Mawr, Wrexham
Clwyd
Dee. Tickets
Maerdy and Ferndale Angling Society
W H Blake
7 Richard Street
Maerdy, Ferndale, Glamorgan
Reservoirs; tickets
Merthyr Angling Association
A Rees
13 Alexandra Avenue
Merthyr Tydfil, Glamorgan
Midland Flyfishers
D M Plea
11 Newhall Street
Birmingham 3
Dee. Tickets
Milford Haven Sea Angling Club
G Betty
113 Haven Drive
Milford Haven, Dyfed
Mold Trout Anglers
K Beaumont
5 Tan y Cae
Nannerch
Mold, Clwyd
Alyn. Tickets.
Mold Kingfishers Angling Club
R W Ambrose
25 Pinewood Avenue
Connah's Quay
Clwyd
Wheeler, Ayn, pools, St only

Monmouth and District Angling Society
B Vickers
13 Clwydd-y
Goldwire Lane
Monmouth
Monnow and Trothy. Members only

**Montgomeryshire Angling Association
(including Llanfair Caereinion FC
Newtown FC, Welshpool AC)**
T J Evans
48 Gungrog Road
Welshpool, Powys
Severn and tribs, canal, lakes. Tickets

**Montgomeryshire Federation of Angling
Associations (seven clubs)**
Edgar Spooner
Memorial Gallery
Newtown, Powys

Moss-Side (Manchester) Angling Society
Water on Dee
(see English list)

Mountain Ash Flyfishers
I Glyn Jenkins
10 Eul-y-Plwyf
Ynysybwll, Pontypridd
Glamorgan

Mumbles Motor Boat and Fishing Club
Ron Edwards
642 Mumbles Road
Mumbles, Swansea

Neath and Dulais Angling Association
A Beasley
10 Neath Road, Tonna
Neath, W Glamorgan

Newbridge Angling Association
K S R Clutton
28 Worseley Avenue
Johnstown
Wrexham, Clwyd
Dee. Members only

New Dovey Fishery Association (1929) Ltd
D Morgan Jones
Plas, Machynlleth   Powys
Dovey; some tickets

Nevern Anglers Association
G A James
Post Office
Moylegrove
Cardigan, Dyfed SA43 3BW

Newport (Mon) Angling Association
P Climo
2 Darwin Drive
Newport, Gwent
Monmouth Canal and pond Tickets
limited

New Quay and District Angling Club
D H Jones
Helbryn
New Quay, Dyfed

Northern Anglers Association
Water on Dee
(see English list)

North Wales Federation of Anglers
G M Williams
The Fisherman's Cabin
11–13 High Street
Bala, Gwynedd

Ogwen Valley Angling Association
Bryn Evans
31 Erw Las
Bethesda, Gwynedd

Pembroke Angling Association
J Price
104 Haven Road
Haverfordwest, Dyfed

Pembroke and District Angling Club
T Caveney
Kilnbac, Angle Village
Angle, Dyfed

Pembrokeshire Anglers Association
M Gibby
22 Greenfield Close
Haverfordwest, Dyfed

Pencoed and District Angling Club
G D John
Railway Inn
Pencoed, Glamorgan

Poncian Angling Society
K Valentine
Bryn-y-Owen
Pentre Buchan
Wrexham, Clwyd
Lakes. Permits

Pontardulais and District Angling Association
E I Williams
Rosemary
Heol-y-Barna
Pontardulais, West Glamorgan
Llwchwr and Dulais

Pontrhydfendigaid Angling Association
D Lloyd Jones
Rhyd Teify
Pontrhydfendigaid, Dyfed

Pontypool and District Angling Association
A Wakeham
7 St Hilda's Road
Griffithstown
Pontypool, Gwent
Afon Llwyd. Tickets

Pontypridd and District Angling Association
T Thomas
3 Barry Road
Pwllgwaun, Pontypridd
Mid-Glam

Porthcawl Sea Angling Association
A Burch
171 New Road
Porthcawl, Glamorgan

Prince Albert Angling Society
  Queen's Hotel
  Albert Place
  Waters Green
  Macclesfield, Chesire
  Dovey, Dulas, Dysynni, Dee, Twymyn
  Some tickets
Prysor Angling Association
  D G Williams
  Bryn Gwyn
  Trawsfynydd, Gwynedd
  Prysor and Trawsfynydd Lake. Tickets
Pwllheli and District Angling Association
  G W Pritchard
  Ednyfed
  30 Lon Ceredigion, Pwllheli
  Gwynedd
  Erch, Soch, etc, tickets
Pyrddin Angling Society
  D M Jones
  4 Moorlands
  Dyffryn Cellwen
  Neath, Glamorgan
  Neath. Tickets
Rhayader Angling Association
  G H Roberts
  Belmullet, Rhayader
  Powys
  Wye, Marteg and lake. Tickets
Rhostyllen Angling Club
  J R Williams
  57 West Grove
  Rhostyllen, Wrexham
  Clwyd
Rhyl and District Angling Association
  Martin Fowell
  'Bon Amie'
  28 Ffordd Tanrallt
  Meliden
  Prestatyn, Clwyd
  Elwy and Clwyd. Permits
Rhymney and District Angling Society
  G H Roper
  72 Penbryn Avenue
  Cefn Forest
  Blackwood, Gwent NP2 1LH
  Lakes
Risca Fly Fishing Association
  Mrs J Mellor
  7 Penllwyn Street
  Cwmfelinfach, Gwent
  Sirhowy. Tickets
River Wygyr Fishing Association
  T Gillham
  2 Crown Terrace
  Llanfechell, Anglesey
Rossett and Gresford Fishers Club
  P H Long
  The Homestead

Hooton Road
  Willaston, S Wirral L64 1SG
  Members only
St Asaph Angling Club
  R C Baldwin
  6 Bryn Elwy
  St Asaph, Clwyd
  Clwyd. Members only
St Clears and District Angling Association
  David J Bryan
  Madras Cottage
  Laugharne
  Carmarthen, Dyfed SA33 4NU
  Taf. Tickets
St Helens Angling Association
  Water on Dee
  (see English list)
Seiont, Gwyrfai and Llyfni Anglers' Society
  H P Hughes
  11 Eryri Estate, Bethel
  Caernarvon, Gwynedd
  Seiont, Gwyrfai, Llyfni lakes. Tickets
Sennybridge Fishing Association
  W J Davies & Son
  Sennybridge
  Powys
  Usk Tickets
South Wales and Monmouthshire Federation of Angling Societies
  J E Palmer
  8 Caerau Park Place
  Ely, Cardiff
  Glamorgan
Strata Florida Angling Association
  D Lloyd Jones
  Rhydteify
  Pontrhydfendigaid
  Ystrad Meurig, Dyfed. Teify. Tickets
Swansea Amateur Angling Association
  D Cohen
  34 Tydraw Street
  Port Talbot
  Towy, Cothi. Tickets
Swansea Sea Angling Club
  Mrs B Walters
  279 Gwynedd Street
  Cockett, Swansea
Talsarnau and District Angling Association
  C R Jones
  4 Cilfor, Talsarnau
  Gwynedd
  Lakes
Talybont Angling Association
  Honorary Scretary
  c/o Central Stores
  Talybont, Dyfed SY24 5ER
Tawe and Tributaries Angling Association
  Michael Matthews
  32 Farm Road

Court Start
Briton Ferry
Nr Neath, West Glamorgan
Teifi Trout Association
C Jones
Emlyn House
Newcastle Emlyn, Dyfed
Teifi. St only
Trawsfynydd Lake Management Committee
H E Lewis
Castle House
Trawsfynydd, Gwynedd
Tredegar Angling Society
A S Davies
68 Queen Victoria Street
Tredegar, Gwent
Tregaron Angling Association
E G Jones
30 Maesyrawel
Tregaron, Dyfed
Teifi. Tickets
Treharris Angling Association
D L Lewis
4 Penlocks
Treharris, Glamorgan
United Usk Fishermen's Association
H J P Candler
32 Monk Street
Abergavenny, Gwent
Upper Rhondda Angling Association
D Rossiter
71 Miskin Street
Treherbert
Glamorgan

Warrington Angling Association
Dee *(see English list)*
Wentwood Reservoir Fly Fishing Association
J Blanco
7 Laurel Park
St Arvans
Chepstow, Gwent
Whitland Angling Association
R M Jones
Ivy House, Spring Gardens
Whitland, Dyfed
Wirral Game Fishing Club
P Liddiard
13 Kingswalk
West Kirby
Wirral L48
Members only
Wrexham and District Angling Association
C C Richards
104 Lear Drive
Wisaton
Crewe CW2 8DS
Alyn. Members' guests only
Wygyr Angling Association
T Gillham
Crown Terrace, Llanfechell
Anglesey
Wygyr. Tickets
Ynysddu and Cwmfelinfach Angling Club
H P Hopkins
2 Brynderwyn
Ridge Cafe
Cwmfelinfach
Sirhowy Tickets

FISHING IN SCOTLAND

District Boards and Close Season for Salmon and Trout

FISHING in Scotland is under the general jurisdiction of the Dept of Agriculture and Fisheries for Scotland, Chesser House, Gorgie Road, Edinburgh EH11 3AW.

The annual close season for **trout** in Scotland extends from October 7 to March 14, both days included. Trout may not be sold between the end of August and the beginning of April, nor at any time if the fish are less than 8 in long.

Visiting anglers are reminded that on Scottish rivers and lochs the owner of the fishing is the riparian proprietor, whose permission to fish should be obtained. The only public right of fishing for brown trout is in those portions of the rivers which are both tidal and navigable, but the right must not be exercised so as to interfere with salmon or sea-trout fishing and can be exercised only where there is a right of access to the water from a boat or from the banks.

Salmon. Provision is made in the Salmon Act, 1986, for the formation and amalgamation of District Boards, composed of representatives of proprietors of salmon fisheries in each district. These boards, the addresses of which are given on pages 274–6, are responsible for the administration and protection of the salmon fisheries in their districts, and boards have been formed for practically all the important salmon rivers. In districts in which boards have not been formed, the salmon fisheries, of which sea-trout fisheries are legally part, are under the direct control of the proprietors.

In the following list, the days fixing the start and finish of the annual close time for net fishing and for rod fishing respectively are in all cases inclusive, and, as in the case of the Add, the first river in the list, the first pair of dates are the limits of the net season and the second pair apply to rod fishing.

Add. Annual close time for net-fishing: From Sept 1 to Feb 15, both dates inclusive. Annual close time for rod-fishing: From Nov 1 to Feb 15, both days inclusive.

Ailort. Aug 27 to Feb 10; Nov 1 to Feb 10.

Aline. Aug 27 to Feb 10; Nov 1 to Feb 10.

Alness. Aug 27 to Feb 10; Nov 1 to Feb 10.

Annan. Sept 10 to Feb 24; Nov 16 to Feb 24.

Applecross. Aug 27 to Feb 10; Nov 1 to Feb 10.

Arnisdale. (Loch Hourn). Aug 27 to Feb 10; Nov 1 to Feb 10.

Awe. Aug 27 to Feb 10; Oct 16 to Feb 10.

Ayr. Aug 27 to Feb 10; Nov 1 to Feb 10.

Baa and Goladoir. Aug 27 to Feb 10; Nov 1 to Feb 10.

Badachro and Kerry (Gairloch). Aug 27 to Feb 10; Nov 1 to Feb 10.

Balgay and Shieldaig. Aug 27 to Feb 10; Nov 1 to Feb 10.

Beauly. Aug 27 to Feb 10; Oct 16 to Feb 10.

Berriedale. Aug 27 to Feb 10; Nov 1 to Feb 10.

Bervie. Sept 10 to Feb 24; Nov 1 to Feb 24.

Bladnoch. Aug 27 to Feb 10; Nov 1 to Feb 10.

Broom. Aug 27 to Feb 10; Nov 1 to Feb 10.

Brora. Aug 27 to Feb 10; Oct 16 to Jan 31.

Carradale (in Kintyre). Sept 10 to Feb 24; Nov 1 to Feb 24.

Carron (W Ross). Aug 27 to Feb 10; Nov 1 to Feb 10.

Clayburn Finnisbay, Avennangeren, Strathgravat, North Lacastile, Scalladale and Mawrig (East Harris). Sept 10 to Feb 24; Nov 1 to Feb 24.

Clyde and Leven. Aug 27 to Feb 10; Nov 1 to Feb 10.

Conon. Aug 27 to Feb 10; Oct 1 to Jan 25.

Cree. Sept 14 to last day of Feb; Oct 15 to last day of Feb.

Creed or Stornoway, and Laxay (Island of Lewis). Aug 27 to Feb 10; Oct 17 to Feb 10.

Creran (Loch Creran). Aug 27 to Feb 10; Nov 1 to Feb 10.

Croe and Shiel (Loch Duich). Aug 27 to Feb 10; Nov 1 to Feb 10.

Dee (Aberdeenshire). Aug 27 to Feb 10; Oct 1 to Jan 31.

Dee (Kirkcudbrightshire). Aug 27 to Feb 10; Nov 1 to Feb 10.

Deveron. Aug 27 to Feb 10; Nov 1 to Feb 10.

Don. Aug 27 to Feb 10; Nov 1 to Feb 10.

Doon. Aug 27 to Feb 10; Nov 1 to Feb 10.

Drummachloy or Glenmore (Isle of Bute). Sept 1 to Feb 15; Oct 16 to Feb 15.

Dunbeath. Aug 27 to Feb 10; Oct 16 to Feb 10.

Earn. Aug 21 to Feb 4; Nov 1 to Jan 31.

Echaig. Sept 1 to Feb 15; Nov 1 to Feb 15.

Esk, North. Sept 1 to Feb 15; Nov 1 to Feb 15.

Esk, South. Sept 1 to Feb 15; Nov 1 to Feb 15.

Ewe. Aug 27 to Feb 10; Nov 1 to Feb 10.

Fincastle, Meaveg, Ballanchist, South Lacastile, Borve and Obb (West Harris). Sept 10 to Feb 24; Nov 1 to Feb 24.

Findhorn. Aug 27 to Feb 10; Oct 7 to Feb 10.

Fleet (Kirkcudbrightshire). Sept 10 to Feb 24; Nov 1 to Feb 24.

Fleet (Sutherlandshire). Sept 10 to Feb 24; Nov 1 to Feb 24.

Forss. Aug 27 to Feb 10; Nov 1 to Feb 10.

Forth. Aug 27 to Feb 10; Nov 1 to Jan 31.

Fyne, Shira and Array (Loch Fyne). Sept 1 to Feb 15; Nov 1 to Feb 15.

Girvan. Sept 10 to Feb 24; Nov 1 to Feb 24.

Glenelg. Aug 27 to Feb 10; Nov 1 to Feb 10.

Gour. Aug 27 to Feb 10; Nov 1 to Feb 10.

Greiss, Laxdale or Thunga. Aug 27 to Feb 10; Nov 1 to Feb 10.

Grudie or Dionard. Aug 27 to Feb 10; Nov 1 to Feb 10.

Gruinard and Little Gruinard. Aug 27 to Feb 10; Nov 1 to Feb 10.

Halladale, Strathy, Naver and Borgie. Aug. 27 to Feb 10; Oct 1 to Jan 11.

Helmsdale. Aug 27 to Feb 10; Oct 1 to Jan 10.

Hope and Polla or Strathbeg. Aug 27 to Feb 10; Oct 1 to Jan 11.

Howmore. Sept 10 to Feb 24; Nov 1 to Feb 24.

Inchard. Aug 27 to Feb 10; Nov 1 to Feb 10.

Inner (in Jura). Sept 10 to Feb 24; Nov 1 to Feb 24.

Inver. Aug 27 to Feb 10; Nov 1 to Feb 10.

Iorsa (in Arran). Sept 10 to Feb 24; Nov 1 to Feb 24.

Irvine and Garnock. Sept 10 to Feb 24; Nov 1 to Feb 24.

Kanaird. Aug 27 to Feb 10; Nov 1 to Feb 10.

Kilchoan or Inverie (Loch Nevis). Aug 27 to Feb 10; Nov 1 to Feb 10.

Kinloch (Kyle of Tongue). Aug 27 to Feb 10; Nov 1 to Feb 10.

Kirkaig. Aug 27 to Feb 10; Nov 1 to Feb 10.

Kishorn. Aug 27 to Feb 10; Nov 1 to Feb 10.

Kyle of Sutherland. Aug 27 to Feb 10; Oct 1 to Jan 10.

Laggan and Sorn (Island of Islay). Sept 10 to Feb 24; Nov 1 to Feb 24.

Laxford. Aug 27 to Feb 10; Nov 1 to Feb 10.

Leven. Aug 27 to Feb 10; Nov 1 to Feb 10.

Little Loch Broom. Aug 27 to Feb 10; Nov 1 to Feb 10.

Loch Duich. Aug 27 to Feb 10; Nov 1 to Feb 10.

Loch Luing. Aug 27 to Feb 10; Nov 1 to Feb 10.

Loch Roag. Aug 27 to Feb 10; Oct 17 to Feb 10.

Loch Sunart. Aug 27 to Feb 10; Nov 1 to Feb 10.

Lochy. Aug 27 to Feb 10; Nov 1 to Feb 10.

Lossie. Aug 27 to Feb 10; Oct 16 to Feb 10.

Luce. Sept 10 to Feb 24; Nov 1 to Feb 24.

Lussa (Island of Mull). Aug 27 to Feb 10; Nov 1 to Feb 10.

Moidart. Aug 27 to Feb 10; Nov 1 to Feb 10.

Morar. Aug 27 to Feb 10; Nov 1 to Feb 10.

Mullanageren, Horasary and Lochnaciste (North Uist). Sept 10 to Feb 24; Nov 1 to Feb 24.

Nairn. Aug 27 to Feb 10; Oct 1 to Feb 10.

Naver and Borgie (see Halladale).

Nell, Feochan and Euchar. Aug 27 to Feb 10; Nov 1 to Feb 10.

Ness. Aug 27 to Feb 10; Oct 16 to Jan 14.

Nith. Sept 10 to Feb 24; Dec 1 to Feb 24.

Orkney Islands (river from Loch to Stenness etc). Sept 10 to Feb 24; Nov 1 to Feb 24.

Ormsary (Loch Killisport), **Loch Head, and Stornaway** (Mull of Kintyre). Aug 27 to Feb 10; Nov 1 to Feb 10.

Pennygowan or Glenforsa and Aros. Aug 27 to Feb 10; Nov 1 to Feb 10.

Resort. Aug 27 to Feb 10; Nov 1 to Feb 10.

Ruel. Sept 1 to Feb 15; Nov 1 to Feb 15.

Sanda. Aug 27 to Feb 10; Nov 1 to Feb 10.

Scaddle. Aug 27 to Feb 10; Nov 1 to Feb 10.

Shetland Islands. Sept 10 to Feb 24; Nov 1 to Feb 24.

Shiel (Loch Shiel). Aug 27 to Feb 10; Nov 1 to Feb 10.

Sligachan, Broadford and Portree (Isle of Skye). Aug 27 to Feb 10; Nov 1 to Feb 10.

Snizort, Orley, Oze and Drynoch (Isle of Skye). Aug 27 to Feb 10; Nov 1 to Feb 10.

Spey. Aug 27 to Feb 10; Oct 1 to Feb 10.

Stinchar. Sept 10 to Feb 24; Nov 1 to Feb 24.

Tay (except Earn). Aug 21 to Feb 4; Oct 16 to Jan 14.

Thurso. Aug 27 to Feb 10; Oct 6 to Jan 10.

Torridon, Balgay and Shieldaig. Aug 27 to Feb 10; Nov 1 to Feb 10.

Tweed. Sept 15 to Feb 14; Dec 1 to Jan 31.

Ugie. Sept 10 to Feb 24; Nov 1 to Feb 9.

Ullapool (Loch Broom). Aug 27 to Feb 10; Nov 1 to Feb 10.

Urr. Sept 10 to Feb 24; Nov 30 to Feb 24.

Wick. Aug 27 to Feb 10; Nov 1 to Feb 10.

Ythan. Sept 10 to Feb 24; Nov 1 to Feb 10.

DISTRICT FISHERY BOARDS

The names, addresses and telephone numbers of the clerks of the various salmon district fishery boards in Scotland are as follows: Please note that their duties are purely to operate the Acts and that they do not have fishing to let.

Alness District Board. W H Cormack, Messrs Mackenzie and Cormack, 20 Tower Street, Tain, Ross-shire IV19 1DZ (Tel 0862 2046).

Annan District Board. James E M Stevenson, McJerrow and Stevenson, Solicitors, 55 High Street, Lockerbie, Dumfriesshire DG11 2JJ (05762 2123/4).

Awe District Board. T C McNair; MacArthur, Stewart & Co, Solicitors, Boswell House, Argyll Square, Oban, Argyllshire PA34 4BD. (Tel 0631 62215.)

Ayr District Board. G Hay, D & J Dunlop, 2 Barns Street, Ayr KA7 1XD, (Tel 0292 264091).

Bervie District Board. R M Ross, SSC, Messrs Campbell, Middleton, Burness & Dickson, Clydesdale Bank Buildings, 112 High Street, Montrose, Angus, DD10 8JH (Tel 0674 72929).

Bladenoch District Board. Peter M Murray, A B & A Matthews, Bank of Scotland Buildings, Newton Stewart, Wigtownshire DG8 6EG. (0671 3013.)

Broom District Board. Middleton, Ross and Arnot, Solicitors, PO Box 8, Mansfield House, Dingwall, Ross-shire IV15 9HJ (0349 62214).

Brora District Board. G J P Mason, Sutherland Estates Office, Golspie, Sutherland, KW10 6RR (Tel 04083 3268).

Clayburn District Board. A G Scherr, Borve Cottage, Isle of Harris PA85 3HT (0859 85202).

Conon District Board. Miles Larby, Finlayson Hughes, 45 Church Street, Inverness (Tel 0463 224343).

Cree District Board. G Davies, Messrs McCormick & Nicholson, Solicitors, 6 Victoria Street, Newton Stewart, Wigtownshire.

Creed or Stornoway and Laxay District Board. G MacDonald, Secretary, Stornoway Trust, Estate Office, 20 Cromwell Street, Stornoway, Isle of Lewis. (0851 2002.)

Creran District Board. J A M Smith, McGrigor and Donald, Solicitors, Pacific House, 70 Wellington St, Glasgow G2 6SB (041 2486677).

Dee (Aberdeen) District Board. J G Innes, 7 Golden Square, Aberdeen AB9 8SP (Tel 0224 641065).

Dee (Kirkcudbright) District Board. J W Campbell, New Cottages, St Mary's Isle, Kirkcudbright (0557 3024).

Deveron District Board. A Gibb, Solicitor, 29 Low Street, Banff AB4 1AX (02612 2457/2101).

Don District Board. G Alpine, Messrs Paull & Williamson, Solicitors, 6 Union Road, Aberdeen AB9 8DQ (Tel 0224 631414).

Doon District Board. H S Campbell, Messrs R & J A MacCallum, Solicitors, 8 Alloway Place, Ayr KA7 2AF (02922 69131).

Dunbeath District Board. Colin Scott, Old Garth, Dunbeath, Caithness (059 33 256).

Eachaig District Board, A T M Cairns, Lochloy House, Nairn, IV12 5LE (Tel 0667 55355).

Esk (North) District Board. R Murray Ross, Messrs Campbell, Middleton Burness & Dickson, Clydesdale Bank Chambers, 112 High Street, Montrose, Angus DD10 8JH (Tel 06747 2929).

Esk (South) District Board.R Murray Ross, Messrs Campbell, Middleton Burness & Dickson, Clydesdale Bank Chambers, 112 High Street, Montrose, Angus DD10 8JH (Tel 06747 2929).

Ewe District Board. Middleton, Ross and Arnot, Solicitors, PO Box 8, Mansfield House, Dingwall, Ross-shire IV15 9HJ (0349 62214).

Fincastle District Board. A J Scherr, Borve Lodge, Isle of Harris PA85 3HT (085985 202).

Findhorn District Board. W A Taylor, Messrs Mackenzie & Grant, Solicitor, Royal Bank Buildings, Forres, Morayshire IV36 0PD (0309 72126).

Fleet (Kirkcudbright) District Board. G Davies, McCormick & Nicholson, Solicitors, 66 Victoria Street, Newton Stewart, Wigtownshire.

Forss District Board. A T M Cairns, Lochloy House, Nairn IV 12 5LE (Tel 0667 55355).

Forth District Board. Henry Robb, LLB, Messrs Hill & Robb, 3 Pitt Terrace, Stirling FK8 2EY (0786 70985).

Girvan District Board. T L Wilson; Murray & Tait, Procurator Fiscal's Office, Girvan, Ayrshire (0465 3118).

Gruide or Doinard District Board. W H Cormack, Mackenzie & Cormack, Solicitors, 20 Tower Street, Tain IV19 1D2 (0862 2046).

Gruinard and Little Gruinard District Board. Messrs. Middleton, Ross and Arnot, Solicitors, PO Box 8, Mansfield House, Dingwall, Ross-shire IV15 9HJ (0349 62214).

Helmsdale District Board. John Douglas-Menzies, Mounteagle, Fearn, Ross-shire IV20 1RP (Tel 086 283 2213).

Hope and Polla District Board. Middleton, Ross and Arnot, Solicitors, PO Box 8, Mansfield House, Dingwall, Ross-shire IV15 9HJ (0349 62214).

Inchard District Board. N W Buchannan, J & F Anderson, Solicitors, 48 Castle St, Edinburgh EH2 3LX (031 225 3912).

Kinloch District Board. A Sykes, Messrs J & F Anderson, Solicitors, 48 Castle Street, Edinburgh EH3 8HA.

Kyle of Sutherland District Board. W H Cormack, Messrs Mackenzie & Cormack, Solicitors, 20 Tower Street, Tain, Ross-shire IV19 1DZ (Tel 0862 2046).

Laxford District Board, J D O Fulton, Todd & Murray WS, 66 Queens Street, Edinburgh EH2 4NE (031 226 4771).

Leven District Board. J Sutherland, McGregor, Donald & Co, Solicitors, PO Box 38, 224 Ingram Street, Glasgow G1 15P (041 248 5981).

Loch Roag District Board. G MacDonald, Stornoway Trust, Estate Office, 20 Cromwell Street, Stornoway, Isle of Lewis PA87 2DD (08 512002).

Loch Shiel District Board. E T Cameron Kennedy, 95 Bothwell Street, Glasgow G2 7JH (Tel 041 204 1231).

Lochy District Board. Messrs MacArthur, Stewart & Co, Solicitors, 87 High Street, Fort William, Inverness-shire.

Lossie District Board. A J McCartan, MacKenzie & Grant, Solicitors, Royal Bank Buildings, Forres, Moray IV36 OPD (0309 72126).

Luce District Board. E A Fleming-Smith, Stair Estate Office, Rephad, Stranraer, Wigtownshire DG9 8BX (Tel 0776 2040).

Mullanagearan District Board. D Shaughnessy, Estate Office, Lochmaddy, Isle of North Uist. (0876 3324.)

Morar District Board. M H Spence, 8 New Square, Lincoln's Inn, London WC2A 3QP (Tel 01-242 4986).

Nairn District Board. A de Candia, Cawdor Estates, Nairn IV12 5RE (Tel 06677 666).

Naver and Borgie District Board. W McEwan, 105 Culduthel Road, Inverness (046 323 0435).

Ness District Board. J O Waddell, Messrs Anderson, Shaw & Gilbert, Solicitors, 20 Church Street, Inverness IV1 1ED (046 3236123).

Nith District Board. E G Fenwick, Messrs Saint & Co, Chartered Surveyors, 26 Castle Street, Dumfries DG1 1EN (Tel 0387 55477/8).

Spey District Board. C D R Whittle, Messrs R & R Urquhart, 121 High Street, Forres, Morayshire IV36 0AB (Tel 0309 72216).

Stinchar District Board. T L Wilson, 1 Church Square, Girvan, Ayrshire KA26 9HB (Tel 0465 3118).

Tay District Board. Condie Mackenzie & Co, Solicitors, 2 Tay Street, Perth PH1 5LJ (Tel 0738 33171).

Thurso District Board, P J W Blackwood, Estate Office, Thurso East, Thurso, Caithness KW14 8HW (Tel 0847 63134).

Tweed Commissioners. J H Leeming ARICS, River Tweed Commissioners, Quayside, Berwick-upon-Tweed TD15 1HE (Tel 0298 305475).

Ugie District Board. C T Macrae, Messrs Gray & Gray, Bath House, Bath Street, Peterhead, Aberdeenshire AB4 6BY (Tel 0779 72376).

Ullapool District Board. Middleton, Ross and Arnot, Solicitors, PO Box 8, Mansfield House, Dingwall, Ross-shire IV15 9HJ (0349 62214).

Wick District Board. T P Buick, Messrs D W Georgeson & Son, Solicitors, 22 Bridge Street, Wick, Caithness KW1 4NL (Tel 0955 2442).

Ythan District Board. Capt C A Farquharson, Estate Office, Haddo House, Aberdeen AB4 0ER (Tel 06515 664/5).

Note. Anglers visiting Scotland to fish for coarse fish should note that it is not, in certain districts, lawful to fish with two or more rods simultaneously. The rule is one rod only.

The characteristic "kype" of a cock salmon in Autumn. *Photograph: John Marchington.*

SCOTTISH FISHING STATIONS

THE nature of Scotland with its many rivers and lochs, especially on the west coast, makes it impracticable in some cases to deal with each river's catchment area separately. Thus some fisheries on the west coast north of the Firth of Clyde are grouped under the heading "West Coast Rivers and Lochs".

The need again arises to decide whether a river should be included in England or Scotland. The Border Esk is dealt with in the English section, together with the Kirtle and the Sark, which happen to fall within the Esk's catchment area on the map. The Tweed and *all* its tributaries are included in this Scottish section. All the Scottish Islands, including Shetland and Orkney, are considered as within one watershed, viz, "The Islands", in which, for convenience, Kintyre is included. The exact position in the book of any river or fishing station can, of course, readily be found by reference to the index.

In a previous edition of this directory all place-name references were changed to reflect the then new terminologies arising from local government reorganisation. As it has been made abundantly clear to us by local referees who supply the information on which "Where to Fish" is based, while these may have taken root in some parts of Britain they have not done so in Scotland north and west of the Forth and Clyde valleys. We have, therefore, reverted in this edition, where appropriate, to the older terminology, to conform with continuing local practice.

ALNESS

Rises 4 miles west of Loch Morie and flows 12 miles to Cromarty Firth at Alness. Salmon, sea trout, brown trout.

Alness (Ross & Cromarty). Highland and Islands Development Board has acquired water here, which is administered by Alness AC. Dt and wt. Worm and fly only. Hotels: Station, Novar Arms, Evanton.

Evanton (Ross & Cromarty). Factor, Novar Estates Office, issues permits for two private beats; fly only; fishing let by the day and the week. Dt from £10–£15, according to month.

ANNAN

Rises in Moffat Hills and flows about 30 miles to Solway Firth. Good spring salmon, sea trout in May and June. Good herling in July and August, and salmon in late autumn; brown trout.

Annan (Dumfries & Galloway). Newbie Estates water. River above bridge; limited dt from Newbie Mill. River south of bridge now let to Annan AC, which also has a reservoir; members only. Castle Milk water: particulars and permits from Castle Milk Estates, Norwood, Lockerbie *(see also Lockerbie)*. Dt £6, £5.25 and £3.30 VAT incl for Hoddom and Kinmount Estate waters at Newbie Mill and Hoddom. Feb, March, April and Oct best for salmon; May, June, July best for sea trout and brown trout; herling in July and Aug. Full details

from Mr T Bayley, Newbie Mill (Tel: 2608). 2½m W of Annan, **Kelhead Quarry:** trout and coarse fish. Dt £2 on site. Queensbury Arms can arrange permits.

Ecclefechan (Dumfries & Galloway). Annan, 2m SW; salmon, herling (late July onwards), brown trout. River preserved from here to sea *(see Annan)*. Dt for Hoddom Castle water (over 2m) may be booked from river watcher, Hoddom Bridge Cottage (tel: 05763 488). Limited to 15 rods daily. Charge £4.50–£6.50 per day. Fly only, except when river height is above white line at Hoddom Bridge, when spinning permitted. Hoddom & Kinmount Estates also own Purdomstone Reservoir, brown trout; dt £6.50 per boat (2 rods per boat): and Kelhead Water, brown and rainbow trout; dt £2. Apply Estate Office, Hoddom, Lockerbie. **Water of Milk,** 4m W *(see Lockerbie).* At a short distance is the **Kirtle Water** trout. *(See Border Esk in English section.)* Hotel: Ecclefechan, where permits are available for Castle Milk waters.

Lockerbie (Dumfries & Galloway). Annan $1\frac{1}{2}$m W; salmon, sea trout, brown trout. Castle Milk Estate water. Three beats on Annan, one on **River Milk.** St £100, £60, £6. Wt £20, £40 and £2. Dt £5, £4 and £1. Full details from Factor (Tel: 057 65 203). McJerrow and Stevenson, Solicitors, Lockerbie, issue permits for Halleaths water; wt £14, st £75; fly only. Hoddom and Kinmoun Estates, Lockerbie, may have rods and fishing cottages to let; inquire of the Factor. **Black Esk Reservoir:** bank fishing only; fly and spinner only; dt £1.50. Apply J D Medcalf, Hart Manor Hotel, Eskdalemuir, Dumfriesshire and J Crowsen, Sandyford Cottage, Sandyford, Lockerbie. Applegirth Water on Annan, **Kinnell Water** and **Dryfe Water;** now taken over by Upper Annandale AA. Limited st £40, wt £20 and £12, dt (until Sep 15) £3. Tackleist: Gordon's Sports, High Street; permits from former for Upper Annan fishing. Hotels: Dinwoodie Lodge (can arrange fishing), King's Arms, Crown, Bluebell, Townhead, Somerton House, Lockerbie House, Queen's, Red House, Wamphray.

Lochmaben (Dumfries & Galloway). Salmon, sea trout, trout, chub (good). Coarse fishing on **Castle Loch**; dt and wt from Warden, Lochfield. Salmon and trout fishing on Annan also available on

Castle Loch Estate, apply to McJerrow & Stevenson, 55 High St, Lockerbie *(advt below).* Royal Four Towns water, Hightae. Salmon seaon, Feb 25 to Nov 15; trout, March 15 to Oct 6. Tickets: restricted (no parties) wt £15, dt £3; from Clerk, Kathleen Ratcliffe, Jay-Ar, Preston House Road, Hightae-Lockerbie. **Kennell Water,** 3m; salmon, sea trout and trout, Upper Annandale AA water. Permits from hotels and J Graham, Millhousebridge. Permits for **River Ae,** from Wilson, Esbie Farm. No Sunday fishing in rivers. Hotels: Kings Arms; Balcastle; Crown.

Wamphray (Dumfries & Galloway). 4m of R Annan *(see Moffat)* controlled by Upper Annandale AA. Permits from hon sec and Red House Hotel: dt £3, wt £25 and £12. Limited st at £30.

Beattock (Dumfries & Galloway). Upper Annandale AA water on river. Auchen Castle Hotel can arrange fishing on river and has trout loch in grounds.

Moffat (Dumfries & Galloway). Upper Annandale AA controls $\frac{1}{2}$m of **Little Annan,** 1m of **Moffat Water,** from Meeting of Waters; 4m **Annan** from Meeting of Waters. Salmon: dt £3, wt £25 and £12, st £30 (no dt for salmon after Sept 15). Tickets from hon sec and other local sources; reductions for juveniles. Fly only for trout, sea trout and herling in April and Sept. Spinning allowed from Feb 25 to Sept 30 when water level is not below white lines marked on bridges. Salmon season best August onwards; sea trout July onwards. No Sunday fishing. Hotels: Elmhill (fishing arranged in Annan, and Moffat), Annandale Arms, Moffat House, Buccleuch Arms, Red House, Balmoral, Star, Moffat Mercury. Tackleist: Helen Smith, Hairdresser, Well St, Moffat.

AWE and LOCH AWE and LOCH ETIVE

A short river, but one of best-known salmon streams of west coast. Connects Loch Awe to sea by way of Loch Etive, which it enters at Bonawe. River fishes best from July onwards.

Taynuilt (Argyll). Salmon, sea trout, trout. Taynuilt Hotel has fishing for salmon and sea trout. Polfearn Hotel is convenient for Loch Etive. Inverawe Fisheries (Tel 08662 262) have 1m on river and three lochs stocked with rainbow trout. Wt and dt, with part-day and father/son concessions. Tuition, tackle for hire and refreshments available. Dalavich, by Taynuilt. Fishing on L Awe is available: **R Avich** dt £2 (trout only to Aug 31 £1), bank fishing **L Avich** £1. Apply Forestry Commission, Cabins Reception, Dalavich, who can also advise on boat hire.

Connel (Argyll). Ossian's Hotel, newly built, overlooks Loch Etive; salmon, sea trout, brown trout. Fishing also from Falls of Lora Hotel.

LOCH AWE:

Lochawe (Argyll). Fishing on Awe and **Orchy,** for guests at Carraig Thura

Hotel. Dt on river for non-residents (as available) £7.

Lochaweside (Argyll). Taychreggan Hotel on lochside, has salmon, sea trout, brown trout and coarse fishing on Lochs Awe and **Etive,** for guests. Fish run to good size. Boat with outboard; a few gillies available. Good sea fishing.

Kilchrenan. Bank fishing on L Nant (two mile walk) bookable from Trading Post. £1 per day. Ardanaiseig Hotel arranges fishing.

Portsonachan (Argyll). Portsonachan Hotel on shore of Loch Awe has fishing in loch; trout, salmon, sea trout, perch pike. Boats £8 per day available to hotel guests. Salmon fishing and fishing on hill lochs also arranged.

Ford (Argyll). **Cam** and other hill lochs: bank fishing dt £2. **R Liever;** dt £2. Permits; in office hours from D Murray, Ford Hotel and Cabins' Manageress, Village Hall, Dalavich.

Tributaries of the Awe

ORCHY: Good salmon, few large trout.

Dalmally (Argyll). River flows into Loch Awe here, excellent salmon fishing in May, June, Sept and Oct. Loch Awe holds salmon, trout, perch, pike, sea trout.

Inveroran (Argyll). On Loch Tulla, but

2m from the River Orchy; salmon, trout. The salmon fishing in the Orchy is good in the autumn but, given good water, July is the best month. Upper Orchy no good before mid-June. There are a few trout in the river and those large. Hotel: Inveroran. Fishing in lake and 2m of Orchy for residents (April 1 to Oct 31).

AYR

Rises in Glenbuck and flows into Firth of Clyde through town of Ayr opposite south end of Isle of Arran. Good brown trout river (av $\frac{1}{2}$ lb) with fair runs of salmon and sea trout.

Ayr. Mostly preserved, but tickets (wt £4, dt £1.50) can be had for $\frac{3}{4}$m water at Ayr from the Director of Finance, Kyle and Carrick DC, Town Buildings, Ayr, and from tackleists *(see below)*. Up-river water club fishing for members only. Wading essential for good sport. Water restocked with brown trout by Ayr AC. About 3m N at Prestwick, dt can be had for Prestwick AC water on **Prestwick Reservoir;** trout, $\frac{3}{4}$ lb to $3\frac{1}{2}$ lb; restocked

monthly; fishes best in evening. Tickets from Red Lion Hotel, Prestwick; Wheatsheaf Hotel, Monkton. St £11, dt £3. Concessions for OAP and jun. Good and free pike and perch fishing can be had on various lochs within 10m of Ayr. At **Drongan** (10m ESE) Drongan Youth Group AC issues permits at small charge for **River Coyle** (sea trout, trout, grayling, few salmon) and **Snipe Loch** (brown and rainbow trout stocked weekly) apply

H Lees, 2 Reid Place and Snipe Loch. Brown trout fishing on **Lochs Bradan, Skelloch, Brechbowie** and **Dhu** (Ayr 20m); Lochs Bradan and Skelloch stocked. Wt £9 (£4.50 jun), dt £3 (£1.50 jun), boat from £3 extra. Pike fishing on **L Linfern:** apply Heaney, Tallaminnoch, Straiton, Maybole, Tel: 06555 7616 or Forestry Commission, Tel 0465 86223. **Penwhapple Reservoir,** near Barr, stocked with brown trout; water of Penwhapple AC. Dt £4, boats £1 per 4 hours, apply J Murray, 3 Dalrymple St, Girvan, or at loch. 3m S of Ayr is **River Doon,** at Alloway. Good salmon and sea trout (July onwards). Burns Monument Hotel, Alloway, has stretch. Otherwise private. Loch Doon is 20m S; 6m long; good free trout fishing early months; boats at Dalmellington village. Tacklelists: Gamesport, 60 Sandgate, Ayr, and James

Kirk, 25 Kyle Street, Prestwick, from whom tickets for town and other waters on Rivers Ayr and Doon can be obtained and for coarse fish lochs. Wt £3.50, dt £1.30.

Catrine (Ayrshire). Trout, grayling; some migratory fish. Club: Catrine AC; limited wt and dt.

Mauchline (Ayrshire). Permits from S Wallace, Kilmarnock Road, for fishing on Ayr and **Cessnock Water.**

Sorn (Ayrshire). Sorn AC has 5m on Ayr, both banks; trout, grayling, some salmon and sea trout late in season. St £6, wt £3, dt £1.50 to visitors staying in town. Accommodation at Sorn Inn.

Muirkirk (Ayrshire). Trout, grayling; tickets, from hon sec, Muirkirk AA; water restocked annually. Association also has fishing on **River Greenock;** trout and grayling.

Tributary of the Ayr

LUGAR: Salmon, sea trout, trout, grayling.

Ochiltree (Ayrshire). Trout, grayling; some salmon and sea trout; Aug and Sept best. Ochiltree AA has Lugar and tributaries: limited membership. Auchinleck AA has 4m on **R Lugar** and 2m on **R Ayr.** Also **Tarmac Lodge** (brown trout). Dt from hon sec.

Cumnock (Ayrshire). Cumnock and Dist AA controls several miles of Lugar and its tributaries (Bello and Glaisnock) and two small lochs. Trout in Lugar and salmon and sea trout; restocked annually from association's hatchery. Tickets: from hon sec. Association also has **Boreland Reservoirs** (2), well stocked with trout; permit from hon sec or tacklelists. Hotels: Dumfries Arms, Royal.

BEAULY

Beauly proper is about 9m long, being formed by junction of Glass and Farrar. Flows into Beauly Firth and thence into Moray Firth. Good salmon and sea trout, April to October.

Beauly (Inverness). All fishing on the Beauly is owned by Lovat Estates and let in various beats. The principal ones are the Home, Falls and the Downie on the lower reaches: salmon, grilse, sea trout, and finnock. Kilmorack Ex-Servicemen's AA fish two days a week on the Tidal

Beat. The river is fly only except estuary beats where spinning is allowed. St £35, wt £15, dt £6–£4. Day tickets from £3 from Lovat Estate Office for tidal, estuary, and other river and loch beats. Good sea trout from the beginning of the season.

POLLUTION

Anglers are united in deploring pollution. To combat it, urgent action may be called for at any time from any one of us. If numbers of fish are found dead, dying, or seriously distressed, take samples of both fish and water and contact the office of the Director of Scientific Services at the appropriate Regional Water Authority.

THE ROYAL MARINE HOTEL
Golf Road, Brora. Tel. No.: 0408 21252
"The North's Favourite Golfing & Fishing Hotel"
Every comfort for River, Sea, Loch, fishers. Own boat, drying room. Bedrooms have Teletext T.Vs, Radios, Tea-makers, Baths, Sports Centre has heated swimming pool, curling rink, billiards, pool. Chef's cuisine in Sir Robert Lorimer dining room. Phone for booking or brochure and breaks tariff. **Telex 76165.**

Tributary of the Beauly

CANNICH:

Cannich (Inverness). At confluence of Cannich and Affric. Guests at Glen Affric Hotel can have salmon fishing on 4m of **River Glass**, 5m on **River Farrar** and trout fishing on **Lochs Benevean, Mullardoch, Monar** and hill lochs. Dt from £3 (T) and £8.25 (S). Permits for Loch Benevean (two rods), also from Sports Stores, Inglis Street, Inverness. Craigard Hotel, Boat of Garten PH24 3BP issues permits (wt £27, dt £9) for 6m of **Spey**, both banks, Dt £8 for **Lochs Vaa** and **Dallas**; £3 for **Avielochan**. Concessions for junior.

BERVIE

Rises on Glen Farquhar Estate and flows 14m to North Sea near Inverbervie. Salmon, sea trout, autumn best for salmon and Aug–Sept for sea trout.

Inverbervie (Kincardine). Trout, sea trout, salmon (best Sept–Oct) permits for foreshore from Joseph Johnston & Sons, 3 America Street, Montrose, for fortnightly periods (restricted; advance booking advised). River permits from Burgh Office, Church St.

Fordoun (Kincardine). Laurencekirk AA has rights upstream to Glenbervie, downstream to Arbuthnott. Limited guest tickets available, wt £10, dt £2.50.

BRORA

After being joined by tributaries Blackwater and Skinsdale, Brora flows through Loch Brora and into sea at Brora. Blackwater enters Brora about two miles above loch (at Balnacoil Lodge) on Gordonbush Estate. All fishing rights on both banks, extending for about 10m, owned by estate. Other tributary, the Skinsdale, flows into Blackwater six miles above Balnacoil. Rights on this river also owned by Gordonbush Estate. Noted salmon and sea trout waters. Good throughout season for salmon; two runs of sea trout, large ones in June to July and finnock in August to Sept. Loch fishing best June to Sept. Brown trout small.

Brora (Sutherland). Salmon, sea trout. Gordonbush Estate owns the sole fishing rights, on both banks, between Loch Brora and Blackwater junction (2m). Salmon catch on this beat averages more than 400. Estate lets north bank from sea to loch and both banks from loch to Balnacoil; also both banks of Blackwater and Skinsdale, with or without Balnacoil Lodge. Also boats by day or longer periods on **Loch Brora** (Brora 21345). Apply Gordonbush Estates Office, Brora, for salmon, sea trout, char and brown trout fishing. Hotels at Brora have boats on loch. Sutherland Estates,

Golspie (Golspie 268) owns south bank of Lower Brora from sea to Loch Brora and let four rods; also Upper Brora for about 5m (both banks) from Balnacoil Ford to Dalreavoch Lodge, let with or without lodge. Loch fishing available. Estate also owns upper **Blackwater** at Benarmine, again let with loch fishing and with Benarmine Lodge. Golspie AC has salmon and trout fishing. Permits from tackleists. Tidal stretch open to public for salmon and sea-trout fishing from 1 June (closed Sundays). Brora and Golspie AC have boats on **Loch Brora**. Also several estate and hotel boats.

Golspie AC has boat on **Loch Lundie,** and **Loch Horn.** Dt £3, st £5, entitling holders to reduced boat charges. Tackleists: Lindsay's, Golspie; Rob

Wilson, Brora. Hotels: Royal Marine *(advt p 281),* Links and Sutherland Arms, Brora.

CARRON (Grampian)

Rises in Glenbervie and flows about 9m to the North Sea at Stonehaven. Trout.

Stonehaven (Kincardine). About $2\frac{1}{2}$m brown trout fishing available to visitors from Stonehaven and Dist AA. Permits also issued for **River Cowie** (about $1\frac{1}{4}$m);

sea trout, finnock. Best July, August and Sept. Good sea fishing. Numerous hotels and boarding houses.

CLYDE

Rises near watershed of Tweed and Annan, and flows about 50m to the Atlantic by way of Glasgow. Once a famous salmon river, but long since spoiled by pollution. Trout and grayling fishing passable, especially in higher reaches. The Clyde's most famous tributary, the Leven,

The R. Orchy at the Bridge of Orchy. *Photo: John Tarlton.*

which connects with Loch Lomond, still has run of salmon and sea trout. In north-west corner of Renfrewshire is Loch Thom, linked by water spill with Loch Compensation, which, when water is high, drains into River Kip in Shielhill Burn. United Clyde Angling Protective Association Ltd, controls much of Clyde and tributaries. Association has hatchery and rearing pond, and restocks annually. Avon AC, Stonehouse, Lanarkshire, controls leases on Avon.

Greenock (Strathclyde). On estuarial Clyde. Greenock and District AC preserves **Loch Thom** (365 acres, trout—three to the pound). Also rights on **Compensation Reservoir** (38 acres, trout). **Yetts, No. 8 and No. 6** (Spring Dam); good trout. Permits from hon sec, tackleist or waterman at Loch Thom, or farmers on loch side. Club membership restricted to persons resident in Greenock and district, but permits available to visitors; Sunday fishing; no parties. Fly only on all club waters during season (March 15 to Oct 6). Good sea fishing—cod, skate, dogfish, conger, haddock and plaice. Tackleist: Findlay & Co, 25 West Stewart St, Greenock, who also issue tickets.

Port Glasgow (Strathclyde). On Clyde estuary. **Lower Loch Gryffe** (72 acres), **Knocknair** (10 acres), **Harelaw** (23 acres) preserved by Port Glasgow AC. Wt £5, dt £1 from hon sec.

Glasgow (Strathclyde). Glasgow has excellent trout, sea trout and salmon fishing within a radius of 60m. Lochs Lomond, Dochart, Awe, Tay, Ard, Leven, Lubnaig, Vennacher, Lake of Menteith, etc, and Rivers Annan, Goil, Cur (head of Loch Eck), Clyde (trout and grayling only), Teith, Tweed, Allan, Dochart, Leven, Kinglass etc, all accessible from here. Coarse fishing in Forth-Clyde canal; roach and perch. United Clyde Angling Protective Association Ltd, issues season tickets for a number of waters locally, apply hon sec or tackleists. **Lochend Loch, Coatbridge** (Monklands Dist water); Pike, perch, some trout. Dt £1 from Drumpellier Country Park Pursuit Centre, Townhead Rd, Coatbridge. At **Kilsyth** Kilsyth FPA issue £3 st and £1 dt for **Birkenhead Reservoir, Townhead Reservoir,** Banton Loch, and **Garrel Burn;** boats on **Banton Loch** (trout); two sessions daily; permits and boats £2 per session from Coachman Hotel, Parkfoot Street, Kilsyth. **Carron Dam,** 5m away; good trout; dt (from boat only): **Carron Water;** free; good trout fishing: **Luggie Water;** trout; dt, details from Central Regional Council,

Viewforth, Stirling. Coarse fishing on Black Loch. Strathclyde RC, Water Dept, 419 Balmore Rd, Glasgow G22 6NU, issues permits at £6.50 per day including boat, for **Loch Katrine, Arklet** and **Glen Finglas Reservoir;** fly fishing from boat only. At **Lennoxtown.** Campsie AC has trout fishing on **River Glazert,** burns and ponds. Dt and st from hon sec. Walton AC has water on **White Cart;** brown trout; members only. At **Airdrie** local club stocks two reservoirs—**Hillend** and **Lily Loch**—with Loch Leven and brown trout average 1 lb. For Hillend Reservoir apply to Airdrie AC and for Lily Loch apply to Clarkston Independent AC. Both waters shared with Blackridge AC; dt £2, st £10 from Auchengray Lodge, Forrestfield Hotel, Truff Inn and Eastercroft Hotel—all at lochside. Boats available on Hillend Loch apply G Scott (tel: 0236 843266). **Whittlemuir Dam** now leased to Howwood Industries, Midton Road, Howwood. **Daer Reservoir** (trout); no bank fishing; fly only; dt £10 for boat (plus £6 for outboard engine), apply McMraw, Mills & Co, 1 Orchard Street, Motherwell. **Roughrigg Reservoir** (pike and perch). For tickets apply to Donald Marketing Services, Trading Estate, 2 Main Street, Caldercruix, nr Airdrie. Glasgow tackleists: Hardy Bros and John Dickson & Son, Royal Exchange Square; Cafaro Bros, 37 Cowcaddens Street; Arthur Allan, 3 West Nile Street; Robertson, 27 Wellington Street; Anglers Rendezvous, 24 Parnie Street; Lawrie Renfrew, 514 Gt Western Road; Scottish Angling Services, 367 Paisley Road; J Pitcher, 402 Dunbarton Road; McKendricks Sports, 8 Alexandra Arcade, East Kilbride.

Paisley (Strathclyde). Good trout fishing in **Glenburn** and **Muirhead Reservoirs,** dt £2, **Camphill Reservoir** (£6.50 per boat, 2 rods), **Rowbank** and **Barcraigs Reservoirs** (dt £4) all tickets from Strathclyde RC, Lower Clyde DIV—Water Dept, 19 Underwood Road, Paisley PA3 1TQ. Tackle and information from Pitcher's Sports Shop, Moss Street. Hotels:

Brabloch and Rockfield, both Renfrew Road.

Strathavon (Strathclyde). Avon and Clyde; trout and grayling; st from UCAPA for water on Clyde. Avon AC controls Avon. *(See also Carstairs.)*

Lanark (Strathclyde). Trout, grayling (trout av 6 ozs, grayling $\frac{1}{2}$ lb). Lanark AA has stretch from Kirkfieldbank Bridge to Upper Shoals. Permits from hon sec and water bailiffs, st and dt. Trout and grayling.

Carstairs (Strathclyde). Trout and grayling; st from United Clyde APA, good baskets of trout on minnow and fly. *(See also Thankerton.)*

Thankerton (Strathclyde). Permits for 9m of water from Thankerton to Roberton

from hon sec, Lamington AIA, bailiffs or Bryden Newsagent, Biggar; st £13, wt £6, dt £2.50; trout and grayling. Concessions for OAP and junior. UCAPA water below Thankerton. *(See Carstairs.)*

Biggar (Strathclyde). $1\frac{1}{2}$m to Clyde; tickets from Lamington AA. Other Assn water at **Lamington, Symington** and **Roberton** *(see Thankerton)*. Hotels: Hartree; Toftcombs; Tinto and Wyndales House, Symington; Shieldhill, Biggar. Tackleist: Bryden, Newsagent, High Street.

Abington (Lanark). Trout and grayling; UCAPA water. Other Assn water at **Crawford** and **Elvanford.** Hotel: Abington.

Tributaries of the Clyde

LEVEN AND LOCH LOMOND: Salmon, trout, pike and perch.

Loch Lomond (Strathclyde). Good trout, sea trout and salmon fishing (also perch and pike) can be had from various centres on loch. Under control of Loch Lomond Angling Improvement Assn, 29 St. Vincent Place, Glasgow G1 2DT (Tel: 041 221 0068). Fishing reserved for full members only (entrance fee £11.50, subscription £72) in Loch Lomond, Rivers Leven, **Fruin** and **Falloch** and some stretches of **Endrick.** Dt are issued for Leven and Loch Lomond (£6.50) at all local centres. St and wt also obtainable for Leven. Wt £20. No Sunday fishing. Dt from tackleists, boat hirers and hotels. Late April and May earliest for fly on Loch Lomond (sea trout and salmon). Permits for pike, perch and roach fishing are free during salmon and trout close seasons. Otherwise £6.50 per day, £20 per week. Apply Loch Lomond AIA. Hotels at **Tarbert** (Dunbarton), **Inversnaid** and **Rowardennan,** by Balmaha (Stirling) are convenient for loch; permits and boats. All prices VAT incl.

Balloch (Strathclyde). Trout, good sea trout and salmon fishing on River Leven and Loch Lomond; large perch and pike in loch; fishing controlled by Loch Lomond AIA *(see Loch Lomond)*. Hotels: Tullichewan, Balloch; boat available.

FRUIN: (tributary of Loch Lomond):

Helensburgh (Strathclyde). Trout, sea trout and salmon fishing; sub £72 + entrance fee, issued by Loch Lomond AIA *(see*

Loch Lomond). Helensburgh AC has water; members only. Tackleist: Le Sport.

Ardlui (Dunbarton). Trout, sea trout and salmon fishing in Loch Lomond. Hotel: Ardlui.

ENDRICK: (tributary of Loch Lomond):

Killearn (Stirling). Good trout, sea trout and salmon fishing. Loch Lomond AIA has water; st £72 covers all assn waters; waiting list and entrance fee of £11.50 payable when vacancy notified. All prices incl VAT *(see Loch Lomond)*.

GRYFE (or GRYFFE): Trout and grayling.

Bridge of Weir (Strathclyde). Bridge of Weir River AC issue mt, wt, dt for 4m of water. Bridge of Weir Loch AC; no tickets.

Kilmacolm (Strathclyde). Strathgryfe AA has trout water here. St £6.50, dt £1.50 and £1; entrance fee for new members £5. Concessions for jun. Permits from Cross Cafe. No Sunday fishing for visitors.

CALDER and BLACK CART:

Lochwinnoch (Strathclyde). St Winnoch AC has stretch of Calder (brown trout). Mt £4, wt £2, dt £1 from hon sec. Sunday fishing. Castle Semple Loch (pike and perch) now taken over by Water Dept. Castle AC has 2m stretch on Black Cart (trout, perch, pike) and $\frac{1}{2}$m stretch on Barbush (salmon, trout, pike, perch, roach, eel); membership £5 and st £6 from hon sec; dt £1 from Walkers (ironmongers), High St, Johnstone. Hotel: Mossend ($\frac{1}{2}$m Lochwinnoch).

CONON (including Orrin and Blackwater)

Drains Loch Luichart and is joined by Orrin and Blackwater before entering the Moray Firth and North Sea by way of Cromarty Firth. Spring fishing has declined and main salmon runs now take place from July to September. Sport then among best in Highlands.

Dingwall (Ross & Cromarty). Sea trout and brown trout. Dingwall District AC has beat on R Conon. Fly only, for salmon, sea trout and brown trout. Season: Jan 26 to Sept 30, best months May, Aug and Sept. Also fishing for brown trout, pike, perch and char on Loch Luichart. Season March 15 to Oct 6. Visitors' tickets from tackleist: H C Furlong, The Sports and Model Shop, Tulloch Street, Dingwall. Wt £15, dt £5. Salmon, sea trout and trout fishing on **Allt Graad River, Alness River** and **Loch Glass** near **Evanton** from Factor, Novar Estates Office *(see under Alness)*. Alness AC also has water on river. Hotels: Conon at Conon Bridge and Aultguish (fishing on **Loch Glascarnoch,** boats).

Strathpeffer (Ross and Cromarty). Salmon and trout on **Rivers Conon and Blackwater;** trout in lochs. Loch Achonachie AC has beats on Upper Conon (April 1 to Sept 30) and Upper Blackwater (ditto) also boats on **L Achonachie** and **L Meig.**

Dt £3–£12, boat £7.50, apply to bookings sec, Malcolm Burr. Both rivers fish better late in the season. Craigdarroch Hotel, Contin (by Strathpeffer) issues permits for Blackwater and lochs (brown and rainbow trout). Best July–Sept. Coul House Hotel, Contin, issues wt and dt (£35–£400 and £5.00–£50, according to date) for beats on **R Conon** and **R Alness** (salmon); and bank fishing on **L Morie,** at the head of the river. Sea trout, brown trout and char. Dt £15 per rod, inclusive.

Garve (Ross & Cromarty). Garve Hotel (Tel 205) has excellent fishing on **Loch Garve,** which holds large trout (fish up to 12 lb taken) also pike to 30 lb and perch, and for brown trout on $1\frac{1}{2}$m of River Blackwater within hotel grounds. Strathgarve Lodge, has fishing on 7m of river (salmon and trout) and five lochs for guests. Own salmon beats April to Sept; other months by arrangement. Aultguish Inn by Garve, issue wt and dt for trout fishing on **Loch Glascarnoch.**

CREE and BLADNOCH

Drains Loch Moan and flows about 25m to sea at Wigtown Bay. Runs of salmon and sea trout in summer and early autumn. **Minnoch,** tributary of Cree, is also a salmon river, joining Cree about six miles from Newton Stewart.

Creetown (Dumfries & Galloway). Hotel: Barholm Arms. Good river and loch fishing in the area; apply proprietor for particulars.

Newton Stewart (Dumfries & Galloway). Salmon, sea trout; best early in season. Newton Stewart AA has fishing for salmon, sea trout and brown trout in Cree, **Bladnoch, Minnoch** and **Penkiln Burn** and on **Kirriereoch Loch** (trout), **Palnure Burn** (salmon, sea trout, herling); **Bruntis** and **Garwachie Lochs, Loch of Fyntalloch, Lochs Ochiltree, Wee Glenamour** and **Kirriereoch** (brown, trout), and **Clatteringshaws Dam** (trout and pike). Charges wt £25, dt £2.50–£6. Tickets from hon sec and tackleists. Spinning and bait

fishing allowed when river in flood. Fishing for carp, tench and other coarse fish on **Barnbarach Loch,** W Whamphill. Plenty of pike fishing in the area can be arranged. Creebridge House Hotel arranges fishing in River Cree and various lochs and burns. Galloway Arms Hotel can also arrange fishing. Corsemalzie House Hotel between Wigtown and Glenluce, has fishing on Bladnoch, **Tarff** and **Malzie Burn.** Fishing arranged on Cree and on nearby coast. Castlewigg Hotel, nr Whithorn, 19m S of Wigtown, can arrange salmon and trout fishing in local lochs and rivers; and sea angling from Port Patrick and Isle of Whithorn. Tel: 098 85-213. Tackle and information from The Gun Shop.

DEE (Aberdeenshire)

Second most famous salmon river of Scotland; for fly-fishing probably the best. Also holds sea trout and brown trout. Rises in Cairngorms and flows into North Sea at Aberdeen. Best months for salmon: February to mid-June. Best for finnock (small sea trout) mid-August to end of September.

Aberdeen. Salmon, sea trout, brown trout; sea fishing. Many owners let for whole or part of season, but some good stretches held by hotels. Some hotel waters free to guests during summer. Lower reaches give good finnock fishing. Aberdeen and Dist AA has 10m of salmon and brown trout fishing on the **Don** (7m away), and trout fishing on **Loch Loirston** (3m away); wt £20 and dt £5 from J Somers & Son (tackleist), 40 Thistle St, Aberdeen. Visitors tickets only available to visitors who reside outside 30m radius of Aberdeen. Sea fishing is good in vicinity of Aberdeen *(see Sea Fishing Stations)*. Other tackleist: Wm Brown & Co, 11 Belmont Street. Hotels: Station, Caledonian, Imperial, Royal, Marcliffe.

Drum (Aberdeens). Dee preserved. **Gormack Burn;** trout; heavily fished; permission of H Q Forbes Irvine, of Drum.

Banchory (Kincardine). Salmon, sea trout and grilse. Fishing let at fortnightly periods on Ballogie stretch; 3m long; four rods allowed from Feb 1 to Sept 30; Carlogie stretch is 2m with three rods allowed; salmon and grilse caught Feb to Sept. Banchory Lodge Hotel by river can

Salmon fishing is not all exertion. A peaceful scene on the R Glass, in Inverness-shire. *Photograph by Eric J Chalker.*

arrange salmon and trout fishing for five rods, bait fishing to April 15, fly only after; at rates ranging from £15 period per day to £300 per week, according to date. Gillies and tuition available. Feughside Inn, Strachan, by Banchory, has 2 rods on 1½m of Dee and can arrange fishing on **Feugh;** salmon and sea trout. Other hotels: Potarch, Torna-Coille (fishing arranged on Dee and Feugh).

Aboyne (Aberdeens). Dee; salmon and sea trout. Hotels: Balnacoil (water on Dee); Huntly Arms (fishing arranged through Scotia Sporting Services on river and lochs).

Ballater and Braemar (Aberdeens). Balmoral, Mar, Glenmuick and Invercauld Estates preserve most of river Dee salmon fishings. The latter lets Crathie, Lower Invercauld and Monaltrie beats, 20m in all, details from The Factor, Invercauld Estates Office, Braemar By Ballater AB3 5XQ. Tel: Braemar 224. Brown trout fishing on **Rivers Gairn** and **Clunie.** St £7–£9, wt £4–£5, dt £1.50–£3, from Invercauld Estates Office, Countrywear Tackle Shop, Ballater, Tourist Office, Braemar. **Lochs Bainnie** and **nan Ean;** permits from Invercauld Estates Office and Gamekeeper. Tel: Glenshee 206. **Loch Vrotichan;** permits from Ballater Angling Assoc, 59 Golf Rd, Ballater, Tel: Ballater 55365. Hotels: Mar Lodge *(advt above)*; Invercauld Arms; Ravenswood.

DEE (Kirkcudbrightshire), including Lochs Dee and Ken

Flows through Loch Ken about 16m to Solway. Salmon, sea trout and brown trout. Netting reduced and river stocked with salmon fry. An area in which acidification problems have been reported. Some lochs affected.

Castle Douglas (Dumfries & Galloway). Dee private. **River Urr** (8m) holds salmon, sea trout and brown trout; Castle Douglas AA has 7m; re-stocked annually; good runs of sea trout and grilse starting in June. Permits from

Tommy's Sports, 178 King Street. Spinning and bait fishing in flood water only. GM Thompson issue permits for **Lairdmannoch Loch,** Twynholm. Several lochs may be fished from Milton Park Hotel *(see Deugh–Dalry).* Lochinvar Hotel also has fishing on loch *(see Dalry).* **Auchenreoch Loch** is 9m away on main Dumfries Road; good pike, some trout; permission from Galloway Arms, Crocketford. **Carling-wark Loch,** on outskirts of Castle Douglas (pike and perch) is free: boats available. Tackleists: as above and M McCowan & Son, 52 King Street. Cul-gruff House Hotel, Crossmichael has coarse fishing on **River Ken** and **Wood-hall Loch** and caters especially for pike anglers in winter. Glaisters Lodge Hotel has fishing.

New Galloway (Dumfries & Galloway). Dee private. Fishing free in **Loch Ken,** W bank only, (2m); holds trout, large pike and perch, and some salmon. New Galloway AA controls stretch of **River Ken,** stretch of **Loch Ken, Blackwater of Dee** (N bank only), **Mossdale Loch** and **Clatteringshaws Reservoir.** Visitors permits, for all except Mossdale Loch, £2 per rod per day or £10 per week; from Craiglea, High St and hotels. Concession for jun. Mossdale Loch, stocked with brown trout; £6 per boat (2 rods) per day; no bank fishing; fly only. Permits

from Craiglea, High St. Ken Bridge Hotel has own stretch on R Ken (Wt £10, dt £2), both this hotel and Cross Keys can arrange fishing on rivers and lochs. **Barscobe Loch;** trout; dt (incl boat) £1 from Hugh Wontner, Barscobe. For **Knockman Loch** and **Lochinvar Reservoir;** good trouting from bank; dt £5 (bank), £10 (boat) from Duchrae Farmhouse.

Dalry (Dumfries & Galloway). Dalry AA has fishing on **River Ken** (left bank from Dalry to Boatknowe), **Carsfad** and **Earlstoun Reservoirs.** Tickets from Glenkens Cafe (wt only for river, dt for reservoirs).

DEUGH: (tributary of Loch Ken):

Dalry (Dumfries & Galloway). Trout. Permits from Dalry AA for **River Ken, Carsfad Reservoir** and **Earlstoun Reservoir;** boats on both. Dt £8 from hon sec. Milton Park Hotel (Tel Dalry 286). Trout fishing (brown and rainbow) on **Lochs Barscobe, Mossroddick, Brack** and **Howie,** boats available with boat also on **Loch Earlstoun** at rear of hotel; all waters stocked with trout. Tickets for non-residents, (£3–£7) but guests have priority. Salutation Hotel (Carsphairn), can arrange fishing on Deugh. Lochinvar Hotel can arrange fishing in rivers, lochs and reservoirs (salmon, trout, pike and perch).

DEVERON

Rises in Cabrach and flows some 45m into the Moray Firth at Banff. A prolific salmon river, but has, in particular, a reputation for its brown trout fishing. There are also some large sea trout, many of 8–10 lb. Sea trout run June to September; finnock mid-July to end of October. Best months: June and July.

Banff. Salmon, sea trout, brown trout. Hotels: Fife Lodge, Banff Springs and County Hotel which can sometimes

arrange fishings. Best months: salmon, March to Oct; sea trout June to Aug; brown trout, April, May and Sept.

Sea trout improving. Local association: Banff and Macduff, which has about 1m both banks of tidal water; wt for visitors resident in Banff or Macduff; dt for others, from hon sec. Sea trout fishing (July onwards) in **Boyne Burn,** 6m away. Tickets from Seafield Estate, Cullen (no charge, but limited).

Turriff (Aberdeens). Turriff AA has salmon, sea trout and brown trout fishing on Deveron; wt (Mon–Fri) for resident visitors only, wt £35 from hon sec. Fly only when level falls below 6 in on gauge. Best months July, August and Sept; also a fishery on opposite bank, dt £1. Tackleist: Ian Masson (Sports) Ltd, 14 Main St. Hotels: Union, White

Heather, Royal Oak, Glenesk. Enquiries to Bell Ingram, 7 Walker Street, Edinburgh for Beldorney Castle Water. (£55 per rod per week).

Huntly (Aberdeens). **Bogie** and Deveron; salmon, sea trout and trout. **Isla:** trout. St £40, mt £30, wt £20, dt £6 from Clerk to Huntly Fishings Committee, 27 Duke Street, Huntly. Only 10 dt per day and none on Saturdaays or Public Holidays. **Kirkney:** Bogie tributary (4m); small trout; permits from Forestry Commission. In late spring upper waters of rivers will be found best for salmon. Hotels: Gordon Arms, Castle *(advt p 288)* (rights on Deveron).

DIGHTY

Drains some small lochs and falls into the Firth of Tay not far from Dundee. Banks built up on lower reaches. Now clear of pollution. Trout, odd sea trout and salmon. Badly weeded and difficult to fish in summer.

Dundee (Angus). Trout with occasional sea trout; free. **Rescobie Loch:** Fly fishing for large trout (brown and rainbow). Bank and boat fishing through Mr J

Yule, South Lodge, Reswallie, Forfar. Tel: Letham (Angus) 384. St £42, dt £4.50. **Monikie** and **Crombie Reservoirs** leased to Monikie AC. Reservations via

Tailing a salmon from the Canary Pool, Middle Blackhall beat. *Photograph by Eric J Chalker.*

the bailiff (tel: Newbiggings 300). **Lintrathen (Backwater) Reservoir** leased to Lintrathen AC. Good trout fishing but a rather complicated system of charges by sessions. 15 boats; catch limit 24 fish (over 10″) per boat. Dt £10–£14, from Water Services Dept, Tayside Regional Council, 10 Ward Road, Dundee. Tel: 21164 or at the loch, tel: 05756327, but phone not permanently manned. Club bookings from Dr Parratt, 91 Strathern Road, Broughty Ferry, Dundee, tel: 0382 77305. Other trout waters within easy reach include **Loch Fitty,** 20 boats and bank fishing, tackle shop, restaurant and fish farm to which visitors are welcome. Boats, including outboard motor, for 3 anglers, day (10 am—5 pm) £15.99; evening (5.30 pm—dark) £18.99 with reductions during

Apl, Aug, Sept; bank permits £6.20 per session. Reduced boat charges for Single Anglers and 'Father and Son/Daughter'. The Lodge, Kingseat, Dunfermline, Fife (Tel: 0383 723162) for both waters. **Ballo, Holl** and **Glenfarg Reservoirs.** Boats for two rods, morning and evening sessions, £7 and £8. Permits from Fife Regional Council Water Division, Craig Mitchell House, Flemington Road, Glenrothes, Fife KY7 5QH. Tackleists: John R Gow & Sons, 12 Union Street, who will give advice on fishing throughout Scotland and issue permits for **Eden** (Fife), st £15, dt £2 and Strathmore AIA water on **Isla and Dean** (15m); restocked; st £7.50, dt £1.50; concessions to OAP and jun. Other tackleists: Shotcast Ltd, Whitehall Crescent.

DON (Aberdeenshire)

Rises near Ben Avon and flows for nearly 80m to North Sea at Aberdeen. Good salmon river which is also noted as a dry-fly trout water. Autumn salmon fishing falling off, but spring fishing improving. Some sea trout.

Parkhill (Aberdeens). Now privately owned. No tickets.

Kintore (Aberdeens). 1m of salmon and trout fishing on both banks of River Don. St £35, wt £18, dt £5. Well stocked with trout 10/12 ozs. Permits from Kintore Arms and J Copland, Newsagent, (open from 6 am) Northern Road. Other hotel: Torryburn. No Sunday fishing.

Inverurie (Aberdeens). River Don (2½ miles) and **River Urie** (3½ miles) salmon, brown trout and occasional sea trout. Permits from E J Duncan & Son, 4 West High Street, Inverurie (Tel: 0467 20310). St £33, wt £16.50, dt £4.50 to £6 according to date. Juniors and OAP approx half price. No Sunday fishing. Salmon best March, April, May and September-October. Hotels: Gordon Arms, Banks of Ury and Kintore Arms.

Kemnay (Aberdeens). Mrs F J Milton, Kemnay House, issues permits for two

beats on Don at Kenmay.

Monymusk. (Aberdeens). Grant Arms Hotel has exclusive rights to 10m of trout and salmon fishing (13 beats).

Alford (Aberdeen). 25m from Aberdeen. Salmon and trout. Hotel: Forbes Arms, Bridge of Alford AB3 8Q5, which has 4½m of Don for guests, and also issues permits. Wt £55, dt £10. Some good trout burns (free) in vicinity.

Kildrummy (Aberdeens). Kildrummy Castle Hotel has good stretch of salmon and brown trout fishing. Trout best early, salmon late. Permits. Dt (S) £10 (T) £5, enquiries to T Hillary (Tel Kildrummy 208). Kildrummy Inn also issues permits.

Glenkindie (Aberdeens). Apply Glenkindie Arms for salmon and trout fishing. Wt (S) £40, (T) £20. Dt (S) £7, (T) £3.50. No Sunday fishing.

Strathdon (Aberdeens). Colquhonnie Hotel has 3m salmon water, 9m of trout fishing. Dt (S) £6.90, (T) £3.50.

POLLUTION

Anglers are united in deploring pollution. To combat it, urgent action may be called for at any time from any one of us. If numbers of fish are found dead, dying, or seriously distressed, take samples of both fish and water and contact the office of the Director of Scientific Services at the appropriate Regional Water Authority.

DOON

Drains Loch Doon on the Solway Firth's watershed and flows right through the old County of Ayr to the Firth of Clyde, near Ayr Town. Good salmon, sea trout and brown trout water.

Ayr. On Doon and Ayr estuaries. Salmon and sea trout July onwards. Burns Monument Hotel, Alloway, has water on Doon. District Council issues permits for Ayr *(see p 279)*. Tackleist: Gamesport (Ayr) Ltd, 60 Sandgate.

Dalrumple. Skeldon Estate, salmon and sea trout; dt £5–£12. Cottages available with fishing. Tel: 029256 656. Lindsayston Farm, dt available. Tel: 029256 240.

Dalmellington (Ayrshire). Good salmon and sea trout (July onwards). **Loch Doon,** 6m; plenty of small brown trout and occasional salmon and char; fishing free; boats for hire. Craigengillan Estate has both banks of River Doon from **Loch Doon** to the Straiton Road Bridge. Tickets from keeper for stretch from Loch Doon to Lynn bridge only. Brown trout and occasional salmon and sea trout. Apply Farm, Craigengillan (Tel: Dalmellington 550 366). Local clubs: Dalmellington AC; fishes Lochs Doon, **Ballochling** and **Bogton.** Loch Doon free; dt for **Bogton** (salmon, sea trout, brown trout and pike) £3 boat; permits from hon sec. Ness Glen AC shares Bogton Loch. Hotels: Loch Doon, Eglinton.

LOCH DOON: Brown trout; free. Dalmellington AC fishes Doon, Ballochling and Bogton *(see Dalmellington).*

LOCH FINLAS: (tributary of Loch Doon): Trout up to 1 lb. Rented by Loch Finlas FC; fishing is strictly for members and members' guests only.

EDEN (Fife)

Rises in Ochil Hills not far from Loch Leven and falls into North Sea in St Andrews Bay. Provides some very fair trout fishing. Slow-flowing stream suitable for dry-fly fishing. Some sea trout below Cupar.

St Andrews (Fife). **Cameron Reservoir** stocked by St Andrews AC (trout av $1\frac{1}{4}$ lb). Fly only. Details of permit and boat charges on application to the secretary. (Tel: 72477.) Permits and boat reservations from bailiff. (Tel: Peat Inn 236). Kenly Burn (ticket water), inquire tackleists. Kinness Burn free. St and dt (£15, £5 and £2) for river from tackleist, J Wilson & Son (tel: 0334 72477). Other tackleist: A Mackenzie & Son. Many hotels.

Cupar (Fife). Trout, sea trout, few salmon. Preserved by Eden AA. Dry fly much used; trout average, $\frac{1}{2}$ lb to $\frac{3}{4}$ lb; best sea trout Aug/Sept, and salmon Sept/Oct; st and dt from Cupar railway station near river or John R Gow and Sons, Union Street, Dundee, and other tackleists in Dundee and Fife. Permits from Crawford Priory Estate, 2,

Bonnygate, Cupar, for trout fishing on **Clatto Loch.** Brown trout, boats. St £35, dt £3.50–£6. Also from Mrs Watson, Waterman's Cottage.

Ladybank (Fife). Fine dry-fly fishing; trout. Some free, but mostly preserved. **Lindores Fishery, Newburgh** (7m NW). Loch holds brown, rainbow and American brook trout; fly only; no bank fishing. Dt £16.50–£17. Sunday fishing allowed. Applications to Kindrochet Fish Farm, St Fillans, Perthshire PH6 2JZ (tel: 076485 337).

Tributary of the Eden

MOULTRAY:
Kilmany (Fife). Trout; mostly free.
Note: *Trout fishing on several reservoirs in area available from Fife and Kinross Water Board* (see under Glenrothes, Loch Leven).

ESK (North)

Formed by junction of Lee and Mark, near Lochlee, and flows for nearly 30m to North Sea near Montrose. Good river for salmon and sea trout.

Montrose (Angus). Sea trout, finnock (whitling) and brown trout. Joseph Johnston & Sons Ltd, 3 America Street,

issue free permits for Morphie Beat (1m) for either Monday and Wednesday, Tuesday and Friday, or Thursday and

Saturday from end of May to end of Aug. Best Aug. Also dt for Gallery and Canterland beats, charges varying from £4 to £16, according to date and day of week. Early months best of all. Local club: Montrose AA. Hotels: Links, Park. Other tackleists: Philips, 122 High Street; Cobb, Castle Place.

Edzell (Angus); ns Montrose. Salmon, sea trout, etc. Permits for beat on S bank from Montrose and Dist AA. Dt for Brechin and Arbroath AC water from

Breans, Commission Agents, Lordburn, Arbroath. Tackleists: The Sports Shop, High Street, Brechin; A de Costa, Post Office, Edzell. Hotels: Glenesk, Central Panmure.

LUTHER WATER:

Laurencekirk (Kincardine). Sea and brown trout. Laurencekirk AA has full rights here; limited guest tickets available. Wt £10, dt £2.50. Jun 12 years old and younger fish free. Best Aug–Oct.

ESK (South)

Rises in Glen Clova and flows some 49m to North Sea near Montrose. Good salmon river with plentiful runs of sea trout. Best months for salmon are February, March and April. Good autumn river (mid-September onwards).

Brechin (Angus). Salmon and sea trout; fishing good, but mostly preserved. South Esk Estates Office, Brechin, let beats on $2\frac{1}{2}$m, usually by the week or longer periods, but limited dt £5.75 available. Dalhousie Estates, Brechin, has boats to hire for trout fishing on **Loch Lee** (Glenesk); no bank fishing, and fly only; also salmon beats to let by the week or longer on North Esk. Justinhaugh Hotel has good salmon stretch; 3m one bank, $\frac{3}{4}$m other; free to guests. Forfar AC have adjacent stretch. **Loch Saugh**, Fettercairn, is 12m; trout. Brechin AA water. Permits from Ramsay Arms Hotel, Fettercairn; Drumtochty Hotel, Auchenblae; and Sports Shop,

22/24 High Street, Brechin, who also issue limited dt for salmon and sea trout on Westwater. Hotel: House of Dun (two beats for guests).

Kirriemuir (Angus). Kirriemuir AC has approx 7 m on S Esk. Salmon, sea trout, a few brown trout. Wt £20, dt £5 from hon sec (tel: 0575 73456). Some fly only water, but much of it unrestricted. Concessions to jun. Strathmore AIA has rights on lower **Isla** and **Dean;** st £7.50 and dt £1.50 from Mrs Dallas, Balbrogie Cottage. Coupar Angus. St (grayling) £4 from Mrs Henderson, 364 Blackness Road, Dundee. Ogilvy Arms has 3m of private water on S Esk, dt, wt and mt available.

EWE

This river has good runs of salmon (best May onwards) and sea trout (end June onwards) up to Loch Maree. Fishing again excellent, after problems caused by disease.

Poolewe (Ross & Cromarty). Salmon, sea trout, trout. Shieldaig Lodge Hotel, by Gairloch, has salmon and trout fishing on **Badachro River** and loch, and hill lochs. Dt (S) £2–£5. (T—bank) £1.50. (T—boat) £2.30. National Trust, Inverewe Visitors' Centre, has fishing on four lochs. Dt £4, boat £3. No Sunday fishing. Reduction for members.

LOCH MAREE (Ross & Cromarty). Ns Achnasheen. Especially noted for sea trout (July to mid-October). Fish run large mostly taken on dap. Spring salmon season (trolling) April and May.

Loch Maree Hotel, Achnasheen, has fishing. Heavy demand for sea-trout season so early booking advised. Hotel owned by anglers' syndicate which provides excellent facilities.

Kinlochewe (Ross & Cromarty). Kinlochewe Hotel has fishing on Loch Maree. Salmon April and May, sea trout July to Oct. Fly only after mid-June At **Torridon** (10m SW) Loch Torridon Hotel, By Achnasheen, Wester Ross, IV22 2EY, has fishing on **Rivers Torridon,** and **Thrail,** on **Lochs an Iascaigh** and **Damph,** and hill lochs. Dt £6–£12.50 for hotel guests. Tel: 044 587 242 for details.

FINDHORN

Rises in Monadhliath Mountains and flows over 60m to Moray Firth. Good salmon river with many rock pools, mostly preserved by owners. Also sea trout and brown trout. Best months: July and August. An area in which acidification problems have been reported: Some lochs affected.

Forres (Moray). Forres AA issues permits for visitors resident in town; from Feb 11 to Sept 30. Good trout fishing on nearby locks; **Loch of Blairs Loch Dallas;** permits from Smokers, and Sports Shop. J Geddes, Tolbooth Street, Forres, issues permits for **River Nairn**. Permits for **Lochindorb** from Moray Estates, Forres. Tackleists: The Smokers, and Sports Shop, W Stuart & Son, both High Street; J Geddes, Tolbooth Street (Findhorn permits). Hotels: Caris-brooke, Carlton, Park, Royal, Brig Motel, Ramnee.

Tomatin (Inverness). Salmon and brown trout. Freeburn Hotel has salmon and trout fishing on river; permits: dt (S) £7.50, (T) £1.50.

Note: *Cawdor Estate Office, Cawdor, Nairn, lets beats on river. Apply to Factor. Moray Estates Development Co, Forres, may also have beats available.*

FLEET (Kirkcudbrightshire)

Formed by junction of Big and Little Water, empties into the Solway Firth at Gatehouse. Good sea trout and herling, and few grilse and salmon; best months July and August.

Gatehouse-of-Fleet (Dumfries and Galloway). N.s. Dumfries, 33m. Sea trout and herling early and some salmon and grilse. River fishing in R Fleet: charges range from st £27 to dt £6, according to beat. Trout fishing on **L Whinyeon**, fly only from boats, spinning from shore permitted. Boat for two £17; dt for bank,. £7. Tickets from Murray Arms Hotel (Tel Gatehouse 207). River and loch restocked regularly. Gatehouse and Kirkcudbright AA controls **Lochenbreck** (6m; stocked annually with 12 in brown trout). Fly only. St £18, wt £12 and dt £4, boat £1 per day from McKinnel, St Cuthbert Street, Kirkcudbright and D Twinhame, High Street, Gatehouse. Hotels: Murray Arms, Gatehouse-of-Fleet; sea trout and herling fishing on Fleet, brown trout on five lochs; Cally (own loch; fishing also arranged on Fleet and other lochs).

FLEET (Sutherland)

Rises east of Lairg and, after run of some 12m, flows into Loch Fleet at The Mound. Middle and lower half of river (north bank) owned by Morvich Estates; middle portion (south bank) by Rovie Lodge and lower portion (south bank) by Cambusmore Estates. Upper reaches owned by Tressady Lodge. Salmon and sea trout. Dt £20 from Morvich Estate Keeper, Rogart, by Golspie.

FORTH (including Loch Leven and Water of Leith)

Formed from junction of Avendhu and Duchray not far from Aberfoyle, and thence flows about 80m to its firth at Alloa, opening into North Sea. Principal tributaries, Teith and Allan, flow above Sterling. A large salmon river, which at times, and especially on upper reaches, provides some good sport. Good run in lower reaches during February and March as a rule. This river and Teith, Balvaig, Leny water and Allan Water being extensively restocked with salmon and sea trout by Forth District Salmon Fishery Board. (Howietown and Northern Fisheries Co, Stirling, providing hatchery facilities.) Trouting in upper reaches and tributaries, particularly in lochs, where salmon also taken.

Stirling. Forth, Allan and Teith may be fished from here. Herling in Forth in spring and autumn. Salmon fishing from Lands of Hood to mouth of Teith ($7\frac{1}{2}$m) including Cruive Dykes is controlled by District Council. Permits for residents and visitors from Chief Exec, Stirling DC, Corn Exchange Road; D Crockart & Son, tackleist, and McLaren's, 4 Allanvale Rd, Bridge of Allan, st £34 and £17, dt £4.75, with concessions to juniors, OAPs etc. Sport on three miles of Teith from Blue Banks to Forth junction. Mon, Wed and Sat, dt for eight rods; salmon, sea trout, trout; permits from tackleist. Good trout lochs within reach by car. Loch Leven *(see under "Tributaries of Forth")*. **Loch Coulter:** Larbert and Stenhousemuir AC; limited dt and evening tickets at £6 and £4; fly only; no bank fishing. **Carron Valley Reservoir:** controlled by The Central Regional Council *(see Falkirk)*. **Lochs Ard** and **Chon:** dt (shore fishing) 50p. **Lake of Menteith:** brown and rainbow trout; boat £16 (9.30–5.30 or 6–11 pm) from Lake Hotel, Port of Menteith FK8 3RA. **North Third Reservoir** is Sauchie Estate water. Tackleist: D Crockart & Son, 35 King Street (tickets for stretches on main river and tributaries and information).

Aberfoyle (Perthshire). Trout; a few salmon taken. GPO and Civil Service ACs control. Dt from Ferguson, Newsagent. Aberfoyle APA (st £15) issues dt for **L Ard,** £1.50 + boat £4, brown trout, fly only. Tickets and boats from newsagent, hotels and Assn (Tel 0877 7261). Dt for **L Chon,** Forestry Commission water, and boat-hire from I Closie, Frenich Farm, Kinlochard. Hotels: Bailie, Nicol Jarvie, Forest Hills, Altskeith. Among other accessible waters are **Lake of Menteith,** brown and rainbow trout, fly only **Dt** for £15. Reservations at Lake Hotel and Loch Lomond *(see Clyde)*. Tackleist: D Crockart & Son, Stirling (permits) *(see Stirling)*. Hotel: Inversnaid (fishing).

Loch Katrine (Perthshire). Good trout fishing (fish av 6–8 oz); fly fishing from boat only. Permits (£6.50 per boat per day, VAT incl) from Strathclyde RC; Lower Clyde Div Water Dept, 419 Balmore Road, Glasgow G22 6NU. Season April–Sept same terms apply to **Loch Arklet,** and **Glen Finglas Reservoir.** *(see also Glasgow).*

FORTH—Tributaries

DEVON: Fair brown trout stream; sea trout and salmon lower down.

Alloa (Clackmannan). Devon AA has salmon and sea-trout fishing from one mile above Devonshire Bridge to below Cauldron Linn. St £6 and dt £2 from hon sec or Scobbie Sports, 4 Primrose Street, Alloa and 90 Stirling Street, Alva.Good centres include **Tillicoultry, Dollar, Rumbling Bridge** and **Crook of Devon,** and in **Glendevon.** Hotel accommodation at each of these places. Water within grounds of Castle Hotel, Glendevon. Rumbling Bridge Hotel and Blackhills Estate is private. Trout fishing on **Glenquay Reservoir,** bank only, by dt £2 obtainable from Wightman, Bookseller, Dollar and Tea Rooms, Rumbling Bridge. No Sunday fishing.

ALLAN: Fair trouting, with sea trout and grilse from July onwards.

Bridge of Allan (Stirlings). Salmon and trout fishing on the river from junction with River Forth to Blackford, all under control of Allan Water Angling Improvement Association, which has rights on full stretch of River Allan, except where indicated by noticeboard. River stocked with both trout and salmon fry.

Wt £10 and £15, dt £2 and £3 according to date from Hardings, Newsagents, Dunblane; D Crockart, King Street, Stirling; McLarens Sports; or Allanbank Hotel, Greenloaning. Hotels: Royal, Queens; Allanbank, Greenloaning.

Dunblane (Perthshire). Trout. Several hotels. Allan Water AIA issues wt and dt. *(See entry above.)* Trout $\frac{1}{2}$ lb to 1 lb; sea trout run from mid-April; grilse and salmon from mid-July on. Best stretches of river near Kinbuck and Greenloaning stations. Hotels: Allanbank, Greenloaning (permits for association waters); Stirling Arms, Dunblane Hydro, Ardleighton.

Blackford (Perthshire). **Carsebreck Loch** (two boats), **Upper Rhynd and Lower Rhynd** (one boat on each). Very good trout fishing; fly only; boats from Simpson at Braco 218. Hotels: Braco and Blackford (trout and salmon fishing). **Frandy Loch** (Glendevon Reservoir) can be fished from here; brown trout; fly only; dt from reservoir keeper, boat extra.

Gleneagles (Perthshire). Gleneagles Hotel Auchterarder PH3 1NF, has access to Lower Scone and Almondmouth beats on

River Tay; salmon, grilse and sea trout; dt £35–£250. Trout fishing on **Fordoun Loch;** dt £35: and also on **Laich Loch,** in hotel grounds, free to guests from mid-Jan to late Oct. Apply to Country Club, Gleneagles Hotel (tel: 07646 2231).

AVON: Flows 18m to estuary of Forth near Grangemouth. Lower reaches polluted; good brown trout elsewhere (av $\frac{1}{2}$ lb with few around 2 lb). River fishes best in late June, July and Aug.

Falkirk (Stirlings). Slamannan Angling and Protective Assn controls 5–6m of water; no permits. Long waiting list for membership. Central Regional Council, Water and Drainage Dept, Woodlands, Stirling FK8 2HB, issues permits for **Carron Valley Reservoir** £15.15 (rate-payers £12.15) per day per boat. No bank fishing. Advance booking essential; apply Director of Finance. At **Larbert** (3m NW), Larbert & Stenhousemuir AC issue dt £3 for **Loch Coulter,** (Loch Leven, brown and rainbow trout). Tackleist: W J Scrimgeour, 28 Newmarket Street (dt issued). Mrs J Jenkins, Northend Bar, and Mrs C Penman, Lochend Farm, issue st. **Nr Linlithgow,** small dt rainbow trout fishery, **Bowden Springs,** Carribber. St £200 and £100. Dt £10, limited. Tel Linlithgow 847269. *(For other reservoir and loch fishing in area, see Edinburgh.)*

TEITH: Noted salmon and brown trout fishery, with good sea trout in summer.

Callander (Perthshire). Stirling District Council controls part of Teith, in which excellent salmon, sea trout and brown trout fishing open to visitors; st £34, dt £4.75 (concessions for residents, OAP, etc), obtainable from James Bayne *(see below).* Brown trout average $\frac{3}{4}$ lb. **Loch Vennacher** controlled by the Town Council; good salmon, sea trout and brown trout fishing: trout average 1 lb; fishing from bank permitted on parts of loch; st £27, dt £3.75, with concessions to OAP, juniors, etc; boats available. Roman Camp Hotel has fishing on river (free to guests). Dt for **Loch Lubnaig** (trout av $\frac{3}{4}$ lb) from James Bayne (tackleist), 76 Main Street; dt (S) £5 and (T) £1.50. Boats on Loch Vennacher also from Mr Bayne at £4 + £3 per rod. Boats can be arranged too on **Linlithgow Loch** (trout; av 1 lb). Good and convenient trout fishing can also be had on the **Lochs Voil, Ard, Chon** and **Drunkie** (Post Office, Brig o' Turk issues dt for Drunkie) *(see below).* Further particulars from Tourist Office, Callander, or tackleist.

BALVAIG and CALAIR (Tributaries of Teith): salmon, trout.

Balquhidder (Perthshire). 2m of Balvaig; st £10, dt £1.50 from A Ferguson, Gartnafuarin Farm, Balquhidder. Boats for **Lochs Voil** and **Doine** from M McNaughton, "Lochs", Balquhidder and Mrs Fergusson, Muirlaggen Farm, Balquhidder.

Strathyre (Perthshire). Midland Counties APA issues st and dt, £3 to £6 for river. From hon sec or Strathyre Inn, Ben Sheann and Munro hotels. **Loch Lubnaig;** trout, also char, and some salmon by trolling; an early loch. Dt (salmon) £3, (trout and char) £1 from J Bayne *(see Callander)* or Strathyre hotels (Station, The Inn, Munro, Rosebank); have boats. Guests at hotels can fish Balvaig (ticket) and Lochs Vennacher *(see Callander),* Voil, Doine, Ard, Dochart and Earn *(see Aberfoyle and Balquhidder).*

LOCHS CHON and ARD

Aberfoyle. (Perthshire). Trout, controlled by Aberfoyle APA *(see Aberfoyle under Forth).*

Check before you go

While every effort has been made to ensure that the information given in "Where to Fish" is correct, the position is continually changing and anglers are urged, in their own interests, to make preliminary inquiries before travelling to selected venues. This is especially important with reference to prices quoted. Inevitably, the rate of inflation is affecting stability in this quarter. Anglers' attention is also drawn to the fact that the hotels mentioned under the various fishing stations do not necessarily have water of their own. Any amendments or further data for inclusion in subsequent editions, and any criticism, will be welcome.

Brig o' Turk (Perthshire). Permits for Lochs **Drunkie** and **Achray** (trout and coarse fish) and for **Lochan Reoidhte** (trout, fly only) from Forestry Commission Aberfoyle District Forest, David

Marshall, Lodge, Aberfoyle, Stirling. Vehicle access to forest £1 (2×50p coins for vending machine), dt £1.50 and £3. Boat on **Lochan Reoidhte**, £4.

Loch Leven

Famous Kinross-shire loch which produces quick-growing trout. Loch is nowhere deep so feed is good, and practically whole area is fishing water. Under efficient management, this has become one of the most notable trout-fishing lochs of Scotland.

Kinross. 16m from Perth, 25m from Edinburgh. Trout average 1 lb; annual catch in 1985, 22,891 trout. Trout up to $9\frac{1}{2}$ lb have been captured on fly. Perch abundant, but pike rigorously exterminated, 40 boats. Fly only; three rods per boat only. There is now a somewhat complex range of charges in force, subdivided into rates for all day, afternoon and evening sessions, differing as between weekdays and weekends, and according to time of year. They span from £8 for a weekday afternoon between the opening and the end of July, through ten progressive levels to £20 for an evening boat in June or July. For full information on charges

and booking conditions, apply to the Manageress, The Pier, Kinross (Tel 63407). Tackle can be bought at the pier. Fishing also available on **Leven Cut** (Loch Leven sluices to Auchmuir Bridge) from River Leven Trust, Sluice House, (Loch Leven (20p day, £1 season). At **Glenrothes** (12m) permits may be had from Fife Regional Council for reservoir trout fishing on **Glenfarg, Upper Glendevon** and **Lower Glendevon Reservoirs.** Morning and evening sessions. Boats (2 rods) £7 and £8. Bank, (lower Glendevon and **Castlehill** only) £2. Permits from Fife Regional Council, Water Division, Craig Mitchell House, Flemington Road, Glenrothes.

Water of Leith

Local people who know river well get fair numbers of trout, but there is some pollution, which is being tackled.

Edinburgh. Lothian Regional Council manage the Water of Leith and thirteen water supply reservoirs in the area. Water of Leith, running through the city, is stocked annually with brown trout. St issued free of charge from Regional HQ, George IV Bridge, Edinburgh. Permits for boat fishing at **Gladhouse, Glencorse, Clubbiedean, Harperrig** and **Crosswood Reservoirs** from Dept of Water & Drainage, "Comiston Springs" 55 Buckstone Terrace, Edinburgh. (031 445 4141) Boat and bank permits are available from the water staff at **Megget Reservoir** (0750 42265) **Rosebery Reservoir** (8300 353) **Talla Reservoir** (08997 209) and **Fruid Reservoir** (08997 225). Bank permits for **Harperrig** from ticket machine on site. Permits for **Whiteadder Reservoir** from Superintendent at reservoir (036 17 257). Boat fishing on **Hopes** and **Donolly Reservoirs** booked through Dept of Water & Drainage, Alderston House, Haddington (062 082

4131). Charges range from £7.20 for a boat for two on a stocked water to £1.30 for a bank ticket on an unstocked one. Whiteadder Reservoir, in the Lammermuirs, is 70m from Edinburgh; Harperrig and Crosswood are W of the Pentland Hills. Rosebery, Clubbiedean, Threipmuir, Glencorse and Gladhouse are within 15m of city, to the S. For details of all above waters contact Director of Planning, Lothian Council, 12 Giles Street, Edinburgh EH1 1PT. St £24 and £15.40, wt £8.80, dt £1.65, for **Threipmuir** and **Harlaw,** are balloted for (contact the Factor, Dalmeny Estate Office, S Queensferry, West Lothian EH30 9TQ), limited dt £1.40 from Alex Fleming, Grocer, 42 Main Street, Balerno. Apply in person. All are fly only waters. Concessions for OAP and jun. Cobbinshaw AA has fishing on **Cobbinshaw Loch,** on Union Canal, *leased from BWT.* **Linlithgow Loch,** close to Linlithgow Palace, is stocked with trout by Forth

Area Federation of Anglers'; limited dt for bank and boat fishing; fly only. West Lothian DC, Dept of Leisure and Recreation, County Buildings, High Street, Linlithgow, issues permits for **Beecraig's Reservoir**. Dt £10 and £5.50. West of Edinburgh is the **River Almond**, controlled by River Almond AA, fishing poor. Blackridge and Dist AC fish **Hillend Reservoir** and **Lily Loch;** st £10 and dt £5 from bailiffs and Forrestfield Hotel, Eastercroft Hotel, Truff Inn. Boats available (tel: 0236 843266). **Avonbridge** and Dist AC has trout water on the Avon between Strathavon and Larkhall. Permits from hon sec and members. Near **Dunfermline** (17m NW) is **Loch Fitty**, good trout water. Boats, including

outboard motor, for 3 anglers Day (10 am—5 pm) £15.99; evening (5.30 pm—dark) £18.99 with reductions for Apr, Aug, Sept; Bank permits £6.20 per session. Reduced boat charges for Single Anglers and "Father and Son/Daughter". The Lodge, Loch Fitty, Kingseat, Dunfermline, Fife. (Tel: 0383 723162). **Raith Lake**, near Kirkcaldy, now fished by Raith Lake AC. **Craigluscar Reservoir and Dam** also provides sport with trout; no boat. Permit at reservoir. Tackleists: John Dickson and Son, 21 Frederick Street; E Miller, Field and Stream, Montrose Terrace; F and D Simpson, 28 West Preston Street, all Edinburgh. D Black, The Hobby Shop, 10-12 New Row, Dunfermline.

GIRVAN

Drains small loch called Girvan Eye and thence runs 25m to the Atlantic at Girvan. Good salmon and sea trout; fair brown trout. Salmon run March onwards; sea trout from July.

Girvan (Ayrshire). Salmon, sea trout, brown trout. Carrick AC issues wt £5, dt £2.50, available from John Murray (tackleist), 3 Dalrymple Street, who also issues dt £2.50 for **Penwhapple Reservoir** (Penwhapple AC) which is 6m away; excellent trout loch; fly only; dt £4 and evening £2.50; boats available £1 per 4 hour session, season opens April 1. At **Barrhill** (5m) are Drumlamford Estate Fisheries comprising 3m salmon and trout fishing on **River Cree**, two stocked trout lochs and two coarse fish lochs. Dt £8 and £3. Boats available. Permits from keeper, A McKeand, The Lodge. (046 582 256). Excellent sea fishing; trips arranged by Girvan Sea AC; contact at

harbour. Hotels: King's Arms, Hamilton Arms, Ailsa, Queen's, Royal. Turnberry Hotel is 4m N.

Maybole (Ayrshire). Salmon, sea trout, brown trout. Garpin AC has $1\frac{1}{2}$m at Crosshill; permits from hon sec or T McCulloch, 50 High Street. Maybole AC has water; no tickets.

Straiton (Ayrshire). Salmon (late), sea trout, brown trout. Dt £8 for Blairquhan Estate water from D Galbraith, The Kennels, Blairquhan Estate, Straiton. Apply A MacGillivray, Broadwood, for permit for Straiton club waters. For loch, trout fishing fly only; (boats available); apply R Heaney, Tallaminnoch, Straiton.

HALLADALE

Rises on north slope of Helmsdale watershed and empties into sea at Melvich Bay. Good and early salmon river. Trout average $\frac{3}{4}$ lb.

Melvich (Sutherland). Melvich Hotel, Melvich, by Thurso, 12m from Forsinard, offers trout fishing on a number of lochs, most of which have boats on them, dt £6 per boat. Salmon fishing by arrangement on Halladale.

Halladale (Sutherland). For salmon beats (wt £100-£400, dt £20) and trout lochs (dt £2-£10) contact J Atkinson, Factor, 8 Sinclair Street, Thurso. Accommodation; self catering in Lodge and various cottages.

Fishing Clubs

When you appoint a new secretary, do not forget to give us details of the change. Write to Thomas Harmsworth Publishing, 13 Nicosia Road, London SW18 3RN. Thank you!

Forsinard (Sutherland). Salmon sport good, especially after freshets. Application for beats can be made to the Forsinard Hotel *(advt above)*, which is on the Helmsdale-Melvich road close to the railway station. Apart from beats on

Halladale, dt (S) £15, (Res £7.50), can arrange fishing on various trout lochs, most with boats, dt £10. Garvault Hotel, **Kinbrace,** has brown trout fishing on burns and lochs; free to guests; gillie, instruction available.

HELMSDALE RIVER

Formed by two headstreams near Kinbrace, this river flows 20m southeast through Strath Ullie to sea. Excellent salmon river, where there is now no netting.

Helmsdale (Sutherland). Salmon and sea trout. Salmon beat lettings from F Holdsworth, Hunt Sporting Agency, 10 Bridge Street, Hungerford, Berks (0488 83222) Lower Helmsdale only: wt £50 and dt £10 from A Jappy, Salmon Contractor, Helmsdale (0431 2654). Information from J A Douglas Menzies,

Mounteagle, Fearn, Ross-shire. Navidale House Hotel arranges fishing for brown trout on six lochs, fly only on all but one. Dt (bank) £1, (boat) £3, ob motor £5 extra. Salmon fishing available on Helmsdale Association Water. Wt £50, dt £10. Other hotel: Belgrave.

INVER (including Kirkaig and Loch Assynt)

Draining Loch Assynt, this river flows into a sea loch on the west coast of Sutherland known as Lochinver (village and loch having the same name), a little north of the old Ross-shire border. Holds salmon and sea trout but fishing is hard to come by.

Drumbeg (Sutherland). 14m from Lochinver or 11m from Kylesku Ferry. Hotel has brown trout fishing for guests. Boats on sixteen good lochs. Boats £4. (Mt and wt available.) **Loch Drumbeg**, in front of hotel, very good; fish average over $3/4$ lb. Best months: May, June, July and Sept. Salmon fishing arranged. Good sea fishing (Hotel: Tel Drumbeg 236). Assynt AC controls thirty-five lochs, including **Loch Roe**, with a run of salmon and sea trout. Mt £25, wt £10, dt £2.50.

Altnacealgach. Altnacealgach Motel, Ledmore has b trout and char fishing on **Loch Borralan.** Boat £10 per day. Tel: 085 486 220.

Lochinver (Sutherland); W Lairg, 48m. The Inver, running out of Loch Assynt (6m) is private. **Kirkaig:** $3\frac{1}{2}$m S of Lochinver, river divided into three beats, available to guests at Culag Hotel. Restocked annually; main run mid-June to mid-July. Trout and sea trout fishing for guests at Culag on lochs such as **Ailsh, Assynt, Culag, Fionn** and **Veyatie** and on small hill lochs. Sea fishing also arranged. Brown trout fishing closes Oct 7, salmon and sea trout Oct 15. Assynt AC has good trout fishing on about 30 lochs. Wt and dt issued for bank fishing; boat extra.

Loch Assynt

Inchnadamph (Sutherland). Salmon fishing (fair) from June on upper end of Loch Assynt and in **Loanan Water,** which runs into it out of Loch Awe. Loch Assynt now developing as sea trout water. Loanan Water holds salmon (good in spate) and brown trout averaging $\frac{1}{2}$ lb, but also large ferox. Assynt AC controls 35 lochs, issuing permits for a number of them. Tickets from hotels. Permit from

Inchnadamph Hotel for celebrated **Gillaroo Loch,** Loch Assynt and Loch Awe (£2.50 day + £5 for boat). Season from May 1 till Oct 10. Best months for trout, mid-May to Mid-July, and Sept; for salmon, mid-June to mid-July, and Sept. Hotel: Inchnadamph; fishing free to guests on loch and on Loanan Water on alternate days. Ten boats available.

IRVINE (and Annick)

Rises near Loudonhill and flows about 20m to Firth of Clyde at Irvine Town. Main tributaries are Cessnock Water, Kilmarnock Water and Annick. Fishing controlled largely by clubs. Salmon and sea trout July onwards; brown trout average $\frac{1}{2}$ lb; early season best.

Irvine (Ayrshire). Salmon, sea trout, trout; Irvine and Dist AA issues st £9, mt £6, wt £4.50, dt £2 for 2m on Irvine and 3m Annick (no dt Saturdays). Irvine Water runs from estuary to Red Bridge, Dreghorn, on north bank and to Bogie Bridge on south bank. Annick Water is from confluence with Irvine to northern boundary of Annick Lodge Estate, except for one private stretch. Tickets from Currie Sports Shop, Townhead and R Gilmour, 58 Muir Drive, both Irvine.

Dreghorn (Ayrshire). Salmon, sea trout, trout; Dreghorn AC issues wt and dt for 12m water on both banks of Irvine and Annick; apply hon sec or R W Gillespie, 16 Marble Ave. July to Sept best for salmon and sea trout. Brown trout average $\frac{1}{2}$ lb.

Kilmarnock (Ayrshire). Salmon, sea trout, trout. Salmon best Aug-Sept. St £8.50, dt £3 from McCririck's, John Finnie Street.

Hurlford (Ayrshire). Salmon, sea trout, brown trout. Hurlford AC issues wt £7 and dt £2 for 3m of water. Salmon and sea trout best from June onwards. Apply J M McVey, Post Office, where tackle is obtainable.

Galston (Ayrshire). Good sport with salmon and brown trout; Aug to Oct for salmon. Galston AC issues dt for salmon and trout but not on Saturdays; 7m of water; Irvine and Cessnock Water.

Newmilns (Ayrshire). Salmon (occasional; best Aug to mid-Oct), sea trout, trout; Newmilns and Greenholm AC has water and issues dt (Mon-Fri only), and wt; apply Valley Sports (tackleists), Main Street, who also issue tickets for Avon and Clyde and tributaries.

A young angler prepares to go afloat on a hill loch. His prospects will be improved if a breeze rises. *Photo: John Marchington.*

Garnock and Lugton

GARNOCK: Trout, sea trout, salmon.

Kilwinning (Ayrshire). Garnock and Irvine join in tidal water and have common mouth. Salmon, sea trout, trout. Kilwinning Eglinton AC has 9m on Garnock and **Lugton** Rivers; Wt £10 and £5, dt £2 and £1 from hon sec and J Gordon Sports, Main St.

Dalry (Ayrshire). Salmon, sea trout, trout. Dalry Garnock AC has 6m plus tributaries (both banks) and **Third Part** Reservoir (trout only; fly only); mt, wt, and dt from hon sec. Hotels: King's Arms, Royal.

Kilbirnie (Ayrshire). Kilbirnie AC has water on river and **Kilbirnie Loch** (trout and excellent roach) and two reservoirs; wt £5, dt £1.50, both excluding Saturdays. The roach fishing in the loch is claimed to be the best in Scotland. Season; trout and coarse, March 15 to Oct 6. Tickets from hon sec, and D Lennie (Watchmaker), Main Street and Glengarnock PO.

ANNICK: Brown trout; small runs of salmon and sea trout Sept–Oct.

Stewarton (Ayrshire). Stewarton AC has water on Annick and tributaries, and **White Loch;** st £12.50, wt £10, dt £3 from hon sec and J Gordon Sports, High Street. Kilmaurs AC has 7m on Annick and **Glaisart** at **Kilmaurs;** sea trout and brown trout, with salmon in autumn; st £5, dt £1. Dreghorn AC issues permits for 12m on both banks *(see Dreghorn)*. Permits for 12m of water on Irvine and Annick from hon sec. Wt and dt; no dt Saturdays. Salmon July onwards.

THE ISLANDS

The term "The Islands" includes the Inner and Outer Hebrides, the Orkney and Shetland Islands and, for convenience, Kintyre.

ARRAN: For all streams and lochs, except **Machrie, Iorsa** and **Blackwater,** apply to Tourist Information Centre, Brodick pier or G Ambler, General Store and PO Lagg. Principal waters: **Sliddery, Kilmory, Rosa, Cloy, Benlister, Monamore, Sannox,** and **Ashdale.** Wt and dt. The Iorsa river and loch, **Tanna Loch,** and **Kilmory Water,** are reserved from Lagg Hotel to sea, but for Machrie River enquiries should be made of J T Boscawen, Strathtay Estate Office, Boltachan, by Aberfeldy, Perthshire.

Brodick. Best stream in Brodick district is Rosa. Brown trout in fair numbers, but very small. Cloy also fairly good for small trout. Small trout seem to be rule in all burns. During July, August and Sept there is good sea-trout fishing. Rods have got as many as 15 in a day, running from 1 lb to 5 lb or 6 lb. Machrie Water well spoken of. Rosa has early run of finnock; Feb to April. Arran AA permits (mt £5, wt £5, dt £2.50) from Tourist Office. Hotels: Douglas, Ormidale.

Kilmory District. Kilmory and Sliddery Waters both good for salmon and sea trout in the autumn. Few brown trout to speak of, although Sliddery is better of two. Some very good sea trout are got in Sliddery in August and Sept. Arran AA permits from Post Office at Lagg. Hotel: Lagg.

Lamlash. Good sea fishing *(see Sea Fishing Section)*. Two fair streams, Benlister and Monamore. Few brown trout worth speaking of, but in July, August and Sept fair number of sea trout can be got. Hill lochs contain numerous small trout, best being Loch Tanna in northern half of island. Hotels: PH Trust and Lamlash. Arran AA permits from Gordon Bros, Ship House. Hotel: Aldersyde. Wt £20 and £15, and dt £4 and £3 for most Arran AA waters.

BENBECULA: Lies between N and S Uist. Numerous lochs, giving good sea and brown trout fishing. Hotel: Creagorry, which has free fishing for guests on several lochs and three sea pools; boats available on some waters; waders useful; trout to 1 lb; farthest water 5m; June to Sept best for brown trout and August and Sept for sea trout. Sea trout up to 8 lb in sea pools; no stream fishing. Hotel has right to fish two rods per day on Loch Bee in South Uist. Permits at small charge from South Uist AC for 15 lochs, four with boats.

BUTE: 5m from Ayrshire coast; 16m long and 3–5m wide. Trout and coarse fish.

Rothesay. Loch Ascog, $1\frac{1}{2}$m pike, perch and roach. Permits: St £5.75, Ft £1.15. **Loch Quien,** 5m first-class trout fly fishing (fish averaging 1 lb); st £11.50, dt £1.15. Fishes best early and late in season for both brown and rainbow trout. Applications to Bute Estate Office, Rothesay (Tel 2627). **Loch Fad,** $1\frac{1}{2}$m rainbow trout fly fishing. St £40, wt £22, dt £8. Applications to Rothesay Seafoods, Ardmalaish, Bute. Permits also available from Bailiff at Loch. Sea fishing from rocky shore popular and good: by boat regularly from Rothesay pier. Kyles of Bute AC and shops in Kames and Tighnabruaich, also Kilfinan Hotel, Kilfinan, issue dt for salmon and sea trout on **Kilfinan River.** Free to guests at hotel.

COLL: 18,500 acres, in extent, is owned by three proprietors, C K M Stewart, J de Vries and Mrs Erskine. Lies within easy reach of Oban and Tobermory (Mull). No stream fishing, but many island lochs, all of which are now preserved for private fishing. Hotel: Isle of Coll, Arinagour; boats. Sea fishing excellent.

COLONSAY: Reached by car-ferry from Oban. The hotel shares fishing rights on East, West and Mid-Loch Fada; fishing and boats, £1.50 per ½ day. Brown trout; best months, May, June and Sept; fish average 10-16 oz; sea fishing with fly and bait. Fishing free to residents of hotel and self-catering accommodation. Tel 09512 316 for full details.

CUMBRAE: Small islands lying between Bute and Ayr coast. Trout fishing in two reservoirs, wt £10 and dt £3 from Mrs B Hill (tobacconist), Stuart Street, Millport. Sea fishing good from shore or boats. Boat hirers also provide tackle.

HARRIS: Southern part of the island of Lewis and Harris, Outer Hebrides. At Tarbert, good sea fishing for haddock, pollack, saithe etc in East Loch Tarbert. Position regarding salmon, sea trout and brown trout fishing uncertain as we go to press. Hotel: Rodel. Leverburgh, South Harris, lets fishing on mill pond, Obbe and Steisavat Lochs, and several others, including Finsbay waters. Brown trout fishing during May and June inclusive. Good sea trout and occasional salmon; best months, July to Oct. Also good sea fishing close by. No stream fishing available. Borve Lodge, Scarista. Sea trout lochs. Dt from £3 sometimes available. Enquire Tony Scherr, Factor, Borve Lodge Estates, Isle of Harris (085985202). Horsacleit Lodge let furnished for six guests with fishing for salmon and sea trout in river; for brown trout on Loch Drinishader. Rents during fishing season run from £100 per week to £250. Bookings to Mr C J Lucas, Warnham Park, Horsham, Sussex RH12 3RU. Limited dt from Manager N MacDonald; Tel Harris 2464. Harris AC issues wt £12 and dt £2 for seven brown trout lochs. Tickets from hon sec or Tourist Information Centre, or 18 Scott Road, Tarbert.

ISLAY: Most southern island of Inner Hebrides. Lies on west side of Sound of Islay, in Argyllshire. Greatest length is 25m and greatest breadth 19m. Sport with salmon, sea trout and trout.

Bridgend. Loch Gorm, 9m from Bridgend, famous for trout. Bridgend Hotel has trout fishing in five good lochs, six boats. St £10, dt £2 + boat £7, from Mr Wiles, Head Keeper, (049681 293) who will also deal with salmon and sea trout fishing enquiries. River fishing, salmon and sea trout can be arranged. Islay Estates have boats on four good lochs, £7 per day, £5 after 2 pm. Dt for bank fishing £2. Tickets from Estate Office or head keeper, Islay House. Tel Bowmore 293.

Port Askaig. By staying at Port Askaig Hotel, trouting can be had in Lochs Lossit, Ballygrant and Allan. Dt (boat) £7. Sport on other lochs by arrangement. Salmon fishing in River Laggan available. Best months: May, June and Sept.

Port Charlotte. Port Charlotte Hotel; trout fishing for guests; six lochs, incl L Gorm.

Port Ellen. Guests at Machrie Hotel can have brown trout fishing on Lochs Gorm, Ballygrant, Lossit, Finlaggan, Solon (salmon and sea trout also) and Glencastle, by arrangement with keepers. Wt £6, dt £2, 3-dt £4. Machrie (salmon, sea trout) free to guests. May, June, July best for trout; Sept and Oct for salmon, sea trout. Also sea fishing.

KINTYRE: This peninsula is part of Argyll and lies between Islay and Arran.

Ardrishaig (Argyll). Guests at Auchendarroch and Argyll Arms hotels can have fishing in ten local lochs; trout. Wt £10, dt £2.50. Fishing (trout) can be had in Crinan Canal, 2m N. *(See also Crinan and Lochgilphead.)*

Campbeltown (Argyll). Salmon and sea trout. Machrihanish Water free but badly polluted by farm effluent. Kintyre FP and AC has concessions on Crosshill Reservoir and on Lochs Lussa, Auchalochy and Ruan; brown trout: and also on Coniglen and Glenbreckerie Waters; salmon and sea trout. St £10 + £1 joining fee, mt £10, wt £3.50, dt £1.25, from tackleists. Boats available on three lochs. Permits from Tangy Farm (J Black) for Tangy Loch (60 acres, boat and bank fishing, trout to 2 lb). Dt £2, boat £3. Sea fishing in harbour and Firth of Clyde. Tackleists: A P McGory, Main Street, and R Armours, Longrow. Hotels: Ardshiel, Royal White Hart and Argyll. Hon sec of club will be pleased to give further information (send sae). *(See also Machrihanish and Southend.)*

Carradale (Argyll). Excellent salmon and sea-trout fishing may be had on Carradale Water. St £25, mt £18, wt £12, dt £3. Apply D Paterson, 17 Tormore, Carradale; J Semple, The Garage; or A Oman, The Pier.

Crinan (Argyll). Near west end of Crinan Canal. Brown trout lochs controlled by Lochgilphead Dist AC. Canal (trout). *(Permits as Lochgilphead, below.)*

Lochgilphead (Argyll). At east end of Crinan Canal *(see Crinan and Ardri-*

shaig). Lochgilphead and Dist AC has rights on eleven hill lochs; good brown trout; wt £10, dt £3 from Hugh MacArthur (Sports), 37 Lochnell Street. Forestry Commission has brown trout fishing on **Lochs Coille Bhar, Barnluasgan, Losgunn.** Boats £4.50–£6.50, £2 per rod. Advance bookings from Mrs Robertson, Barnluasgan (tel: 054 67 608). Stag Hotel can arrange fishing on **River Add** and various lochs. Salmon and sea trout in river, brown trout in lochs. Permits for other waters. Ford Hotel can arrange fishing on 5m of R Add. Dt £5 are available from Robin Malcolm, Dunhrune Castle, Kilmartin, Argyll. Lochgair Hotel is good centre for Lochs Fyne and Glashan; boats available. Tackleists: K Milton, Lochnell Street; Hugh MacArthur, 37 & 41 Lochnell Street.

Machrihanish (Argyll). Free salmon and sea trout fishing in Machrihanish Water. Permits for Kintyre FP and AC lochs from Ugadale Arms. Good sea fishing *(see Campbeltown).*

Southend (Argyll). Salmon and sea trout fishing in Conieglen and part of Glenbreckerie; st £10, wt £3, dt £1.25. Permits (and for Kintyre FP and AC lochs) from Argyll Arms and club hon sec *(see also Campbeltown).*

LEWIS: Some salmon, much trout fishing on lochs.

Stornoway. Little salmon fishing for visitors. For salmon and sea trout fishing in **River Creed, Loch Clachan** and **Loch an Ois** enquire of the Factor, Stornoway Trust, Estate Offices, Stornoway. For **Loch Valtos** and **Laxay River** enquire of John Macleod, Valtos Cottage, Laxay. (Tel 0851 83248). For Soval Angling Association enquire of Mr J M Macleod, 15 Balallan. Wt £2, dt £1. Sport with brown trout on numerous lochs within easy distance of Stornoway. Claitair Hotel, Sheildenish, has trout fishing. Uig Lodge Hotel has salmon, sea trout, brown trout fishing. The Garynahine Estate advertising salmon, sea trout and brown trout fishing in rivers and lochs. Apply to A Miller Mundy, Garynahine Lodge (tel: 085 172 209). The **Grimersta** belongs to Grimersta Estate Ltd, who occasionally have salmon, sea trout and brown trout fishing available for individuals or small parties in April, May and early June. Hotels: Country, Caledonian, Royal Lewis, Commercial.

Caberfeidh Hotel has private beats for guests on loch or river for salmon, sea trout and brown trout.

Uig. The Scaliscro and North Eishen Estates have salmon, sea trout and brown trout fishing; also sea angling. Booking agents Finlayson Hughes (tel: 031 220 1800).

MULL:

Tobermory. Mishnish Lochs: 2m excellent brown trout fishing; Tobermory AA has three boats. Mt £11, wt £7, dt £2. Boats, £2 per 4 hours hire. **Loch Frisa:** good brown trout, some salmon and sea trout. 7m of fishing; boats. Good sea fishing. Permits for **Mishnish** from tackleist A Brown, 21 Main Street. Accommodation: Glengorm Castle, Mishnish Hotel, Macdonald Arms, Western Isles Hotel; Heanish Chalets and guest houses.

Salen. 10m south of Tobermory, is good centre. Salen Hotel has boat on Loch Frisa, 5m away; excellent trout fishing, best months May and June, with few sea trout and odd salmon later. For the **R Forsa,** a spate river, Glenforsa Hotel issues dt £7.50 when conditions suitable. 5m of fishing for salmon and sea trout. Preferential terms for residents.

Bunessan. Argyll Arms Hotel has good salmon, sea trout and brown trout fishing on Loch Assapool and brown trout fishing on Loch Poitee at £5 per day for non-residents. Work in hand to improve sea trout access to L Assapool.

Dervaig. Sea, rainbow and brown trout fishing; permits from D Fairbairns, Cuin for **Loch Torr, Loch Frisa, Aros Loch, Mishnish Lochs** and **River Bellart.**

NORTH UIST: Island in Outer Hebrides, 17m long and 3–13m broad. Lochs and sea pools (numbering hundreds) well stocked with salmon, sea and brown trout. Lochs to north controlled by Department of Agriculture, and to south by North Uist Estates Ltd, Lochmaddy. Both issue permits. Main salmon lochs may be fished by visitors at Lochmaddy Hotel *(advt p 304).* Fly only, except for sea pools holding sea trout. Twenty boats on lochs. Gillie for boats if required. Best months: March to May, and July to October. Apply Manager for permits.

SOUTH UIST:

Lochboisdale. The hotel here offers ten salmon/sea trout beats on seven lochs, boats £16.50 (2 rods), £11 (1 rod) + gillie's fee. Fishing for brown trout of above average size on eight others. Boats £11 (2 rods), £7.50 (1 rod). Bank-fishing on brown trout lochs for non-residents by arrangement; wt £5, dt £1.50. Hon Sec South Uist AC will help visitors in respect of other waters. *All in all, there are 70 fishable lochs in S. Uist. Uist Community Press has published a guide to them, written by John Kennedy. Profits from the sale are ploughed back into angling protection and improvement.*

ORKNEY

While sea fishing for skate, ling, halibut (British record), haddock, cod, etc, is general in waters about Orkney, and good fun may be had in the evenings with saithe comparatively close to the shore anywhere, good quality trout fishing is confined to the mainland and Rousay for both brown and sea trout, but in the latter island the lochs are private, in contrast to the mainland, where all but one (Loch of Skaill) of the best lochs are "open" water. Sea trout, for which the east shores of the island of Hoy also have a good reputation, may be found at any point where fresh water enters the sea as well as in the Lochs of Stenness and Harray in March and April and from July to the end of October, and may be taken from a boat in the lochs. Wading trousers are useful in the estuaries.

Principal fishing lochs on the mainland are **Loch of Stenness**, 12m from **Kirkwall** and 3m from **Stromness**, which yields brown and sea trout, from March to October, the average weight being nearly 1 lb. The best part of the season for this loch is probably June to August. **Loch of Harray**, 11m from Kirkwall and 4m from Stromness, is connected to Loch of Stenness and fishes well from April to end of September, the average being about 1 lb. The **Lochs of Swannay, Broadhouse** and **Hundland** are in close proximity to each other in the north of the mainland, about 20m from Kirkwall, and fish well, particularly Swannay, which yields good brown trout of more than 1 lb average weight. All three lochs are fairly early in form and good sport may be had from April until the end of September. Boats are available for hire on all of these lochs, in most cases without boatmen, though in certain cases this may be arranged. Free fishing is also available on the Lochs of Wasdale, Kirbister and Bosquoy.

Accommodation is available in Kirkwall at several hotels including the Kirkwall Hotel, and there are taxi services to fishing waters. Anglers might prefer to stay closer to the waters they want to fish, however.

Merkister Hotel, Harray, is close to Loch of Harray (now the best of the Orkney Lochs) and affords excellent free loch fishing: boats, outboards, gillies (Tel 366). The Standing Stones Hotel, Stenness (fully licensed and under new management; boats, outboards, gillies) stands on the shores of Loch of Stenness and is also convenient for Loch Harray, while Smithfield Hotel (Dounby) and The Barony (Birsay), are convenient for the Lochs of Boardhouse, Hundland and Swannay. Keldroseed Guest House, Sandwick, By Stromness, overlooks Loch Stenness.

Orkney Trout Fishing Association operates a trout hatchery. Restocking has yielded excellent results, notably in the Loch of Swannay. Information from hon sec R Windwick, 36 Quoybanks Crescent, Kirkwall.

RAASAY:
The Isle of Raasay is near Skye. Free trout fishing in lochs and streams; spare tackle and waders should be taken.

RUM:
The fishing in the streams and lochs of the Isle of Rum is all preserved by the Nature Conservancy.

SHETLAND

The following notes have been compiled mainly with the aid of *Manson's Shetland Guide* but help has also been sought from a booklet written by James Coutts and published by The Highlands and Islands Development Board (20p). They should be read in the light of the fact that reports from our local correspondent now underline the fears expressed by conservationists on the bearing oil-related development would have on the famous Shetland sea trout fishings. Now, it is suggested, visitors might do better to think in terms of loch fishing for brown trout. There is also a threat of unrestricted netting which the Shetland AA is fighting to the best of its ability.

The sea trout fishing season in Shetland extends from February 25 to October 31, and that for the brown-trout fishing from March 15 to October 6. Nearly all mainland waters are controlled by The Shetland Anglers' Association (Hon sec Andrew Miller, 3 Gladstone Terrace, Lerwick) and remainder are usually available on request or for a small fee. St for association waters £7. There are no monthly, weekly, or daily permits as such. Juniors are free. Season tickets are available from hon sec, hon treasurer, tackle shops and the Tourist Office, Commercial Street. Association waters now include **Spiggie Loch,** the largest loch in the islands and a famous sea trout fishery.

Where the sea trout fishing so far remains unaffected, late March to early May, then July, August and September are the prime months. As regards size, fish up to 3 lb are not uncommon; fish up to 7 lb are not altogether rare; bigger fish are within the orbit of possibility, though perhaps scarcely within that of probability; but all these bigger fish are generally shy and difficult to capture.

Sea trout fishing , like all branches of this sport, cannot be made the subject of hard and fast rules, and both the methods and equipment used are entirely a matter for personal choice. It is not essential to have any special equipment apart from the ordinary outfit of a trout fisher, except perhaps such safeguards as are necessary against the corrosive effects of the salt water on certain types of aluminium reels and fitments of that nature. The sea trout takes a fly in salt water as readily as a brown trout takes it in the waters of a loch; and any of the standard types of sea-trout flies will, in favourable conditions, produce results until such time as the fisher develops those faiths and fancies to which all anglers are prone. He may then swear by his teal and red, or his blae and black, as his personal experience will no doubt have taught him to swear; or he may have become a disciple of the lure, which is often used to good effect, especially in weather which does not permit easy control of a lighter fly. He may even have recourse to bait-fishing to discover that the use of worm or strips of mackerel are not unproductive of good baskets.

There are two methods of fishing with mackerel. The easiest and most popular is to mount a strip of it on one of the hooks of the treble of any spoon or lure. The second approach is to use a rod of at least 12 feet, with fly-line and long tapered cast, and to attach a piece of mackerel strip to the hooks of Stewart or Pennel tackle. Fished in tidal water, allowing the current to work the bait as in salmon fishing, mackerel strip is the nearest thing to a live sand-eel.

The brown trout are more or less native to the freshwater lochs, of which literally thousands are populated by brown trout, most of them *under*-fished. Generally speaking, they average about $\frac{1}{2}$ lb. There are bigger fish—in fact, there are individual lochs which occasionally produce exceptionally big ones; but most of the many lochs which have fish in any quantity rarely produce a higher average weight, and often a lower one, a re-stocking programme is in progress. Only in exceptional cases is a boat available for fishing the lochs; but almost in every case fishing can be done from the bank or shore, by wading. It is often desirable to wade, rather than to fish from the bank, in order to clear heather slopes which can so effectively wreck a light fly cast.

The failure of a fishing holiday in Shetland at the proper time of year can scarcely ever be attributed to lack of fish. Occasionally, as in all places, there are spells of weather which result in poor baskets; but as the Shetland weather is rather noted for its changeability, the day for the angler is usually not long to wait. At a time when trout fishing is becoming increasingly difficult to procure, Shetland has a hundred spots to offer the angler where he is more or less free to fish at will, and a hundred more when these are exhausted. It is true there is a growing tendency among landowners to regard these fishings as a possible source of revenue, but, with the habits of sea trout what they are, there will always remain in the islands the possibility of fishing untrammelled by the restrictions which have placed so many of Scotland's rivers beyond the reach of the average fisherman. Shetland regards her trout fishings as an attraction which will result in visitors discovering the islands for themselves, and the measure of freedom she has to offer in an age of increasing restriction may well be the measure of her future prosperity.

Sea fishing off the Shetlands is excellent—large skate, also ling, tusk, cod, haddock, pollack, etc. *(See under Sea Fishing Stations.)* The fishing is done invariably by boat, and the rock fishing, popular at some places on the mainland of Scotland, is practised only occasionally in the capture of young saithe (called "pilticks") which can be taken on fly from the shore. Boats and equipment are easy to obtain and comparatively inexpensive. The fish caught consist mainly of haddock and whiting, while at certain places the catch may include rock-cod, ling, flounder—in fact, a general assortment of fish which makes very interesting fishing indeed.

Generally speaking, the fishing grounds lie beyond the limits of the voes, but during July and August, in certain of the larger voes, good fishing can be had without going farther afield. Fishing is by rod or hand-line at a depth between 20/50 fathoms; and, when the fish are plentiful, big catches, numbering scores, are taken. Also generalising, early and late months provide the best fishing. Tackleists on the island are J A Manson; Stove and Smith, both Commercial Street, Lerwick; and Hay & Co, Commercial Road.

NOTE: Anglers are recommended to bring their own cars, owing to the lack of public transport. Ferry services from Aberdeen and Leith. Shetland Tourist Organisation, Market Cross, Lerwick, will help with accommodation and other details. The association also issues a leaflet on angling. Shetland AA reports a disturbing decline in sport with sea trout and grilse following the advent of commercial fishing and fish processing. Association conducting vigorous campaign against netting.

Unst. Balta Sound Hotel, most northerly in British Isles, offers sea and trout fishing to guests.

Bressay. Loch and foreshore fishing leased from Garth Estate by Shetland AA; fishing by permit from hon sec; brown trout in Loch of Brough and Loch of Setter.

Delting. Lerwick 20m. Brown trout in lochs as follows: Mill Loch, Loch of Glen, Seawater; Loch of Voe. Sea trout at Dales Voe and Collafirth. Good sea trout fishing also at Garths Voe, Orka Voe, Voxter, Scatsta, Toft, Firth and Swinister Voes.

Dunrossness. Sea trout fishing at Spiggie, St Ninian's Isle, Channerwick, Cunningsburgh; also in Loch Spiggie during the fall fishing *(see also Scousburgh)*. Hotel: Spiggie.

Laxo. Laxo Voe, once one of the finest grilse and sea trout waters in the islands, now poached so heavily that Sumburgh Estates have given up the fishery.

Lerwick and District. The Shetland AA controls most of loch and sea trout fishing in Shetland (including Bressay). Best brown trout lochs (six in number) are located in valley of Tingwall. Tingwall is about 6m from Lerwick and 1 to 2m from Scalloway. Sea trout run into two of the above-mentioned lochs in season. Sea trout also obtained in nearby voes. Following voes (with distances from Lerwick) all contain sea trout. Full body waders are recommended. Laxo Voe (20m), Laxfirth (6m), Wadbister (8m). Hotels: Grand, Queen's Hotel, Lerwick Hotel, both Lerwick; Royal Hotel, Scalloway Hotel, both Scalloway. Information regarding other fishing readily given to visiting anglers by hon sec. Shetland AA Association issues permits at £7. Boats have been placed in the care of crofters for hire to anglers at moderate charges in the vicinity of the lochs **Girlista, Spiggie, Tingwall, Grunnavoe** and **Punds Water.** Enquire locally and apply. Fly only on most lochs. Accommodation from Information Centre, Lerwick. Tackleists: Stove and Smith; J A Manson & Son, both Commercial Street; Hay & Co, Commercial Road.

Lunnasting. After a bad history of poaching, attempts are now in progress to restore this water by a re-stocking programme.

Northmavine. Good brown trout fishing in Eela water, near Ollaberry and Bardister, and in many neighbouring lochs. In Pundswater, S of Hillswick, fish run larger. Good fishing and shooting over Lochend Estate. Sea trout in all lochs and numerous burns. Fishing and shooting can be rented with accommodation (contact A P Cromarty, Lochend House, Lochend). Sea trout also at Queyfirth, Ronas Voe, Ollaberry, Bardister, Sullom, Mangaster, Hillswick. Also at Hamar Voe, Gunnister and Nibon. Good brown trout in numerous lochs between Nibon and Mangaster (Busta Estate). Limited but good accommodation at Mrs Mowat's Fair View, North Roe. Car advised. Close to Busta Estate brown and sea-trout fishing.

Sandness, Bridge of Walls, etc. Brown trout and sea trout in lochs and voes.

Scalloway. Numerous lochs and voes. Hotel: Scalloway (excellent fishing in lochs and voes).

Scousburgh. Famous Loch of Spiggie holds good brown trout and sea trout in season. Fishing by Assn season ticket, £7. Best months: brown trout, May and June; sea trout, late Aug and Sept.

Weisdale. John White, Kergord (Weisdale 6) gives permission to holders of assn permits to fish the Burn of Sandwater— reputed one of the best in the islands— and four lochs, including **Sandwater,** when the fishing is not required by himself or his guests. Sea trout run through burn to reach Sandwater, 3m inland. Mr White or the manager at the Kergord Estate Salmon Hatchery (Weisdale 305) should also be approached for permission to fish Weisdale Burn and the Burn of Strom.

SKYE

Trout and salmon fishing generally preserved, but some good free fishing for hotel guests. Sea trout especially good in places. Excellent sea fishing.

Bracadale. Stores at Struan will give information on excellent salmon, sea trout and brown trout fishing; river and loch.

Broadford. Broadford Hotel. Fishing on **Broadford River** (salmon, sea trout) free to hotel guests.

Duntulm. Hotel has salmon, grilse, sea trout, brown trout fishing on **Kilmartin** and **Kilmaling Rivers** and various lochs. Excellent sea fishing; boats available.

Dunvegan. Numerous streams in area can be very good for sea trout in May and June. Dunvegan Hotel has rights and issues day and weekly permits for **Caroy River, Claigan Lochs, Hamara River** (Glendale) and **Rivers Haulton** and **Hinnisdale** (also shooting over 23,000 acres). Best salmon months July through to mid-Oct. Sea angling excellent May to Sept. Capt Henderson, 17 Skinidin, Glendale (Tel 268) arranges boats.

Sleat. Hotel Eilean Iarmain (Isle of Ornsay Hotel) has trout and sea trout fishing on a number of small rivers and lochs in the parishes of Sleat and Strath in the South of Skye. Boats also

available for sea fishing. July–Sept best for sea trout and June for brown trout. St £20, mt £15, wt £7.50, dt £2. Toravarg House Hotel has trout fishing on **Horavaig River;** free to guests. Dt issued.

Portree. Lochs Fada and **Leathan** have good trouting (big trout occasionally); **Storr Lochs** are 4m away on good road. Bank fishing; seven boats. Mid-May to Mid-July best. Further information from hon sec Portree AA. There is salmon fishing in **Staffin River** and numerous small brown trout lochs in the north of the island. St and dt for these fishings. Enquiries to hon sec Portree AA. Also sea fishing, for pollack and saithe in harbour. Sea trips from Portree daily, apply Tourist Office. Hotel: Cuillin Hills.

Skeabost. Skeabost House Hotel has 8m of salmon and sea trout fishing on **Snizort River** and trout fishing on Storr lochs; dt £7, other sport arranged. Hotel launch available for trips on Loch Snizort. (Sea fishing.) Tackle and bait supplied.

Sleat. Kinloch Lodge Hotel has trout and sea-trout fishing by arrangement with Clan Donald Lands Trust.

Sligachan. Sligachan Hotel has salmon and sea trout fishing in 2m **Sligachan River** and brown trout fishing in **Loch na-Caiplaich** free for guests; salmon few, sea trout quite plentiful; best months, mid-July to end-Sept. Brown trout fishing by arrangement in Storr Lochs (15m); boats available; season, May to end Sept. Dt for non-residents £6, ½ day, £3.

Staffin. Salmon, sea trout, brown trout. Portree AA hold the fishing rights. Tickets from D Burd, College of Agriculture, Portree.

Struan. Ullinish Lodge has salmon, sea trout and brown trout fishing in three lochs (boats available on two of them) and on **Rivers Ose** and **Snizort** *(advt above)*.

Uig. Uig Hotel can arrange fishing on north bank **River Hinnisdale** and **Storr Lochs;** also on various hill lochs on which Portree AS has rights. Wt £20 and dt £5 from Pier Garage. River Hinnisdale is run by newly formed angling club. A blocked fall has been cleared, restocking undertaken and 1987 showed a most worthwhile improvement with good sport fish between 4lb – 8lb.

LOCHAR

A sluggish stream, 15 to 16m long, which holds trout and some sea trout in season. Empties into Solway few miles east of Nith. Occasional salmon and herling caught near mouth during floods. River runs mostly through Lochar Moss. Fishing stations: **Ruthwell** (Dumfries). Near mouth: **Amisfield** (Dunfries). Trout: free on farmers' permission.

LOCHY (including Nevis)

Drains Loch Lochy and, after joining the Spean at Mucomir, flows about 8m to salt water in Loch Eil close to Fort William. Very good salmon and sea trout river but affected by hydro works at Falls of Mucomir. Best months: July, August and Sept. Inquire Manager, River Lochy Association, 5 Wellington Square, London SW3, and for lower water and Spean apply to Rod and Gun Shop, Fort William. Permits also from Benmore Restaurant, **Crianlarich.** Fly only *(see also Spean).*

Tributaries of the Lochy

SPEAN: Flows from Loch Laggan. A rocky river with good holding pools. Good fishing for salmon and sea trout from May to October. For lettings and permits inquire at Rod & Gun Shop, 18 High Street, Fort William.

Spean Bridge (Inverness). Beats available on dt £5 for left bank only, also for **Lochs Arkaig** and **Lochy.** Inquire of Spean Bridge Hotel or hon sec, River Lochy Association. Boats for lochs available from Mrs Duck, Poplar Cottage, Bunarkaig (tel: 039 782 283). Hotel: Spean Bridge. *(Advt above.)*

ROY (tributary of Spean): Salmon. A spate river; fishes best July onwards. Lower half let to Roybridge AC; and Glenspean Lodge. Upper half owned by Roy Fisheries; wt £60 and dt £10, from The Manager, R J Tapp, Braeroy, Roybridge (tel: 039 781 210) and Roybridge Hotel.

NEVIS: A short river flowing around south side of Ben Nevis and entering Loch Linnhe at Fort William, not far from mouth of Lochy. Very good salmon and sea trout fishing.

Fort William (Inverness). River Nevis; salmon, grilse, sea trout. Fort William AA has about 6m; dt from local tackleists (limited); no spinning; best June onwards. Good brown trout fishing on **Loch Lundavra** 6m from town. Dt £1.50 and boats £7.50, from Mrs MacCallum, Lundavra Farm (Fort William 2582). For **Loch Arkaig** (15m away); sea trout and brown trout, St £23, wt £5, dt £1, and boats £8.05 (with o/b motor £11.50) per day from A G Duck, Poplar Cottage, Achnacarry by Spean Bridge. Tackleists: Rod & Gun Shop (licences and permits for town beat on River Lochy). Hotels: Imperial, Grand, Alexandra, West End, Milton.

LOSSIE

Drains Loch Trevie and flows about 25m to the Moray Firth at Lossiemouth. A good trout stream; salmon runs improving, July onwards. Provides good sport with sea trout from June onwards, especially near estuary.

Lossiemouth (Moray). Salmon, sea trout. Lossiemouth AA now amalgamated with Elgin and Dist AA, has water; estuary and sea; sea trout and finnock only; st £4, visitor's ticket £2 and information on other fishings available from hon sec or DIY, Queen Street; and Elgin Angling Centre. Hotels: Stotfield Laverock Bank, Rock House, Huntly House.

Elgin (Moray). Lossie; salmon, sea trout and brown trout. Elgin AA has 15m of water; wt £10, dt £4, can be had from local tackleists. Kellas Estates office issues permits for stretch. Loch fishing for brown trout can be had on the Town Council's Milbuies Estate: dt £3.25 from Dept of Recreation, 30 High St, or on site. Loch fishing for brown trout may also be had by private arrangement at **Loch na-Bo** ($3\frac{1}{2}$m E). Numerous hotels.

LUNAN

Rises near Forfar and flows about 13m to North Sea between Arbroath and Montrose. Some good trout, dry fly good. Sea trout and finnock in autumn. A Protection Order now in force requiring all anglers to be in possession of proper permits.

Arbroath (Angus). Lunan and its tributary, the **Vinney,** about 8m of water, leased to Arbroath AC by riparian owners; restocked each year, holds good head of brown trout, $\frac{1}{2}$ lb to 1 lb. St £10, dt £2 from Tackle Shop, 274 High Street. Good sea fishing.

West Water. A tributary of North Esk, leased to Arbroath AC for sea trout and salmon. Best months, Aug, Sept, Oct.

Brothock Burn, about 4m long, lies on east side of town. Holds good trout up to $\frac{1}{2}$ lb. Free fishing; fly; spinning, bait.

Elliot Burn, also about 4m long, lies on west side of town. Holds good trout up to $\frac{1}{2}$ lb and sea trout at mouth. Free fishing in town stretch; fly, spinning, bait.

Rescobie Loch, 250 acres, has been developed jointly by Arbroath and Canmore AC as high-class fly-fishing loch for brown and rainbow trout. Lies about 11m from Arbroath. Brown trout up to 3 lb and rainbows up to $2\frac{1}{2}$ lb. Best months are Aug, Sept, Oct. Visitors' tickets for bank and boat fishing from bailiff at loch. Prices of tickets on application.

NAIRN

Rises in Monadhliath Hills and flows about 36m to Moray Firth at Nairn. Salmon, sea trout, finnock and yellow trout.

Nairn. Tickets for the lower reaches (estuary to Cantray Bridge $8\frac{3}{4}$m) can be had from Nairn AA; st £25, ft £30, wt £18, dt £5. Best months: July to September for salmon. Permits from Pat Fraser, High Street; Clava Lodge Hotel. Culloden Moor in Inverness, also issues permits for hotel stretch. Lochs **Lochindorb, Allan,** and **Loch-an-Tutach** privately owned; brown trout; dt and boat. Tackleist: Sporting Stores. Other hotels: Meallmore Lodge, Daviot (private stretch of river); Newton (river and loch fishing by arrangement).

NAVER (including Borgie and Hope)

Drains Loch Naver and flows about 24m to north coast at Naver Bay. The Borgie, which also debouches into Naver Bay, drains Loch Laighal and has course of about 7m. Both are good salmon and sea trout rivers; all preserved, but beats can be arranged, usually for fortnightly periods.

Bettyhill (Sutherland), via Lairg and Thurso. Bettyhill Hotel provides fishing for guests on Loch Naver, **Loch Rimsdale** (salmon, sea trout and brown trout) and on nine smaller brown trout lochs. No Sunday fishing; trout run to good size in several lochs; boats available on five, including Loch Naver (salmon, sea trout, brown trout; salmon very good March to June; sometimes July; sea trout good Aug/Sept) and Loch Rimsdale; trout; fishing free (and restricted) to hotel guests. Dt (S) £5 and 50p to non-residents for smaller lochs. Naver FC has sea trout and salmon fishing above Naver Bridge. Hotel: Lewiston Arms.

Altnaharra (Sutherland); ns Lairg. Altnaharra Hotel (postcode: IV27 4UE), which specialises in catering for fishermen, provides salmon fishing in Loch Naver and **Rivers Mudale** and **Mallart;** sea trout fishing in Loch Hope and brown trout fishing in a number of lochs, most of which have boats and are close to the road. Some are open to non-residents. Dt (river) £8.50; boats on lochs from £7 to £16.50, special terms for residents. Permits for Loch Hope also from Tongue Hotel *(see Tongue).* Excellent sea trout water; also holds salmon. No bank fishing; fly only.

Lochs Slaim and Craggie

Tongue (Sutherland). Tongue Hotel has salmon fishing on Loch Slaim and River Borgie, and fishing for wild brown trout on Slaim, Craggie, **Loyal** and **Cormac.** Dt (boat for 2 rods) £13 and £10, but fishing often included at no extra charge in hotel's special package offers. Also excellent salmon and sea trout fishing on **Loch Hope.** Boat for 2 rods £25. Many small burns. Ben Loyal Hotel (Tongue AA HQ) offers trout fishing on 12 lochs. St £15, wt £8 and dt £2.

NESS

Drains Loch Ness and flows to North Sea close to Inverness. Notable salmon and sea-trout river. Best July to October.

Inverness. Salmon, sea trout, brown trout. Inverness AC has stretch from estuary upstream for about $2\frac{3}{4}$m and **Loch Ruthven.** Wt £25, dt £5 (not available for Sat only); from J Graham & Co (tackle shop), 71 Castle St. Hotels: Glen Mhor, Culloden, Kingsmills. At **Fortrose** (10m NE) is good sea trout fishing from the seashore; fly and spinner; best June–July; Fortrose & Rosemarkie AC; tickets from A Gow (chemist), High Street, Fortrose.

LOCH NESS: Sea trout at Dochfour and Aldourie; salmon, especially out from Fort Augustus and where Rivers **Moriston, Enrick** and **Foyers** enter the loch. Brown trout all round the margins. Boats and boatmen from hotels at Fort Augustus, Drumnadrochit, Foyers, Lewiston and Whitbridge.

Drumnadrochit (Inverness). Salmon and brown trout. Enquire of J Menzies, Lewiston Garage for dt and boats. **River Enrick,** which enters loch here; best months, April, May, June. Sea fishing on Moray Firth by arrangement. Further

details from hotel. Glenurquhart Lodge can arrange fishing; Clansman Hotel, Lochness-side, has fishing; boats available. Ancarrig Chalets can arrange fishing on River Moriston, Loch Ness and several hill lochs. Tackle sale hire.

Foyers (Inverness). Salmon and brown trout fishing in Loch Ness. River Foyers enters loch here; preserved. Foyers Hotel has fishing on Loch Ness. Boat with ghillie: £20. Several other lochs may also be fished, including **Lochs Bran, Garth** and **Farraline** (£3 day).

Invermoriston (Inverness). River Moriston enters loch here. Permits from Estate Office for river and 20 hill lochs. Hotel: Glenmoriston Arms.

Fort Augustus (Inverness); ns Spean Bridge (bus service). Salmon and brown trout. Salmon season opens Jan 15. Trout season, March 15. Dt for River Oich (S) £6, (T) £3, for Fort Augustus AA Water (dt 50p). Hotels: Lovat Arms, Caledonian, Brae, Inchnacardoch.

Tributaries of Loch Ness

LOCH MHOR (Inverness). 18m from Inverness. Loch is 4m long by $\frac{1}{2}$m broad, and contains trout averaging $\frac{1}{2}$ lb. Accommodation $\frac{1}{2}$m away at the Old Manse Guest House, Gorthleck and Whitebridge Hotel, Whitebridge ($2\frac{1}{2}$m); *(see Whitebridge).* Boats available. **Loch Ruthven** can be fished, also **Loch Bran** and **River Fechlin.** Outlet from loch enters Loch Ness via River Foyers.

Whitebridge (Inverness). Whitebridge Hotel has boats for use of guests on **Loch Knockie** and **Loch Bran.** Daily charge £8.50. Arrangements also made for guests wishing to troll on **Loch Ness.** River and burns dried out in course of

hydro-electric development. Other hotel: Knockie Lodge.

MORISTON: Salmon; brown trout.

Glenmoriston by Loch Ness. Glenmoriston Estates Ltd, IV3 6YA, offer excellent salmon fishing on Loch Ness and River Moriston at prices from £6–£12 per rod. Brown trout fishing is also available on 9 miles of Moriston, Loch Ness and 22 hill lochs, at prices from £3 for a bank dt to £14 for a boat with ob motor. Discounts for occupants of the Glenmoriston Arms Hotel, Cluanie Inn and the Estate's Holiday Homes. Trout permits, salmon and boat bookings from Glenmoriston Estates

Office Tel No: (0320) 51202. Hotel: Glenmoriston. (Tel: 0320 51206.)

GARRY: Rises in loch SW of Loch Quoich and runs into that loch at western end, thence to Lochs Poulary and Garry. Good salmon and trout river. Outlet to Loch Garry dammed by North of Scotland Hydro-Electric Board. At Loch Poulary are fish traps; at Invergarry, a hatchery.

Invergarry (Inverness). For fishing in **River Oich** (salmon and trout) and in **Loch Oich** and **Loch Lundie** (brown trout); st £25, wt £9, dt £3 from Miss Ellice, Taigh-An-Lianach, Aberchalder Farm (tel: 287) and W Wernham, Larigan, Aberchalder (tel: 373). Glen-

garry Castle Hotel also offers fishing. **Loch Quoich** (brown trout), permits and boats from Lovat Arms Hotel, Fort Augustus. Glen Garry FC has fishing on River Garry and **Loch Inchlaggan;** boats on loch through hon sec or to guests at Garry Gualach Hostel or Tomdoun Hotel. Loch stocked with brown and rainbow trout, fly only *(see also Tomdoun).*

Tomdoun (Inverness); ns Invergarry. Free fishing on $3\frac{1}{2}$ miles of river and on Lochs **Garry, Poulary** and **Inchlaggan** (18 lb 4 oz trout taken in 1965) for guests at Tomdoun Hotel. Wt £15, dt £3 for non-residents. Boats on **Loch Quoich** by arrangement. Best months: May and June.

NITH

Rises on south side of Ayr watershed and flows south and east to Solway, which it enters by an estuary with Dumfries at its head. Carries a good head of small trout and has runs of sea trout and salmon in spring, summer and autumn. Salmon fishing has improved since netting was suspended in 1947.

Dumfries (Dumfries & Galloway). Dumfries Town Water, 3m on Nith, $1\frac{1}{2}$m on **Cairn** (tributary); salmon, sea trout, brown trout and grayling; best, March–May and Sept–Nov. St £69, wt £34.50, dt £11.50 from Director of Finance, Nithsdale DC; Municipal Chambers. **Glenkiln Reservoir** (trout) now controlled by Dumfries and Galloway Regional Council, Director of Water and Sewage, DG2 9BB. St £12, wt £6, dt (bank) £1.50, dt (boat) £3.50. Dumfries and Galloway AA has 3m on Nith and 20m on Cairn (brown trout, good; av $\frac{1}{2}$ lb). Salmon and brown trout. Wt £50 and £30, dt £12 and £10. (£20 and £5 for Cairn only, above Irongray Bridge.) No visitors' tickets at week-ends. Tickets from McMillan, tackleist *(see below)*. Tackleists: D McMillan, 6 Friar's Vennel; Malcolm Tathe, Queensberry Street. At **New Abbey** (Kirkcudbright), about 6m off, New Abbey AA has herling, sea trout and brown trout fishing in a small tributary of Nith; tickets from PO, Abbey Arms Hotel and Criffel Inn. Visitor's st £6, wt £3, dt £1.

Thornhill (Dumfriesshire). Salmon, sea trout, brown trout; some grayling. Mid-Nithsdale AA has 3m on Nith and tributaries **Scaur** and **Cample**. Visitors' tickets, wt £33–£75 (resident visitors

only), dt (limited) £7 and £10; no dt on Saturdays; fly only in low water. Tickets from hon sec. Buccleuch Estates Ltd has four beats and trout fishing on two lochs (with boats). Apply to The Factor, Drumlanrig Mains, Thornhill, Dumfriesshire DG3 4AG (tel: 084 86 283). Hotels: Buccleuch & Queensberry (fishing arranged in Nith and Scaur); Trigony House (private fishing on Nith)

Sanquhar (Dumfries & Galloway). Upper Nithsdale AC has approx 11 miles of Nith; and stretches on tributaries Kello, Crawick, Euchan and Mennock. Salmon, sea trout, brown trout and grayling. Monday–Saturday wt for bona fide visitors, £30–£55, dt £7–£12, (£1 grayling only, winter). Tickets from W & W Forsyth, Solicitors, 100 High Street, Sanquhar. Dt for grayling fishing. Dec–Jan, from W Laidlaw, 22 Renwick Place. Hotel: Glendyne; Drumbringan; Nithsdale House.

New Cumnock (Ayrshire). Salmon, trout, New Cumnock AA fishes the Nith, **Afton Water** and **Reservoir**, and other reservoirs and lochs (trout) and parts of **Rivers Deugh, Ken, Nith, Carsphairn Lane Burn.** Club also has some good coarse fishing, including grayling in Nith. St issued. No Sunday fishing.

OYKEL (including Carron, Cassley, Shin and Loch Ailsh)

Rises at Benmore Assynt, flows through Loch Ailsh and thence 14m to enter the Kyle of Sutherland at Rosehall. Excellent salmon and sea trout fishing. The Lower Oykel has produced an average catch of over 780 salmon in recent years. Much water managed by Renton Finlayson, Estates Office, Bonar Bridge, Sutherland

October on the Garry. *Photo: John Marchington.*

Oykel Bridge (Ross & Cromarty). Lower reaches of Oykel are fished from Oykel Bridge Hotel which also has salmon beats on **Upper and Lower Oykel, Einig,** and boats on **Loch Ailsh, The Kyle of Sutherland,** and hill trout lochs. Lower reaches fish very well for salmon early on and good grilse and sea trout run usually begins in the latter half of June. **Loch Ailsh.** Good sea and brown trout fishing with occasional salmon. Best months— Lower Oykel, March to September. Upper Oykel and Loch Ailsh, mid-June to September.

CARRON: Rises near Ben Dearg and flows 20m to enter Kyle of Sutherland opposite Bonar Bridge. Salmon and very good sea trout. Strathcarron Hotel (Lochcarron 228) controls 3m beat. Best months June, July and August. Dt £9 from Mrs MacKinnon, whose house is close to hotel. Several beats, and occasional dt through Renton Finlayson, Bonar Bridge.

Bonar Bridge (Sutherland). Caledonian Hotel has fishing through Kyle of Sutherland AC on Kyle of Sutherland (sea trout and brown trout, best months for former, mid-July onwards, for latter, June to Sept), fishing for brown trout on **Migdale Loch.** Wt £20, dt £5 for the Assn water; Assn tickets from Mackenzie-Harris Leather Shop, Bonar Bridge and Macleod, Ironmonger, Tain. For about 12m of sea-trout fishing above Bonar Bridge (Kyle of Sutherland) and 1m below bridge apply R L Henderson, East End. (Corrimulzle Estates Water.)

CASSLEY: Some 10m long, river is divided at Rosehall into upper and lower Cassley by Achness Falls. Below falls fishing starts early. Upper Cassley fishes well from May to Sept. Sea trout July and Aug. Rods let by week (av £105) on both banks. Sole agents: Bell-Ingram, Isla Rd, Perth. Hotel: Achness House, Rosehall.

SHIN (Loch Shin and Kyle of Sutherland): Brown trout in loch av $\frac{1}{2}$ lb, but very large fish taken early in season. Outlet from Loch Shin controlled by hydro-electric works. River flows about 7m and

empties into Kyle of Sutherland at Invershin. Salmon fishing privately let. Upper: Lairg Estates with some periods through Sutherland Arms Hotel. Lower: under private ownership, but a 3-rod beat available through Sutherland Arms Hotel in mid-Aug and Sept. Trout fishings on Loch Shin and hill lochs. Lairg AC has 10 boats for hire, o/b motors if required; £6 per day + £6 for motor and tankful of fuel. Bookings from hon sec (tel: 0549 2010). Sea-trout fishing in Kyle from Dornoch AA. Other hotel: Invershin.

Lairg (Sutherland). Trout fishing in Loch Shin (av: $\frac{1}{2}$ lb and up to 12 lb). This is largest freshwater loch in Sutherland—16 miles long. Lairg AC issues wt £6 and dt £2 via local tackleists for bank fishing and for boat fishing, with or without outboard motor. Best mid-May to end of July. Hotel: Sutherland Arms (salmon fishing on **River Shin,** sea and trout on Kyle of Sutherland, trout fishing on Loch Shin and hill lochs).

Overscaig Hotel (Sutherland). Ns Lairg (16m). On shore of Loch Shin. Hotel has boats on loch and others on Lochs **Ghriam** and **Merkland** with many hill lochs within walking distance. Facilities usually available for sea trout and salmon fishing on **Lochs Stack and More.** Hotel gillies, advice and instruction. Large brown trout caught on hotel waters in recent years. Fishing free to residents. Boats with ob motors. £9 per day. Wt for non-residents £5, dt £1.

DORNOCH FIRTH:

Dornoch (Sutherland). At entrance to Firth. Burghfield House Hotel has rights on **Lochs Migdale** and **Buidhe;** brown trout (av $\frac{3}{4}$ lb) Dt. Sea trout fishing in **Kyle of Sutherland** from Creich to Cassley mouth; permits from local hotels; best mid-July onwards. Permits from Dornoch AA for sea-trout at **Little Ferry;** wt £2.50, dt 50p and brown trout on **Lochs Lannsaidh, Buidhe, Laoigh, Lagain, Laro** and **Cracail Mor,** boat, £6 per day and bank (on Buidhe, Laoigh and Lagain) 50p.

KYLE OF DURNESS

Durness (Sutherland); ns Lairg. Cape Wrath Hotel at Keodale has good salmon and sea trout fishing on **Rivers Dionard, Grudie** and **Dall,** and **The Kyle** of Durness. Best for salmon and sea trout mid-June to mid-Sept. Big brown trout in Lochs **Calladale, Crosspool, Lanlish,** and **Borralaidh**—well-conditioned fish of

8 lbs in weight have been taken—and there are several hill lochs, two with boats. Lochs and rivers stocked with salmon, sea trout, brown trout fry. Dt for Dionard £16.50; for Grudie, £9. For Kyle, with boat, £9, for Limestone Lochs, £8. Bank fishing £5. Hotel open throughout year.

SCOURIE (including Laxford River and Lochs Stack and More)

Scourie (Sutherland, via Lairg). Excellent centre for sea-trout, brown-trout and salmon fishing. About 200 trout lochs. Scourie Hotel has extensive fishing rights on over 100; four with salmon and sea trout. Boats available on many. Gillies may also be employed. Dt varies between £7 and £28. Days on Loch Stack and Loch More (by permission of Duchess of Westminster) available to guests during July, Aug and Sept. Salmon, sea trout (good), brown trout. Charges on application. Laxford River is preserved. Scourie & Dist AC has rights on 31 lochs to N of village; trout around half-pound mark, but some larger fish. Wt £12.50 and dt £3 (boat £3 extra) from A Thomson, 4 Handa Terrace. Tackle available for hire.

Laxford bridge, over the famous Sutherland river. *Photo: John Tarlton.*

SHIEL (Argyll/Inverness-shire) (including Moidart and Loch Shiel)

Short but good salmon river, only about 3m long, draining Loch Shiel. Moidart is a good spate river with excellent holding pools. Loch Shiel is fed by four major rivers, **Slatach, Finnan, Callop** and **Alladale,** which all tend to be spate rivers. The Loch is best for salmon from April 1 till end May or early June. The sea trout run from July onwards and fishing closes at the end of October.

Acharacle (Argyll). River preserved. Loch Shiel, 17m long, holds salmon and sea trout, and a few brown trout; best mid-May to end of October; good late run. Boats for Loch Shiel and Salen from Forestry Commission, Strontian.

Shiel Bridge (Acharacle, Argyll). On loch and river. Loch fishing good for salmon, grilse, sea and brown trout. Lower end best. Sea, brown and rainbow trout

fishing. Glenborradale Farm. Tel 246. River Shiel strictly preserved.

Glenfinnan (Inverness). Stage House Inn (Kinlocheil 246) has 7 boats all with outboards available for hire £10. The hotel has recently been completely modernised and refurbished. Glenfinnan House Hotel has two boats with outboard available and Glenalladale Estate occasionally has a boat available with chalet accommodation.

LOCH SUNART

Strontian (Argyll). Salmon and sea-trout fishing on Lochs Shiel, **Doilet** and **Sunart;** Rivers **Carnoch** and **Strontian;**

boats available from Forestry Commission, Strontian.

SPEY

Rises mile or two above Loch Spey and flows NE about 100m to North Sea, emptying between Banff and Elgin. Historically, one of the great salmon rivers, but spring run much diminished of late. Well organised facilities for visitors, though, including tuition. Good sea trout and brown trout in places.

Fochabers. Salmon fishing leased by Gordon Castle Estate; all beats privately let. Fochabers AA lease a stretch ($1\frac{1}{4}$m) from May 16 to Aug 31; resident members only; limited number of permits for members' friends staying locally. Best months, July and Aug. Hotels: Gordon Arms, Grant Arms; some permits for trout and finnock in estuary. Tackleist: Speyside Tackle Shop.

Craigellachie (Banffs). Salmon, sea trout, trout. Craigellachie Hotel has over 2m beat, residents only; best mid-April to mid-June; grilse, July to Sept. Mt £300, wt £75, dt £13.

Aberlour (Banffs). Salmon, sea trout, finnock. Burgh water for visitors here. Best season usually March till June but can be very good in July and August too. Hotels: Aberlour; Lour; Downans. Fishings arranged on Spey, Avon and Lochindorb (14m). Dt £4 from tackleist: J A J Munro.

Grantown-on-Spey (Moray). Salmon and sea trout. Strathspey Angling Improvement Association leases stretches on **Spey** and **Dulnain;** over 40m in all on both banks. Wt £30 and £6 (jun) for salmon and trout. Inquiries to hon sec. Private beats on Spey on daily or weekly basis from following: Seafield Estate Office, The Square; Tulchan Estate, Advie (10m from Grantown), Ballindalloch Estate, Ballindalloch (15m) and Pitchroy Estate, Ballindalloch (17m). Boats on brown trout lochs in the area from tackleist G G Mortimer, 61 High Street, Grantown on Spey. Twelve licensed hotels; twenty guest houses; see Seafield Lodge *(advt p 317)* and Haugh Hotel and excellent caravan site. Many hotel proprietors themselves keen anglers.

Nethy Bridge (Inverness). Salmon, trout. Abernethy AIA has 6m of Spey and two good trout lochs. Best months, May, June, July. Courses for beginners run by

Seafield Lodge Hotel

Spey Valley Holidays — Salmon and Brown Trout Fishing, Golf, Hill Walks and Highland Touring combine with comfortable accommodation, good food, wine and congenial company at the Seafield Lodge Hotel — Spey Valley's premier fishing hostelry. Where **Arthur Oglesby**, noted fisherman and author, hosts his celebrated springtime salmon fishing courses. Less than ten hours motoring from most of Britain!

For brochure and holiday details contact Nancy or Peter Austen —

Seafield Lodge Hotel,	AA ★ ★
Grantown-on-Spey, Moray PH26 3JN	RAC ★ ★
Telephone (0479) 2152	RSAC ★ ★

Nethy Bridge Hotel in May and Sept. Hotels: Heatherbrae Hotel, Mount View Hotel.

Boat of Garten (Inverness). Salmon, trout,

Abernethy Angling Improvement Assn issues tickets for $5\frac{1}{2}$ mile stretch of Spey (both banks) for those staying locally, wt £28, dt £10 from hotels. Hotels: The

Spring salmon fishing on the Spey at Craigellachie, by the old bridge. *Photo: Eric J Chalker.*

Boat; Craigard, Nethybridge. Fishing schools spring and autumn. *For Loch Garten see Grantown.*

Aviemore (Inverness). The principal Spey Valley tourist centre. Aviemore Osprey Fishing School, Chief Instructor James Cornfoot, provides courses and accompanied fishing outings on Spey, **Feshie** and a number of lochs. St £30, wt £12, dt £4. A leaflet is issued. Tel Aviemore 810911.

Kingussie and **Newtonmore** (Inverness). Badenoch AA has rights on more than 15m of trout and salmon fishing on Upper Spey, several lochs (brown trout),

and **Spey Dam** (brown trout). Boat available on **Spey Dam**. Membership cards covering all waters, £15. Visitors £2.50 day, £10 week from local tackle shops and hon sec. Trout protection order in force.

Kinloch Laggan (Inverness). Trout fishing on loch controlled by Badenoch AA. Fish average $\frac{3}{4}$ lb. St £15, wt £10, dt £2.50. For possibilities on Spean, Roy, Treig and Cour inquire of hotel or Rod & Gun Shop, Fort William.

Glenmore, by **Aviemore, Loch Morlich**. Permits from Warden, Glenmore Forest Park; wt £8.40, dt £2.10. (Junior wt £3,90, dt 80p).

Tributaries of the Spey

FIDDICH:
Dufftown (Banffs). Dullan trout; free. Hotel: Fife Arms, Elms (temperance), Commercial.

AVON;
Tomintoul, by **Ballindalloch** (Banffs). Sea trout, grilse and salmon. Richmond Arms has 6m of fishing on Avon and $2\frac{1}{2}$m on **Livet** for guests. Gordon Arms guests can fish 5m of Avon and 1m of

Livet; dt £10. A beat on Avon (1m) is available for Tomintoul residents and visitors, and permits can be obtained from hotels and tackleist *(see below)*. Permit includes trout fishing on **Conglass Water.** Permits also issued to guests at Delnashaugh Hotel, Ballindalloch. Free trout fishing on Avon and three streams; Conglass Water, Chabet and Burn of Lochy. Tackleist: J Ross, Main Street.

STINCHAR

One of west coast streams, rising on western slope of Doon watershed and flowing about 30m to Atlantic at Ballantrae. Has a very late run of salmon, lasting till middle of October. Also good sea trout and brown trout.

Ballantrae (Ayrshire); ns Girvan, 13m. Trout, sea trout, salmon. Beats readily obtainable. River rises and falls rapidly after rain. Barr AC has water (salmon, sea trout, brown trout) on Stinchar; dt £4–£8: late July to Sept best. Dt for Knockdolian. Beat can be had from S Scobie, head gamekeeper, Colmonell (Colmonell 248) and other rods let by

riparian owners and Kings Arms Hotel, **Barr,** arrange fishing on Stinchar, **Girvan** and various lochs. Salmon and sea trout in rivers, brown trout in lochs. Dt £4. Colmonella guest house, Colmonell, also arranges fishing in Stinchar and lochs. Daljarrock Hotel, Pinwherry (by Girvan) has fishing on Stinchar.

CROSS WATER OF LUCE

Dependent on flood water for good salmon fishing, but very good for sea trout after dark. Best July onwards.

Stranraer (Dumfries & Galloway). Excellent centre for river, loch and sea fishing **Loch Ryan** and open sea. Stranraer AA has about 8m of salmon and sea trout fishing on Cross Water of Luce, and on

five trout lochs. Wt and dt issued. Waters are restocked. The lochs are: **Dindinnie, Knockquhassan** (boat), **Penwhirn Reservoir** and **Soulseat Loch** (rainbow and brown trout; av $1\frac{1}{2}$ lb).

Sunday fishing on lochs only. Wt £16, dt £4 from hon sec, tackleists and numerous hotels. Boat bookings through the secretary. One of the best lochs is at **Lochnaw Castle**, by **Leswalt**, where a dt is issued for boat-fishing on the loch. Brown trout, av 12 oz. Refreshments available. Phone bookings to Leswalt 227. Tackleists: Sports Shop, George Street.

TAY

A prestigious salmon river. Tay proper runs out of Loch Tay, but its feeder, the Dochart, at head of loch, takes its head water from slopes of Ben More. River fished mainly from boats, but certain beats provide also spinning and fly-fishing from banks. Notable in particular for run of spring fish, though autumn fishing often gives good results. After a course of some 120m it empties into North Sea by a long firth. Netting extends as far as Stanley, some miles above Perth. At least half a dozen of its tributaries are salmon rivers of little less repute than main stream. An excellent run of sea trout, big brown trout (less often fished for), grayling, and coarse fish (scarcely ever fished for).

Perth. Salmon plentiful in Tay from Jan 15 until Oct 15, when river closes, but best fishing is Feb to April and Sept/Oct. Permits (dt 50p non-residents) for river within city boundaries from City Chamberlain (roach increasing; no permits required). From Almond Mouth, some 2m above the town, to Aberfeldy, fishing strictly preserved. Tackleist: Bob Sime, 57 South Methven Street issues tickets for Perth and Dist AA water on Earn; wt £8, dt £2. Dt for trout fishing on **Horn Loch** (8m) from Forester in charge, Glenalmond. Hotel: Isle of Skye, Queens Bridge.

Stanley (Perthshire). Some of the best salmon pools are near here, such as Cat Holes and the famous Pitlochry Pool. In spring preserved baits, devons and plugs, mainly used. All waters strictly preserved. Beats always let in advance but occasional sub-lets available. Mark Clements & Associates, Commissioners House, Shore Road, Perth, let Taymount Estate. Fishing by week; two beats, five rods each; 26 named pools. Gillie usually available. Hotels: Ballathie House (salmon fishing), Tayside.

Meikleour (Perthshire); ns Cargill. The **Isla** here joins Tay; trout, salmon, pike and grayling; all preserved. Isla in upper water above Airlie Castle contains plenty of small trout; fishing free. From its junction with the Water of Dean, a few miles below Airlie Castle, to where it joins Tay, it is very sluggish, and full of pike, large trout, grayling and perch. **Water of Dean** contains capital trout.

Birnam (Perthshire). Fishing available by arrangement with Mrs E Redford, Homelea, Station Road, Errol (Tel 0821 2312) and Mr Michael Smith, at Dalguise, (dt £20). Hotel: Birnam.

Dunkeld (Perthshire). Post Office and R Scott-Miller, "Top Shop", Atholl Street, issue wt £4 and dt £1 for Tay and **Braan**. The latter arranges salmon fishings and issues dt from £5 for stocked hill lochs, also pike and perch, dt £1, for lochs **Cluanie** and **Freuchie**. Permits for **Loch Marlee** from Marlee Hotel, by Blairgowrie. Dunkeld House Hotel (salmon fishing). Atholl Arms can arrange trout fishing for guests.

Ballinluig (Perthshire). Salmon and trout, with good grayling Oct–March. Tummel here joins Tay. Fishing preserved. Hotel: Logierait, which has $2\frac{1}{2}$m of the Tay near hotel and other stretches including Grandtully Castle beats, to let to residents; salmon (March to June best; mostly spinning), trout (wet and dry fly).

Aberfeldy (Perthshire). Salmon, trout and grayling fishing on 3m of Upper Tay. Salmon, dt £8–£15; trout and grayling, mt £20, wt £5 and dt £2. Permits from D Campbell, The Square. Various hill lochs can be made available. Hotels: Guinach House, Moness House.

Weem (Perthshire). Hotel: Weem, which has trout and salmon fishing available free to guests on Weem Water. Dt for others.

Kenmore (Perthshire). Tay here leaves Loch Tay. Salmon and trout fishing on river and loch for guests at Kenmore Hotel: boats available.

Killin (Perthshire). **Dochart** and **Loch Tay;** salmon (Jan 15 to early May; average 18 lb; trolling on loch), trout (Mar 15 to Sept 30); average $\frac{1}{2}$ lb; wet and dry fly and dapping. Killin AC has trout fishing on west half of Loch Tay, on **Lochan-na-Laraig** and on stretches of **R Lochay** and R Dochart. St £20, wt £8 and dt £2. Club also has salmon fishing on 4m of R Dochart; wt £20 and dt £5. Permits from Des Allen, The Tackle Shop. Hotels with boats and fishing rights on loch are: Killin (also Lochay River), Bridge of Lochay, Clachaig. Ardeonaig Hotel has 12m of fishing and

boats on loch. Wt and dt.
Crianlarich (Perthshire). Trout fishing on **Loch Dochart** (good early in the season), **Loch-an-Nubhair** and **River Fillan.** In summer, salmon find their way into loch and up Fillan and tributaries. Best months: May, June, July and Sept. Ben More Restaurant issues permits.
Tyndrum (Perthshire). Fillan, Loch Lyon, Loch-na-Bhe (boats), Loch Tulla.

Tributaries of the Tay

EARN: Salmon, sea trout, brown trout (av $\frac{1}{2}$ lb) and excellent grayling.
Crieff (Perthshire). Crieff AC has 4m of north bank and 6m of south bank available to visitors. Feb 1 to July 31: mt £22, wt £12, dt £3. Aug 1 to Oct 15: mt £37, wt £20, dt £5 from tackleists, Wm Cook & Son, 19 High Street. No tickets on water. Best months: sea trout June to August; salmon, April, Sept and Oct. No Sunday fishing. No worms or gaffs before May 1. Other hotels: Arduthie, Kingarth, Drummond Arms (St Fillans), George, Victoria, Star.

Comrie (Perthshire). Salmon, sea trout, trout in Earn, **Ruchill** and **Lednock.** Salmon best Aug, Sept, Oct; sea trout best May and June. Rivers overfished and visitors' permits strictly limited. Tackleist: D McNaughton, Bridge Street. Hotels: Royal, Comrie, Ancaster Arms.
St Fillans (Perthshire). Trout fishing for visitors in **Loch Earn** and river; boats. Whole of loch controlled by St Fillans & Loch Earn AA, which also has $\frac{3}{4}$m of trout fishing on River Earn and Glentarken Burn; mt £5, wt £3 and dt £1 from post office (also tackle).

The Ardeonaig Hotel Loch Tay

AA ** RAC

12 miles of Salmon and Trout fishing on Loch Tay. River fishing can be arranged on several local rivers. For brochure contact Stephen or Sian Brown Killin (05672) 400

Dapping for loch trout under the eagle's eye. Suilven dominates the back-drop. *Photograph: John Tarlton.*

Lochearnhead (Perthshire). **Loch Earn;** brown trout ($\frac{1}{2}$-$\frac{3}{4}$ lb); permits from St Fillans and Lochearnhead Post Offices.
ISLA: Trout (av $\frac{1}{2}$ lb and up to 3 lb) and grayling. Pike also in lower reaches.
Dundee (Angus). Permits for trout and grayling fishing from Strathmore AIA; from local tackleists. Assn also issues permits for **Dean Water,** tributary of Isla; holds large trout and grayling, and is good for dry-fly. **Glamis** is useful centre. Assn also has short stretch of **Kerbet** and salmon fishing on **Isla;** members only. St £7.50, dt (S) £5.50, (T) £1.50, (G) £4, from local tackle shops and Glamis PO and for Isla from Mrs Dallas, Balbrogie Cottage, Coupar Angus. Forfar Canmore AC has water on **Dean, Kerbet** and **Noran** waters and on **Forfar Loch** and **Glenogil Reservoir;** st £5, mt £2.50, wt £2, dt £1 from C Kerr, West High Street. Other tackleist: E Mann, 44 Sheriff Park Gardens (permits for Glenogil Reservoir and Rescobie Loch; trout).

ALYTH (tributary of Isla):
Alyth (Perthshire). Several streams in neighbourhood. Isla contains trout and grayling in lower reaches. Above Reekie Linn trout very numerous but small. Hotel: Lands of Loyal.
Glenisla (Perthshire). Trout and grayling on Isla, **Melgum** and **Blackwater** from Glenisla Hotel.
ERICHT (tributary of Isla):
Blairgowrie (Perthshire). Blairgowrie, Rattray and Dist AC have salmon and good trout fishing, esp April and May. St £30, wt £12 (S) and £3 (T), dt £6 (S) and £1 (T), from local tackleists. Salmon fishing only available on certain days for non-club members. Loch fishing in area; many lochs hold pike and perch (**Marlee** best; boats at Marlee Hotel). At **Kirkmichael** (13m NW), Edelweiss Hotel issues permits for **Ardle River.** Other hotels: Royal, Bridge of Cally.
Blacklunans (Perthshire). Dalrulzion Hotel, Glenshee, PH10 7LJ, has salmon and

trout fishing on own river free to guests; dt £3. Other fishings available.

BRAAN:

Dunkeld (Perthshire). Several stretches of river free. Merryburn Hotel, Station Rd, Birnam, can arrange fishing on Braan and **Loch Craigluish.** Loch Freuchie lies near. Hotels: Atholl Arms, Royal Dunkeld, Stakis Dunkeld House.

TUMMEL: Salmon, trout and grayling.

Pitlochry (Perthshire). Boats for **Loch Faskally** from E Yule, two rods in each case. Salmon fishing mainly trolling; no Sunday fishing. Bank fishing (fly only), tickets also available; trout fishing April 15 to Sept 30; salmon fishing usually starts May 1, but not until 300 salmon have been counted through fish pass. Tickets can be had for Pitlochry AC water on **River Tummel** below Pitlochry Dam; salmon and sea trout on Port-na-Craig beat, limited dt £25–£6: trout and grayling in Tummel, dt £2; **Lochs Bhac** and **Kinardochy,** trout, boat £10; **Loch Garry,** trout, bank dt £1, but not available after July 31. Apply West Tempar Estate, Kinloch Rannoch, for other fishing on Tummel. Tickets for Tummel from Information Centre,

Malloch's tackle shop and Ballinluig PO. Tickets for lochs from Airdaniar Hotel, Atholl Road. General advice (by phone, evenings) from Harriman (2484) or Gardiner (2157). **Loch Moraig** available except Sat and Sun; excellent trout fishing; permits from W G Gordon, Lude, Blair Atholl. Permits for **Dunalastair Reservoir** (trout; boats) from J and H Mitchell, WS, 28 Atholl Road and Dunalastair Hotel *(see Kinloch Rannoch).* Other hotel: Pine Trees (Tummel fishing).

Strath Tummel (Perthshire). **Loch Tummel** holds excellent brown trout, some pike and perch and occasional salmon and sea trout. Fishing from Loch Tummel Hotel; N Campbell, Ardgnalich Farm; and Mr Scott-May, Croft Douglas; boats.

GARRY (and Ericht): Ruined as fishery by North of Scotland Hydro-Electric Board scheme.

Blair Atholl (Perthshire). Atholl Arms Hotel issues wt and dt, obtainable by non-residents from The Gun Shop, Blair Atholl.

Dalwhinnie (Inverness). Fishing on **Loch Ericht** (22m long) and rivers; st £15, wt £10, dt £2.50. Hotel: Loch Ericht.

LOCH RANNOCH: Trout, some large but averaging 9 oz; best May to October.

Kinloch Rannoch (Perthshire). Dunalastair Hotel has fishing free to guests on Tummel, on Loch Rannoch and on **Dunalastair Reservoir.** Dunalastair Res, fish to 5 lb; fly only; boat only (£12.50 per day). Conservation permits on R Tummel and L Rannoch; wt £5 and dt £1.50. Boats on L Rannoch £10 per day. Bunrannoch Hotel has fishing on Loch Rannoch and **River Tummel.** St £15, wt £5, dt £1.75. Concession to OAP and jun. Fishing and boats on other local lochs arranged. Moor of Rannoch Hotel, Rannoch Station PH17 2QA, has trout fishing on **L Laidon, R Gaur** and **Dubh Lochan,** which is stocked with brown trout. Dt £1.50 and £10 (Dubh Lochan). Rannoch AC has trout fishing on **Loch Eigheach,** Rannoch Station; dt £1.50 from J Brown, The Square, Kinloch Rannoch. Boat on **Loch Monogan** and **Loch Finnart** £6. Boat on Loch Rannoch (from Dunalastair Hotel) £8.

LYON (near Loch Tay): Good salmon and trout river in lovely valley.

Coschieville (Perthshire); ns Aberfeldy. Tay, Lyon, Keltney Burn; some trout fishing on request.

Fortingall (Perthshire); ns Aberfeldy. Fortingall Hotel has 3m on **Lyon; dt** (S) £12.50 and (T) £1.50. Also River Tay and Loch Tay by arrangement from £15 per day.

DOCHART (feeds Loch Tay):

Killin (Perthshire). At confluence of Dochart and Lochay, near head of Loch Tay. Salmon fishing best in July, Aug and Sept. Trout numerous and run to a fair size. Water is very deep and sluggish from Luib to Bovain, but above and as far as Loch Dochart there are some capital streams and pools. Mr G Coyne, Keeper's Cottage, Auchlyne and Glendochart Caravan Park issue £4 dt and wt by arrangement for Dochart. Trout fishing best April–May, good run of autumn salmon. Ardeonaig Hotel, **Ardeonaig,** has boat on Loch Tay. Morenish Lodge and Achray and Drummond Arms Hotel, **St Fillans,** can arrange fishing. W Allan, newsagent, Main St, issues permits for Kinnell Estate waters.

THURSO

A noted salmon river and one of the earliest in Scotland. However, the spring run has not been so good in recent times. Water level is regulated by a weir at Loch More on the upper reaches. The river is entirely preserved.

Thurso (Caithness). Salmon fishing (fly only) can be arranged through Thurso Fisheries Ltd, Thurso East (Tel: Thurso 63134). Bookings usually by week, fortnight or month, but day lets arranged. Weekly charges, including accommodation, range from £247 to £423, according to date. Excellent accommodation at Ulbster Arms, Halkirk. Fishing improves progressively from opening on Jan 11 to close on Oct 10. First-class loch, burn and river fishing for trout from hotel at attractive terms. Thurso AA has one beat; members only, but possibility of permit if no members fishing. Hotels: Royal Hotel has rights on **Loch Calder;** free to guests; trout. Pentland Hotel has rights on **Lochs Watten, St John's** and **Stemster,** and can arrange fishing on

Loch Calder; boats available; trout. St Clair Arms Hotel, Castletown, has rights on all these lochs and **Loch Hielan.** Tackleists: Harper's Fly Fishing, Sinclair Street issues st £3 and wt £1.50 for L **Calder, Watten,** etc, and arranges boats.

Halkirk (Caithness). The Ulbster Arms Hotel has fishing on Loch Calder and many other hill lochs; accommodation and fishing, £212–£384 per week. Salmon fishing on Thurso River. Information from Secretary, Thurso Fisheries Ltd, Thurso East, Thurso, Caithness.

Dunnet (Caithness); ns Thurso. Hotels: Northern Sands—own boats on Lochs **St John's** and **Scarmclate.** Fishing arranged on most others; also some river fishing for salmon and sea trout.

TWEED

Rises in corner formed by watersheds of Clyde and Annan, and flows over 100m to North Sea at Berwick-on-Tweed, forming, for much of its course, boundary between England and Scotland, Tweed is second only to Tay in its fame as a Scottish salmon river. It contains over 300 named casts and its salmon harvest is considerable. Sport more affected by height of the water than most rivers. Tweed produces strain of sea trout which are remarkable both for size and distance they are known to travel in sea. Formerly called bull trout, they rise badly to fly. Excellent brown trout in main river and tributaries, and grayling.

Berwick-on-Tweed (Northumberland). Salmon, sea trout, trout, grayling, coarse fish. Tidal Tweed gives free fishing for roach and grayling. Berwick and Dist AA has fishing in **Whiteadder,** which joins Tweed 1½m from here; brown trout only. Good bus service on both sides of Whiteadder and to Norham from Berwick. St £20 (£5 OAP & jun), wt £5, dt £3.50. **Till** enters Tweed 2½m above Norham, 9m from Berwick. A day or two's salmon fishing can sometimes be

Not a rod-caught fish, but claimed to be the biggest sea trout ever taken in Britain. $38\frac{1}{2}''$ in length: 28 lbs. 9 ozs. in weight. Netted from the Tweed at Norham, near Berwick. *Photo: D M Smith, Berwick and Alnwick.*

had from the lessees of the fisheries, on payment. Tillmouth Park Hotel, Cornhill-on-Tweed, Northumberland, has 4m on Tweed, divided into five beats; salmon and sea trout; boats and gillies available, wt £275 and £475, according to date (boat and gillie incl). Dt £50 and £80. (Coldstream 2255.) **Coldingham Loch,** near Great North Road, Ayton. Brown and rainbow trout, 5 boats, bank fishing for 6 rods. Dt £7.50 (boat extra) and evening £5.50. Permits from Dr E J Wise, West Loch House, Coldingham, Berwickshire (tel: 08907 71270), who has chalets and cottages to let. Coldingham is noted for the quality and size of the trout caught there. Berwick hotels: Castle, Kings Arms.

Norham (Northumberland). Salmon, trout; preserved. Ladykirk & Norham Angling Improvement Association has lot of water in the district—brown trout, grayling and coarse fish. Reputed to be one of the best waters along border. St £5, wt £2, dt £1 from hotels. Hotels: Masons Arms, Victoria.

Coldstream (Berwick). Tweed and **Leet Water**; salmon, trout. Details of salmon beats from J H Leeming, Chartered Surveyor, Stichil House, Kelso. Trout and coarse fishing permits from Tweed Tackle Shop, Market Street, Coldstream, and Crown Hotel, Market Square. Hotels: Majicado, Newcastle Arms.

Kelso (Roxburghshire). Salmon and sea trout preserved, trout and grayling. Also excellent sport with roach (av $\frac{3}{4}$ lb). Kelso AA has about 8m of Tweed and **Teviot,** and water on **River Eden.** Tickets (trout, grayling, coarse fish) from hon sec. No Sunday fishing; size limit 9 in; restrictions on spinning; trout season, April 1 to Sept 30. Trout fishing good. St £7, wt £4, dt £1.50. Concessions for OAP and jun. Tackleists: J Dickson & Sons, 35 The Square, TD5 7HL and Redpath

& Co, Horsemarket; from both tickets and information may be obtained. Sportswise, Roxburgh St, Kelso, also issues permits; others from river watchers. Trout fishing (brown and rainbow) on **Wooden Loch,** nr Kelso. Boat available. For reservations after April 10 apply A H Graham, Gamekeeper's House, Eckford, Kelso. Hotels: Cross Keys, Ednam House (fishing arranged in Tweed, **Teviot, Bowmont** and **Kale Waters),** Black Swan, and Sunlaws House, by Kelso.

St Boswells (Roxburgh). Brown trout. St Boswells, Newtown & District Angling Association have $4\frac{1}{2}$m. St £7, dt £1.50. Apply hon sec, Laws (electrician), Main Street, St Boswells, Christines (newsagent), Newtown St Boswells; Buccleuch Hotel, St Boswells; Dryburgh Abbey Hotel, Dryburgh. With a protection order in force anglers must not fish without first obtaining a permit. Salmon fishing all private. Hotels: Railway and Dryburgh Arms, Newtown; Buccleuch, St Boswells; Dryburgh Abbey, Dryburgh.

Melrose (Roxburghshire). Melrose and Dist AA has several stretches open to visitors for trout and grayling fishing. Fish average three to the pound. St £6, wt £4 and dt £1.50, with concessions to juniors. No Sunday fishing; no spinning or use of natural minnow or maggot permitted. Tickets from Anglers' Choice, High Street. Holders of these tickets eligible for dt on new waters at Cowies and Ravenswood, but numbers restricted. Season: April 1 to Oct 6 (Sept 30 on new waters). Hotels: Bon Accord, Waverley Castle, Tweedmount. Guest House: Craig Friarshall, Gattonside.

Earlston (Berwickshire). A good centre for **Leader** and Tweed trout fishing. Earlston AA controls about 5m of Leader adjacent to Earlston, with the exception of two small private stretches; st £4, dt £1 (OAP free), from Earlston newsagents, no salmon fishing; no Sunday fishing and Saturday fishing for st holders only. 4 day permits available at £1 each on River Tweed at Gledswood Estate for st holders. Melrose AA has excellent trout water *(see Melrose).* Other portions of Tweed are reserved. No salmon or seatrout fishing is available on trouting portions of Tweed. Hotel: White Swan. Tackleist: J Rutherford & Son.

Galashiels (Selkirk) Rods for Boleside beat from L Bald, Fisherman's Cottage, Boleside. Wt £115 and £86.25 according to date. Feb 1 to Sept 10. Tel: 2792. Salmon, brown trout and grayling. Gala AA has trout fishing on 10–12m of Tweed; st £5, wt £2, dt £1.50 (no Sunday tickets; no spinning). Tickets from hon sec or J and A Turnbull (tackleist), Bank Street. April to Sept provides best daytime sport; mid-June to Aug best evenings. **Gala Water** is included in permit. Hotels: Douglas, Clovenfords, Thornilee, Kingsknowes.

Selkirk (Selkirkshire) Salmon fishing preserved. Good centre for Tweed, **Yarrow** and **Ettrick,** covering 80m of trout fishing. Selkirk and Dist AA restocks annually from own hatchery. St £5.50, mt £4, wt £2.50 and dt £1.25 from any post office, or hotel in district. Trout average four to the pound and go up to 3 lb. No spinning allowed. Hotels: Shaws, Broadmeadows, Gordon Arms, Glen, Heatherlie House, Woodburn, Philipburn, Heatheray Hill, Whitmuir Hall. Some in the town, some in the surrounding countryside.

Ettrickbridge. Hotel: Ettrickshaws.

Clovenfords (Selkirk). Tweed here controlled by Gala AA *(see Galashiels).* Caddon Water; trout. Gala Water; trout.

Check before you go

While every effort has been made to ensure that the information given in "Where to Fish" is correct, the position is continually changing and anglers are urged, in their own interests, to make preliminary inquiries before travelling to selected venues. This is especially important with reference to prices quoted. Inevitably, the rate of inflation is affecting stability in this quarter. Anglers' attention is also drawn to the fact that the hotels mentioned under the various fishing stations do not necessarily have water of their own. Any amendments or further data for inclusion in subsequent editions, and any criticism, will be welcome.

Walkerburn (Peebles). Salmon, trout. Peebles TFA has water. Also Peebles Salmon FA water *(see Peebles)*. Tweed Valley Hotel, EH43 6AA, which offers rod hire, tuition and specially arranged fishing holidays, has access to much private water for salmon, sea trout and brown trout fishing on a variety of terms ranging from £3 per day for loch fishing to £72–£311 per week for a salmon beat. Gillies and instruction by arrangement. Tel: 089687 636. *(Advt above.)*

Innerleithen (Borders). Salmon, trout. Peebles TFA has water *(see Peebles)*. Leithen Water; trout; free. Quair Water; trout; preserved. Hotel: Traquair Arms.

Peebles (Borders). Salmon fishing on approx 2 miles of Tweed. Season Feb 21 to Nov 30. Tickets (limited in number) issued by Peeblesshire Salmon Fishing Association. Enquiries Blackwood & Smith WS, 39 High St, Peebles. St £50, dt £10 and £20. Also salmon and trout fishing on Town Water; st (BT) £1, wt (S) £20 and £50 (only Mon to Fri). Enquiries District Council Offices, Rosetta Road, Peebles. Peebles Trout FA has approx 25m on Tweed and 5m on **Lyne;** trout and grayling; restocked. Season April 1 to Sept 30. No spinning or float fishing. Fly only April and Sept and all season on upper reaches. Fish under 9 in must be returned. Waders desirable. Good trout April/May on wet fly then dry best. Tickets issued by hon sec. St £14 (per beat), ft £14, wt £9, dt £3. Hotels: Cringletie House, Tontine, Park, Green Tree, Cross Keys, Peebles Hydro.

Broughton (Borders). Trout; preserved. Holmes Water. Broughton Burn. Crook Inn, Tweedsmuir, by Biggar, convenient for Upper Tweed and **Talla, Fruid** and **Megget Reservoirs,** £2 per day (bank), boat £2. Permits from Victoria Lodge, Tweedsmuir. Dt for river (S) £15, (T) £2.50, from Crook Inn.

Tributaries of the Tweed

WHITEADDER: Runs from Chirnside Bridge to Edington Castle via Allanton Bridge. A good trout stream. Upper waters, from Ninewells (Chirnside) to source, including tributaries, are largely controlled by Whiteadder AA; st £6, dt £2 from hon sec, bailiffs and hotels. Tickets must be obtained before fishing begins. Concessions to OAP, ladies and juniors. Assn has restocked water with brown and rainbow trout. Trout av ¼ lb. Best months June–August. Many burns.

Allanton (Berwick). 1¼m Berwick and Dist AA water from ½m above Allanton Bridge to Cantie's Bridge; trout; visitors living outside 15m radius, wt and dt. St and dt for water above Allanton Bridge obtainable locally. Blackadder joins river here. Fishing reported good. Whiteadder AA has from above Allanton Bridge to source. Hotel: Red Lion, Allanton, Chirnside, Berwickshire *(see Chirnside)*.

Duns (Borders). Trout. The following streams are within easy reach: Blackadder (preserved by private association), Whiteadder, **Fasney, Bothwell, Dye, Blacksmill, Monynut** and **Watch.** These, except Blackadder, are, with main stream, largely controlled by Whiteadder AA. Assn also has fishing on **Watch Reservoir;** bank dt £2, boat for two, £5; is stocked with brown and rainbow trout.

Tickets and boats from bailiff Amos, Longformacus *(see Chirnside)*. Riparian owners may grant permission. Tackleist: R Welsh, 28 Castle Street. Hotels: Bungalow, Blanerne, Duns. 1m both banks in Whiteadder reserved for hotel guests. White Swan, Barnikin.

Chirnside (Borders). Trout. Chirnside is good centre for Whiteadder, provided that angler has car. From here to source, except for stretches at Abbey St Bathans Estate, Chirnside Paper Mills and Cumledge Bridge, river is controlled by Whiteadder AA, including all tributaries entering above Chirnside, except (1) the Monynut above Bankend; (2) the Fasney above Fasney Bridge; and (3) certain stretches of the Dye. Tickets from hon sec.

Longformacus (Borders). Some 7m from Duns. On Dye, Watch and Blacksmill burns. Whiteadder runs near Hotel: Rathburne (permits for Whiteadder AA fisheries), *(see Chirnside for fishing)*.

BLACKADDER (tributary of Whiteadder): Very good for brown trout early in season.

Greenlaw (Borders). About 12m held by Greenlaw AC. Tickets from hotels, PO and Doigs Store; st £4.50, dt £1.50. Concessions for OAP and jun. Hotel: Castle.

TILL and BREAMISH: Trout, sea trout, salmon, good grayling, some pike and perch.

Etal (North'land). Accommodation at Red Lion. Millfield (about 3m), but all fishing round Etal strictly preserved.

Wooler (North'land). Good centre for Till (2m N) and **Glen,** which join below Wooler, running through Millfield Plain into Tweed, and are open for sea trout and salmon angling from Feb to Nov. Whitling early summer if conditions right; later on large fish numerous. Wooler and Doddington AA preserves 2m of the Till and 1m of **Wooler Water;** limited dt £4 issued to visitors staying locally, but not for Sundays; fixed-spool reels prohibited; no maggot fishing; fly only, Feb–April inclusive and from Sept 14 to Nov 30. Tickets from hon sec. Some miles from Wooler, at Bewick Bridge, Breamish becomes Till. Wading in Till dangerous. White Swan Inn, Yetholm, can give details of fishing on **Bowmount** and **Kale Waters.** Trout (small), grayling, with good sea trout in wet season.

Chatton (North'land). Trout, grayling; and some fine roach: preserved by Chatton AA for $6\frac{1}{2}$m. Limited number of associated members' tickets; st £7.50, apply by Jan 1 to hon sec for st; dt from hotel. Other centres: **Lilburn, Chillingham.** Hotel: Percy Arms, whose guests may fish Assn water for £5 per day. *(See English section under Otterburn).*

EDEN: Trout.

Ednam (Borders), ns Kelso, 2m. Trout: Kelso AA has water *(see Kelso)*. Tweed 1m E.

TEVIOT: Good salmon spring and autumn, and first-class for trout and grayling.

Roxburgh (Borders). Kelso AA controls some miles of brown trout fishing on Teviot and Tweed *(see Kelso)*. Tweed, 2m W.

Eckford (Borders). Eckford AA issues dt for Teviot; salmon and trout. The Buccleuch Estate has 1m on Treviot; dt (S) £10 and (T) £1.50: $1\frac{1}{2}$m on **Kale Water;** dt (T) £1: and **Wooden Loch;** dt (T) £7. Tickets from waterkeeper, Keeper's Cottage, Eckford (tel: 08355 255).

Nisbet (Borders). Salmon, bull trout, brown trout, pike, perch, grayling. Oxnam Water. Jed Water, 2m S: trout.

Hawick (Borders). Teviot and tributaries **Slitrig, Borthwick, Rule** and **Ale.** Hawick AC issues tickets for these and for **Lochs Alemmor, Hellmoor, Williestruther, Acreknowe** and **Akermoor;** st £9, wt £5, dt £2 and £10 (S), from hon sec or Stotharts, High Street. Rivers all contain brown trout and grayling; all lochs contain trout but Alemoor is primarily pike and perch water.

Jedburgh (Borders). St £10, wt £6 dt £10 and £1.50 for visitors for Rivers Jed (trout) and Teviot (salmon, trout and grayling) through Jed-Forest AA. Grayling fishing permitted on Teviot only, except in Oct, Nov, and Feb. Tickets from hon sec; Game and Country Enterprises, 6/8 Canongate and W Shaw, Cannongate. Jedforest Hotel has stretch of **Jed Water,** which runs by hotel (brown trout). Royal Hotel can arrange fishing in Jed Water and Teviot. Tackleists: Jedburgh Gun & Sports Shop.

LEADER: Trout (4 to lb).

Lauder (Borders). Lauderdale AA controls 6m of Leader and 20m of tributaries upwards from Whitslaid Bridge to Carfraemill with the exception of waters in Thirlestane Castle policies. St £4, wt £3, dt £2 from hon sec, bailiffs and Post Office. Earlston AA has water *(see Earlston under Tweed)*. Hotels: Tower, Oxton; Carfrae Mill (4m from Lauder); Lauderdale; Black Bull; Loanside, Eagle.

Oxton (Borders). Lauderdale AC has burns; small trout *(see Lauder)*.

GALA WATER: Popular trout water; fish average about 5 to lb.

Stow (Borders). Edinburgh is 26m distant by rail. There is a good hotel (Royal Hotel) standing on banks of Gala. Fishing on 5m below Stow, and 4m above. Ludgate Water, $1\frac{1}{2}$m; trout; 6m off is the Leader; trout.

Fountainhall (Borders). Gala Water; trout. Armet Water. Within easy reach of Edinburgh.

ETTRICK WATER (and Yarrow): Salmon fishing preserved. The Buccleuch Estate has fishing on **Bowhill Estate** and Upper Loch, Bowhill. Tickets from Estate Office, Bowhill, Selkirk TD7 5ES (tel: 0750 20753). All trout fishing in Ettrick and Yarrow by ticket; water being restocked with brown trout by Selkirk AA. Good fishing on some 50m besides

many burns. Dt for **Clearburn Loch,** Hawick, £2.50 + £2.50 per boat from Tushielaw Inn. Association tickets from Tushielaw Hotel (Ettrick), Gordon Arms (Yarrow), Rodono, Tibbie Shiels *(see Megget Water)* and bailiffs, and hotels and tackleists in Selkirk.

St Mary's Loch (Selkirk). Rights on **Megget Water** held by Rodono Hotel. Trout; chance of a salmon. Fishing free to guests. Ticket charges for non-residents: wt £4 and £6, dt £1 and £2. Loch (into which Megget Water runs) leased and stocked by St Mary's Loch AC. Trout, pike and perch. Residents at Rodono and Tibbie Shiels hotels have free fishing. Boats available. **Loch of the Lowes** is also St Mary's AC and Rodono Hotel water; also feeder burns; brown and rainbow trout (few pike and perch); permits from bailiffs, hon sec, Gordon Arms Hotel and The Glen Café.

EDDLESTON WATER: Situated near Eddleston village on bus route. Equal distance from Peebles and Leadburn (5m). Trout; but of little account; fishable also from Peebles.

TYNE (Lothian)

Rises on north slopes of Lammermuir Hills and flows about 25m to North Sea a little south of Whitberry Ness, known best as brown trout stream.

Haddington (Lothian). Trout; East Lothian AA controls most of water in county. St £4 and dt £1.50 from J Main, High Street, and L Walker, 3 Bridge Street, East Linton; also river watchers. No Sunday fishing; no spinning. Permits for **Whiteadder Reservoir** (trout) from

Reservoir Superintendent. Fishing on two other reservoirs — **Donnally** and **Hopes** — also available from Dept of Water and Drainage, Alderston House, Haddington (tel: 062 082 4131). Good sea fishing at **North Berwick** (10m).

UGIE

A small river entering the sea at Peterhead. Salmon, good sea trout, some brown trout. Salmon and sea trout best from July to October; good run of finnock in February and March.

Peterhead (Aberdeens). Permits available for approx 13m of fishing owned by Capt Curzon, Daluaine, Huntly. St £39, wt £14, dt £6 from Robertson Sports, 1–3 Kirk Street, Peterhead; Gavin Milne, Newsagent, 3 Ugie Street, Peterhead; or Dick's Sports, 54 Broad Street, Fraserburgh. Small Angling Assn surcharge. Juniors and OAP half-price. 12m N of Peterhead is **Loch of Strathbeg;** Loch Leven trout (av $\frac{3}{4}$ lb). Boat for one

£6; for two £8; for three £10; apply J Moir, Gamekeeper, Wood Cottage, Crimonmogate Estate, Lonmay (tel: 0346 32367) or Brown & McRae, solicitors. **Crimongate Fishery** 6m S Fraserburgh; six acre lake; wild brown trout and stocked with rainbow. Dt £12 (limit 4 fish), wt and st also available. Tel: 0346 32225. Hotels: Alexandra, High St; Royal and Station, Broad St.

Tributary of the Ugie

STRICHEN (or North Ugie):
Strichen (Aberdeens). Free trout fishing

(subject to permission of riparian owners). Salmon fishing strictly preserved.

URR

Drains Loch Urr and flows to Solway. Late run of salmon; also sea trout, herling and brown trout.

Rockcliffe (Dumfries & Galloway). On Urr estuary. Baron's Craig Hotel can arrange fishing on river and hill lochs (7m from hotel).

Dalbeattie (Dumfries & Galloway). Dalbeattie AA has 3½m both banks; salmon, grilse, sea trout, herling and brown trout; wt £16 and dt £6. Assn has Loch Leven and rainbow trout fishing on **Dalbeattie Reservoir;** fly only; wt £15 and dt £5. Full-water permits (limited) £27. Permits from M McCowan & Son, 43 High Street. Concession to jun. Glenshalloch Burn free fishing. Southwick AS has fishing on **Southwick Water;**

sea trout, brown trout, herling; dt and wt from the hon sec. Hotels: Maxwell Arms, Galloway Arms, Kings Arms, Glaisters Lodge, Corsock. The Pheasant, Dalbeattie. At **Castle Douglas** (5m W) the Angling Assn has about 5m of Urr. Dt £5 and wt £15 from Tackleist: Tommy's Sports Goods, 178 King St, Castle Douglas.

Crocketford (Dumfries & Galloway). Trout lochs; Corsock, Glenkiln and various others; boats available. Pike and perch fishing on **Auchenreoch** and **Milton Lochs.** Hotel: Galloway Arms (tickets for local fishing).

WEST COAST STREAMS AND LOCHS

Some complex fisheries and one or two smaller—though not necessarily less sporting—streams are grouped here for convenience. Other west coast waters will be found in the main alphabetical list.

AILORT

A short but very good sea trout river which drains Loch Eilt and enters sea through saltwater Loch Ailort. One of the very few rivers where run of genuine spring sea trout takes place.

Lochailort (Inverness). 27½m from Fort William. Salmon and sea trout fishing on **Loch Eilt** and River Ailort preserved. **Loch Morar,** a few miles north, provides excellent sport with salmon, sea trout

and brown trout. Fishing from banks free. Boats £10 day from Morar Hotel, Morar, Mallaig, when not wanted by guests.

LOCH BROOM (including Rivers Broom, Dundonnell, Garvie, Oscaig and Ullapool)

Achiltibuie (nr Ullapool). (Ross & Cromarty). Sea trout, brown trout and sea fishing. Summer Isles Hotel has much fishing for guests on rivers and lochs in the vicinity. Sea trout, brown trout Loch Oscaig and Lurgain: boat £20 and £15, River Garvie,

dt £10, brown trout lochs, dt £5. Gillies can be arranged £17 per day extra. Own boats for sea fishing. Permits from Badentarbat Lodge for left bank River Garvie; fly only; dt £5: and also six brown trout lochs; fly only; dt 75p.

The Royal Hotel, Ullapool

Situated on the shores of Loch Broom and commanding superb views, the Royal specialises in fresh local produce for its fine restaurant.

Sea angling. Fishing rights to 2 excellent Hill Lochs. Boats and outboards available for Hill Lochs.
Ghillie on request.

ULLAPOOL (0854) 2181

Ullapool (Ross & Cromarty). **Ullapool River,** sea and brown trout; dt £15 (upper beat) and £4 (lower beat). **Loch Achall,** salmon, sea and brown trout; dt £10 (boat) and £4.50 (bank). Permits from tackleist *(see below).* Royal Hotel has fishing for guests on **River Polly** (20m away); **River Garvie** salmon and sea trout; **Loch Sionascaig** (20m), brown trout; and **Loch Lurgain** (12m). For salmon, sea trout and brown trout fishing on River Garvie, **Polly Lochs** and **Loch Sionascaig** apply to Estate Office, Inverpolly (tel: 05714 252). Tackleist: Lochboom Hardware, Shore Street. Hotel: Royal.

Dundonnell (Ross & Cromarty). **Dundonnell River;** salmon and sea trout. Hotel Dundonnell, by Garve.

Inverbroom. River Broom; best July and August. Also hill lochs. Beats sometimes available on Inverbroom Estate water; inquiries to Sharpe or Matheson, Inverbroom.

LOCH DUICH, including Shiel and Croe

Glenshiel (Ross & Cromarty); ns Kyle of Lochalsh. Salmon and sea trout. Fishing available on **River Croe,** a spate-river with late runs. Dt £7.50 from Nat

Trust for Scotland, Morvich Farm House, Inverinate, By Kyle IV40 8HQ. Reductions for members. Sea fishing on Loch Duich.

ECHAIG (Loch Eck and to Holy Loch)

Drains Loch Eck and flows about 5m into Atlantic by way of Holy Loch and Firth of Clyde. Salmon and sea trout.

Kilmun (Argyll). On Holy Loch and Firth of Clyde. Echaig enters sea here. Salmon, sea trout in Loch Eck (5m), where Whistlefield Inn, Loch Eck, has boats for guests: fly best at head of loch where **River Cur** enters. Other hotel: Coylet.

Dunoon (Argyll). River fishing now preserved. Coylet and Whistlefield Hotels have salmon (mainly trolling), sea trout and brown trout fishing on **Lock Eck** for guests (preferential terms for residents); st £10, wt £5 and dt £1.50; boats available at hotels. Loch Eck is about 7m long. No good for salmon until early June; best in August, Sept. Whistlefield Inn also has fishing by arrangement in Rivers **Cur, Finnart** and **Masan. Loch**

Tarsan and **Loch Loskin** fishing for brown trout, fly only. **Dunoon Reservoir,** rainbow and brown trout, fly only. Rivers **Massan, Cur** and **Finnart** salmon and sea trout any legal lure. Dt £2.50 to £8. Wt: L Tarsan £6; R Cur £10; R Finnart £6. Seven day rover permit allows fishing on all above £25. Permits from Purdies of Argyll, 112 Argyll Street (tel: 0369 3232). Permits for **River Finnart,** sea trout, and occasional salmon, £2 per day ($\frac{1}{2}$ day £1), from Forest Office, Benmore Forest, Kilmun by Dunoon. Glendaruel Hotel at **Glendaruel** (18m) has salmon, sea trout and trout fishing on **River Ruel** (best July to Sept). Permits £1 day.

LOCH FYNE (including Rivers Douglas, Shira, Garron, Kinglas, Fyne and Dubh Loch)

Large sea loch on west coast of Argyll, which provides good sea fishing and first-class salmon and sea trout in streams. These are spate rivers; best from June to September.

Inveraray (Argyll). Argyll Estates, Cherry Park, Inveraray (Inveraray 2203) issue dt as follows and as available: R Aray £15, R Shira £7, R Douglas £6, R Garron and Dubh Loch £15, hill lochs, £2. No Sunday fishing.

Knipoch by Oban (Argyll). **Dubh Loch** and **Loch Seil,** dt £5 with boat. L Leven and brown trout. River Euchar, salmon and sea trout; dt from J T P Mellor, Barndromin Farm (tel: 085 26 273).

Cairndow (Argyll). **River Fyne** tidal water: Wt £70, dt £14 from Ardkinglas (Tel: Cairndow 217), but fishing may be let to single tenant for whole season.

GAIRLOCH

A sea loch on the west coast of Ross. Gairloch Hotel has trout fishing on lochs. Shieldaig Lodge Hotel has trout fishing on lochs and salmon fishing on one loch and short stretch of river. Limited permits for visitors. Salmon and sea-trout fishing on **River Kerry** from Creag Mor Hotel. Dt £8. Dt for hill loch brown trout fishing from tackle shops.

GLENELG

Rises in Glen More and flows about 10m to the sea at **Glenelg.** Salmon and sea-trout fishing preserved by owner of Scallasaig Lodge. Rod occasionally let for the day at owner's discretion.

LOCH INCHARD

Kinlochbervie (Sutherland). Garbet Hotel has extensive rights of high standard; over 40 lochs; sea trout (July to Sept), brown trout (April to Sept) and small spate river (the **Shinary**). Stock of flies and casts at hotel. Fishing free to guests. Boats from £2 day. Trout average 1 lb.

LOCH LONG (including Rivers Finnart and Goil)

A sea loch opening into the Firth of Clyde. Good sea trout, some salmon in streams. Finnart good in spates. Forestry Commission intend to lease Rivers Finnart and Goil to local angling clubs but arrangements have not yet been finalized.

Ardentinny (Argyll). Finnart, $1\frac{1}{2}$m fishing, enters Loch Long here. Salmon, grilse and sea trout, season July to mid-October: May–September.

Arrochar (Argyll). Arrochar House hotel (Tel 238) overlooks Loch Long, where good sea fishing obtainable. Hotel has trout fishing in **Loch Lomond** ($1\frac{1}{2}$m). Vale of Leven & Dist AC issues permits for trout fishing on **Loch Sloy.** Dt £2.50; fly only. Apply to hon sec (tel: 0389 57843).

Carrick (Argyll). Carrick Castle Hotel has salmon, sea trout and brown trout on River and **Loch Goil,** free to guests. Boat on loch.

Lochgoilhead (Argyll). For fishing on **Lettermay Loch,** brown trout, contact D Campbell, Faillte, Lochgoilhead. Sea fishing in **Loch Goil.** Hotels: Lochgoilhead, Drimsynie House (private stretches free to guests).

CUILFAIL HOTEL
KILMELFORD
BY OBAN, ARGYLL
Tel: KILMELFORD 274

Nestling between sea and hill. A delightful country hotel combining Victorian charm with modern comfort.

Come and stalk trout in hill lochs and burns. Then return for a refreshing dram and a delicious home cooked dinner.

FIRTH OF LORN (including Loch Nell)

Forming the strait between Mull and the mainland on the west coast. Lochs Linnhe and Etive open into it. Good sea trout and a few salmon.

Oban (Argyll). **Loch Nell** (4m). Good sea trout, occasional salmon, July–Sept. Heavier sea trout run towards end of June, and later on finnock appear in numbers. Boats from Mrs MacIlwraith, Torinturk, Glenloan (Kilmore 212) by Oban. **Oban Reservoir,** at Loch-na-Gleanna Bhearraidh, 1½m of Ardrishaig Road, gives reasonable sport with brown trout (av 1 lb). Loch Nell, Oban Reservoir and many other lochs and lochans in the area managed by Oban and Lorn Angling Club; tickets from local tackleists. Brown trout fishing in **Black Loch;** dt from Halfway House, Caravan Site, Dunbeg, Connel. At **Kilninver** on **Euchar** estuary (10m south of Oban on A816), good salmon, sea trout and some brown trout fishing may

be had from Mrs M McCorkindale, Glennan, Kilninver. Dt £2 for river, boat £6 for 2 rods for loch. Bank £2. As the Euchar is a spate river, bookings are not accepted more than a week in advance. Price concession for full week booking. Lt Col P S Sandilands also issues dt for river. Boat on **Loch Scammadale** dt £2 + £2 per rod from Mrs M McCorkindale. J T P Mellor, Barndromin Farm, Knipoch (by Oban) has 1m, for which permits are issued three days a week only. Sea trout best mid-June to end of Sept; salmon first week of July to early Oct. Tackleist: D Graham, 9–15 Combie Street and 123 George St. Hotels: Alexandra; Shieling Guest House, Kilmore; Cuilfail, Kilmelford *(advt above)*; Tighantruish, Clachan Bridge.

LOCH MELFORT

A sea loch opening into the Firth of Lorn south of Oban. Sea trout, mackerel, flounders, etc.

Kilmelford (Argyll) 15m from Oban. Cuilfail Hotel can arrange fishing on Lochs **nan Drimnean** (10 min walk, trout; March–May, Aug–Sept best; fly only; 10 in limit), **a'Phearsain** (15 min walk; trout, char; fly only; April–June, Aug–Sept best), **Avich** (5m by road; trout; May–Oct best), **na Sreinge** (8m by road and 35 min walk; trout; May–Oct

best), **Scammadale** (8m by road; sea trout, salmon; end June–Sept), Melfort (10 min walk; sea trout, mackerel, flounders, skate, etc; June–Aug best), and five hill lochs (hour's walk and climb; trout; June–Oct). Wt £12, dt £2.50. Season: March 15 to Oct 15. *(Advt above.)*

MORVERN

Lochaline (Argyll). At mouth of Loch Aline; salmon and sea trout in loch and **R Aline,** whiting, mackerel etc, in Sound of Mull. Ardtornish Estate, Morven, by Oban PA34 5XA, has fishing on river and boats on **L Arienas;** (brown and sea trout:) and on self-stocking hill lochs. Dt from £2 to £13.20. Inquiries to factor.

LOCH MUDLE

Ardnamurchan (Argyll). Kilchoan Hotel, on the Ardnamurchan peninsula, by Fort William, issues dt (boat and bank) for

Loch Mudle. Glen Lochs, about $\frac{1}{2}$m from Kilchoan, free of charge (brown trout).

WICK

Good salmon and sea-trout fishing on Wick River controlled by Wick AA *(see Wick)*. Famous Loch Watten (trout) is 7m from Wick. Also many other excellent trout lochs, including St John's Calder, and Stemster. Apply to Pentland and Royal Hotels (both Thurso), Northern Sands Hotel (Dunnet, by Thurso), Ulbster Arms (Halkirk), John O'Groats House Hotel and Loch Watten Hotel, Watten.

Wick (Caithness). Wick AA permits for visitors. Wt and dt. River well stocked from association's own hatchery. Trout fishing on several lochs.

Lybster (Caithness). Lybster is 12m S of Wick at mouth of Reisgill Burn. Guests at Portland Arms Hotel can have salmon and sea trout fishing on **Berriedale River** and trout fishing on six lochs by arrange-

ment. Best months for loch: May and Sept. Permits for (**Loch Watten** also from Lochview Farmhouse and for **St John's** from Northern Sands Hotel, Dunnet, St Clair Hotel, and A A MacDonald, both Sinclair St, Thurso. Thrumster Garages, Thrumster, issue permits for **Hempriggs** and **Sarclet.**

YTHAN

Rises in "Wells of Ythan" and runs some 35m to North Sea at Newburgh. Late salmon river which used to fish best in autumn, but now has good spring run (February, March, April). All netting on the Estuary has been stopped since 1979 so now seeing a marked difference in the stocks returning each year. River of no great account for brown trout, but noted for sea trout and finnock, which run up from June through to September, with some fish in October. Ythan has very large estuary for so small a river and is markedly tidal for the lower five miles or so of its course.

Newburgh (Aberdeenshire) 13 miles from Aberdeen, sea trout and finnock and salmon. Fishing the large estuary here controlled by Fishing Manager, Mr E I Forbes, Ythan Fisheries, 3 Lea Cottages, 130 Main Street, Newburgh, Ellon AB4 03N. (Tel: Newburgh 035 86 297). Sea trout average $2-2\frac{1}{2}$ lbs run up to 12 lbs; finnock May onwards with large ones in September. Fly fishing and spinning only; spoons. Ythan Terrors, devons and Sutherland Specials fished on a 7-8 ft spinning rod with 8-12 lb line as most usual tackle. Worm, maggot, bubble float and other bait not allowed. Lead

core lines, sinking lines not allowed. Floating line with sinking tip allowed. Much fishing from bank, but boats available. Prices on application to Fishery Office, 3 Lea Cotts, Newburgh, Aberdeenshire (Tel: 035 86 297), who also stocks tackle. Best months June to September.

Methlick (Aberdeens). Still some spring fish, but the main run now Sept/Oct. Good early run of finnock; a second, smaller run in the autumn. Sea trout; June–Oct. Fishing on Haddo Estate water; now leased to Haddo House Angling Association. Dt £3 to £7.

Enquiries to hon sec (*see club list*). Hotel: Ythanview.

Ellon (Aberdeens). Salmon, sea trout, trout. Buchan Hotel issues permits for fishing at Ellon Castle; st £60, wt £24, dt £5: and at Meikle Mill; st £50, wt £20, dt £4. Concession for OAP and jun. Spring good for finnock (to mid-April) and Aug to Oct good for sea trout. Tributaries: Ebrie *(see Auchnagatt)*, Forvie; trout,

free. Loch of Strathbeg stocked with Loch Levens (av ¾ lb) *(see Ugie—Peterhead)*.

Fyvie (Aberdeens). Sea trout, finnock, salmon, brown trout. Sept and Oct best months for sea trout. Fyvie AA issues st £10 and dt £1.50 (Oct £2), obtainable from Vale Hotel; Sheiling Tor Café, Ythan; Spar Grocer; Clydesdale Bank.

Tributary of the Ythan

EBRIE:
Auchnagatt (Aberdeens). Parts of the river are free; sea trout, finnock, trout. Sea

trout fishing fairly good in the back end when there is plenty of rain; fly or lure. Hotel: Baron's Inn.

Angling, from time immemorial, has offered inspiration to writers and artists. This photograph is of a fine bronze sculpted by David Hughes, well-known Midland artist craftsman, and keen angler.

SEA FISHING STATIONS IN SCOTLAND

IT is only in recent years that the full sea angling potential of the Scottish coast, indented by innumerable rocky bays and sea lochs, has come to be appreciated. Working in conjunction, tourist organisations and local sea angling clubs smooth the path for the visiting angler. He is well supplied in matters of boats and bait, natural stocks of the latter remaining relatively undepleted in many areas.

Note: The local name for coalfish is "saithe" and for pollack "lythe".

Further details on sea fishing in Scotland may be had from the Scottish Tourist Board, who provide a useful guide.

Stranraer (Dumfries & Galloway). Loch Ryan, the W coast of Wigtownshire and Luce Bay offer first-class sea fishing, boat and shore. Loch Ryan: codling, whiting, plaice, flounders, dabs, skate, conger, tope and dogfish. Other species found in Luce Bay and off Irish Sea coast include pollack, bass, wrasse, mackerel and tope. No sea bait sold locally. Tackleist: Sports Shop, George St, Stranraer.

Girvan (Ayrshire). Mostly saithe, haddock, cod, pollack and mackerel, which run quite heavy towards Ailsa Craig; July onwards best. Shore fishing and boats from harbour; inquire of Harbourmaster. Tackleist: J H Murray, 3 Dalrymple Street. Six boats take out parties. £3.50 per 4 hours.

Ayr (Ayrshire). Saithe, haddock, whiting, skate, cod, mackerel, conger, eels, flounders; from pier, shore, or boats which can be hired in the town. Good mackerel fishing (trolling) in July and August. Tackleists: James Kirk, 5 Union Arcade; Game-sport, 60 Sandgate; J A Newbiggin, 19 Aitken St, Largs.

Saltcoats and Ardrossan (Ayrshire). Cod, haddock, conger, saithe, flatfish. Good beach fishing in Irvine Bay and small bay between Saltcoats and Ardrossan. Boatmen include: A Gibson, 1 Fleck Avenue, Saltcoats. Tackleist: "Leisure Time", 42 Hamilton Street. Clubs: Saltcoats SAA and Ardrossan and District SAC.

Lamlash (Isle of Arran). Growing centre. Horseshoe Bay popular. Good cod, haddock, whiting, flatfish, etc. Boats at St Molios Boatyard, Old Pier, or Pier Cafe. N C McLean, Torlin Villa, Kilmory, will answer inquiries. Angling festivals at Whitsun and in August.

Campbeltown (Argyll). Good sport with cod, haddock, flatfish, etc, in Kildalloig Bay and from The Winkie, causeway between Davaar Island and mainland. Some boats; trips arranged. Further details from the Tourist Information Office. Tackleists: R Armour & Sons, Longrow; A P MacGrory, Main Street.

Oban (Argyll). Accessible beaches overfished, but good sport in Firth of Lorne and tidal waters near Kerrera Island with saithe, pollack, mackerel, huss, conger and flatfish. D McLeod, 2 Castle Road, runs fishing trips. Several other boat hirers. Tackleists: D Graham, Combie Street.

Mallaig (Inverness). Good centre in beautiful area. Flatfish, pollack, conger, mackerel, coalfish in bay and from rocks and new piers. Boats from John Henderson & Son. Tackleists: Johnston Bros; D W Maclean, The Pier.

Shieldaig (Ross & Cromarty). Skate, cod, conger, saithe, ling, huss, dabs, sole and mackerel. Fishing in sea lochs of Shieldaig, Torridon and Upper Torridon; sheltered water nearly always. Outside lochs conditions can be dangerous. D N Cameron, "Hillcroft", takes boat parties out.

Gairloch (Ross & Cromarty). Cod, haddock, whiting, pollack, saithe and flatfish in sea loch here, especially around Longa Island. Many boatmen catering for anglers. Hotels: Gairloch; Myrtle Bank; Creag Mor; Millcroft; Old Inn. Tackleists: Gairloch Sands Holiday Centre; Stores; The Wild Cat, Achtercairn; K Gunn, Strath. Gen information from Ross & Cromarty Tourist Organisation (Tel: Gairloch 2130).

Ullapool and Summer Isles (Ross & Cromarty). Noted for large skate, fish over 100 lb have been landed from boats. Also haddock, whiting, codling, pollack, coalfish, mackerel, gurnard, flatfish, thornback ray, conger, dogfish, turbot and wrasse. Excellent sport inshore from dinghies and in charter boats around the Summer Isles. Good shore fishing at Morefield, Rhu and Achiltibuie. Charter boats from I McLeod, Achiltibuie. Tackleist: Lochbroom Hardware, Shore Street, Ullapool.

Lochinver (Sutherland). Cod, halibut, skate, tope, saithe, codling, lythe, mackerel. N A Mackaskill, Cruimer, operates launches; other boats available. Tackleist: M B Turnbull, newsagent, and Lochinver Fish Selling Co. Bait available from pier: Hotel: Lochinver. Tourist Information Centre supplies details of accommodation.

Portree (Isle of Skye). Good sport in harbour, loch and shore, with great variety of fish. Boats available. Most hotels will arrange facilities *(see Skye freshwater section).*

Stornoway (Lewis). Cod, haddock, whiting, saithe, skate, etc. Fastgrowing centre with local club, Stornoway Sea AC, South Beach Quay, whose secretary will gladly help visiting anglers, offers weekly membership £5. Tackleist: The Sports Shop, 6 North Beach Street; and C Morrison and Son, Point Street. Hotels: County, Caledonian, Royal, etc.

Kirkwall (Orkney). Sheltered waters in Scapa Flow hold variety of fish (record skate; halibut over 150 lb; ling over 30 lb; large cod and pollack). Boats available. Orkney Tourist Board, Broad Street, Kirkwall, will supply further details.

Lerwick (Shetland). Superb skate fishing: Nearly 200 skate over 100 lb taken. Also excellent mixed fishing for ling, cod, tusk, haddock, pollack, etc, and chance of halibut. Area holds British records for tusk, homelyn ray, grey gurnard and Norway haddock. Also Scottish hake record. For boat hire contact Kennie Manson, Mizpah House, Bressay,

Shetland. Hotels: Lerwick Hotel, Kveldsro House, Grand, Queens, etc. Club: Lerwick and Bressay Sea AC. Other centres in Shetland include **Whalsay, Unst** and **Burra.** Boat: H Smith, Buness, Baltasound, Unst and Berry Hotel, Scalloway. Hotels: Baltasound, Unst; Lingaveg Guest House, Whalsay. Further details from R H Johnson, Hon Sec, Shetland ASA.

Wick (Caithness). Mainly rock fishing for conger, pollack, saithe, cod, haddock, mackerel and flatfish. Good points are: Longberry, Boathaven, Sandigoe and Helman Head. Excellent cod fishing off Noss Head. Best months: June to Sept. Hotels: Rosebank, Nethercliffe, Mackay's, Station, Queen's Club: Tourist Information Office, Whitechapel Road.

Lossiemouth (Moray). Notable centre for sea-trout fishing off east and west beaches; spinning into breakers provides splendid sport. Also mackerel, saithe, flatfish from beach, pier and boats. Tackleists: Homecraft, 16 Queen Street.

Aberdeen. Excellent rock fishing for codling, saithe, mackerel, whiting, haddock and flatfish. Few boats. Tackleist: John Dickson & Son, 35 Belmont Street. Hotels: Caledonian, Imperial, Royal.

Stonehaven (Kincardine). Rock fishing for haddock, saithe, lythe, flounder and mackerel very good. Cod, haddock, ling, etc, from boats; available from Mrs E Cargill, 1 The Cross. Bait may be dug or obtained from Mrs Cargill. Tackleists: Davids, Market Square. Numerous hotels. Further data from Mrs Cargill.

Dundee (Angus). Fishing from rocks, pier and boats at Broughty Ferry, Easthaven and Carnoustie for mackerel, saithe, lythe and flatfish. Tackleist: John Gow & Sons, 12 Union Street. Club: Dundee and Dist Sea AA.

Dunbar (Lothian). Excellent rock, pier and boat fishing. Saithe, cod (up to 10 lb), codling, dabs, plaice, flounders, eels and, at times, small whiting, gurnard and mackerel can be caught.

Fishing Clubs

When you appoint a new secretary, do not forget to give us details of the change. Write to Thomas Harmsworth Publishing, 13 Nicosia Road, London SW18 3RN. Thank you!

FISHING CLUBS & ASSOCIATIONS IN SCOTLAND

INCLUDED in the list of fishing clubs and associations in Scotland are those organisations which are in England, but which have water on the Tweed and its tributaries or on the Border Esk. Further information can usually be had from the secretaries, and a courtesy which is appreciated is the inclusion of a stamped addressed envelope with postal inquiries.

NATIONAL BODIES

Anglers' Co-operative Association
Malcolm W Thomson
21 Heriot Row
Edinburgh EH3 6EN
Dept of Agriculture and Fisheries for Scotland
Chesser House
500 Gorgie Road
Edinburgh EH11 3AW
Forestry Commission
21 Church Street
Inverness
Salmon and Trout Association
2 Queens Road
Aberdeen AB9 8BD
Tel: 0224 6444276
Scottish Federation of Coarse Anglers
c/o J B Angling
Townhead
Kirkintillich,
Glasgow G66
Scottish Federation of Sea Anglers
H A Sharp
11 Rutland Street
Edinburgh EH1 2AE

Scottish National Angling Clubs' Association
David A Biggart CA
Taylor & Ireland
307 West George Street
Glasgow G2 4LB
Tel: 041 221 7206
Scottish Record Fish Committee (Saltwater)
R B Burn
7 Oswald Road
Ayr
Tel: 0292 81648
Aims as British Record Fish Committee
Scottish Record Fish Committee (Freshwater)
Alan Armstrong
57 Iona Way
Kirkintilloch
Glasgow G66 3QB
Scottish Tourist Board
23 Ravelston Terrace
Edinburgh EH4 3EU
Tel: 031-332 2433
Gives information on fishing holidays in Scotland

CLUBS

Abercorn Angling Club
D Marshall
10 Glendee Road
Renfrew, Gryffe
Tickets
Aberdeen and District Angling Association
Messrs Clark & Wallace, Solicitors
14 Albyn Place
Aberdeen
Dee, Don and loch. Tickets
Aberfeldy Angling Club
D Campbell
The Square

Aberfeldy
Perthshire
Tay. Tickets
Aberfoyle Angling Protection Association
E A Howell
Tigh na Cruinn
Aberfoyle, Perthshire
Lochs. Tickets
Abernethy Angling Improvement Association
John McInnes
"Balnafoich"
Boat of Garten
Spey. Tickets

337

Airdrie and District Angling Club
R Burgess
21 Elswick Drive
Caldercruix
Airdrie, Lanarkshire ML6 7QW
Trout reservoirs. Tickets
Allan Water Angling Improvement Association
T McKenzie
12 Charles Street
Dunblene
Perthshire FK15 9BY
Scotland (Central)
Allan. Tickets
Alness Angling Club
J B Paterson
33-35 High Street
Alness, Ross and Cromarty
Alness River. Members only
Annan and District Anglers' Club
Dennis Hartley
63 High Street, Annan
Dumfries
Annan, lochs, reservoir
Arbroath Angling Club
G Talbert
The Old Toll House
Clockbriggs
Forfar, Angus
Ardrossan and District Sea Angling Club
D Arnott
6 Winton Buildings
Ardrossan, Ayrshire
Ardrossan Eglinton Angling Club
W Withnall
22 Hunter Avenue
Ardrossan, Ayrshire
Trout reservoirs
Arran Angling Association
E Robertson
Mill House
Lamlash, Brodick
Isle of Arran KA27 8NJ
Tickets
Arran Sea Angling Association
Mrs M S McLean
Torlin Villa
Kilmory, Isle of Arran
Assynt Angling Club
S McClelland
Baddidarroch, Lochinver
Sutherland
Numerous lochs. Tickets
Auchinleck Angling Association
John McColm
21 Milne Avenue,
Auchinleck
Ayrshire
Ayr and Lugar. Tickets

Avon Angling Club
J Leggate
41 Strathaven Road
Stonehouse, Lanarkshire ML9 3EN
Avon
Ayr Angling Club
J H McClement
149 Whitletts Road
Ayr
Badenoch Angling Association
c/o J Dallas (Jewellers)
16 High Street
Kingussie
Scotland (Highland)
Spey. Tickets
Ballater Angling Association
c/o 59 Golf Road
Ballater
Aberdeenshire
Banff and Macduff Angling Association
R Pederson
3 Simpson Place
Macduff, Banffshire
Deveron. Tickets
Barr Angling Club
c/o Kings Arms Hotel
Barr by Girvan
Ayrshire
Stinchar. Tickets
Barra Angling Club
Desmond J Dunn
Seaview
Castlebay, Isle of Barra
Lochs. Tickets
Barrhead Angling Club
G Haydock
20 Graham Street
Barrhead, Renfrewshire
Beauly Angling Society
J MacKenzie
Viewfield Avenue
Beauly, Invernessshire
Berwick and District Angling Association
David Cowan
23 Bridge Street
Berwick-upon-Tweed
Northumberland
Whiteadder. Tickets
Blackridge and District Angling Club
Allan Neil
9 Murdostoun Crescent
Harthill, Lanarkshire
Lochs. Tickets
Blairgowrie, Rattray and District Angling Association
W Mathew
4 Mitchell Square
Blairgowrie, Perthshire
Ericht. Tickets

Brechin Angling Club
W Brooks
20 Nursery Lane
Brechin, Tayside
Lochs. Tickets
Bridge of Weir Loch Angling Club
G Scott
10 Park Road
Bridge of Weir
Renfrewshire
No tickets
Bridge of Weir River Angling Club
J Milne
8 Beech Avenue
Bridge of Weir
Renfrewshire
Gryffe. Tickets
Broughty Angling Club
D A Adams
8 Bridge Lane
Barnhill
Dundee, Angus
Buckie Angling Association
W Reid
5 High Street
Buckie, Banffshire
Bute Angling Association
J McVey
"Ardlerag"
Academy Road
Rothesay, Bute
Caithness Sea Angling Association
J Campbell
29 Castlegreen Road
Thurso, Caithness
Caledonian St Andrew Angling Club
A P Philip (match secretary)
Caledonian Club
Princes Street
Edinburgh
Campsie Angling Club
W McKie
36 Holyknowe Crescent
Lennoxtown, near Glasgow
Glazert and burns. Tickets
Carradale AC
D Paterson
17 Tormore
Carradale
Argyle
Carrick Angling Association
T L Wilson
1 Church Square
Girvan, Ayrshire
Carsphairn Angling Club
J A Hunter
The Knowe
Carsphairn, Castle Douglas
Galloway

Castle Angling Club
Ian Morris
20 Bute Drive
Sandyflats
Johnstone, Renfrewshire PA5 8NP
Black Cart. Tickets
Castle Douglas and District Angling Association
I Bendall
178 King Street
Castle Douglas, Galloway
Urr. Tickets
Catrine Angling Club
R M Miller
35 Sloan Street
Catrine, Ayrshire
Chatton Angling Association
A Jarvis
New Road
Chatton Alnwick
Northumberland
Till. Members only
Clarkston Independent Angling Club
S Armstrong
16 Luing
Airdrie, Lanarkshire
Coatbridge Angling Club
James Thom
24 Drumpellier Avenue
Coatbridge, Lanarkshire
Cobbinshaw Angling Association
M W Thomson
21 Herriot Row
Edinburgh EH3 6EN
Cockburn Angling Club
J S Stirling, WS
27 Buckstone Terrace
Edinburgh
Coldstream & District Angling Association
E M Patterson
27 Leet Street
Coldstream, Borders
Tweed, Leet. Tickets
Commissioners of Royal Four Towns Fishings
W Graham
Glenelg
Hightae, Lockerbie
Dumfries, Annan
Tickets
Crianlarich Angling Association
R Leleux
58 Benbecula
St Leonards, East Kilbride
Crieff Angling Club
G Smith
Leesthorpe
Barrell Square, Crieff, Perthshire
Earn. Tickets

Cumbrae Angling Club
J Pope
7 Hastie Avenue
Millport
Isle of Cumbrae KA28 0BS
Cumnock and District Angling Association
D Stevenson
57 Avisyard Avenue
Craigens
Cumnoch, Ayrshire
Lugar. Tickets
Cupar Angling Club
R L Duncan
"Hame"
3 Hill Street
Cupar, Fife
**Cupar, St Andrews and District Sea
Angling Club**
P Hannigan
Brighten Place
South Union Street
Cupar, Fife
Dalbeattie Angling Association
G W Garroch
Doon Cottage
William Street
Dalbeattie DG4 4EE
Dalmellington Angling Club
J Coughtree
40 Ness Glen Road
Dalmellington, Strathclyde
Dalry Angling Association
Sholto Douglas
49 Main Street
Dalry, Kirkcudbrightshire
Dalry Garnock Angling Club
J S Martin
146 St Margaret's Avenue
Dalry, Ayrshire
Garnock. Tickets
Dalrymple Angling Club
W A Crosbie
30 Barbieston Road
Dalrymple, Ayrshire
Devon Angling Association
D M Beveridge
5 Dirleton Gardens
Alloa, Clackmannanshire
Devon
Tickets
Dingwall and District Angling Club
H Furlong
Sports and Model Shop
Tulloch
Dingwall, Ross and Cromarty
Conon and loch. Tickets
Dornoch and District Angling Association
W A MacDonald
Castle Street

Dornoch, Sutherland
Sea trout and brown trout. Tickets
Dreghorn Angling Club
Michael Fullerton
12 Rigfoot
Girdle Toll
Irvine, Strathclyde
Irvine and Annick. Tickets
Drongan Youth Group Angling Club
J Hunter
76 Coyle Avenue
Drongan KA6 7DW
River Coyle; permits
Drumgrange and Keirs Angling Club
Samuel Taylor
27 Reicawr Avenue
Dalmellington, Ayrshire
Doon. Members only
Dumfries and Galloway Angling Association
D G Conchie
46 Barrie Avenue
Cresswell, Dumfries DG1 2ND
Nith. Cairn. Tickets
Dundee Angling Club
A S Nicoll
PO Box 84
51 Meadowside, Dundee DD1 9PQ
Dundee and District Sea Angling Club
D P Wilson
118 Ellengowan Drive, Dundee
Dundee West Angling Club
J Greig
Sibbald
8 Hillcrest Road
Dundee, Angus
Dunfermline Angling Club
N G Smith
34 Queen Anne Street
Dunfermline, Fife
Dunfermline Artisan Angling Club
W Beveridge
59 Maitland Street
Dunfermline, Fife
Trout reservoirs.Tickets
Dunoon and District Angling Club
A H Young
7 Blair Lane
Stewart Street
Dunoon, Argyll PA23 8DS
Earlston Angling Association
P Hessett
2 Arnot Place
Earlston,
Berwickshire
Tweed. Tickets
East Lothian Angling Association
J Crombie
10 St Lawrence
Haddington, East Lothian

Eckford Angling Association
R B Anderson, WS
Royal Bank Buildings
Jedburgh, Roxburghshire
Teviot. Loch. Tickets
Eden Angling Association
John Allen
10 Ardross Place
Glenrothes, Fife
Eden. Tickets
Edinburgh Amateur Angling Club
C Turcan, CA
64 Queen Street
Edinburgh
Edinburgh Saturday Angling Club
Michael McKinnell
16 Almondbank Terrace
Edinburgh EH11 1SS
Loch Leven, Linlithgow Loch, Lake of
Menteith. Members only
Edinburgh Walton Angling Club
Malcolm W Thompson
21 Heriot Row
Edinburgh EH3 6EN
Elgin Angling Association
F J Rind
Birch View
Longmorn
Elgin, Morayshire IV30 3SL
Lossie. Tickets from tackleists
Ellem Fishing Club
Jas D Lyon
Murray Street
Duns, Berwickshire
Esk and Liddle Fisheries Association
c/o Stevenson and Johnstone's Office
Langholm
Dumfriesshire
Border Esk and Liddle
Weekly and season tickets
Fochabers Angling Association
John Cruickshank
Hursleigh
Fochabers, Morayshire
Forestburn Fishing Club
J Gardner
6 Watt Avenue
Armadale, West Lothian
Forfar Canmore Angling Club
E Mann
44 Sheriff Park Gardens
Forfar, Angus
Dean Water. Tickets
Forfar East End Angling Club
J Grewar
25 John Street
Forfar, Angus
Fort William Angling Association
c/o Rod and Gun Shop

High Street
Fort William, Inverness-shire
Nevis. Tickets
Fortrose and Rosemarkie Angling Club
Mrs P M Wilson
5 Ness House
Ness Road
Fortrose, Ross
Fyvie Angling Association
G A Joss
Clydesdale Bank PLC
Fyvie, Turriff
Aberdeenshire AB5 8PB
Gairloch Angling Association
F Kelsey
Whindley
Achtercairn Gairloch
Gairloch Sea Angling Club
I Cox
23 South Erradale
Gairloch
Gala Angling Association
S Grzybowski
3 St Andrews Street
Galashiels
Selkirkshire TD1 1EA
Tweed. Gala Water. Tickets
Galston Angling Club
J Nisbet
26 Orchard Street
Galston, Ayrshire
Irvine. Tickets
Garpin Angling Club
A Mackay
6 Ladyland Road
Maybole, Ayrshire
Girvan. Tickets
**Gatehouse and Kirkcudbright Angling
Association**
J L Gormley
2 Dunblane Strand
Kirkcudbright
Dumfries and Galloway
Glasgow Academical Angling Club
J B Elder
Abbotsford
Loch Road
Milngavie
nr Glasgow G62 8BB
Glenburn Angling Club
J Williamson
228 Braehead Road
Paisley
Glenburn Reservoir
Glen Garry Fishing Club
Capt E F Grey
Garry Gaulach
Invergarry, Invernesshire
Loch Garry. Tickets

Golspie Angling Club
The Secretary
Golspie Angling Club
Golspie
Sutherland
Salmon and trout fishing. Permits

Greenlaw Angling Association
J Purves
9 Wester Row
Greenlaw, Berwickshire
Blackadder. Tickets

Greenock and District Angling Club
B Peterson
22 Murdieston Street
Greenock PA15 4DS
Loch Thom. Tickets

Gretna Angling Association
W G Graham
126 Currock Park Avenue
Carlisle
Cumberland
Kirtle and Sark. Tickets

Haddo House Angling Association
J French
Kirkton
Methlick
Ellon, Aberdeenshire

Harris Angling Club
Honorary Secretary
Harris Angling Club
Isle of Harris

Hawick Angling Club
Ronald A Sutherland
20 Longhope Drive
Hawick
Roxburghshire TD9 9DW
100m or rivers. Tickets

Helensburgh Angling Club
A Nicol
"Hillview"
36 Ardencaple Drive
Helensburgh, Dunbartonshire
No tickets

Hurlford Angling Club
J Miller
25 Knowehead Road
Hurlford
Ayrshire
Irvine. Tickets

Inverness Angling Club
G M Smith
50 Nevis Park
Inverness IV3 6PP
Ness. Tickets

Inverurie Angling Association
J E Duncan
4 West High Street
Inverurie
Aberdeenshire AB5 9SA

Irvine and District Angling Club
R Gilmour
58 Muir Drive
Irvine, Ayrshire
Irvine. Tickets

Irvine Angling Improvement Association
Wm H Caldow
26 Drumleyhill Drive
Hurlford, Ayrshire

Jedforest Angling Association
A Whitecross
42 Howden Road
Jedburgh, Roxburghshire
Teviot and Jed. Tickets

Kelso Angling Association
C Hutchison
53 Abbotseat
Kelso, Roxburghshire
Tweed and Teviot. Tickets

Kelvinside Academical Angling Club
F G Seligman
"Eastwood"
Kilcreggan, Dunbartonshire

Kilbirnie Angling Club
I Johnstone
12 Grahamston Avenue
Glengarnock, Kilbirnie
Ayrshire KA14 3AF
River, loch. Tickets

Killin Angling Club
Des Allan
The Tackle Shop
Killin, Perthshire

Kilmarnock Angling Club
T Morrison
39 Tinto Avenue
Kilmarnock, Ayrshire

Kilmaurs Angling Club
J Watson
7 Four Acres Drive
Kilmaurs, Ayrshire
Annick and Glaisart. Tickets

Kilsyth Fish Protection Association
P Clark
47 Belmont Street
Kilsyth, Stirlingshire
Garrel Burn, reservoirs. Tickets

Kilwinning Eglinton Angling Club
R Irvine
88 Duddingston Avenue
Whitehurst
Kilwinning, Ayrshire
Garnock. Tickets

Kincordie Fly-Fishing Club
J Miller
15 Bright Street
Lochee, Dundee

Kinross-shire Fishing Club
H Gardiner

7 Sorley's Brae
Dollar, Clackmannanshire
Kintyre Fish Protection and Angling Club
S Martin
Dunallister
Killkerran Road
Campbeltown, Argyll
Lochs. Tickets
Kirriemuir Angling Club
H F Burness
13 Clova Road
Kirriemuir, Angus DD8 5AS
Kyle of Sutherland Angling Association
R L Henderson
East End
Bonar Bridge, Sutherland
Tickets for Kyle
Kyles of Bute Angling Club
A Morrison
Menteith, Kames
Tighnabruaich, Argyll
Ladykirk and Norham Angling Improvement Association
R G Wharton
8 St Cuthberts Square
Norham-on-Tweed
Northumberland
Tweed. Tickets
Lairg Angling Club
J M Ross
Post Office House
Lairg, Sutherland
Lamington and District Angling Improvement Association
B Dexter
Red Lees
18 Boghill Park
Biggar,
Lanarkshire ML12 6EY
Clyde. Tickets
Lanark and District Angling Club
M A Murrie
11 Castlebank Gardens
Lanark, Lanarkshire
Clyde. Tickets
Larbert and Stenhousemuir Angling Club
R Baird
29 Beech Crescent
Larbert, Stirlingshire
Loch Coulter. Tickets
Largs and District Angling Club
32 Pantonville Road
West Kilbride, Ayrshire
Lauderdale Angling Association
D M Milligan
1 Newbyth House Stables
East Linton
E Lothian EH40 3DU
Leader Water. Tickets

Laurencekirk and District Angling Association
W Davidson
26 Provost Robson Drive
Laurencekirk
Kincardineshire
Lerwick and Bressay Sea Angling Club
E Lockwood
26 Russell Crescent
Lerwick, Shetland
Leith Fly-Fishing Association
W K Moncur
Royal Bank of Scotland
Bernard Street
Leith, Edinburgh EH6 6SN
Lintrathen Angling Club
J Christie
51 Broadford Terrace
Broughty Ferry
Dundee, Angus
Loanhead and District Angling Club
John Thompson
19 McKinlay Terrace
Loanhead, Midlothian
Loch Achonachie Angling Club
D MacRitchie
Scarasdal
Park Road
Strathpeffer, Ross-shire
Upper Conon, Upper Blackwater,
Loch, Achonachie and Meig. Tickets
Loch Brora Angling Club
Rob Wilson
(Rods and Guns)
Brora, Sutherland
Loch Finlas Fishing Club
N Martin
2 Wellington Square
Ayr
Lochgilphead and District Angling Club
D MacDougall
23 High Bank Park
Lochgilphead, Argyll
Lochs. Tickets
Loch Leven Fisheries
Sir David Montgomery
Kinross Estates Office
Kinross
Tickets for Loch Leven
Loch Lomond Angling Improvement Association
224 Ingram Street
Glasgow G1 1HH
Loch Lomond, Rivers Leven, Fruin,
Endrick, Gareloch. Waiting list
Lochryan Sea Angling Club
J G Powys BEM
18 Laurey Drive
Stranraer, Wigtown

Lossiemouth Angling Association
J Stewart
8 Seatown
Lossiemouth, Moray
Lossie (tidal). Tickets
Mauchline "Ballochmyle" Angling Club
Robert Anderson
85 Mary Morrison Drive
Mauchline
Ayrshire,
Ayr. Tickets
Maybole Angling Club
James Harper
54 Kirkoswald Road
Maybole, Ayrshire
Girvan. No Tickets
Melrose and District Angling Association
A Brown
Kenilworth
3 High Cross Avenue
Melrose, Roxburghshire
Tweed. Tickets
Midland Counties Anglers Protection Association
J Neilly
2 Cornish Street
Coatbridge, Lanarks.
Balvaig. Tickets
Midlothian Angling Association
S H G Glennon
32 Glendevon Road
Edinburgh.
Mid-Nithsdale Angling Association
Pollock & Day, Solicitors
West Morton Street
Thornhill, Dumfries
Nith. Tickets
Montrose Angling Club
G S Taylor
Braes
Russell Street
Montrose, Angus
Muirkirk Angling Association
R Shaw
3 Connel View
New Cumnock, Ayrshire
Ayr. Tickets
Nairn Angling Association
Mrs W R Mackay
36 Mill Road
Nairn
Nairn. Tickets
Ness Glen Fishing Club
J Semple
160 Merrick Drive
Dalmellington, Ayrshire
New Abbey Angling Association
I D Cooper
West Shambellie

New Abbey, Dumfries DG2 8HG
Dumfriesshire
Trout Stream. Tickets
New Cumnock Anglers' Association
Allan Lockhart
79 Dalhanna Drive
New Cumnock, Ayrshire
Nith. Tickets
New Galloway Angling Association
K J Dahl
"Craiglea"
High Street
New Galloway
Kirkcudbrightshire
Dee. Tickets
Newburgh Angling Club
A F Buchan
Ythanbank
Knockhall Road
Newburgh, Ellon
Aberdeen AB4 0BL
Newmilns and Greenholm Angling Club
H Smith
3 Loudoun Road West
Newmilns, Ayrshire
Irvine. Tickets
Newton Stewart Angling Association
J Cronnie
10 Loudon Place
Creetown
Newton Stewart
Wigtownshire
Cree. Tickets
North Berwick Angling Club
George B Woodburn
29 Craigleith Avenue
North Berwick, East Lothian
Trout Lake. Members only
North Uist Angling Club
David Cockburn
Dunrossil Place
Lochmaddy, North Uist
Oban Sea Angling Club
E Finyland
Great Western Hotel
Oban
Oban and Lorn Angling Club
Dr J Mauchline
Connel
Oban, Argyll
Ochiltree Angling Association
John Brown
38 Brown Crescent
Ochiltree. Ayrshire
Lugar. Tickets
Orkney Islands Sea Angling Association
A J B Scholes
32 Dundas Crescent
Kirkwall, Orkney

Orkney Trout Fishing Association
R Windwick
36 Quoybanks Crescent
Kirkwall, Orkney
Tickets
Paisley and District Angling Club
E Semple
7 Maree Road
Foxbar, Paisley
No water
Peeblesshire Trout Fishing Association
Messrs Blackwood & Smith
39 High Street
Peebles, Peebblesshire EH45 8AH
Tweed and Lyne Water. Tickets
Peeblesshire Salmon Fishing Association
Messrs Blackwood & Smith
39 High Street
Peebles, Peeblesshire EH45 8AH
Tweed. Tickets
Penwhapple Fishing Club
J H Murray
3 Dalrymple Street
Girvan, Ayrshire
Loch. Tickets
Perth and District Anglers' Association
R M Black
1 Schoonieburn Hill
Friarton, Perth
Perth Anglers' Club
R R Thom
10 Blackfriars Street
Perth
Phoenix Angling Club
D A Biggart, CA
307 West George Street
Glasgow G2 4LB
Pitlochry Angling Club
R Harriman
Sunnyknowe
Nursing Home Brae
Pitlochry, Perthshire
Tummel. Tickets
Port Glasgow Angling Club
J Tucker
39 Marloch Avenue
Port Glasgow
Lower Loch Gryffe, Harelaw, Mill
Dams, Knocknair. Tickets
Portree Angling Association
D Burd
College of Agriculture
Portree, Isle of Skye
River Staffa and lochs. Tickets
Prestwick Angling Club
C Hendrie
12 Glen Park Avenue
Prestwick, Ayrshire KA9 2EE
Reservoir. Tickets

Prestwick Sea Angling Club
W R Phillips
48 Underwood
Kilwinning, Ayrshire
Rannoch Angling Club
J Brown
The Garage, The Square
Kinloch Rannoch
Perthshire PH16 5PQ
Renfrewshire Angling Improvement Association
H Young
41 Glentyan Avenue
Kilbarchan, Renfrewshire
River Lochy Association
General Sir William Morgan
5 Wellington Square
London SW3
Fishing on Lochy
Rowbank Angling Club
A C Wilson
c/o C Davidson & Son Architects
15 Forbes Place
Paisley, Renfrewshire PA1 1UT
Reservoirs
Roybridge Angling Club
J MacDonald
Blar-a-cha,
Spean Bridge, Inverness
Water on Roy
St Andrew's Angling Club
P F Malcolm
54 St Nicholas Street
St Andrews, Fife
Reservoir. Tickets
St Boswells and Newtown and District Angling Association
Q McLaren
Rowansbrae
Tweedside Road
Newton St Boswells
Roxburghshire TD60 P1
Tweed. Tickets
St Fillans' and Loch Earn Angling Association
J McPherson
Rannoch
4 Earnview
St Fillans, Perthshire
Loch and River Earn. Tickets
St Mary's Angling Club
J Miller
6 Greenbank Loan
Edinburgh 9
Loch. Tickets
St Mirin Angling Club
R Lindsay
12 David Place
Paisley, Renfrewshire PA3 4QL

St Winnoch Angling Club
J Eadie
19 Glenpark Road
Lochwinnoch, Renfrewshire
Castle Semple Loch. River Calder.
Tickets
Saltcoats Sea Angling Association
W L Currie
8 McNay Crescent
Saltcoats, Ayrshire
Scourie & District Angling Club
J B Hepburn
Duartmore
Scourie, Lairg, Sutherland
Selkirk and District Angling Association
A Murray
40 Raeburn Meadow
Selkirk
Yarrow and Ettrick. Tickets
Shetland Anglers' Association
Andrew Miller
3 Gladstone Terrace
Lerwick, Shetland
Lochs. Tickets
Slammanan Angling and Protective
Association
M Penman
8 Drumclair Avenue
Slammanan, Stirlingshire
No tickets; waiting list for membership
Sorn Angling Club
J Gray
62 Glenshamrock Drive
Auchinleck, Ayrshire
Ayr. Tickets
South Uist Angling Club
Dr I Jack
The Surgery, Griminish
Isle of Benbecula, Western Isles
Lochs. Tickets
Southwick Angling Association
J Thomson
Mainsmill
Southwick, Dumfries
Southwick Water. Tickets
Soval Angling Association
E Young
1 Goathill Crescent
Stornoway, Isle of Lewis
Stewarton Angling Club
S T Lynch
101 High Street
Stewarton, Ayrshire
Annick. Tickets
Stonehaven and District Angling Association
Honorary Secretary
19 East Glebe
Stonehaven AB3 2HW
Cowie, Carron. Tickets

Stonehaven Sea Angling Association
J B Robertson
Solicitor and Town Clerk
Cameron Street
Stonehaven
Stornoway Angling Association
Robt G Morrison
37 Keith Street
Stornoway
Isle of Lewis
Stornoway Sea Angling Association
Roderick Macleod
11 Battery Park Road
Stornoway
Isle of Lewis
Straiton Angling Association
R P Rae
The Cottages
Straiton, Ayrshire
Girvan. Limited Tickets
Stranraer and District Angling Association
John A Cairney
8 Oakland Avenue
Stranraer, Wigtownshire
River and lochs. Tickets
Strathgryfe Angling Association
C Browning
3 Hillside Avenue
Kilmacolm
Renfrewshire PA13 4QL
Gryfe. Tickets
Strathmore Angling Improvement Association
Mrs Henderson
364 Blackness Road
Dundee DD2 1SF
Strathpeffer Angling Club
W Brown
1 Park Terrace
Strathpeffer, Ross
Strathspey Angling Improvement Association
G G Mortimer
61 High Street
Grantown-on-Spey, Moray
Spey. Tickets
Thistle Angling Club
John Robertson
Public Library
Stirling
Thurso Angling Association
J Robertson
of A A MacDonald
23 Sinclair Street
Thurso, Caithness
Thurso. Tickets for visitors only
Tongue and District Angling Association
c/o Ben Loyal Hotel
Tongue, by Lairg
Sutherland
Trout fishing. Tickets

Townhill Angling Club
J Lightfoot
39 Whitelaw Road
Dunfermline, Fife
Reservoir; trout; visitors may accompany
members

Turriff Angling Association
Ian Masson Fishing Tackle
6 Castle Street
Turriff, Aberdeenshire
Deveron. Tickets

Ullapool Angling Club
E G Woodfield
5 Seaforth Road
Ullapool, Ross and Cromarty
Ullapool River. Tickets

Ullapool and Loch Broom Sea Angling Club
C F R Browne
3 Castle Terrace
Ullapool IV26 2XD

United Clyde Angling Protective Association Ltd
R C Sharp
20 Cunningham Street
Motherwell
Clyde and tributaries, and Springfield
Reservoir. Tickets

Unst Anglers' Association
Honorary Secretary
Beltersound
Unst, Shetland

Upper Annandale Angling Association
J Black
1 Rosehill
Grange Road

Moffat, Dumfriesshire
Annan. Tickets

Upper Nithsdale Angling Club
W Forsyth
100 High Street
Sanquhar, Dumfriesshire D64 6EA
Nith. Tickets

Vale of Leven & Dist Angling Club
G Mackenzie
11 Hardie Street
Alexandria
Strathclyde

Waterside Angling Improvement Association
P Daly
56 Burns Road
Harestones
Kirkintilloch, Dumbartonshire
Luggie Water. St only

Waverley Angling Club
A J Dickson
10 Kingsknowe Avenue
Edinburgh

Whiteadder Angling Association
J Boyd
St Leonards
Polwarth
Duns, Berwickshire
Whiteadder. Tickets

Wooler and Doddington Angling Association
T Whitlock
6 Cottage Road
Wooler,
Northumberland NE71 6AA
Till. Tickets

Check before you go

While every effort has been made to ensure that the information given in "Where to Fish" is correct, the position is continually changing and anglers are urged, in their own interests, to make preliminary inquiries before travelling to selected venues. This is especially important with reference to prices quoted. Inevitably, the rate of inflation is affecting stability in this quarter. Anglers' attention is also drawn to the fact that the hotels mentioned under the various fishing stations do not necessarily have water of their own. Any amendments or further data for inclusion in subsequent editions, and any criticism, will be welcome.

FISHING IN NORTHERN IRELAND

Boards of Conservators, Close Seasons, etc.

FOR game fisher and coarse fisher alike, Northern Ireland is still largely undiscovered country. There is a wealth of lakes, large and small; miles of quiet unpolluted river plentifully stocked with large, healthy fish anything but well-educated to anglers and their methods. By the standards of most other part of Britain, all of it is underfished. In recent years, coarse fishermen have begun to find out what Northern Ireland has to offer: there is much for the game fisherman, and frequently at a price so low that it can almost be described as "free". The visitor as yet unfamiliar with the country is recommended to concentrate on the waters owned and managed by the Department of Agriculture, possibly the largest single fishery proprietor in the country. They include some of the very best.

Statutory Bodies. The Dept of Agriculture (Fisheries Division, Hut 5, Castle Grounds, Stormont, Belfast BT4 3TA) is the ultimate authority for fisheries in Northern Ireland. In addition to the department, and working in co-operation with it, there are two Conservancy Authorities, The Foyle Fisheries Commission; and The Fisheries Conservancy Board for Northern Ireland. They operate in separate areas.

The Foyle Fisheries Commission (8 Victoria Road, Londonderry BT47 2AB, Tel: 0504 42100) act as conservator and issues rod licences in the Foyle area: i.e. the North-Western parts of the country drained by the Foyle/Mourne/Camowen river systems and the rivers Faughan and Roe. The Foyle Fisheries Commission is controlled jointly by the Governments of Northern Ireland and The Republic of Ireland, including in the total area the former Moville District in the Republic and the former Londonderry District in N.I.

The Fisheries Conservancy Board for Northern Ireland (1 Mahon Road, Portadown, Co Armagh BT62 3EE, Tel: Portadown 334666). This board acts as conservator and issues licences for the remainder of the country.

The Northen Ireland Tourist Board (River House, 48 High Street, Belfast BT1 2DS, Tel: 0232 31221) is also involved in angling, concerning itself with development and promotion. It issues literature on travel and accommodation; also angling guides.

Under the provisions of The Fisheries Act (N.I.) 1966, **The Fisheries Conservancy Board** and **The Foyle Fisheries Commission** co-operate with the **Dept of Agriculture** in the development and improvement of fisheries. As a result, there has been in recent years a dramatic improvement in the quantity and quality of angling, game and coarse, available to visitors. The department's Drainage Division is also actively engaged in the improvement of fisheries in watercourses under its control. Works include the construction of fishery weirs, groynes and deflectors; restoration of gravel, landscaping of altered watercourses and comprehensive schemes of tree-planting.

Rod Licences. With the following exceptions, anglers are required to take out a rod licence. 1. Anglers under 18 years of age fishing exclusively for coarse fish are not required to take out a licence in the Conservancy Board area. 2. Rod licences do not have to be taken out in the Foyle area by *any* angler fishing exclusively for coarse fish. Rod licences are issued by The Foyle Fisheries Commission and The Fisheries Conservancy Board in their respective areas. The holder of a licence in one area *may obtain on payment an endorsement to cover the other area.* (Charge included in the details below.)

A Game Fishing Rod Licence in The Fisheries Conservancy Board area is valid for both game and coarse fishing, *but a coarse fishing rod licence is valid for coarse fishing only on designated coarse fishing waters.* A list of these is obtainable from the Board. Licences may be obtained directly from the Authorities, or from tackle dealers.

Charges. Foyle Fisheries Commission. S, MT, NT; s £9.50, ft £6, s (juv) £4.75. FF; no licence required. Endorsement to Fisheries Conservancy Board annual game-fish licence £7.05.
Fisheries Conservancy Board. S, MT, NT; s £12.25, ft £8.50, FF, s £4.75, ft £3.25. Endorsement to Foyle Fisheries Commission annual game-fish licence £9.80.

Seasons. There are no statutory close seasons for coarse fish in Northern Ireland, nor for rainbow trout in designated rainbow trout waters in the **Conservancy Board** area. (List of such waters from Board and displayed by licence-sellers.)
For salmon, sea trout and brown trout, the OPEN seasons are: **Foyle area;** rivers: April 1 to Oct 20: lakes: March 1 to Oct 20. **FCB area: Lough Melvin:** Feb 1 to Sept 30. **Lough Erne system and Bush:** March 1 to Sept 30. **Other waters,** in general, March 1 to Oct 31, but late openings and early closings introduced on some stocked trout lakes.

Dept of Agriculture permits; *separate from and in addition to licences.* For Dept of Agriculture fisheries, of which there are more than 60 throughout the country. Charges. (All inclusive of VAT.) St (game) £28.50. St (game) juv £5. Ft (game) £12. Dt (game) £5. St (game, one water only) £17.50. St (coarse) £8. NB: "Ft" = 15 days. "Juv" = under 16 yrs of age.
River Bush—Town Stretch: daily permits
(a) for holders of Dept's season, local or 15-day game permit: March 1—June 30 = £12: July 1—Sept 30 = £25.
(b) others: March 1—June 30 = £17.50: July 1—Sept 30 = £35.
River Bush—Leap Stretch: daily permits
(a) for holders of Dept's season, local or 15-day game permit: March 1—June 30 = full day £5, half day £4: July 1—Sept 30 = full day £9.50, half day £6.
(b) others: March 1—June 30 = full day £7, half day £5: July 1—Sept 30 = full day £15, half day £10.
River Bush—New Stretch: daily permits
(a) for holders of Dept's season, local or 15 day game permit: March 1—June 30 = £9: July 1—Sept 30 = £18.
(b) others: March 1—June 30 = £12: July 1—Sept 30 = £25.
R Shimna, for holders of the Dept's season or 15-day permit (game) March 1 to July 31: No charge, Aug 1 to Oct 31: £8. Other members of the public, March 1 to July 31: No charge, Aug 1 to Oct 31: £13.
R Margy, for holders of the Dept's season, local or 15-day game permit: Aug 1—Oct 1 = £1.

I wonder if this one will do the trick? Hope springs eternal within the angler's breast.

FISHING STATIONS IN NORTHERN IRELAND

AS in other sections, principal catchment areas are dealt with in alphabetical order and details of close seasons, licences, etc, will be found on preceding page. Anglers wanting further details of accommodation, etc, should write to the Northern Ireland Tourist Board, River House, 48 High Street, Belfast, BT1 2DS, or 11 Berkeley Street, London (01-493 0601).

BANN (Lower)

(For close seasons, licences, see p 349 and 350)

A mainly sluggish river running approx 30m from where it leaves Lough Neagh to where it enters the sea below Coleraine. Good coarse fish population; sea trout fishing in the tideway. Salmon stretches in private hands and not usually available to visitors.

Coleraine (Co Derry). River tidal below Cutts. Good coarse fishing above tidal stretches. Bann Systems Ltd, The Cutts, has beats which are available to certain clubs on Fri, Sat and Sun; and will have nominated beats available to tourists from 1989. Agivey AA has 12m stretch on R Agivey. Hotels: Lodge; Bohill Auto Inn.

Kilrea (Co Derry). Pike and perch in local canals and loughs. Permits for **R Agivey** (small brown trout, late salmon and dolaghan) from Hon Irish Society, 8 Shipquay St, Londonderry.
Portglenone (Co Antrim). **Clady River** joins Bann below town. Brown trout,

late salmon and dolaghan. Permits from Clady & Dist AC. Accommodation: Bannside Farmhouse, 268 Gortgole Road.
Toomebridge (Co Antrim). Here, the Lower Bann leaves L Neagh. **Lough Neagh,** with an area of 153 sq miles, is the largest sheet of inland water in the British Isles. It supports an immense commercial eel fishery, but apart from that, its potential is as yet largely untapped. The bottom-feeding habits of Lough Neagh trout and the exposed conditions on this enormous stretch of water have so far discouraged anglers from trying to exploit it. A principal problem is the absence of sheltered bays.

BANN (Upper)

Flows west and north from its source in the Mourne Mountains to enter Lough Neagh near the middle of its southern shore at a point north of Portadown.

Portadown (Co Armagh). For several miles above and below the town the river is sluggish, offering only coarse fishing. Hotel: Carngrove; Seagoe.

Hilltown (Co Down). From here for 20m downstream the river offers good trout fishing. Gilford AC, Banbridge AC, and Rathfriland & Dist AC all have water. Good trout fishing also in **Cusher,** for

first three miles from confluence. Dept of Ag have four good trout lakes, totalling more than 350 acres in the area. Banbridge AC has 76 acre **Corbet Lake** (brown trout). **Lough Shark** (pike, perch and bream) free to licence-holders. Tackleist: J Coburn, 32 Scarva Street, Banbridge; W R Trimble, 25 Downpatrick St, Rathfriland. Hotels: Downshire Arms and Belmont, Banbridge.

BLACKWATER

(For close seasons, licences, see p 349 and 350)

The largest of the rivers flowing into L Neagh, rising in S Tyrone to enter the lough at its SW corner. Coarse fish and trout.

Blackwatertown (Co Armagh). Dept of Ag has $1\frac{1}{2}$m, mainly coarse fishing but short stretch of good game fishing. Permits from Sports Centre, 19 Thomas St, and K Cahoon, 2 Irish St, both Dungannon.

Benburb (Co Tyrone). Trout for $2\frac{1}{2}$m downstream. Armagh & Dist AC leases or owns stretch on river, and seven lakes. Dep of Ag has **Bantry Lough** (brown trout); and Loughs Creeve and Enagh (pike, perch, eel). Permits from Hamilton's, James St, Cookstown.

Accommodation: Salmon Leap View, 22 Carrickaness Mills.

Clogher-Augher-Aughnacloy. (Co Tyrone) Trout fishing down to Caledon. Permits from Aughnacloy AC, Clogher/Augher AC, Augher Dist & Upper Blackwater AC and landowners. Permission from landowners for tributaries **Callan, Oona** and **Torrent**. Dept of Ag has coarse fishing on **White Lough**. Permits from R Morrow, 48 Rehaghey Road, Aughnacloy. Accommodation: Mrs K Hillen, 48 Moore St, Aughnacloy.

SMALLER RIVERS EMPTYING INTO LOUGH NEAGH

MAINE (Co Antrim): Flows 25m from source in Glarryford Bogs to enter lough south of Randalstown, Co Antrim. With tribs **Kellswater, Braid, Clough** and **Glenwhiry** provides good fishing for salmon, trout and dolaghan. Permits from Randalstown AC, Gracehill, Galform & Dist AC and Maine AC. Also from some landowners. Dept of Ag has brown trout fishing on **Dungonnell** and **Killylane Reservoirs.** Tackleist: J Matthews, 72 Ballymoney Street, Ballymena; who issues dt for various club-waters in the area and is a particularly reliable and helpful source of information. Hotels: Adair Arms; Leighinmore House and Tullyglass House, Ballymena.

SIXMILEWATER: Flows 15m from Ballyclare to enter lough at Antrim, at its NE corner. A heavily-fished but highly productive trout water. Antrim & Dist AC issues permits for water below town; landowners for upper reaches. Dept of Ag has trout fishing on **Woodburn Reservoirs,**

nr Carrigfergus. Permits from J. Hill, 4 West St, Carrigfergus. Hotel: Deer Park Antrim.

CRUMLIN AND GLENAVY (Co Antrim): small rivers which flow west through these villages to enter lough. Trout fishing near their mouths. Centre: Crumlin. Accommodation: Hillvale Farm, 11 Largy Road.

BALLINDERRY: Flows east for approx 30m, through Cookstown, to enter lough about midway along W shore. Good fishing for brown trout and dolaghan for 20m up from the mouth. Permission from Cookstown AC and landowners. Hotel: Glenavon House, Cookstown, Co Tyrone.

MOYOLA (Co Londonderry): Flows east and south from its source in S Derry to enter lough at NW corner. Some brown trout in lower reaches and a reasonably good run of salmon from July. Permission from landowners. Centre: Castledawson. Accommodation: Moyola Lodge, 9 Brough Road.

BUSH

(For close seasons, licences, see p 349 and 350)

The Bush flows 30m west and north through Bushmills, Co Antrim, to enter the sea near Portballintrae. The fishing rights of the entire catchment (except the stretch from the sea to Bushmills) have been acquired by the Dept of Agriculture primarily as an experimental river for studies into the biology and management of salmon. Within the terms of this programme, salmon angling is maintained at the highest possible level. Trout in the Bush and its tributaries are small but plentiful: there is a modest run of spring salmon and a grilse run for which the river is best known which begins in June or July, according to flow.

For angling management, the river is divided into three sections: the *Special Stretch* about 200 yds downstream of the Project Centre at Bushmills; the *Restricted Stretch* upstream (approx 400 yds of water) and the *Unrestricted Stretch*, the remaining 24m of fishing water. Special daily permits, bookable in advance, are required for the Special and Restricted stretches, as shown under "Licences, permits and close seasons." Tributary: **River Dervock,** flowing through the village of that name, offers 2m of good trout fishing. Centre: **Bushmills.** Hotel: Antrim Arms, Ballycastle; Manor, Ballymoney. Guest house: Montalto, 5 Craigboney Rd, Bushmills. *(For details of permit-charges, see p 350).*

LOUGH ERNE (Upper and Lower)

(For close seasons, licences, see p 349 and 350)

Upper and Lower Lough Erne, with the R Erne and tributaries feeding the loughs, comprise 37,800 acres of mixed game and coarse fishing owned and annually restocked by the Dept of Agriculture and offering some of the best sport in Europe. The flow is in a NW direction, through the beautiful and largely unspoilt Fermanagh countryside, via Belleek, to where the R Erne reaches the sea at Ballyshannon. Infinitely varied fishing in the lakes, with innumerable secluded bays, inlets and small islands. Rich, unpolluted waters teeming with fish-life, the Erne system is truly an angler's paradise. Centres: Belleek; Kesh; Enniskillen; Bellanaleck; Lisnaskea; Newtown Butler.

BELLEEK (Co Fermanagh). River heavily populated with large bream and roach, pike of record-breaking proportions. Good salmon runs in late summer and autumn. A good centre for fishing Lower Lough. Hotel: Carlton, where boats may be hired.

LOWER LOUGH ERNE. The trout fishing areas, in which the fish may run very large, are in the north and west of the lake. South and east of a dividing line, the lake may be fished on coarse fishing licence and permit only.

TRIBUTARIES FEEDING LOWER LOUGH: Ballinamallard River flows south through the village to enter the lake near St Angelo Airport. Coarse and game fishing by Dept of Ag permit and permission of landowners. **Colebrook** and **Tempo** enter lake from the West. Coarse fish in lower reaches; trout in upper. Permission from landowners.

UPPER LOUGH ERNE: Principally coarse fish. Centres: Lisnaskea; Newtown Butler; Enniskillen. Tackleist: J Richardson Ltd, East Bridge Street, Enniskillen, who are a particularly useful source of information and Erne Tackle, Main Street, Lisnaskea. At Castle Coole, **Lough Coole,** National Trust Fishery. B and rb trout to 5 lbs. $\frac{1}{2}$ dt (boat) £3. Hotels: Killyhevlin; Manor House; Railway; all Enniskillen; and Ortine, Lisnaskea.

TRIBUTARIES FEEDING UPPER LOUGH ERNE: Swalinbar River flows north from Co Cavan to enter the lough midway on the S side. Coarse fish in lower reaches, trout in upper. Permission from landowners. The Silies River flows from above Derrygonelly to enter the lough between Enniskillen and Lisgoole Abbey. Excellent coarse fishing, some trout. The **Arney** flows from **Upper and Lower Loughs McNean** (large trout and exceptional pike fishing) to enter Upper L Erne near Bellanaleck. Dept of Ag mixed fishery from Drumane to Arney Old Bridge, then good mixed fishing all the way to **Lough McNean.** Also ten Dept trout lakes of various sizes in the area (5 acres to 100 acres), including the famous **Navar Forest Lakes,** and **Mill Lough** at Bellanaleck which holds trout to 5 lbs.

FOYLE

(For close seasons, licences, see p 349 and 350)

The Foyle system is half in Northern Ireland, half in the Republic. It is formed by the **Derg** (draining **Lough Derg**) and the **Strule,** constituting the **Mourne,** which unites with the **Finn** at Strabane to become the Foyle proper, which enters the sea at Londonderry. That part of the system in Northen Ireland, including the **Faughan** and **Roe**, is the largest salmon and trout fishery in the country. It drains the north and west slopes of the Sperrin Mountains and most of Co Tyrone.

Londonderry. River tidal here, with fishing for salmon in tidal pools from July. Also a run of sea trout. Permits from Foyle Commission. Tackleist: Fitzpatrick Sports & Tackle, 145 Spencer Road, Waterside. Hotels: Everglades, Broomhill House.

Strabane (Co Tyrone). Here **Mourne** and **Strule** unite to form Foyle. Salmon and sea trout. Permits from Foyle Commission. Dept of Ag has five lakes in the area. Tackleist: R Cunningham, 10 Bridge Street. Hotel: Fir Trees Lodge

Tributaries of the Foyle

MOURNE: Excellent fishing in the 10m between Strabane and Newtownstewart, but largely private and unavailable to visitors. At Sion Mills, Dept of Ag has stretch and some farmers give permission. Brown trout; salmon and sea trout from June/July. At Newtownstewart, the **Owenkellow** and **Glenelly** enter, offering 30m of ideal game fishing waters noted for their sea trout. Permission from Omagh AA and landowners. Membership £10, wt £20, dt £5 and £7 from Tyrone Tackle, Black Market, Armagh; J Graham, 1 Plumbridge Road and D Campbell, Main Street, both in Newtownstewart. Some stretches of **Owenkellow** available on lease. Hotels: Royal Arms; Silver Birch; Knock-Na-Moe; all in Omagh.

STRULE: Very good trout fishing from Omagh to Newtownstewart. Dept of Ag water at Victoria Bridge, otherwise permission from Omagh AA. More good

fishing upstream of Omagh, to Camowen, but fish smaller. Salmon in season. **Owenragh, Quiggery/Fintona** and **Drumragh** enter near Omagh. More good trout fishing by leave of Omagh AA and landowners. Hotels: see above, under **Mourne.**

FAIRYWATER: Flows E from Drumquin (trout) to enter **Strule** below Omagh. Remarkably good roach fishing in lower reaches. Small brown trout and salmon in season in **Burndennett.** Permission for this and Fairywater from landowners. Tackleists, Tyrone Angling Supplies, Bridge Street, Omagh.

DERG: flows E from Donegal for 50m to enter **Mourne** N of Newtownstewart. Good trout water for 15m to above Castlederg, Co Tyrone. Permission from Castlederg AA, Mournebeg & Derg AA. Tackleists: J Grahame, 1 Plumbridge Road, Newtownstewart.

FAUGHAN and ROE

(For close seasons, licences, see p 349 and 350)

The Faughan flows N for 20m to enter the Foyle area E of Londonderry city; the Roe flows the same distance in the same general direction to enter the Foyle Estuary N of Limavady, Co Londonderry. Salmon, sea trout and brown trout in Faughan; principally sea trout in Roe, but also salmon from July.

FAUGHAN: Good fishing for 15m from Londonderry up to Clady on ticket issued by Londonderry & Dist AA.

ROE: Good fishing for 15m from Limavady to Dungiven. Permission Roe AA. Dept of Ag has short stretch at O'Ca-

han's Rock, S of Limavady. Ft £35, wt £20 and dt £5. Tackleist: S J Mitchell, 29 Main St, Limavady, who displays map of all local fishings, issues permits and is a reliable source of local information. Hotels: Gorteen House, Limavady; Finvola Arms, Dungiven.

GLENS OF ANTRIM RIVERS
(For close seasons, licences, see p 349 and 350)

GLENARM: Short privately-owned spate river. Salmon and sea trout. No permits.
GLENARIFF: Small sea trout river which flows into Red Bay at Glenariff. Permission from Glens AC.
DUNN: enters sea at Cushendun. Fair run of late salmon and sea trout. Permission from Glens AC.
MARGEY/CAREY/GLENSHESK: a system of small rivers entering the sea at Ballycastle. Sea trout and salmon. Dept of Ag waters. Hotels: Antrim Arms, Ballycastle; Thornlea, Cushendun. Tackleist: R Bell, 40 Ann St, Ballycastle.

LAGAN
(For close seasons, licences, see p 349 and 350)

A productive river which flows into the **Belfast Lough.** Trout fishing upstream from Magheralin, Co Down, for 12m. Permission from Iveagh AC and Dromore AC. Twelve Dept of Agriculture brown and/or rainbow trout lakes, totalling more than 700 acres, in the Lagan Valley area. Near to Belfast, these waters are fished more heavily than most in N Ireland. Abundant coarse fishing on canals and loughs. Tackleist: Lisburn Sports, 9 Smithfield Square, Lisburn.

LOUGH MELVIN
(For close seasons, licences, see p 349 and 350)

A 5,000 acre natural lake, approximately one fifth of which lies in Northern Ireland, (Co Fermanagh). A good spring run of salmon starts in February and a grilse run in June, but the lake is famous chiefly for the variety of its native brown trout. In addition to fish of orthodox appearance, there are dark "sonaghan" caught over the deeper water and the yellow-bellied "gillaroo", found in the shallows near the shore. Regarded as the Dept of Agriculture's best all-round fishery, Garrison is the centre for fishing the lough and **Lough McNean,** Upper and Lower, also in the vicinity. (Pike, large trout, general coarse fishing.) Accommodation: Lough Melvin Holiday Centre and Heathergrove Guest House, Garrison. Small trout in **L Lattone** pronounced "Latoon") may be caught from the roadside between Belcoo and Garrison.

NEWRY RIVER
(For close seasons, licences, see p 349 and 350)

A small system flowing into the head of **Carlingford Lough** at **Newry,** Co Down. 3m of fair brown trout water above Carnbane Industrial Estate. Permission from Newry & Dist AC and landowners. Club also issues dt £4 for **Guinan Lake,** stocked with brown and rainbow trout and **McCourt's Lake.** 3m from town, **Cooper's Lake,** fly fishing for brown trout. Good coarse fishing in **Newry Ship Canal,** free to licence-holders. Two Dept of Agriculture trout lakes in area: Lough Brickland and Glassdrumman. Tackleist: J C Smyth, 7 Kildare Street, Newry.

Keep the banks clean

Several clubs have stopped issuing tickets to visitors because of the state of the banks after they have left. Spend a few moments clearing up.

QUOILE

(For close seasons, licences, see p 349 and 350)

Flows into top of **Strangford Lough** at **Downpatrick.** Coarse fish and some trout in lower reaches; fair trout waters between Annacloy Bridge and Kilmore. Permits from landowners. Dept of Ag has fishing rights on **Quoile Basin** (100 acres); pike, perch, rudd, eels and brown trout; bank fishing only. Permits from T West, Comber Sports Centre, Castle St, Comber and W F Magee, Sports & Toys Store, Market St, Downpatrick. Downpatrick & Dist AA hold fishing rights to Laughin-Island Lake and Magheraleggan Lake; guests only when accompanied by a member. Tackleist: Down Sports Centre, Market Street, Downpatrick. Hotel: Abbey Lodge, Downpatrick.

SHIMNA

(For close seasons, licences, see p 349 and 350)

Small attractive river with deep rocky pools flowing from E slope of Mournes to enter sea at **Newcastle,** Co Down. Sea trout and salmon from July. Dept of Agriculture fishery in forest areas, Shimna AC in lower reaches. Hotels: Slieve Donard; Enniskeen. Tackleist: J Mackie, Main Street, Newcastle.

WHITEWATER

(For close seasons, licences, see p 349 and 350)

Small attractive sea trout water flowing into sea W of Kilkeel, Co Down, 3m of good fishing. Permission: landowners. Hotel: Kilmorey Arms, Kilkeel.

BELFAST, not mentioned specifically in connection with any river system, is a good centre for much of the fishing in the east of Northern Ireland. It is plentifully supplied with hotels and tackle shops. Tackleists: J Braddell, 9 North Street; K Rankin, 131 Royal Avenue; Rod & Wheel, 37 Smithfield Market. Hotels: Culloden, Wellington, La Mon House.

Good news for somebody. Fresh stock arriving from the trout farm. Great care is necessary in making the introduction. The fish here are in carriage – probably in a sample of the water in which they will henceforth live – from the tanker to the lake.

SEA FISHING STATIONS IN NORTHERN IRELAND

THE popularity of sea fishing in N Ireland has grown immensely in recent years, leading to the discovery of new and exciting possibilities. 300 miles of unpolluted coastline offers fishing for a variety of species from rock and beach alike. Sheltered inlets of which Strangford and Belfast Loughs are the largest and best known, offer protection to the boat angler when the open sea may be unfishable due to adverse weather. Twenty-four species of sea fish are caught regularly, including blue shark, skate, tope, cod, bass and flatfish. The Tourist Board, well aware of anglers' needs (boats, bait, etc) spares no effort to assist visitors in finding both sport and comfortable quarters.

Portrush (Antrim) and **Portstewart** (Derry). Near mouths of Lough Foyle and River Bann. Rock, pier and beach fishing for pollack, mackerel, garfish, coalfish, flounder, plaice, sea trout and bass. Good bass fishing from Castlerock Strand. Plenty of boats and bait. Tackleists: Joe Mullen, 70 Main Street; J Minahan, 3-5 Bath Street, both Portrush. Hotels: Northern Counties; Royal; Skerry-Bhan; Lismara; all Portrush (and many more). Carrig-na-Cule; Golf House; Strand; etc, Portstewart.

Glenarm (Antrim). Pier, rock and boat fishing for pollack, mackerel, plaice, flounders and codling. Plenty of bait.

Larne (Antrim). Belfast 25m. Pollack, mackerel, whiting, cod, coalfish, etc, with jigging for herring off The Maidens, some miles off shore. Plenty of boats. Trout fishing in Town Reservoir. East Antrim AA has salmon and trout fishing; inquire hon sec. Club: Larne & Dist SAC. Hon Sec B Renshaw, 22 Elisabeth Ave. Hotels: Kings Arms; Highways; Laharna.

Whitehead and Carrickfergus (Antrim). Opposite Bangor at entrance to Belfast Lough (Belfast 16m). Pollack, mackerel, coalfish, garfish, cod, whiting, sea trout from rocks, beach and boats. Good trout July onwards (depending on spates);

mostly free. **Castlewellan Lough;** brown and rainbow trout, boats. Dept of Ag water; permits from forest office. Marks for cod are Black Head and Gobbins. Tackleist: Sports & Leisure, 31 High Street, Carrickfergus.

Bangor (Down). Bangor is on Belfast Lough, 12m from capital. Haddock, whiting, pollack, cod, coalfish and, after June, mackerel; fresh bait (cockles, mussels herring and mackerel) plentiful; lugworm can be dug. Some local boatmen now offer charter facilities as well as scheduled trips for holiday anglers. Visitors should contact Bangor Sea AC, which will take them out for a trip of roughly six hours if space available. Other clubs with boats: RNA, Mountbatten House, and BETS Angling Section, Queen's Parade. Many hotels. Club: Bangor SAC, Hon Sec J Bradley, 27 Rosemary Drive.

Donaghadee (Down). Belfast 18m. Fishing from pier or rocks for pollack, codling and mackerel. Motor boats available for deep-water fishing about 3m offshore, where some large cod have been caught. Boats: Simpsons and others. Usual charge, £5 per day. Rag and lugworm and mussels are good baits. Numerous hotels. Club: Donaghadee SAC, Hon Sec W Greer, 29 Ravenscroft Avenue, Belfast. Tel: Belfast 657816.

POLLUTION

Anglers are united in deploring pollution. To combat it, urgent action may be called for at any time from any one of us. If numbers of fish are found dead, dying, or seriously distressed, report the matter to the Dept. of Agriculture, Fisheries Conservancy or Commission.

FISHING CLUBS & ASSOCIATIONS IN NORTHERN IRELAND

THE following is an alphabetical list of angling clubs and associations in N. Ireland. Particulars of the waters held by many will be found by reference to the index, in the section headed "Fishing Stations in N. Ireland", and information about the others, which may not have their own water, could be had from the secretaries. A courtesy appreciated by secretaries is the inclusion of a stamped addressed envelope for reply.

Agivey Anglers' Association
D B Williamson
1 Moneydig Road
Aghadowey, Co Londonderry
Antrim and District Angling Club
T Wilson
15 Brantwood Gardens
Greystone Road, Co Antrim
Armagh and District Angling Club
R Priestley
12 Main Street
Bessbrook, Newry
Augher District and Upper Blackwater
Angling Club
J A Russell
Old Manse, Clogher
Aughnacloy Angling Club
G Hamilton (chairman)
Creaton House
Ballygawley, Co Tyrone
Ballycastle and District Anglers' Club
Mrs Alice Ferguson
Kern House
Armoy, Ballymoney
Co Antrim
Banbridge Angling Club
B McMaster
Iveagh Drive
Banbridge, Co Down
Bangor Anglers' Association
B Rutherford
3 Bayview Road
Bangor, Co Down
Bangor Sea Angling Club
J Bradley
27 Rosemary Drive
Bangor, Co Down
Belfast Anglers' Association
R C Woods
Dhu Fin
Hawthorn Gardens
Belfast BT4 2H7
Belfast Reservoir Angling Club
M Eardley
38 Eblana Street
Belfast

Belfast Waltonians Angling Society
W Bird
60 Fernwood Street
Ormeau Road
Belfast BT15 3AN
Belleek and District Angling Association
P J Farren
HM Customs
Belleek, Co Fermanagh
Bessbrook and District Angling Club
B Priestley
Main Street
Bessbrook, Co Armagh
Bushmills and District Angling Club
G Quinn
14 Heronshaw
Bushmills
Carrickfergus and District (Sea) Angling Club
R Craig
56 Craigowen Road
Carrickfergus, Co Antrim
Castlecaldwell and District Anglers' Club
B Faughan
Leggs
Enniskillen, Co Fermanagh
Castlederg Angling Association
S P Mannion
Mount Bernard
Castlederg, Co Tyrone
Castlewellan and Annsborough Angling Club
H J Hutchman
23 Greenhill Park
Newcastle, Co Down
Clady and District Angling Club
D Hoy
8 Fendale
Culleybackey, Co Londonderry
Clogher/Augher Angling Club
Matt Ferguson
Augher, Co Tyrone
Coleraine Anglers' Association
W J Walker
23 Boulevard
Coleraine, Co Derry
Crossmaglen and District Angling Club
Michael O'Brien

359

Newry Road
Crossmaglen, Co Down
Donaghadee Sea Angling Club
W Greer
29 Ravenscroft Avenue
Belfast
Downpatrick and District Angling Association
R A Hall
6 Castlehill Drive
Belfast
Dromore Angling Club
R Russell
49 Ravenscroft Avenue
Belfast
Dundonald Angling Club
G Legge
Moatview Park
Dundonald, Co Down
Dungannon and District Angling Club
J Arthur
Glenadush
Dungannon, Co Tyrone
Dungiven Anglers' Club
S McCloskey
40 Station Road
Dungiven, Co Londonderry
East Antrim Angling Association
A V Gardiner
22 Bengore Gardens
Craigyhill
Larne, Co Antrim
Fairhead Fishing Club
E C Redmond
Atlantic Avenue
Ballycastle, Co Antrim
Fermanagh Anglers' Association
I Brown
12 Drumday Road
Enniskillen, Co Fermanagh
Fermanagh Fishery Federation
R E Bracken
Lisblake, Florencecourt
Co Fermanagh
Finn Angling Club
H Curran
Glebe
Sion Mills, Co Tyrone
Gilford Angling Club
J Thompson
24 Ann Street
Gilford, Co Down
Glebe Angling Associations
Edward Neeson
6 School Terrace
Glebe, Sion Mills, Co Tyrone
Glens Angling Club
M C Bedwell
3 Thorndale Park
Carryduff, Co Antrim

Gracehill, Galgorm and District Angling Club
N Anderson
50a Ballykennedy Rd
Gracehill, Co Antrim
Iveagh Angling Club
W Knox
1 Drumnamoe Avenue
Lurgan, Co Down
Permits from
M Harrison
12 Donard Gardens
Lurgan
Kells and Connor Angling Club
T Bell
32 Candiere Avenue
Connor
Kells, Ballymena
Co Antrim
Kilkeel Angling Club
M McErlean
8 Dunavan Park
Scroog Road
Kilkeel, Co Down
Kilrea and District Angling Club
J Templeton
Main Street
Garvagh, Co Londonderry
Lisburn and District Anglers' Club
N Kennedy
99 Tisowen Drive
Knockmore
Lisburn, Co Antrim
Londonderry and District Anglers' Association
J H Wallace
86 Spencer Road
Waterside, Londonderry
Maine Angling Club
C Wright
109 Dunminning Rd
Glarryford, Co Antrim
Mournbeg and Derg Anglers' Association
J Davie
Main Street
Castlederg, Co Tyrone
Moy Angling Club
D Towney
The Square
Moy, Co Tyrone
Newcastle and Ballynahinch Anglers' Association
R C Masaroon
44 Devon Parade
Belfast BT4 1LT
Newry and District Angling Club
R McAllister
89 Drumgullion Avenue
Newry, Co Down

North West Angling Federation
Dr B Deeney
The Bowling Green
Strabane
Omagh Anglers' Association
J Fergy
4 Strahulter Road
Newtownstewart, Co Tyrone
Pickwick Angling Club
R Vint
21 Beechgrove Park
Belfast, 6
Randalstown Angling Club
Elaine Hamilton
15 Rathmore Road
Muckamore, Co Antrim
Rathfriland and District Angling Association
D A Crory
5 Castlewellan Road
Rathfriland, Co Down
River Faughan Anglers' Association
Club Office
26 Carlisle Road
Londonderry, Co Londonderry
Roe Angling Association
S Maxwell
51 Scroggy Road
Limavady, Co Derry
Rostrevor and District Angling Club
P J Magee Snr
55 Murne Drive
Warrenpoint, Co Down
Shimna Angling Club
W Irwin
9 Shimna Road
Newcastle, Co Down
South Derry Anglers' Association
J Swann
Castledawson Road
Magherafelt, Co Derry

Strabane Angling Association
Eric Wilson
Provincial Bank
Main Street
Strabane, Co Tyrone
Ulster Coarse Fishing Federation
H Kearns
Scots House
Clones, Co Cavan
Upperlands Angling Club
W J Cochrane
Boyne Row
Upperlands, Co Derry
Warrenpoint and Rostrevor District Angling Club
J F Carroll
93 Rosmara Park
Warrenpoint
Newry, Co Down
Warrenpoint and Rostrevor Sea Angling Club
H J Rice
13 Clonallon Gardens
Warrenpoint
Newry, Co Down
Whiterock Angling Club
B Donnelly
18 St James's Road
Belfast
Whitewell Angling Club
J Hoyles
71 Station Road
Whiteabbey, Co Antrim
Woodvale Angling Club
R Baillie
43 Disraeli Road
Belfast

Check before you go

While every effort has been made to ensure that the information given in "Where to Fish" is correct, the position is continually changing and anglers are urged, in their own interests, to make preliminary inquiries before travelling to selected venues. This is especially important with reference to prices quoted. Inevitably, the rate of inflation is affecting stability in this quarter. Anglers' attention is also drawn to the fact that the hotels mentioned under the various fishing stations do not necessarily have water of their own. Any amendments or further data for inclusion in subsequent editions, and any criticism, will be welcome.

362

FISHING IN THE IRISH REPUBLIC

THE Irish Republic, still relatively free from pollutive industry, is world famous for the quality of its fisheries. Salmon, sea trout, brown trout, pike and other coarse fish are to be found there at their best. The seas around Ireland contain very good quantities of many varieties of fish which provide excellent sport for visiting and native sea anglers. Where to fish in Ireland is virtually everywhere. Fisheries are administered by a Central Fisheries Board and by seven Regional Fisheries Boards answering to the Central Board *(advt p 362)*. The function of each Regional Board is to conserve, protect and develop every aspect of the inland fisheries (salmon, trout, coarse fish, eels), including sea angling, within the Board's fisheries region. Each fisheries region consists of one or more of the seventeen traditional fishery districts and for legal reasons licences to fish for salmon (including sea trout) continue to relate to the fishery district named on each licence. Salmon and sea trout may not be fished except under licence issued by the relevant Regional Fisheries Board for the fishery district named on the licence. A salmon fishing licence to cover all seventeen fishery districts may be purchased from any Regional Fisheries Board. The cost of rod licences for salmon and sea trout is as follows:

Annual licence valid in all seventeen fishery districts, £17.
Annual licence valid for one named fishery district, £8.
Seven-day licence (all fishery districts), £6.
Late-season licence valid 1 July onwards (all fishery districts), £11.50.
Late-season licence valid 1 July onwards for one named fishery district only, £6.

The modified close seasons now in force for salmon, sea trout and brown trout differ not only as between regions, but also within regions, in a formulation too complex for reproduction here in detail. The general pattern is as before, in that seasons for migratory fish tend to open early and close early, while that for brown trout opens early in many places (Feb 15) and does not close until a date in October. There are, however, important exceptions and anglers proposing to visit the Republic, especially early or late in the year, should make careful enquiries with the appropriate Regional Board before making firm plans, whether the intention be to fish for salmon, migratory or brown trout.

No licence is required for brown trout, coarse fish or sea fish angling.

There is no annual close season for angling for coarse fish or for sea fish.

Overall responsibility for the country's fisheries rests with the Department of the Marine, Leeson Lane, Dublin 2.

The Central Fisheries Board consists of the Chairman of the seven Regional Boards and from four to six members nominated by the Minister for Fisheries and Forestry. The functions of the Central Board are prescribed in the Fisheries Act 1980 and include such things as co-ordination and, where necessary, direction of the regional boards in the performance of their functions; management of any fishery, hatchery or fish farm possessed by the Central Board; preparation of an inland fisheries development programme, etc. Amongst other things the fisheries owned and operated by the former Inland Fisheries Trust are now controlled by the Central Fisheries Board. **Inquiries about fishing those waters (location, fees etc) should be addressed to The Chief Executive Officer, Central Fisheries Board, Balnagowan House, Mobhi Boreen, Glasnevin, Dublin 9.**

The Central Fisheries Board owns and operates an important commercial and rod salmon fishery on the River Corrib at Galway, Co Galway (inquiries to the Manager, The Fishery, Nun's Island, Galway, Co Galway), and the famous Erriff Fishery in Co Galway. Enquiries for fishing and accommodation here—at Aasleagh Lodge or Cottage—to the Manager, R Erriff Fishery, Aasleagh Lodge, Leenane, Co Galway.

The Electricity Supply Board also holds extensive fishing rights: principal salmon waters are the River Mulcair and the Shannon at Parteen, above Limerick, and at Castleconnell, Co Limerick. The Board preserves and develops the fisheries under its control. Inquires to the Secretary, Electricty Supply Board, Fisheries Division, Lower Fitzwilliam Street, Dublin 2.

Inquiries about accommodation and general tourist angling information (e.g. leaflets, brochures about local angling resources and amenities throughout the country) should be addressed to **Bord Failte (The Irish Tourist Board), Baggot Street Bridge, Dublin 2** or **The Irish Tourist Board, 150 New Bond Street, London.**

THE REGIONAL BOARDS

The Eastern Regional Fisheries Board. Consists of the fishery districts of Dundalk, Drogheda, Dublin and Wexford, and covers all lakes and river systems entering the sea including coastal waters between Clogherhead, Co Louth and Kiln Bay, Co Wexford. Inquiries to the Board's Regional Fisheries Manager, Balnagowan House, Mobhi Boreen, Glasnevin, Dublin 9.

The Southern Regional Fisheries Board. Consists of the fishery districts of Waterford and Lismore and covers all lakes and river systems entering the sea, including coastal waters, between Kiln Bay, Co Wexford and Ballycotton Pier, Co Cork. Inquiries to the Board's Regional Fisheries Manager, Anglesea St, Clonmel, Co Tipperary.

The South Western Regional Fisheries Board. Consists of the fishery districts of Cork and Kerry and covers all lakes and river systems entering the sea, including coastal waters, between Ballycotton Pier, Co Cork and Kerry Head, Co Kerry. Inquiries to the Board's Regional Fisheries Manager, Nevilles Terrace, Massey Town, Macroom, Co Cork.

The Shannon Regional Fisheries Board. Consists of the Limerick fishery district and covers all lakes and rivers entering the sea, including coastal waters, between Kerry Head, Co Kerry and Hag's Head, Co Clare. Inquiries to the Board's Regional Fisheries Manager, Thomond Weir, Limerick, Co Limerick.

The Western Regional Fisheries Board. Consists of Galway, Connemara and Ballinakill fishery districts and covers all lakes and rivers entering the sea, including coastal waters, between Hag's Head, Co Clare and Pigeon Point, near Westport, Co Mayo. Inquiries to The Board's Regional Fisheries Manager, The Weir Lodge, Earl's Island, Galway.

The North Western Regional Fisheries Board. Consists of Sligo, Ballina and Bangor fishery districts and covers all lakes and rivers entering the sea, including coastal waters, between Pigeon Point, near Westport, Co Mayo, and Carrickgarve, Co Sligo. Inquiries to the Board's Regional Fisheries Manager, Ardnaree House, Abbey St, Ballina, Co Mayo.

The Northern Regional Fisheries Board. Consists of Ballyshannon and Letterkenny fishery districts and covers all lakes and rivers entering the sea, including coastal waters, between Carrickgarve, Co Sligo and Malin Head, Co Donegal. Inquiries to the Board's Regional Fisheries Manager, Station Road, Ballyshannon, Co Donegal.

SEASONS

The matter of open and close seasons for salmon and trout in the Republic of Ireland presents an extremely complicated picture. The season for rod & line fishing for salmon is closed uniformly by law on Sep 30, but local extensions are at times given. The season opens, according to locality, at some date between Jan 1 and June 1. The season for trout closes district by district on the following dates: Aug 31, Sep 15, Sep 30, Oct 9, Oct 10, Oct 12 and Oct 31. As far as we have been able to trace, April 1 is the earliest opening date. Brown trout fishing is prohibited by law on all waters before February. The opening date for brown trout fishing is usually the opening date for salmon fishing on that water, unless the salmon season opens before Feb 15. In that case, Feb 15 is the opening date for brown trout. Most commonly, the open season for brown trout is from Feb 15 or March 1 to Sep 30. Where rainbow trout are present the season may be extended to some later date.

The position cannot be clarified merely by asking one of the Regional Boards listed above for the situation prevailing in its area. It is necessary to state in detail the water(s) one proposes to fish. Central Fisheries Board issues a most helpful booklet covering a number of waters accessible to the general public on permit.

There is no close season anywhere in the Republic for coarse fishing.

FISHING STATIONS IN THE IRISH REPUBLIC

DETAILS of close seasons and licences, etc, for Irish rivers and loughs, listed alphabetically here, will be found in pages 363–4. Anglers wanting further details of accommodation should write to Bord Failte (Irish Tourist Board), Baggot Street Bridge, Dublin, 2.

ANNAGH and ANNAGEERAGH

(For close seasons, licences, etc, see The Shannon Regional Fisheries Board, pp 363–64)

Best centre for these streams is **Milltown-Malbay** (Clare). Fishing free; brown trout plentiful, odd salmon and many sea trout in autumn. Near source of Annageeragh is Doolough; brown trout to $\frac{1}{2}$ lb; boat available.

AWBEG

(For close seasons, licences, etc, see The Southern Regional Fisheries Board, pp 363–64)

A very good trout stream, especially for dry fly. Castletownroche AC issues visitors tickets for lower reaches.

BANDON

(For close seasons, licences, etc, see The South Western Regional Fisheries Board, pp 363–64)

From above Bandon Town to Desert Bridge, **Enniskeane** (about 6m), river controlled by River Bandon Salmon and Trout AA, except one small fishery on north bank; wt and dt for salmon and trout. A portion of river between **Bandon** and **Innishannon** also rented by association. (Hotels: Munster Arms, Bandon; and Innishannon; salmon, white and brown trout fishing). **Brinny** and **Argideen** in this district are white trout rivers. Tickets issued by association and obtainable (with salmon licences) from tackleists in Bandon: F Begley, South Main Street, and Mr Lee, Bridge House. Hon sec will be pleased to advise visiting anglers. The 4m stretch of river to about 1m above **Ballineen Bridge** is controlled by Ballineen and Enniskeane AA; salmon and trout. Mt £10, wt £5, dt (trout) £1, from Mrs Fehily, Bridge Street, Ballineen. A further stretch of 2m, known as Manch (property of District Justice Henry Conner of Manch House), provides best salmon angling in district. Above **Manch Bridge** is Dunmanway Salmon and Trout AA water. St £10 (S) £5 (t). River fishable for about 8m. Trouting also on **Caha River,** which joins Bandon 3m north of **Dunmanway.** $4\frac{1}{2}$m SW, **Drinagh Lake.** Trout mt £2. Guests staying local hotels and guest houses for periods not exceeding one month may fish association waters for salmon and trout (salmon £5, trout £1). **River Argideen,** flowing into Courtmacsherry Harbour, has salmon and sea trout. Permit from J E Spiller, tackleist, 39/41 Pearse Street, Clonakilty, who also issue permits for Bandon, including the tidal water, and for **Shepperton Lakes,** (brown trout). Hotels: Emmet, Inchydoney, O'Donovans.

BARROW (including Suir and Nore)

(For close seasons, licences, etc, see The South Western Regional Fisheries Board, pp 363–64)

Rises well up in the centre of Ireland on the eastern slopes of the Shannon watershed and flows over 120m southerly to the sea at **Waterford** Harbour, entering by a long estuary. Salmon and trout. Salmon fishing fair and many stretches free. Good brown trout river suitable for dry fly. From Waterford, **Belle Lake** (pike, tench, rudd) and **Knockaderry Reservoir** (trout) may be fished. **Mahon River** (15m) holds sea trout and salmon, and mackerel, bass and pollack abound along the coast. Dunmore Deep Sea AC, Co Waterford, welcomes visitors. Tackleist: Sports Shop, Quay, Waterford. Other fishing stations: **Graiguenamanagh** (Kilkenny), **Borris** (Carlow), **Carlow.** Hotels: Royal, Crofton. Salmon fishing free to licence-holders in this area. Trout fishing on **Rivers Lerr, Greese, Douglas** and **Burren,** which fish well wet or dry, controlled by Barrow AC and restocked yearly (membership £2 from local tackleists). Good free coarse fishing in Barrow; perch, rudd, bream, pike, tench. Club: Carlow AA. Annual membership £2. Tackleists: S O'Neill and John Boyd in Kennedy Street; Sports Shop and R Atkinson in Tullow Street and all in Carlow. **Athy.** Several tributaries, including **Bauteogue** and **Boherbaun,** within easy reach. There is some good free dry-fly water. About **Portarlington,** Portarlington-Monasterevan Dist AA have 10m water; visitors welcomed. Tackleists: M O'Donoghue, 14 Castle Street, Carlow; Byrne & Dawson, Main Street, Tullow.

SUIR

(For close seasons, licences, etc, see The Southern Regional Fisheries Board, pp 363–64)

Runs into the same estuary as Nore and Barrow, and is much better salmon river. Noted also for its trout fishing. Record salmon for Ireland, 57 lb, was caught in Suir, in 1874. Best months for spring salmon, which are usually heavy, are Feb to April. Usually good run in May. Grilse from June on, with occasional runs of small salmon to end of season. Principal stations on river are following: **Clonmel.** Hotels: Hearn's, Ormonde, Larkins. Clonmel and Dist AC controls good deal of water on river. Clonmel Salmon AA also has water; apply hon sec. **Nier** and **Tar** trout streams are within easy reach, but **Clogheen** and **Ardfinnan** are best for latter; contact hon secs, Clonmel and Clogheen AC respectively for further information. Mountain loughs can also be reached from this centre. **Cahir.** Cahir

Spinning on the Suir. *Photograph: Bord Failte.*

and Dist AA controls 6m of salmon fishing above town and 1m below. Association also has 3m of tributary **Aherlow;** trout. Hotels: Cahir House, Galtee and Kilcoran Lodge; 8m salmon and trout water. Licences from D Kavanagh, West Gate, Clonmel. Salmon and brown trout flies from E Heavey, Cahir Park, and R J Watkins, Castle Street. **Cashel.** Cashel, Tipperary and Golden AA issues visitors' permits; some spring salmon; grilse July and Aug; trout good (av $\frac{1}{2}$ lb); pike up to 25 lb in upper reaches. Mar, April and May best months usually for trout. Salmon mid-Mar to June; grilse, July/Aug. Hotels: Zetland Hotel ($3\frac{1}{2}$m of private sea trout and salmon fishing and on several lakes), Longfield House (1m of own fishing; many other waters), Royal Tipperary. **Carrick-on-Suir.** Start of tidal water. Carrick-on-Suir AA has developed fishing in vicinity; £1 week. Up river there is good trout fishing and occasional sea trout; mostly free. About 4m to south mountain loughs, largest of which are **Coumshingaun** and **Crotty's,** provide very good fishing as also does **Clodiagh River,** which springs from loughs and is close to road for part of way. Angler in search of good salmon and trout fishing would be advised to seek it anywhere from Carrick to Cashel. Most of river preserved for salmon, but some owners give permission to fish for trout. **Thurles** is good centre for upper river. Hayes Hotel can arrange fishing by the day or week. Club: Thurles, Holycross and Ballycamas AA. Wt £15 and dt £5. Fly only. At **Templemore** is Templemore AA water; visitors' dt for Suir (trout only, av $\frac{1}{2}$ lb). Tackleists: O'Keeffe, OK Garage, New Street, Carrick-on-Suir; Morgan Carroll, The Square, Ballybricken, Waterford; O'Bowman & Sons, 6 Mary Street, Dungarvan.

NORE

(For close seasons, licences, etc, see The Southern Regional Fisheries Board, pp 363–64)

Lies between Barrow and Suir, and runs into same estuary. Salmon fishing now mainly preserved and overnetting has lowered stocks. Spring fish are heavy; big grilse run from June onwards. Trout fishing good (regularly restocked), fish average $\frac{1}{2}$–$\frac{3}{4}$ lb. Tributaries also have been restocked and sport excellent. Fishing stations: **Thomastown** (Kilkenny), **Kilkenny** (Kilkenny). Thomastown AA has excellent salmon and trout stretch of Nore and issues temporary cards to visitors. Kilkenny AA has some excellent salmon and trout fishing on 12m of Nore and **Dinan** and issues permits to visitors. Other stretches free. **King's River;** good brown trout. Hotels: Carmel Club House, Imperial, Metropole, Newpark and Rose Hill. **Abbeyleix** (Leix). Guest houses with fishing: Mrs S Pratt, Dealgrove; Mrs H M Seale, The Glebe, Attanagh, Portlaoise. Fishing much deteriorated due to pollution and drainage works. **Mountrath** (Leix), Nore; brown trout, pike, perch. **Coppal-Bawn River;** brown trout. Hotels: The Arch Bar, Hibernian, de Vesci Arms. Tackleists: M McGrath, 3 Lower Patrick Street, Kilkenny; Kilkenny Sports Scene, 1 Irishtown, Kilkenny.

BLACKWATER

(For close seasons, licences, etc, see The Southern Regional Fisheries Board, pp 363–64)

Perhaps most famous salmon river in Southern Ireland. Rises west of Killarney Mountains and flows eastwards about 70m until it reaches town of Cappoquin, where it becomes tidal and turns sharply south, entering sea by estuary 15m long at Youghal Bay. Salmon (best stretches mainly between Mallow and Lismore), sea trout, brown trout, but large quantities of dace, bream, perch and pike in some parts. Best fishing strictly preserved. Big runs of spring salmon from Feb to April; grilse June to Sept; and often good run of autumn salmon during Aug and Sept. Sea trout in Blackwater and Bride, June onwards.

Youghal (Cork). On Blackwater estuary. **Turig River** enters estuary here; for fishing apply to hon sec, Turig AC. Other club: Youghal Sea AC. At **Killeagh** (6m) Glenbower Trout AC has river and lough; sea trout; fly, bait; Cappoquin AC issues permits for trout and coarse fishing off Lismore Estate waters. Coarse fishing free to visitors. **Ballyduff** (4m Lismore) is popular centre. Best months for salmon: Feb, Mar, April and Sept. Sea trout June, Sept. Inquire Cappoquin AC (Tel: Cappoquin 22). **Fermoy** (Cork). Salmon, sea trout, trout; also dace and rudd. 12m of excellent salmon (record results), sea trout, brown trout and coarse fishing on Lower Blackwater Fishery between Ballyhooley Bridge above Fermoy and Killavallen. Salmon fishing on Blackwater at Careysville Fishery, Fermoy *(advt below)*. Also 2m of very good sea and brown trout fishing (few salmon) on **River Bride** at Tallow Bridge. Permits for Blackwater from Blackwater Lodge Hotel, Upper Ballyduff, Co Waterford. Dt for **R Bride**, £1. Clubs: Fermoy and Dist Trout AA; Fermoy Salmon AA. Hotels: Royal, Grand, both Fermoy; Blue Dragon, Kilworth; Royal, Mitchelstown. Guests at Toby Jug, **Cappoquin**, may enjoy good sport with salmon, trout and coarse fish. Cappoquin AC issues permits for salmon fishing on Blackwater and Bride; and arranges accommodation; inquire hon sec for details. **Araglin** holds brown trout; good dry fly. **Funshion** runs in near Careysville on north bank; trout, dace, rudd. **Bride,** holds salmon and sea trout as well as brown trout; also dace, rudd. All these tributaries can be fished on nominal payment to local angling associations. Kilworth Trout AA is for Araglin and Funshion, and Mallow Trout AA for the Bride. Mitchelstown and Kildorrey Trout AA has upper reaches of Funshion. **Mallow** (Cork). Salmon (preserved); trout and coarse fishing good (roach and dace are main species); all coarse fishing free. Clubs: Mallow Trout AA; Mallow Coarse AA. For trout fishing club membership only required; £5 per year. Salmon licences from Pat Hayes (tackleists), Spa Square. Hotels: Hibernian; Central; Longueville House (Georgian Mansion with own fishery); Isle of Skye, **Kanturk** (1½m of Blackwater, salmon, sea trout, coarse fish). At **Castletownroche,** Castletownroche AC has good trout fishing; apply hon sec. Tackleists: J O'Sullivan, 4 Patrick Street, Fermoy; Mallow Sports Centre, 21 Bridge Street, Mallow; Mrs P Twohig, Strand Street, Kanturk.

BOYNE

(For close seasons, licences, etc, see The Eastern Regional Fisheries Board, pp 363–64)

Rises near Edenderry and flows for about 70m, entering the sea near Drogheda north of Dublin. Very good early salmon, although fresh-run fish are now caught throughout

season in deep pools of Lower Boyne Fishery. Spring fish run large, a few over 30 lb being killed every year, but salmon fishing adversely affected by drainage operations. Sea trout only in lower part, running mainly up a tributary, the **Mattock**, fishable only after heavy spates. Main river preserved, though good number of beats are let.

Drogheda (Louth). Drogheda and District AC has game and coarse fishing on Boyne and Nanny; and also Reservoirs Killineer and Barnattin which are stocked with brown and rainbow. Permits from Jim Donegan Sports, Stockwell Street and Frank Smyth Sports, Shop Street. Lower parts of Boyne and Mattock preserved. Brown trout in two reservoirs; st from Drogheda Corporation. Hotels: Central, White Horse, Boyne Valley, Rosnaree, Cooper Hill House (Julianstown). Tackleist: Olraine Agencies, Abbey Shopping Centre. **Navan** (Meath). Kilbride AA has salmon and trout fishing on 5m; St £12, dt £1. Hotels: Central and Russell Arms. **Slane** (Meath). Fishing good, but preserved. Hotel: Conyngham Arms. **Trim** (Meath). Good trout in main river and tributaries. Trim, Athboy and Dist AA preserves and restocks **Athboy River** and some stretches on Boyne itself; st £15, wt £5, dt £1. Hotels: Wellington Court, Central and Railway. Deel and Boyne AA has trout and salmon water on tributary **Deel**. Hotels: Central, Railway (both Trim); Greville Arms (Mullingar). Longwood Anglers also have salmon and trout fishing on Boyne. **Kells** (Meath). Good trout fishing on **River Blackwater**; dry fly. Mayfly fishing good. 15m preserved and restocked by Kells AA; st £10 and dt £2.50. Trout up to 7 lb may be had in the river, also large pike and salmon, $1\frac{1}{2}$m of free fishing from source. Hotel: Headford Arms. **Virginia** (Cavan). On headwaters. **Lough Ramour** gives good trout fishing and excellent fishing for bream, rudd, perch and pike; boats available, two tributaries. Ten lakes and four rivers within 5m; trout and coarse fish. Hotels: The Park, Virginia. (Salmon and trout fishing on **Blackwater**; trout in loughs and three small rivers; course fishing on **Lough Ramour**). Tackleists: Rod & Gun Sports Shop, Abbeylands, Navan; "Tomas", Farrell Street, Kells.

CORRIB SYSTEM

(For close seasons, licences, etc, see The Western Regional Fisheries Board, pp 363–64)

River Corrib drains **Lough Corrib** and runs $5\frac{1}{2}$m to Galway Bay passing virtually through the city of Galway. Salmon, trout. Salmon fishing very good. For particulars as to present conditions and rods apply Central Fishery Board, Nuns Island, Galway. Best fishing for springers early in season; grilse, May–June. Rods let by the day, the week and the month. Fishing station: **Galway**. Hotels: Great Southern, Atlanta, Skeffington Arms. Tackle and salmon licences from Naughton's, Shop Street. **Kilcolgan River** (10m E) part tidal, salmon and sea trout. Free downstream of old bridge; preserved elsewhere, good free fishing higher up.

LOUGH CORRIB

This, the largest sheet of water in Republic (41,617 acres, 68 sq m), is dotted with islands, around which are shallows which make for good fishing. Specially noted for large brown trout. Trout fishing opens on Feb 15 and is mainly by trolling until April. Wet fly good in April and early May, but lough best known for dapping with mayfly (beginning last week in May) and daddy-longlegs (mid-July to end of season). Good dry-fly fishing on summer evenings. Salmon taken mainly by trolling, and in June on wet fly in many of bays. Also big pike and other course fish in Corrib, so that angling of some kind is available all year. Fishing free, but salmon licence required. Many hotels issue licences. Boats and boatmen at Portacarron, Oughterard, Baurisheen, Derrymoyle, Glan Shore, Cong, Greenfield, Doorus, Carrick, Salthouse, Carey's and Inishmacatreer.

Oughterard (Galway). Currarevagh House (tel: 09182 313) provides boats, gillies, ob motors with fuel and tackle if necessary for a charge of £30 per day, also has boat on top lake of Screebe sea trout fishery. Oughterard House (free fishing on Corrib; private water within 12m; salmon and sea trout); Corrib, Angler's and Egan's Lake. Also new motel: Connemara Gateway (Reservations: Tel: 01-567 3444) and Ross Lake Hotel, Rosscahill (boats and boatmen). **Owenriff River** flows through Oughterard; good in high water late

The class of trout – the sort of fish which used to be termed "ferox" – which has been drawing anglers to the West of Ireland for generations. This one, taken from L. Mask on a trolled copper and silver spoon in 1983, weighed $17\frac{3}{4}$ lb. Shown with it is a typical $1\frac{3}{4}$ lb specimen taken on a fly. *Photograph: by courtesy of Bord Failte.*

summer. Tackleist: Tucks, Main Street. **Headford** (Galway). Convenient for the east side of Lough Corrib. **Black River** (limestone stream) provides excellent if somewhat difficult dry fly water. Affected by drainage work. Best near village of **Shrule.** Accommodation at Angler's Rest Hotel and guest houses. **Greenfield** (Galway). First-class centre for eastern bank. Ower House Apartments, Greenfield, Ower PO, stand on lough shore and are very popular with anglers; boats with boatmen available £30 per day. **Lough Hackett** (large pike, perch) is 9m away. **Maam Cross** (Galway). Hotels: Peacock's, Maam Cross (*see also Ballynahinch–Mid-West Coastal Streams*). **Cong** (Mayo). Good for Lough Mask also. Hotels: Ashford Castle (*advt p 368*) which provides boats and gillies £25 per day. Ryan's Corrib Guest House. Tackleists: S Ryan, Cong; T Cheevers, Northgate Street, Athenry; K Duffy & Son, Main Street, Headford.

LOUGH MASK

Limestone lake of 20,496 acres connected by underground channel with Lough Corrib holding large brown trout, pike, eels, perch and a few char. Trout to 15 lb are taken by trolling and on dap (5–6 lb not uncommon). Mayfly, May, June, and July; daddy-longlegs and grasshopper, late June to Sept; wet fly, Mar–April and July–Sept. **Ballinrobe, Cong, Clonbur** and **Tourmakeady** are good centres. At Cong is Cong AA; (st £5), at Ballinrobe is Ballinrobe and Dist AA (st £5) and at Tourmakeady is Tourmakeady AC. All are open to visitor-membership. Tackleists: Mr Ryan, Cong; D O'Connor, Main Street, Ballinrobe; O'Toole, Tourmakeady and J J O'Connor, Staunton Sports Shop and Pat Quinn Tackle, all Castlebar. Boats for hire at Cushlough Pier, Bay of Islands Park, Rosshill Park, Caher Pier. Good accommodation at Tourmakeady Lodge, recently converted into guest house and which caters especially for fishermen. Also Mask Lodge and Mask Villa on lake shore. River fishing on **Finney** and canal joining Mask and Corrib. At Tourmakeady are some good spate rivers, and mountain lake fishing can be had in **Dirk Lakes**; brown trout. Connected to Mask are **Lough Carra** (4,003 acres, limestone, brown trout run large; boats at Flannery's Pier and Brownstown) and **Lough Nafooey** (good coarse fish). Good trout, perch, pike in three tributaries of Mask: Robe, Finney, Bulkaun.

CLARE-GALWAY

Flows into Lough Corrib, near Galway, and was considered one of best spawning streams for Galway River fish. Best season: Spring salmon, mid-April to mid-May; grilse, third week June to third week July; brown trout, April to June. Holds large trout and suitable for dry fly. Fishing station: **Galway,** for lower reaches. Tackleists: "Great Outdoors", Eglinton Street; Freenys, High Street and Duffy, Mainguard Street. (*For hotels, see Corrib*). 25m W of Galway on coast road is new Carraroe Hotel; sea and lake fishing. **Tuam** (Galway). For upper waters. Some free fishing. Club: Tuam and Dist Trout AA. A private club (Corofin Association) has salmon and dry-fly trout water on river; particulars from hon sec. **Castlegrove Lake**; pike, perch, bream, rudd.

SPIDDAL

Short river 12m W of Galway. Salmon, sea trout. Fishing formerly owned and let by Lord Killanin now unavailable. Remainder of bank is property of Mrs McDonagh, Villa, Galway. Headquarters are property of Irish Land Commission (to let by season with shooting); some free fishing. Inquire Herbert Buckley, Spiddal House, **Spiddal. Boliska Lough** (sea trout, some salmon) is free.

NORTH DONEGAL (streams)

(For close seasons, licences, etc, see The Northern Regional Fisheries Board, pp 363-64)

Donegal is mostly salmon and sea trout country. Its waters are generally acid; rocky or stony streams and small lakes in which the brown trout run small—though there are one or two fisheries where they may be taken up to 2 lb and more.

LENNON (or LEANNAN)

Rises in **Lough Gartan** and flows through south end of **Lough Fern** into sea on west coast of **Lough Swilly**. Salmon, trout. From **Lough Fern** to town of **Ramelton**, Co Donegal, provides 4 to 5m of good salmon water. Permission may be obtained from various landowners. St and dt local club water from P Cullen, Kilmacrennan. Salmon run from January (given mild weather) to June, followed by grilse and sea trout to season's end. Lower portion of river at Ramelton owned and fished privately by Ramelton Fishery Ltd. Free brown trout fishing on various loughs. **Lough Fern**, midway between towns of **Milford** and **Kilmacrennan**, usually provides excellent free salmon fishing during April and May (by boat only). Boats usually obtainable at Milford and Kilmacrennan Hotels or at McFadden's at Lough Fern. Kilmacrennan and **Churchill** are for Upper Lennon. Loughs Gartan, Akibbon and Nacally (trout) may be fished from here, some free, some by ticket. Trout fishing in Lennon equally good on both upper and lower reaches. Best season: April to July. At **Letterkenny** local association has salmon, sea trout and brown trout fishing on rivers and lakes, trout average $\frac{1}{2}$ lb; st and dt from hon sec and local tackleists (*see below*). **River Swilly** provides good salmon and trout fishing and is free. Hotels: Angler's Haven and Fern Arms (Kilmacrennan); McClafferty's and Wilkin's (Churchill); McFadden's (Lough Fern), McCready's Arm (Milford). Licences from hotels and H P Whorisky, The Bridge, Ramelton. Tackle and permits, Ed Barr (information), M Speers, both Upper Main Street, Letterkenny; Wm Gardiner, Milford; Bernard Harte, Lifford; Doherty's (Churchill); Doherty's Leannon Stores and Gorman's Stores (Kilmacrennan).

LACKAGH

Excellent salmon, sea trout and brown trout fishing in **Lackagh River**, **Owencarrow** and **Glen Lough**. Free fishing on **Lough Fern** (10m) and **Doe Estuary** (4m). Glen Lough is early and Owencarrow late. In former, fishing is best in April, May and June, and in latter in July and Aug. Glen Lough is 4m from hotel. Owencarrow is 8m distant by road, but can be reached by boat up lough. Numerous other lakes and streams in neighbourhood. Hotel: Rosapenna.

CRANA

Crana enters tidal water of **Buncrana** on Lough Swilly. Salmon and sea trout few until May; good fishing June onwards. Season: Mar 1 to Oct 12. (MT) Sept 7 (S). Buncrana AA issues mt, wt and dt for salmon and sea trout; brown trout (plentiful, but small). Other waters: **Mill River**; brown trout to $\frac{1}{2}$ lb numerous; free. **Lough Inch** (6m); good sea trout; free. **Dunree River** (6m); free; brown trout, occasional salmon and sea trout. **Clonmany River** (5m); free salmon and sea trout fishing; fair sport in good water; best June onwards. Further information, and flies, from hon sec, Buncrana AA. Tackleist: D McLaughlin, 7 West End, Buncrana.

WEST DONEGAL (streams)

(For close seasons, licences, etc, see The Northern Regional Fisheries Board, pp 363–64)

GWEEBARRA

Drains Lough Barra and flows south-west about 7m to Doochary Bridge, where it becomes tidal and flows hence through long estuary between high hills a further 6m to the Atlantic. Salmon, sea trout. Best season: Spring salmon, Feb–May; grilse and sea trout, end of June to Sept. Fishing belongs to riparian owners, leave obtainable. Salmon and sea trout run into Lough Barra in large numbers and into tributaries. Fishing station: **Doochary** (Donegal). Bridge here marks end of tidal water; several trout lakes in vicinity. **Rosses Fishery** at **Dungloe**, controlled by Rosses AA, offers magnificent facilities to the visitor. Rivers and over 130 lakes; all stocked with brown trout av $\frac{1}{2}$ lb (to 4 lb). **Loughanure Lake** now part of the Rosses Fishery, salmon, sea trout and brown trout. All lakes on **Dungloe** and **Derrydruel** systems have sea trout. Derrydruel and **Crolly,** salmon and sea trout from late May onwards. 5 lakes stocked rainbows to 4 lbs. St £10, dt £3 + £3 boat hire; from C Bonner (tackle shop), Bridge End, Dungloe. Hotels: Ostan na Rosann, Sweeney's.

OWENEA AND OWENTOCKER

Short rivers running into head of Loughrosmore Bay near Ardara, Co Donegal. Salmon, sea trout. Lower beat of Owenea leased by Ardara AA (who also control fishing on 22 lakes in the area); remaining beats (about 5m in all, both banks) leased by Glenties AA. Ardara AA also has Owentocker Fishery 14m, both banks. St £20, wt £10 and dt £2 available from hon sec and tackleists. When in condition Owenea is one of best in country for salmon; many pools. River restocked annually from hatchery in Glenties. Boats on several. Salmon: best months April–June. Grilse and sea trout: June, July–Sept. Free salmon and sea trout fishing on **Rivers Brackey** and **Duog.** Many lakes also free. Fishing stations: **Ardara** and **Glenties,** both Donegal. Tackleists: John McGill, Main Street, Ardara and P O'Donnell, Main Street, Glenties. Hotels: Highland and Kelvon House (Glenties), Nesbitt Arms and Woodhill Guest House (Ardara). Other hotels (seaside) at Maas and at Narin; Portnoo and Rosbeg.

CLADY AND GWEEDORE

Clady drains **Lough Nacung** and runs to sea in about 5m. Formerly good salmon river, but fishing affected by hydro-electric works. Commercial salmon fishing now prohibited to conserve stocks. Small run of sea trout, good brown trout. Best seasons: salmon, April–May; grilse, June–July; sea trout, Sept. Gweedore is good salmon and sea trout water, Mar to Sept. Electricity Supply Board now controls Clady, Gweedore Estuary, **Lough Nacung** and **Dunlewy Lough.** Salmon fishing on Rivers Clady and Crolly; st £17, wt £5.50, dt £2.50; trout fishing free; permits from Regional Manager, Hydro Generation Region, Ardnacrusha, Nr Limerick; Mrs P Boyle, Seaview Hotel, Bunbeg and C Bonner, Bridgend, Dungloe.

ESKE AND INVER

Eske River provides free fishing for salmon (July–Aug) and good sea trout. It drains **Lough Eske,** 3m from **Donegal Town,** which holds brown trout of above average size for this area. Inver Fishery embraces **Eany Water** and tributaries and drains into Inver Bay, 7m west of Donegal Town. Salmon, sea trout, small brown trout. Pike, perch and bream lakes in the vicinity. St £60, wt £25 and dt £5 for game fishing from C Doherty, Tackleist, Main Street, Donegal Town. Two mountain lakes now stocked with rainbow trout and fishable on the Central Fisheries Board £5 general permit. Dt £1.50. **Bradley** and **Tubber Loughs** (10m) hold good trout, especially Bradley. Other good loughs: **Lough A'Capall** and **Lough Suibhne.** Much free lake fishing in area for trout and coarse fish.

GLEN AND OWENEE

These rivers in the Carrick district of south-west Donegal are well stocked with salmon and sea trout. Guests at Slieve Liag Hotel, **Carrick,** can fish them, and good lake and rock fishing available.

For other Donegal centres see pp 356 and 387 (Lough Melvin)

CO. DUBLIN and CO. MEATH (streams)

DARGLE RIVER. Dublin District. Association has boats for trout fishing (members only) on **Vartry Reservoirs at Roundwood** (11m from Bray; see Vartry) and **Bohernabreena Reservoir,** 10m from city centre. Permits can be obtained from Dublin Corporation, Block 1, Floor 3, Civic Offices, Dublin 8. St £10, wt £4, dt £1.50. Associate members' st or visitors' dt can be had for Dargle at **Bray**. Salmon, sea trout, small brown trout, salmon licences from Owens Sports Shop, Bray.

BROADMEADOW RIVER. Dublin District. Trout; rights held by Swords AC in lower reaches of river which enter tidal water at **Swords;** limited membership. Drainage scheme has affected sport.

DELVIN RIVER. In Drogheda District. Fair brown trout stream entering sea at **Gormanstown;** Holds few sea trout. Gormanstown and Dist AA has water. River being stocked and developed with co-operation of landowners and members. **Balbriggan** is convenient centre. (Hotel: Grand.)

DODDER. Dublin District. **Dublin;** brown trout (av 9 ozs, but fish to 2 lbs caught), with some sea trout fishing in tidal portion. Dodder AC annual sub £5 controls all fishing; free to visitors; best months Aug/Sept sea trout; no best months for brown trout, wet fly March/April and superb dry fly all season. Fishing on Dublin Corporation's **Bohernabreena Reservoirs** (10m from Dublin); by Dodder AC membership card or st £10, wt £4, dt £1.50 from Waterworks Office, 28 Castle Street. Open 8.30 to 4 pm on weekdays and 8.30 to 2 pm at weekend.

GLENCREE RIVER. In Dublin District. **Enniskerry** is a centre; small brown trout. Mostly free.

NANNY RIVER. In Drogheda District. River enters sea at **Laytown**, Co Meath. Fair brown trout fishing; some sea trout in lower reaches. Drogheda and Dist AC has water and issues permits at small charge.

TOLKA RIVER. In Dublin District. A once-excellent trout stream dying of pollution in the lower reaches; eutrophication and urban development in the higher. Fishing for the remaining fish free.

ERNE

(For close seasons, licences, etc, see The Northern Regional Fisheries Board, pp 363–64)

A large hydro-electric scheme has turned the River Erne into two large dams. Trout permits (free) from Electricity Supply Board, Lower Fitzwilliam Street, Dublin 2 or Generating Station, Ballyshannon. **Lough Melvin** is best fished from **Bundoran;** boats; free fishing; gilaroos and brown trout that rise freely to fly. Sea trout fishing in estuary from June to Sept. Coarse fishing excellent; bream, rudd and perch abundant and roach multiplying following their introduction in recent years. Hotel: Hamilton. **Lough Erne** is in Northern Ireland; noted for pike and perch. **Enniskillen** is a centre. Trolling usual method to catch trout, but mayfly season is best. Tackleists in Ballyshannon: J Gormley, Main Street (Ballyshannon AA); Rogan's; Timothy's. Hotels in Bundoran: Central, Palace, Atlantic, Imperial, Hamilton (for Bundrowes River; see Bundrowes and Lough Melvin), Maghera. Hotel in Ballyshannon, Millstone. **Dunduff River** is $3\frac{1}{2}$m from Bundoran; dt available; good salmon late June–July. There is some sea fishing out from Bundoran.

Lough Oughter, fed by the Erne, is maze of lakes; holds large trout (av $2\frac{1}{2}$–3 lb, mayfly best but wet fly improving) and a wealth of coarse fish; bream, rudd, pike and roach. Tench in Killmooney Lake. Fishing free. Fishing stations: **Cavan** (two hotels on lake shore), **Swellan Lake** ($\frac{1}{4}$m); coarse fish (tench, rudd, perch, pike). **Lavey Strand Lake** (5m SE). 37 acres; brown trout. Lough Oughter fed by **Annalee** (3m); good coarse fishing (bream, rudd, perch, pike) from **Butlersbridge** ($3\frac{1}{2}$m) to the **Erne**; good trout fishing upstream; has rise of mayfly and is suitable for dry-fly fishing; free. **Annagh Lake, Butlersbridge**, 100-acre water; trout averaging 1 lb and more; boats. **Lough Gowna** accessible from Cavan, which is also a good station for Lough Oughter, Erne and Annalee. Further details from Cavan District Tourist Association. **Belturbet** (Cavan). Salmon and trout in Erne (Aug to Sept), fly fishing upstream and excellent coarse fishing downstream. Numerous lakes. **Annagh Lake**, fishing well on trout; six boats. Hotel: Seven Horse Shoes, many guest houses. **Annalee** gives good trout fishing; has rise of mayfly and is suitable for dry-fly fishing. Free. **Cootehill** (Cavan). Good trout fishing with wet and dry fly on Annalee and Dromore rivers; 16 lakes provide trout and coarse fishing. Club: Cootehill AA. Hotel: White Horse. **Barnagrove Lake** ($4\frac{1}{2}$m) holds good trout. Numerous lakes hold large pike, perch, rudd, bream, fishing free. **Lough Sillan** (8m) holds big trout (to 6 lb and over); free; fishable from entire shore. On the **Finn**, a sluggish tributary of Upper Lough

Erne, is **Clones**. Within 5m of town are six lakes; pike, perch, rudd, bream. River Finn good for bream, and tench recently introduced; all free fishing; boats. Club: Clones and Dist AA. Hotels: Creighton, Hibernian, Lennard Arms and others, and private house accommodation. In **Monaghan** districts are tributaries of the Ulster Blackwater, and lakes. Brown trout in the **Monoghan Blackwater** av $1\frac{1}{2}$ lbs, with fish to 4 lbs not uncommon. Monoghan AA controls 15m, fishable on £10 st. Excellent coarse fishing in 12 lakes in the area. Pike, bream, rudd, tench, roach. Many specimen fish taken, with bags to 80 lbs in a session. Tackleists: Pat Barret, Bundoran, T J Hanberry, 3/4 Fermanagh Street, Clones.

FANE (including Glyde and Dee)

(For close seasons, licences, etc, see The Eastern Regional Fisheries Board, pp 363–64)

Flows from Castleblayney, Co Monaghan, to enter sea at Blackrock. 3m south of Dundalk. Salmon, sea trout, trout; late river; good dry-fly water. Dundalk Salmon AA has about 20m of rivers; salmon, sea trout up to $5\frac{1}{2}$ lb; particulars from hon sec. Fishing station: **Dundalk** (Louth); Dundalk Brown Trout Assn stock heavily and issue st £5 for over 20m of **Fane**. Permits from hon sec. Good points at **Blackstaff, Inniskeen, Culloville**. Excellent late salmon and sea trout water on **Blackwater** at **Castledown**. Tackleists: O'Neill and Emerald Sports, both Earl St, Magee Sports, The Shopping Centre, all Dundalk. Hotels: Imperial, Williams', Lorne, Fairways, Derryhale. **Castleblayney** (Monaghan). Several mostly coarse fishing loughs in area: **Lough Muckno**, large pike, good trout and perch; **Lough Egish** (5m), pike, perch and eel. Castleblayney Trout AA has trout fishing on **Milltown Lake** (3m); st £15, wt £10 and dt £4 from hon sec. Tackleist: J Flanagan, Main Street. Hotels: Glencarn, Central. **Ballybay** (about 7m W) is good coarse fishing centre: **Dromore River** and loughs; details from hon sec, Ballybay AA.

GLYDE

Drains Ballyhoe and Rahams Lakes in Co Monaghan and runs roughly parallel to and south of River **Fane**. Salmon, sea trout, brown trout, with pike, some bream and perch near lakes. Has now recovered from drainage work. Salmon best in spring, depending on spates June onwards. Brown trout (small) in fast water; larger fish (up to 2 lb) in deep water, but slow risers (little fast water on river). Heavily stocked by Dee and Glyde FDA, which owns extensive rights on both rivers. Water well fished in spring, mostly free, except for Bellingham Castle estate, one stretch at **Tallanstown** and two stretches downstream from **Castlebellingham** (Dee and Glyde FDA). Hotels: Ardee Castlebellingham, Dunleer. Also guest house at Castlebellingham.

DEE

Rise in Co Meath and joins sister River Glyde $\frac{1}{4}$m from common mouth. Salmon, sea trout, brown trout, some pike. Now recovered from drainage operations, but has become dependent on spates for salmon; best in spring (Mar–June; Sept good if spates). Well stocked with brown trout by Dee and Glyde FDA; heavily fished; trout average less then $\frac{1}{2}$ lb. Sea trout (early July onwards) only from Willistown Head Weir ($1\frac{1}{2}$m, upstream from mouth) to Cappoge Bridge (main Dublin-Belfast road). Mostly free. Fishing stations: **Ardee, Aclare, Castlebellingham, Dunleer**. Hotels: Aclare, Ardee, Dunleer.

FEALE

(For close seasons, licences, etc, see The Shannon Regional Fisheries Board, pp 363–64)

Rises on north-west slopes of Blackwater watershed and runs into Atlantic near extreme end of Shannon estuary on south shore. Salmon, sea trout, brown trout (small). Best seasons: Salmon, Mar to May; sea trout June on. Fishing stations: **Abbeyfeale** (Limerick). Best centre for Feale. Waders essential. Abbeyfeale Salmon AA has water; st £10, wt £5 and dt £2 from M Doody, Colbert Road. Brosna AA has 6m upstream; trout permit from S Quinlan, Kilmanahan, Abbeyfeale. Hotel: Leen's. Several guest houses. Tackleists: P

Ryan, New Street; Rochés, Bridge Street; Lane (manufacture of the famous "Lane" artificial minnow) New Street. **Listowel** (Kerry). North Kerry AA has 7m; salmon, sea trout and brown trout; wt and dt. Tralee AA has 2m, both banks; dt issued. Fly fishing for salmon quite good from mid-Aug. Salmon licences from P Horgan, 41 Charles Street. Other tackleists: Cantys Sports Shop, William St; Feale Sports Centre, Church St. Hotels: Stack's, Listowel Arms. **Traslee** AA has water; salmon, sea trout; wt and dt; keeper on duty. Tackle: W Benner, 28 Bridge Street.

ILEN

(For close seasons, licences, etc, see The Southern Regional Fisheries Board, pp 363-64)

Swift river rising on watershed of Bantry district and flowing into sea through long estuary, at head of which is fishing station: **Skibbereen** (Cork). Salmon, sea trout. Small spring run of salmon as rule, followed by big run of grilse. Sea trout fishing very good in summer and autumn. Night fishing usually provides best of sport. R Ilen AA have fishing on river. Wt £20 and dt £5. Several trout loughs nearby. Two good hotels: West Cork, Eldon; also Ilenside Guest House. Tackleist: Fallon's Sports Shop, 20 North Street. At **Glandore**, 8m E, **Roury River** provides fair sport with salmon and sea trout, and numerous lakes and small rivers hold brown trout. Excellent sea fishing. Kilfinnan Castle Hotel provides boats for shark fishing and tackle may be hired.

LAUNE and MAINE (including Killarney Lakes)

(For close seasons, licences, etc, see The South Western Regional Fisheries Board, pp 363-64)

LAUNE

Drains **Killarney Lakes** and flows N and W to Dingle Bay on Atlantic, about 14m. Tralee & Dist AA issues wt £15, st £3 for Feale, Laune and **Broderick's Fishery**. Salmon and sea trout. Best months March–May and Sept. Apply Henberry Sports Centre, Ashe Street, Tralee. Dt from Office of Public Works for 4m of Laune, salmon, sea trout, brown

River Laune and the mountains of Killarney. *Photograph: J. A. Cash.*

trout. Fishing stations: **Killorglin** (Kerry) for lower reaches; tidal. Club: Killorglin AA. Hotels: Laune, Taylors. **Beaufort** (Kerry) for upper reaches. Near here is the **Black Valley** with several brown trout lakes. Farm accommodation. At **Glenbeigh** are Glenbeigh and Towers Hotels: salmon, sea trout and brown trout fishing for guests on the lower **Caragh,** Laune, **Blackwater, Feale, Flesk, Behy** and ten lakes, including **Caragh Lake.** For 5m down from Lough Lein (*see Killarney Lakes*) Laune is State fishery. Good for sea trout and brown trout; good mid-April to Oct for salmon. Coolgown Guest House, Beaufort, adjoins fishery. (*See Caragh.*) Tackleist: Henberry Sports, Ashe Street, Tralee.

MAINE

Maine and tributary, **Brown Flesk,** hold salmon, sea trout and brown trout. Salmon fishing fair; sea and brown trout fishing often good. River is late. Best months: Salmon, April to June; sea trout, Aug to Sept. About 15m of free fishing. Anglers can have accommodation at **Castleisland,** on headwaters, and at **Tralee,** 11m distant. At Tralee is Tralee and Dist AA; (*see Feale*).

KILLARNEY LAKES

Consist of three lakes: **Upper Lake, Muckross Lake** (middle), **Lough Lein** (lower), last being much the largest, connected with sea by Laune. Salmon and trout fishing good; free. Best season for salmon: Lough Lein, Feb to July; Muckross and Upper, Jan 17 to April or May. Mayfly hatch in June. **Flesk** feeds Lough Lein; inquire Lough Lein AA, which also has 7m on Flesk (restocked annually); dt £2, special ticket for duration of holiday: £5. Spinning best for salmon. Many small mountain lakes; free trout fishing. **Kilbrean Lake** is well stocked with brown trout, fishing by permit only. Fishing stations: **Killarney.** Hotels: Dunloe Castle and Hotel Europe (both issue salmon and trout permits and arrange deep sea excursions; Hotel Europe has gillie available), Castlerosse convenient for lakes and River Laune. Licences and tackle from The Handy Stores, Main Street. Guests at Lake Hotel, Killarney, can exchange fishing with Butler Arms (*see Waterville*). Tackleists: Handy Stores, Kenmare Place; Mrs M O'Neill, 6 Plunkett Street; D N Foley, 2 Main Street; all Killarney.

LEE

(For close seasons, licences, etc, see The South Western Regional Fisheries Board, pp 363–64)

Draining **Gougane Barra Lake** and flowing 53m to Cork Harbour, Lee was formerly notable early salmon river (Feb to May) but fishing spoilt by hydroelectric schemes; salmon sport restricted to lower 6m.

Cork (Cork). Salmon fishing on lower R Lee at Inniscarra Dam and below Millbro; season Feb 1 to Sept 30. Fishing is privately owned or leased and controlled mainly by Lee Salmon A and Cork Salmon A. A salmon fishing licence is required, obtainable from tackle shops. Trout fishing on **R Shournagh, Martin, Bride** and **Dripsey;** small brown trout; fishing mostly free. For information contact Blarney AA and tackle shops. Tackleists: T W Murray & Co, 87 Patrick St; Roche's Leisure Shop, 17 Patrick St; The Tackle Shop, 6 Lavitts Quay. Hotels: John Barleycorn Inn, Jurys, Gabriel House, Imperial. **Macroom** (Cork). Trout and coarse fishing on **Inniscarra** and **Carrigohid Reservoirs;** dt 50p and boat £15. Permits from ESB Office, Macroom and ESB Generating Station, Inniscarra. Also trout and coarse fishing on middle River Lee, **Rivers Sullane, Laney** and **Foherish;** and on Gougane Barra lake and **Lough Allua.** Hotels: Castle, Victoria.

LIFFEY

(For close seasons, licences, etc, see The Eastern Regional Fisheries Board, pp 363–64)

Winding river with two reservoirs along its course, rises some 13m SW of Dublin but flows over 80m before entering sea at Islandbridge, Dublin. Subject to hydro-electric floods, it has salmon, brown trout and some sea trout in lower reaches. Recorded salmon run about 3000 pa with rod catch of 500-800. Mayfly hatch end of May. Best trout fishing from Lucan upstream. Best salmon between Straffan and Islandbridge. Most water controlled by clubs. Dublin & Dist Salmon AA has St Raphaels, Celbridge; Castletown; Sarsfield Demesne; Laraghcon; Avondale; Fonthill; Wrens Nest; and Islandbridge fisheries. Trout fishing available from Dublin Trout AA; Clane AA; North Kildare Trout & Salmon AA; Ballymore Eustace AA; and Kilbride AC. Tickets from tackleists *(see below)*. **Poulaphouca Reservoir**, 6000 acres, has been developed as a trout fishery by ESB. Fishing rights leased to Dublin Trout AA and Kilbride AC; st £10 and dt £2 (for non-club members), from hon secs and tackleists. Dublin Corporation controls fishing on **Roundwood Reservoir** (20m) and on **Bohernabreena Reservoir** (8m); the former leased to Co Wicklow AA and the latter to Dublin Trout AA; fly only; bank fishing; st and dt. **Grand Canal**, which runs alongside Liffey for some distance, holds brown trout, bream, rudd, perch and pike. Tackleists: Garnetts & Keegans, 31 Parliament St, Dublin 2; Moorkens, 11 Upper Abbey St, Dublin 7; Rory's, 17a Temple Bar, Dublin 2.

MID-WEST COASTAL STREAMS

(For close seasons, licences, etc, see The Western Regional Fisheries Board, pp 363–64)

BALLYNAHINCH

Salmon, sea trout. Rights on this famous fishery and associated waters held as follows: **Ballynahinch River, Lower Ballynahinch Lake** and **Snaberg** belong to Ballynahinch Castle Hotel, **Ballinafad**, Co Galway. Dt (S) £60 and (T) £30, each per beat (2 rods per beat). 10 year membership: £3,500, which includes night fishing for sea trout. Priority given to club members. **Glendalough** is private, together with **Lough Lehanagh**, and parts of **Owentoey** and **Bealnacarra Rivers. Upper Ballynahinch Lake** is private, together with part of river. **Loughs Inagh** and **Derryclare** are let; inquire of Ashford Castle Hotel, **Cong**, Co Mayo. **Loughs Cappahoosh, Derryneen, Shanakeela, Loch-o-dheas, Oorid** and part of the **Owentooey** and **Recess** rivers are owned by Mr L Lyons and Mrs Iris Lyons-Joyce, Tullaboy House, **Maam Cross**, Connemara, who let fishings, Wt (boat) £90, dt (boat) £15, dt (bank) £8, with or without accommodation; salmon, trout and sea trout. A little south lie a number of loughs which can be fished from **Carna** (Galway), including **Skannive** and **Glenaun**. Season on Ballynahinch is from mid-June to Oct 12. A few springers run from mid-Mar onwards; grilse, summer salmon and sea trout mid-June and July; sea trout, grilse, salmon Sept–Oct *(see Owengowla)*.

OWENGOWLA

This river, with its chain of lakes, forms **Gowla Fishery**, one of best sea trout fisheries in Ireland; also contains salmon. The fishery is owned by the Zetland Hotel, Cashel Bay, Connemara. Four beats on the river and five boats (ten rods) on the lakes. The hotel also owns the **Athry Lakes** on the **Upper Ballynahinch** system with three boats (six rods); salmon and sea trout. No spinning. Boats and gillies available for all waters. Wt £70, dt £12. Full details from the hotel (Tel Cashel 8) or Scafco Ltd, Jamestown Road, Finglas, Dublin 11. Tel: 342211. Hotel Telex 28853: Scafco Telex: 31388.

SCREEBE

Screebe Fishery owned by Screebe Estates Ltd, Screebe, Co Galway is a vast undertaking including 21 lakes and its own hatchery. Dt for 2 rods, £25. Two head lakes, **Shindilla** and **Ardery**, reserved for guests at Currarevagh Guest House, **Oughterard**, Co Galway and Peacock's Hotel, Maam Cross, respectively. Screebe House has first-class salmon and sea trout fishing; own hatchery. For details apply Manager, tel: 09174110.

Costello and Fermoyle Fishery

This Sea-trout fishery has been renowned as one of the finest in Ireland for over 100 years. Reserved for Fly Fishers and under careful private ownership, approximately 3,000 sea-trout are taken per season (50–100 salmon). The sixteen miles of river and lakes are divided into twelve beats, which only allows a maximum of twenty-four rods a day.

For full details write to:

**The Manager,
Costello and Fermoyle Fisheries Co.,
Costello, Connemara, Co. Galway.
Tel: 091-72196**

CASHLA (COSTELLOE)

At head of next large bay to east, Cashla Bay, lies Cashla River and lakes, an exceptionally good sea trout fishery, the **Costelloe and Fermoyle Fisheries:** *(advt above).* Salmon, sea trout. Best months for Costelloe: salmon, June to Oct; sea trout, June to Oct, fly only. Inquire of Manager, Bridge Cottage, Costelloe, Co Galway (Tel Galway 72196). Dt (2 rods) £25–£30. Boat on lake, with gillie, £40–50. Licences from Fishery Office. Nearest hotels: Carraroe (3m). Oughterard (17m). Guest house in Costelloe village. On the north-west shore of Ballyconneely Bay, near **Roundstone** (Galway), lies **Doohulla Fishery** which consists of short river and several lakes, chief of which are **Lough Maumeen** and **Lough Emlaghkeeragh**, both readily accessible. Sea trout, brown trout and occasional salmon. Dt £10. Apply to proprietor: N D Tinne, Emlaghmore, Ballyconneely. Hotel accommodation at **Roundstone** (6m) or **Clifden** (9m). Clifden House Hotel arranges salmon fishing on **Owenglen River**, and trout fishing on Clifden Trout Anglers lakes and other salmon and trout fishing farther afield. Also cruiser for deep sea angling. Boats £8 per day, book through P Pyrce. Owenglen now good for salmon following erection of fish pass. Tackleist: Gerald Stanley & Son, Clifden. Clifden Trout AA fish numerous loughs; boats on some. Clifden AA are developing salmon and sea trout fishery; wt, dt and boats. Fishery opens after first June flood; 100,000 rainbow trout stocked into local lakes. Inquiries of G P Stanley. Clifden hotels include Clifden Bay, Central, Ardagh, Rock Glen, Alcock & Brown, Celtic, Atlantic Coast, Clifden House, Abbey Glen. Several good guest houses.

CARROWNISKY

(For close seasons, licences, etc, see The Western Regional Fisheries Board, pp 363–64)

Rises in Sheefry Hills and flows 6m to sea beyond **Louisburgh** (Co Mayo). Louisburgh and Dist AC has water on river; salmon, sea trout (June to Oct). Tackle, tickets and

A local angler fishing at Ballynahinch, with the "Twelve Bens" forming the back drop. *Photograph: Bord Failte.*

licences from hon sec, Bridge Street. Salmon and trout in Altair Lake. Good shore fishing for bass, pollack, etc; boats available at Roonagh and Old Head. **Bunowen River**: Sea trout and late salmon; preserved by Marquess of Sligo. Five beats available, mt £100, wt £30, dt £6, inquiries to Estate Office, Westport, Tel 09825141. Season: May–Oct. Hotels: Old Head (*for fishing on Delphi Fisheries, see Erriff*), Clew Bay and Durkans. For sea fishing Bay View Hotel, Clare Island, recommended; boats available.

ERRIFF

Good salmon and sea trout river lying short distance north of Ballynahinch country and flowing westwards from Corrib watershed to sea at head of Killary Harbour. **Erriff Fisheries, Leenane**, now taken over by Central Fisheries Board. Dt £10 (April–mid-June), £20 (mid-June–Sep 30). Three boats on **Tawnyard Lough** (sea trout), July 1–Sep 30, boat for 2 rods, £18. River season April–Sept, on lough, July 1–Sept 30. Accommodation at Aasleagh Lodge. Enquiries to Erriff Fishery Office, Aasleagh, Leenane, Co Galway (tel: Leenane 11). Salmon and trout fishing at **Delphi Fishery** (Glencullin, Doolough, Finlough and River Burdorragha). Dt £15 + boat £10. Gillies available. Apply to Peter Mantle, Delphi Lodge, Leenane, Co Galway (tel: 095 42213).

GLENAMOY

Strictly preserved by Lord Digby (lower) and Irish Land Commission (upper), which lets fishing. Further information from owners. Principal tributary is **Muingnabo**. Salmon, sea trout.

BURRISHOOLE SYSTEM

Boat fishing for salmon and sea trout on **Loughs Feeagh** and **Furnace** with short tidal stretch of river. Fishery owned and administered by Salmon Research Trust of Ireland; fishing season effectively mid-June to end September. Boats available with or without boatmen, package holidays arranged by request incorporating local accommodation of varying grades. Rates from £30 to £50 per day for two rods (without/with boatman) or £150–£250 per week (6 days). Full details from SRTI, Newport, Co Mayo. Tel (098) 41107. Newport House Hotel has **Lough Beltra** and, for guests, can also book boats on Lough Furnace and Feagh from Salmon Research Trust. Boat (with o/b and gillie) £43 per day. Fly only. Other hotels: Abbeyville Guest House, Burrishoole, and Anglers', **Newport** (*see also Newport River*).

OWENMORE

Owenmore, 20m long and principally spate river from Bellacorick Bridge, rises near Ballycastle and flows into Blacksod Bay. Principal tributary is **Oweniny** (Crossmolina AA). River divided among number of owners. Good for spring salmon from April 1, given really high water; good grilse and sea trout from mid-June to end of Sept, if water is right. Upper and middle reaches owned by syndicate. Information from Dr I R Moore, 20 Temple Gardens, Dublin 6, and Michael Varian, Glasthule Lodge, Adelaide Road, Glengeary, Co Dublin. Lodges and fishings let by the fortnight when syndicate-members are not fishing. Part of fishery let to Bangor FC. Dt from hon sec. Enquiries respecting **Carrowmore Lough**, Bangor Erris, salmon, sea trout and brown trout, to Seamus Henry, Bangor Erris PO Ballina. Accommodation at Altnabrocky Lodge, **Bellacorick**, Ballina, Co Mayo, and at Glenmore Lodge, **Bangor Erris**, Co Mayo. For lower reaches inquire of Mr W J Sweeney, Bridge House, Achill, Westport. Tackleists: O'Connor, Main Street, Ballycastle.

OWENDUFF AND OWENGARVE

Owenduff good for salmon from end of Mar. Grilse and sea trout, mid-June to end of Sept. Provides excellent all-round fishing when water right. Upper reaches managed by F Chambers, Rock House, Ballycroy, Westport; 4½m both banks and **Bellaveeny River** (sea trout). Wt £175 and dt £18; both for 4 rods and to be accompanied by gillie, £10 per day. Middle reaches: Owned by Craigie Bros, Finglass, Co Dublin (no lettings) and Lagduff Lodge (lower beat). All privately held but occasional letting by lodges named. Lower down, a small beat is owned by Mr Justice Barra O'Brien of Enniskerry, Co Wicklow. Good accommodation, Shranamanragh Lodge, let with fishing and shooting by the month. Good for salmon (April/May), grilse and sea trout (July onwards).

Owengarve is a spate river. Grilse and sea trout, early June to early Oct. Most of river controlled by Newport AC, which has mutual agreement with Dr J Healey (Rosturk Castle, **Rosturk**, Westport, Co Mayo) whereby whole river can be fished. Daily, weekly and monthly rods available from club hon sec.

NEWPORT

Drains **Lough Beltra** and runs into Clew Bay, at **Newport**, Co Mayo. River over 7m long and usually fished from banks. Good for salmon and very good sea trout. There are about 20 pools, some for both day and night fishing. Fly only. River known for length of season April to end of Sept. Some 15m of fishing held by Newport House, 4m on **Skerdagh**, a tributary. Beltra is good early lake for salmon, and from late June very good for sea trout also. Fishing station: **Newport** (Mayo). Hotel: Newport House (fishing on Newport River and five loughs; cabin cruisers on Clew Bay *(advt p 382)*. Wt £60, dt £12, evening £6, from hotel. Major fishery improvement plans in progress. Other hotel: Anglers'. Various small trout loughs around Newport. Newport AC, whose members are free to fish Newport River by concession of Newport House, issues permits for salmon and sea trout fishing (June to Sept) on small spate river near **Mulrany**. Hotel: Moynish House (*see also Sea*

Fishing Stations). **Castlebar** (Mayo) is central also for **Loughs Conn** and **Cullen** (good for salmon and very good for brown trout, 1 lb to 7 lb); free; and for **Loughs Mask** and **Carra** (very good brown trout; good wet fly; best months, April-June, Aug, Sept; free; inquire hon sec, Lough Carra Trout AA for boats etc). Extensive lake system to south-west now reduced by drainage works to a single lake, but good trout can still be taken on **Islandreavy/Bilberry Lough**. Book with Austin Gibbons, Cloggernagh, Islandeady. Good coarse fishing in **Castlebar** area. Club: Castlebar and Dist Trout AA. Lough Conn AA, **Crossmolina**, Co Mayo, has been implementing an ambitious scheme for developing sport on lough; inquire of hon sec. Tackleists: J J O'Connor, 15 Spencer Street; Stauptons Sports Shop, Main Street; Pat Quinn, Main Street, all Castlebar. Hotels: Travellers' Friend, Imperial, Breaffy House.

Achill Island, off Mayo coast, has become famous in recent years for its sea fishing (*see Sea Fishing section*). Good brown trout fishing on four lakes, fish plentiful but small. St £20, wt £10, dt £2. Club: Achill Sporting Club. Hotel: Amethyst, Keel.

MOY

(For close seasons, licences, etc, see The North Western Regional Fisheries Board, pp 363–64)

Drains **Loughs Conn** and **Cullen** with numerous smaller loughs and joins Atlantic at Killala Bay through long estuary, at head of which stands Ballina. Salmon, sea trout. Very good salmon river and noted for grilse. Season: Spring fish, February to May; grilse, July onwards; good autumn run, Sept and Oct, sea trout in estuary (best July and Aug). Salmon fishing in famous Ridge Pool owned by Moy Fishery Co, **Ballina.** From May to September boat fishing only; £15–£25 per boat per day + £20 for gillie. 6 fish limit. Hotels: Mount Falcon Castle *(advt p 383)*, Moy, Imperial, Hurst, Beleek Castle, Central and Downhill, the latter having its own cruiser for Moy Estuary and Killala Bay. At **Foxford** the Pontoon Bridge hotel offers salmon and trout fishing on 4m of water, including famous salmon

pool at Pontoon Bridge, and on fresh water lakes, Conn and Cullen. Dt £5. Boats on lake, with or without motor and gillie £8-£28 per day. In 1987 Michael and Margaret Waller started a Fishing School based at Pontoon Bridge Hotel; the only residential school in the country. Cost weekly for 6 days £80. Other hotels: Hely's, Foxford, Anglers' Rest, Dolphin and Hughes' Guest House, Crossmolina for Lough Conn. East Mayo AA has 6m of river near **Swinford**; tickets £5 a day. Spring salmon best from mid-Mar, grilse June onwards. Hotel: O'Connors, numerous guest houses. **Palmerstown River**, 6m from Ballina, good for sea trout July to Oct, if there is a spate; free fishing, except for portion by Palmerstown Bridge leased by Ballina Dist AA; dt 75p from waterkeeper. **Loughs Conn** and **Cullen** provide good free fishing for salmon, trout and pike; trout fishing much improved since coarse fish clearance started by Inland Fisheries Trust. Record Irish pike (53 lb) caught in Lough Conn. Trout up to 5 lb. Boats at Gortnorabbey. Crossmolina (car park and caravan site); Cloghans, Gilbroo Bay and Phuilawokouse Bay. Boats also available on L Cullen but fishing not so good as Conn. **Lough Talt**, 10m east of Ballina, is good brown trout lake; free; boats available. **Crossmolina** is good centre for district. Club: Crossmolina AA. Tackleists: J Walkin, Tone Street; V Doherty, Bridge Street, both Ballina. Hotel: Enniscoe House, on lough shore.

SHANNON

(For close seasons, licences, etc, see The Shannon Regional Fisheries Board, pp 363-64)

Largest river in British Isles, 160m long with catchment area covering greater part of central Ireland. Enters Atlantic on west coast through long estuary. A typical limestone river, rich in weed and fish food, of slow current for most part, and though of some of its sources rise in peat, acidity counteracted by limestone reaches. Many of the adverse effects of hydro electric scheme introduced 45 years ago now overcome by re-stocking and other forms of fishery management. With exception of famous Castleconnell Fisheries, Shannon mostly sluggish. In free stretches, however, reasonably good salmon and grilse fishing can be obtained. Trout fishing poor except during mayfly rise, when excellent sport can be enjoyed, free of charge, in **Loughs Derg** and **Ree** at **Athlone**; trout grow large. River has well-deserved reputation for its coarse fishing. Excellent pike, perch, bream and rudd at many centres. Coarse fishing can also be had in Derg and Ree. **Lough Allen**, northernmost lake of Shannon, specially good for pike.

Limerick (Limerick). On tidal Shannon. Good spring salmon fishing at **Parteen** (1m); and **Plassey** (2m); st and boats from ESB. 6 m above city is **Muclair River**, a tributary of the Shannon; excellent fly water; best months June, July and Sept; st, wt and dt from Regional Manager, Hydro Generation Region, Ardnacrusha, Nr Limerick. Limerick tackleists: McMahon, Roches Street; Nestor Bros, O'Connell Street and Limerick Sports Stores, 10 William Street.

Castleconnell (Limerick). Principal centre for salmon angling on Shannon and within 3m of Muclair River. Traditional big fish water; catches improved recently. Fishing on six Castleconnell beats controlled by Regional Manager, Hydro Generation Region,

Ardnacrusha, Nr Limerick, who will book beats and provide information. Permits available from Head Warden, M Murtagh, O'Briens Bridge. Advance booking advisable. Best months for salmon and grilse, May, June, July and Sept. Trout fishing free. Coarse fishing in area good, especially for bream. Hotels: Lakeside, Killaloe; Cruises and Ardhu House, Limerick (8m).

Killaloe (Clare). At outlet from Lough Derg, good centre for trout and coarse fishing on lake. Trout angling can be very good in May and autumn; fish average 3 to 4 lb. Boats available. Tackleists: McKeogh's.

Dromineer (Tipperary). Best centre for middle sections of **Lough Derg**. Large trout taken spinning or trolling; also good centre for dry fly and dapping; trout up to 10 lb caught. Mayfly starts about first week in May. Coarse fishing very good; large pike and perch. Boats and gillies available; fishing free on lake, but small annual fee payable to Ormond AA for fishing, on **Neagh River,** which flows in at Dromineer. Salmon and trout, with coarse fishing, lower down. Salmon fishing free to licence holders. Hotels: Sail Inn, Dromineer; Ormond, O'Mearas, Carmel and Central in Nenagh. Tourist centre in Pearse Street, Nenagh, will give details of further accommodation.

Portumna (Galway). At north (inlet), end of **Lough Derg**. Hotel: Clonwyn (see Dromineer for fish, etc). Some good dapping bays within reach. Good centre for pike and perch in autumn. Tackleists: Garry Kenny, Palmerstown Stores. Towards Galway (19m from Portumna) is **Loughrea**; trout, pike and perch. Fishing open to members of Loughrea AA, which has improved and restocked water; trout average 2 lb, pike over 30 lb; best months (trout), April, May, June; good evening rise mid-Aug, mid-Sept, fly only for trout; pike fishing by arrangement, July-Aug; st £10 and dt £2; boats available. Accommodation at Lake Villa House. Further information from hon sec. Hotels at Loughrea: Central, Railway.

Banagher (Offaly). Hotel: Shannon. Salmon and trout. May to July. Coarse fishing good; boats obtainable. **Brosna** improving as salmon river, after trouble with drainage and peat pollution; permits £8.25 season from local office at ESB. Good fly fishing for brown trout (wet and dry) in tributaries **Clodiagh** and **Big Silver**. Good dry fly trout water and coarse fishing. **Tullamore** (Offaly) is good centre. Club: Tullamore and Dist AA. **Little Brosna**, which comes in some miles lower down, can best be fished from **Birr** (Offaly). Club: Birr and Dist AA. For salmon fishing, permit needed from Electricity Supply Board. Little Brosna gives good trout fishing throughout season, but especially good during mayfly (June-July); dry fly good. **Cam-Cor** river also at Birr, gives fine sport with large Shannon trout (end of June to end Sept) on large wet flies and spinner; another fishery, improved by IFT management is 25-acre **Pallas Lake**; brown and rainbow trout; wet fly in spring and large dry patterns useful in Aug and Sept; fly only; bank only. Hotels: Dooley's, Egan's, County Arms.

Athlone (Westmeath and Roscommon). Athlone AA has water within 20m radius; restocked with trout. Some salmon. Shannon and **Lough Ree** abound with trout (good rise to mayfly, late May to late June), pike, roach and bream; bank or boat. Tench plentiful on Lough Ree. **Lough Garnafailagh**, which has produced remarkable catches of tench and bream, may be fished from here. Hotels: Royal, Prince of Wales, Hodson's Bay, Shamrock, Lodge and several smaller places. Tackleists: Foy's, Church Street, Denis Connell, Dublin Gate Street and Sean Egan, 59 Connaught Street.

Lanesboro (Longford). Best station for upper Lough Ree. Hotels: Anchor; Lough Ree Arms. Other Shannon centres: **Rooskey** (coarse fish; accommodation at Killianker House); **Carrick-on-Shannon** (trout, coarse fish). Hotels: County (run by anglers). Bush, Cartown House, Brogans. **Clondara**: good trout water below Termonbarry Weir; also coarse fish; free. **Elphin**: coarse fish, trout. Graffa House has good accommodation.

Principal Tributaries of the Shannon

DEEL. Enters estuary near Askeaton some miles below Limerick. Fishing stations: **Rathkeale** (Limerick), and **Askeaton** (Limerick), (best Feb to May), white trout (on summer floods), a few salmon and good brown trout (best mid-Mar to Sept). Parts of river preserved by Mrs R Hunt, Inchirourke, Askeaton, and Altaville Estate. Hotels at Rathkeale: Central, Madigan's. Deel AA issues st £5 for 15m water at Rathkeale. Nearest tackleists at Limerick.

MAIGUE. Enters estuary between mouth of Deel and Limerick. Salmon, trout, mostly preserved. Major drainage-work in progress, fishing possible at week-ends only. Fishing station: **Adare** (Limerick). Hotel: Dunraven Arms ($1\frac{1}{4}$m fishing free to guests). Above Adare road bridge to Croom preserved. Some free tidal water below town. **Croom** (Limerick), Maigue AA issue st £10. Further information from hon sec. Preserved water below town, free above to Bruree and beyond, wet and dry-fly water. **Bruree** (Limerick). Hotel: Murphy's. Tributaries **Camogue, Loobagh** and **Morningstar** mostly free and very good for trout. Centres: **Killmallock**, where hon sec of angling association will help. **Kilfinane** (inquire hon sec. Development Assn, re cottages to let).

FERGUS. Limestone stream with gin-clear water, trout fishing good; few salmon in spring. Fishing free. Fishing station: **Ennis** (Clare). Good centre for fishing principal waters of Co Clare, including several coarse fish lakes and rivers (tench, pike, perch, rudd). Good brown trout fishing in Fergus and lakes it drains: **Loughs Inchiquin, Dromore, Atedaun,** and numerous smaller loughs. Inchiquin holds good stock of trout averaging $1/1\frac{1}{4}$ lb; in Dromore fish run larger; big duck fly hatch in Mar–April. On coast between **Doonbeg** and **Liscannor** are several rivers with fair runs of sea trout. Part of **Quin** at **Dromoland** and fishery in Falls Hotel grounds at **Ennistymon** preserved; latter free to hotel guests. Aberdeen Arms Hotel at **Lahinch** caters for anglers. Tackleist in Ennis: M Tierney, Church Street. Accommodation: Auburn Lodge, Old Ground, Queen's, West Country Inn. **Corofin** (Clare; Ennis 8m). Numerous lakes very good for trout, others for perch, rudd and tench, and all for pike. Accommodation at a number of family guest houses. **Lakes Inchiquin, Atedaun** and **Ballycullinan** and River Fergus close by; boats. Excellent bream and pike fishing in **Tulla** area; fishing free in about 40 lakes within 10m radius (Ennis 10m). Inquire hon sec, Tulla Coarse AA.

SUCK. Joins Shannon at **Shannon Bridge** between Banagheer and Athlone. Holds large brown trout in parts. Pike, bream, rudd and perch fishing very good. Fishing stations: **Ballinasloe** (Galway and Roscommon). Suck and tributaries, including Lough O'Flynn, controlled by CFB. Hotels: Hayden's, Holloway's, O'Carrolls's. **Bunowen** and **Shiven** good early season waters. **Lough Acalla,** 8m from Ballinasloe; rainbow trout up to 7 lb, good for wet fly in June (CFB). **Castlerea** (Roscommon), station for upper reaches, which hold good trout. Hotels: McCormack's, O'Reilly's. **Lough O'Flynn** now excellent trout fishery thanks to IFT improvement work. Trout and coarse fish in **Lough Glinn. Roscommon** also good centre for Suck (3m; unlimited coarse fishing) and **Lough Ree** (5m). **Strokestown**, to north, is centre for fine coarse fishing on streams and loughs. River is good for trout in mayfly season. Irish record rudd (3 lb 1 oz) caught in nearby **Kilglass Lake**. Hotels: Greally's Royal, Central. Roscommon Gun and Rod Club have **River Hind**; trout; dry-fly water.

INNY. A slow-flowing river densely populated with roach, large bream and large tench. Trout between **Abbeyshrule** and **Shrule Bridge**. Fishing stations: **Ballymahon, Multy-farnham, Ballinalach, Granard, Castlepollard, Mullingar**. Inny AA control much fishing. **Mullingar** a good centre for the famous limestone lakes **Ennell, Owel** and **Derravaragh**, of large acreage and offering fly fishing of the highest order as trout rise freely to the succession of chironomids, ephemera and sedges which hatch almost continuously from April to the end of September. Average size of trout large: e.g. 3 lbs 4 ozs on L Ennell in 1980. All developed by the IFT, now succeeded by the new Central Fisheries Board. Smaller private lakes, e.g. **Lough Lane** and **Lough Shelvior**, privately managed for trout and coarse fishing. St from J O'Malley, tackleist, 33 Dominick Street, Mullingar, covers much water; information given on others. Hotels in Mullingar: Greville Arms, Broders. Hotels in Castlepollard: Pollard Arms, Brogan's, Kearney's. Near **Ballyjamesduff** lies **Lough Sheelin**. Sheelin Shamrock Hotel, Mountnugent, on lakeside, and guest-houses, can provide boats and services. Boats £7 per day, ob motors £5 extra. **Lough Kinale** (CFB; pike, perch, rudd, tench, some trout). **Cornagrow Lake** and **Bracklough** also afford good coarse fishing (pike, perch, rudd, tench). **Lough Gowna** (trout and coarse, including bream) is accessible from Granard. Hotels: Greville Arms, Macken's Guest House. Park Hotel, **Virginia**, is convenient for **Lough Ramor** (trout, coarse fish); also **River Blackwater** and other loughs.

BOYLE. Connects **Lough Gara** and **Key**. Trout (good). Fishing station: **Boyle** (Roscommon). River, 6m long affected by drainage scheme. **Lough Arrow**; excellent trout fishing (av $2\frac{1}{4}$ lb). Lough Key abounds in coarse fish. Hotel: Rock House.

SLANEY

(For close seasons, licences, etc, see The Eastern Regional Fisheries Board, pp 363–64)

Rises in corner between Barrow and Liffey watersheds and flows south 73m to Wexford Harbour. During most of course has rocky beds, rapids alternating with deep pools. Good salmon river, especially in Tullow-Bunclody reaches (Mar, April, May best; no autumn run) but of little account for brown trout save in upper reaches and in some tributaries. Good sea trout lower down and in tributaries **Urrin** and **Boro**. Best sea trout fishing around Enniscorthy. Most salmon fishing private, but certain parts let from season to season and no permission needed to fish for salmon or sea trout from Enniscorthy Bridge to Ferrycarrig (Feb 26 to Sept 15). Fishing station: **Wexford Lough.** Garman AC has made efforts to restock. **Owenduff**; good white trout fishing in June, July and Aug. **Sow River** near **Castlebridge** good for brown trout and sea trout; permits from angling club. Fishing for brown trout on **Wexford Reservoir.** Sea fishing (including sea trout, bass and mullet) in estuary. Tackleist: Bridges of Selskar, North Main Street. Hotels: Talbot, White's County. **Enniscorthy.** Sea trout good; brown trout poor; free fishing downstream of bridge. Tackleists: Paddy Lennon, 26 Main Street, Nolan, 3 Wafer Street, and C L Cullen, 14 Templeshannon. Hotels: Portsmouth Arms, Slaney Valley. **Tullow** (Carlow), Tullow Salmon and Trout AA have water on Slaney; st £8 (T), wt £5 (T), dt £12 (S), from hotel and Bridge Sports Shop. Trout and salmon fishing is free on Slaney from Rathvilly to Baltinglass, and also on River Derreen. Hotel: Slaney. At **Bunclody** (Wexford), Bunclody Trout AC has fishing for visitors. Tackleist (licences): Mrs Nolan, Irish Street, The Square.

SLIGO and LOUGH GILL

(including the Bonet, Ballysodare, Lough Arrow, Bundrowes and Lough Melvin)

(For close seasons, licences, etc, see The Eastern Regional Fisheries Board, pp 363–64)

Garavogue River connects Lough Gill with sea, which it enters in Sligo Bay to south of Donegal Bay and Erne. Salmon, trout, coarse fish. Fishing station: **Sligo** (Sligo). Hotels: Great Southern, Imperial, Grand, Kelley's, Clarence, Silver Swan, Jury's. Tackleists: Barton Smith Ltd, Hyde Bridge. **Lough Gill**, 2m away, holds salmon (spring), trout (av 2 lb, mayfly only) and pike, perch and bream. Fishing free except on preserved parts under control of Sligo AA. Permits from hon treasurer, E Armstrong, 68 Riverside and tackle shops. Lough Gill not a good fly water; trolling best for trout and salmon. Permits also cover fishing on south shore of Sligo portion of **Glencar Lake**, 7m; salmon (grilse), sea and brown trout; boat available. **Lough Colga**, 4m; brown trout, free; boat available to Sligo AA members. Tackleists in Sligo: F Nelson & Son Ltd; Barton Smith. Hotels: Innisfree, Sligo Park, Silver Swan and others.

BONET

Feeds Lough Gill. Salmon, trout. Best for salmon in summer. Fishing station: **Dromahaire** (Leitrim). Abbey Hotel has free, all-round fishing for guests. Manorhamilton AA also preserve some water on river and **Glencar Lake**. St £12, dt £5, from A Flynn, Post Office, Manorhamilton. Also abundance of coarse fishing, in which club members show little interest; comments and advice from visiting coarse anglers would be welcomed.

BALLYSODARE

Formed by junction of three rivers, **Unshin** or **Arrow, Owenmore***, and **Owenbeg**, near Collooney. Unshin drains Lough Arrow and district lying south of Lough Gill. Near mouth of river, at Ballysodare Falls, is earliest salmon ladder erected in Ireland (1852). Salmon, trout, very few sea trout. Dt at times from Collooney and Dist AA. Best season, May to July. Fishing dependent on sufficient rain. Leave for sea and brown trout sometimes obtainable. Good dry fly. River contains sizeable pike; permission from riparian owners. Fishing station: **Collooney** (Sligo). **Lough Bo** fished from here (trout).

LOUGH ARROW

Lough Arrow is a rich limestone water of 3,123 acres on the border of Sligo and Roscommon. It is about 5m long and varies in width from $\frac{1}{2}$m to $1\frac{1}{2}$m. Unshin or Arrow River drains the lake into Ballysodare Bay. Arrow River joins Owemore from Templehouse Lake near Collooney and the combined rivers from what is known locally as **Ballysodare River**. This is a well-known 2m salmon stretch. The lough is almost entirely spring-fed and has a place of honour among Ireland's best known mayfly lakes. Nowhere else is the hatch of fly so prolific or the rise so exciting. Three and four-pounders are common. Trout rise to mayfly from late May to mid-June and sport is varied at this time by dapping, wet-fly and dry-fly fishing with green drake and the spent gnat. This is followed soon after (mid-July to mid-Aug) by a late evening rise to big sedge called the Murrough and Green Peter, which may give the lucky angler as much fun as mayfly. The marked improvement in fishing at Lough Arrow can be attributed to the removal of coarse fish from these waters by the Central Fisheries Board and regular stocking with trout. Boats and gillies may be hired at all times and at many centres on lake shore. At **Ballinary** (Arrow Cottage) boats available and nearby at **Ballindoon** is Rock House (*advt p 386*), a modernised and re-equipped hotel on the the lakeside run by an angler of considerable experience, willing to help others. Boats arranged. Salmon and sea trout fishing on Ballysodare River available to guests. **Feorish**, good trout stream nearby. Boats and accommodation also at **Ballinafad, Castlebaldwin, Heapstown Cross** and at **Boyle** and **Ballmote**. The last-named is in centre of Sligo's coarse fishing district. It caters for anglers to **Templehouse Lake** and **Cloonacleigha Lake** (good pike fishing, boats) and **Owenmore River**, Ballymote is also centre for **Lough na Leibe,** Ireland's first rainbow trout lake, and **Feenagh Lake**, where 2 lb trout will often appear among limit of six which CFB prescribes. Excellent hotel, guest house and private accommodation. Inquiries to Hon Sec, Tourist Assn, Ballymote, Co Sligo. **Lough Bo**, near Lough Arrow, provides good shore fishing for brown trout. Tackleist: M J Creegan, 2/4 Main Street, Ballymote.

BUNDROWES AND LOUGH MELVIN

(For close seasons, licences, etc, see The Northern Regional Fisheries Board, pp 363–64)

About 4m south of Erne, Bundrowes River carries water of Lough Melvin to sea in Donegal Bay. **Bundoran** (Donegal) is $1\frac{1}{2}$m from Bundrowes River and 3m from west end of Lough Melvin. Hotels: Great Southern, Central, Hamilton ($6\frac{1}{2}$m of salmon, sea trout and gillaroo trout fishing; boats and boatmen available). Sport with brown trout very good at times. River opens Jan 1 for salmon, Feb 15 for trout. Club: Bundoran AA, hon

---

* *Not to be confused with Owenmore River, Co Mayo.*

sec of which will be pleased to give information. Dt (S) £6, (T) £3. Tackleist: Pat Barret, Bundoran.

Part of Lough Melvin is in Northern Ireland and is served by village of **Garrison**. Hotels: Lakeside, Melvin; lake is free fishing except for two bays which are private. Other hotel: Casey's Lake. Lake has excellent run of early spring salmon and holds perch, brown trout (av $\frac{3}{4}$ lb), sonaghan (av $\frac{3}{4}$ lb), gillaroo (to $3\frac{1}{2}$ lb), lake trout (to 9 lb), sea trout and a few char. For **Drowes Fishery** apply T Gallagher, **Kinlough**. For salmon and trout permits for **Rossinver Bay**, apply T Bradley, Rossinver.

SOUTH-WEST COASTAL STREAMS

(For close seasons, licences, etc, see The South Western Regional Fisheries Board, pp 363–64)

WATERVILLE (or Currane) and INNY

Waterville River, short river joining **Lough Currane** and sea in Co Kerry. Popular with visitors. Salmon, sea trout, brown trout. All migratory fish running to Lough Currane go through this river, which also has spring run of large sea trout. There is a commercial fishery, traps of which are lifted on July 15. Lough Currane (excellent trout and salmon fishing) free to licence-holders. Boats available. Inny River is late salmon river with sea trout; best season for salmon May to Oct. Fishing station: **Waterville**. Butler Arms has preserved fishing on four loughs (Derriana, Cloonaughlin, Coppal and Namona) plus six beats on the R Inny. Dt for guests and others. Lake Hotel has rights on Waterville River (Butler's Pool) and Inny and **Cummeragh Rivers**, and on Loughs Derriana, **Cummeragh**, **Nahiska**, Namona and Cloonaughlin; salmon, sea trout, brown trout. Season, Jan 17 to Oct 13. (Salmon: Sept 7). Boats and boatmen available at both hotels for freshwater and sea fishing. Bay View Hotel has similar extensive rights and facilities. Dt issued at hotels. Guests at Butler Arms can interchange meals and fishing with Lake Hotel, Killarney. Tackleists: Mrs A J Huggard, Anglers' Rest, Waterville; D Foley and Mrs M O'Neill, Killarney.

KENMARE BAY RIVERS

Several small salmon rivers empty into this bay, which provides excellent sea fishing (large skate, tope, etc). Best season, May to August. Fishing station: **Ardtully**. Kenmare Salmon AA owns part of **Roughty**. Permits from T O'Shea, Kenmare: dt £3 and wt £10, few spring salmon (March/April); good grilse runs (June to Aug); fly, spinning, prawning and worming permitted; fish average 9 lb. **Sheen** runs in on south shore and is preserved by owner. **Finnihy**, on north shore, is free fishing for brown trout, grilse and some sea trout in floods. **Kilgarvan SA** fish 10m of Roughty and **Slaheny** (salmon, sea trout, some brown trout); particularly good after spates. Wt £10; dt £3. Visitors welcome. These rivers are all close to **Kenmare** (Kerry). Hotels: Great Southern, Lansdowne Arms, Central, Kenmare Bay (sea fishing especially catered for); Riverdale House; and guest houses. **Cloonee**, on the south shore, drains four lakes; permits to fish some from Derreen Estate Office, Kenmare also for **Lough Inchiquin** and **Glenmore River** and **Lake**, for salmon and sea trout. Best months April, May, June and September. Daily charges range from £7 to £20 + the boatman's services. **Cloonee Lakes**, 8m south, provide excellent brown trout fishing with occasional salmon; boats and boatmen, accommodation, etc; apply to Lake Hotel, Lake House, Kenmare. **Loughs Uragh** and **Barfinnihy** and Finnihy River are fished by Kenmare AA; hon sec willing to help visitors. For fishermen with taste for mountain climbing there are at least 40 lakes holding brown trout on plateau of Caha Mountains, all easily fished from Kenmare. **Kerry Blackwater** drains **Lough Brin** and is preserved, but permission can be obtained from Estate Office, Kenmare. Blackwater is excellent salmon river, at its best in July and August, and also holds good stock of sea trout from June onwards. Ceimeen or **Glass Lakes** are easily fished from Kenmare; brown trout. **Sneem River**, farther west, is preserved by owner. Further information from hon sec, Kenmare Salmon AA, who issue wt £3 covering all their waters. *For tackleists, see Killarney.*

CARAGH

River runs through **Caragh Lake** to sea at Dingle Bay. Salmon, sea trout, trout (small). Salmon best Feb–April and Sept–Oct; sea trout best Sept–Oct. Bass and mullet in estuary. Fishing stations: **Glenbeigh** (Kerry) for lower water; wt £20 and dt £4, from Towers Hotel. Hotel also issues permits for 6m of **Laune** (single bank only), $8\frac{1}{2}$m of **Feale**, 3m of **Flesk**, and **Behy** and **Loughs Caragh** and **Currane** (Waterville). **Glencar** (Kerry) for upper river. Hotel: Glencar, which has 7m of upper river (both banks) reserved for guests only; salmon; best months, Feb to end of June; grilse June onwards; sea trout. The hotel has also **Loughs Cloon, Acoose, Rea** and **Drombrain**, and Rivers **Meelagh, Brida, Owbeg, Owenroe** and **Small Caragh**; salmon, brown trout. Many smaller rivers and lakes holding brown trout. Gillies and boats available; wt £77, dt £18, also tackle and licences at hotel *(advt below)*.

BANTRY BAY RIVERS

Rivers within easy reach of **Bantry** are **Ilen** (*see Ilen*), **Dunnamark** (private), **Owvane** ($3\frac{1}{2}$m; spate stream, fair salmon run in March; sea trout late May; mostly free; Ballyhahill AA welcomes visiting anglers), **Snave** (5m; similar to Owvane), **Glengariff** (11m; spate river; salmon and sea trout only fair but good early run of latter; Glengariff AA has water). Brown trout fishing in rivers poor, but good sport sometimes had on loughs: **Bofinna** (3m; fish average 6 oz and reach 1 lb; best March, April, May). **Farnamanagh** (17m; free; fish average 9 or 10 oz; late evening usually best; fancy flies). Loughs **Avaul** (Upper and Little; tickets from keeper; trout to 2 lb; boat on upper lake from keeper). Numerous other lakes hold trout of 4 oz to 1 lb. **Reenydonagan L** (between Bantry and Ballylickey, 6 acre tidal lake stocked with brown trout averaging $1\frac{1}{2}$ lb; two boats). Boats for sea fishing can be hired; inquire Bantry Bay Sea AA. Tackleists: Atkins & Co, The Square, Dunmanway.

VARTRY

(For close seasons, licences, etc, see The Eastern Regional Fisheries Board, pp 363–64)

Small river which drains **Roundwood Reservoir** and flows into sea near Wicklow. Sea trout in lower reaches, brown trout (small). Co Wicklow AA control Varty River and Roundwood Reservoir, the latter on lease from Dublin Corporation. Fishing station: **Rathnew** (Co Wicklow). Hotels: Hunter's, Tinakilly.

The tailer in use on the Blackwater. Generally speaking a much under employed item of landing equipment. *Photograph: S. J. Newman.*

SEA FISHING STATIONS IN THE IRISH REPUBLIC

As elsewhere, the sea fishing in the Irish Republic has been growing in popularity. The inshore potential of these waters is now widely appreciated. Bass are much sought after along the south and west coasts, and pollack are abundant off the rocks. Deep-sea boats land specimen skate, conger, halibut, turbot and so on. Fishing facilities are improving all the time. Space will not permit more than a few centres to be listed, but club secretaries and local tackleists will be pleased to give further information and to help visitors.

Rosslare (Wexford). Fishing from shore and pier, but mainly from boats up to 50 ft. Latter can reach Tuskar Rock, famous offshore mark; smaller craft, 18-20 ft, fish Splaugh Rock, excellent bass mark. Apart from bass, main species are flatfish and tope. Many bass taken on spinner from boats. Several boatmen. Tackleist: Bolands Garage, Rosslare Harbour, John Murphy and also Bridges, both N Main Street, Wexford. Club: Rosslare Harbour SAC, which holds competitions.

Kilmore Quay (Wexford). Bass from shore; boat and pier. St Patrick's Bridge, reef of rocks to east of harbour, is good boat mark. Excellent pollack, bass and tope around Saltee Islands. Surf fishing for bass and tope at Ballyteigne Bay. Mullet and flatfish abound. Lugworm from harbour. Trawlers and lobster boats available for parties and bookable in advance. Other boats from Fethard. Club: Kilmore Quay SAC. Tackleists in Rosslare, Wexford and Kilmore Quay.

Dungarvan (Waterford). Harbour popular venue for mullet; also good bass and flounders. Pier at Helvick provides good sport with congers, and mullet taken in Helvick Harbour. Bass now spasmodic. Fewer blue shark than there were. Also pollack off Black Rock, flatfish and dogfish bottom fishing. Conger, ling and bottom-feeding species in general off Helvick and Mine Head. Crab and lugworm on foreshore. Boats from Bowmans (Fishing Tackle Dept.). Tel 05841395, £12 per day. Other tackleist: Casey, Tel 05841738.

Youghal (Cork). Fishing in Youghal Harbour; shore; pier mainly for bass (April–Oct), pollack (July–Sept), mackerel (July–Sep), codling (Sep–Nov), and sea trout (June–Aug). Flatfish the year year round. Youghal Bay: bass

(April–Oct), pollack (May–Nov), mackerel (May–Nov), and sea trout (June–Aug). Deep-sea fishing, skate, conger, ling, pollack, dog and spurdog, thornback ray, blue and porbeagle shark. Many specimen fish. Charter-boats 6/8 anglers: £70. Rods for hire. Hotels: Hilltop Hotel, Devonshire Arms, Monatrea House. General inquiries to Capt M Vastenhout, Stonebridge Cottage.

Ballycotton (Cork). One of the best-known of Irish sea fishing centres; large catches of prime fish and excellent facilities. Skate, blue shark, tope, porbeagle, cod, ling, pollack, coalfish, bass, conger are among species taken. Fishing from shore, pier, rocks or boat; best shore fishing at Ballymona; big bass. Good mullet in harbour. Ballycotton Angling Centre for boat bookings (£10 per angler, £50 per boat min.) tel: 021 646733 and 41292. Tackleist: J A Connolly, Corner Shop, who will be pleased to give local information. Monthy competitions May to Oct. Hotel: Bay View.

Kinsale (Cork). Best-known centre on the south coast for deep-sea fishing, especially for shark. Famous marks at Ling Rocks, Pango Reef, off the Old Heads, and the wreck of the "Lusitania". Blue shark, ling, conger, dogfish, rays, pollack, coalfish, red bream and wrasse. Well-equipped boats and experienced skippers. £16 per angler daily; £70–£90 boat charter; from Kinsale Marine Services, Trident Hotel & Angling Centre and Blue Haven Hotel. All operators offer rod and tackle hire. Kinsale Sea AC run many competitions during season. Other hotels: Actons, Perryville House.

Rosscarberry (Cork). Noted for surf fishing for bass; three fine beaches. Bass and mullet also taken in small harbour, and from mouth of estuary. Lugworm and ragworm in estuary, sandeel from beach. Boats for inshore fishing. Club: Rosscarbery SAC.

Baltimore (Cork). Shark (very good, July–Oct), skate, conger, tope, ling, cod, pollack and mackerel from boats; pollack, bass and mackerel from shore. Best June–Oct. Deep-sea angling boats for parties of up to six rods from T Brown, Baltimore House Hotel, Tel 028 20164. Hire charge £75 max (up to 6 rods). Tackleists: Fuller & Co.

Castletownbere (Cork). Good sheltered fishing in Berehaven and offshore at marks in Bantry Bay. Shark, pollack, ling, conger, ray, skate, pouting, bass, bream, wrasse, spurdog, gurnard, flounder, plaice, grey mullet, whiting and mackerel. Tackleist and tourist agent: C Moriarty, The Square. Hotel: Cametrignane House.

Cahirciveen (Kerry). For **Valentia Island**. Catches include conger (up to 72 lb), turbot (to 26 lb), halibut (to 152 lb), skate (to 218 lb), red bream (to 9 lb), bass (to 16 lb). Also large gurnard, mackerel, garfish, tope and blue shark. Boat fishing most popular, but good sport also from shore. International Deep Sea Festival at Caherciveen in Aug. Club: Valentia Harbour Sea AC. Information from Tourist Office, Caherciveen and Atlantic Holidays (Caherciveen 107); Kerry Boats Ltd (Caherciveen 122); Rod & Reel Ltd (Caherciveen 120).

Dingle Peninsula (Kerry). Provides some of best surf fishing for bass in British Isles; good centres are **Smerwick, Cloghane** and **Castlegregory**. Offshore fishing also very good; large pollack, coalfish, sea bream, conger and ling caught off rocky ground. Big skate, tope, turbot and halibut also taken. Late autumn, winter and early spring best for bass. Club: Dingle SAC.

Clifden (Co Galway). First-class boat and shore angling in sheltered conditions. Blue shark, tope, coalfish, pollack, skate, ray, ling, cod, turbot, brill and plaice. Good marks include: Slyne Head; Barrister wreck off Inishark; Inishbofin; Inishturk and Fosteries Shoals. Other good bays are Mannin, Ballinakill, Killary, Roundstone, Cleggan and Bunowen. Tackleists: E Sullivan, Main Street, and P Stanley, Market Street. Boats from F Mannion, J O'Grady, G Jeffries, all Market Street, and J Ryan,

Main Street. Sea trout and brown trout fishing available (*see freshwater section*). Club: Clifden Sea AC. Hotels: Clifden Bay, Alcock & Brown, Abbeyglen, Clifden House, Atlantic Coast and Celtic. Boats available at Bunowen and Roundstone.

Westport (Mayo). Good boat and shore fishing. Local clubs run nine of forty-eight sea angling competitions in the area each year. Fish caught include: the record monkfish (69 lb), skate (up to $167\frac{1}{2}$ lb), tope and conger (to 40 lb and more), cod, codling, pollack, flounders, plaice, gurnard, coalfish, bass, wrasse, turbot, dogfish, white skate (146 lb), and blue shark (up to 206 lb) and porbeagle shark and tunny. Dr O'Donnell Browne's 365 lb porbeagle was taken here. Good marks include Tower in Inner Bay, off Lighthouse, Pigeon Point, Cloghormack Buoy. Sheltered sport in Clew Bay. Boats available from Francis Clarke (tel: 098 25481). Tackleists: Hewetson's, Dyar's Bridge Street; Clarke's, The Octagon; Mulloy's & Gibbons, Shop Street. Club: Westport Sea AC and Westport Boat Club. Hotels: Westport Ryan, Olde Railway, Helm (especially suitable for angling groups).

Achill Island (Mayo). Excellent boat fishing; pollack, conger, ling, ray, cod, etc; fish run large. Noted area for blue shark; July–Oct best; also thresher and porbeagle. Tunny also reported in area. Pollack fishing off rock produces specimens in 15 lb class. Flatfish from Tullaghan Bay on north side of island. Good shore fishing; sea trout late June to early Aug (plentiful and good size); mackerel; plaice etc. Boats from McHugh, Bullsmouth; Bradley and Jim O'Gorman. both Dooagh. Tackleist: Sweeny and Son, Achill Sound. Hon sec, Achill Tourist Development Ltd and Achill Sea AC, will supply further details. Hotel: Achill Head, Keel; Atlantic, Dooagh.

Newport (Mayo). One of Eire's finest sea fishing centres. Large mackerel, tope, skate, conger, dogfish, monkfish, whiting, coalfish, pollack, gurnard may be taken in Clew Bay. Boats from SAC, st £3. Boats for six anglers, £50 per day. Hotels: Black Oak Inn, Newport House.

Belmullet (Mayo). Rapidly rising in popularity as sea-fishing centre. Sheltered water. Turbot, bream and pollack especially good. Belmullet Sea AC developing facilities; inquire hon sec. Deep-sea cruisers available. Annual festival.

Moville (Donegal). Foyle Sea AC arranges Lough Foyle Festival of Sea Angling. Tope, conger, skate, pollack, cod, gurnard, plaice, ling and others. Plenty of boats (20 ft–30 ft) and bait. At

Rosapenna (Donegal) is excellent boat fishing for tope. For deep-sea bookings apply Mrs C O'Donnell, "The Fleets Inn", Downings (Tel: 21). Other information from Donegal Deep Sea Angling Ltd, 1 Mount Southwell, Letterkenny. Tackleists: Co-operative Stores: Many hotels.

Fishing the long-awaited evening rise. *Photo: John Tarlton.*

FISHING CLUBS ETC. IN THE IRISH REPUBLIC

THE following is an alphabetical list of angling clubs and associations in the Irish Republic. Particulars of the waters held by many will be found, by reference to the index, in the section headed "Fishing Stations in the Irish Republic", and information about the others, which may not have their own water, could be had from the secretaries, whose addresses are given. A stamped/addressed envelope should be enclosed with inquiries.

NATIONAL BODIES

Anglers' Information Service Bord Failte (Irish Tourist Board)
Baggot Street Bridge
Dublin 2
Tel: Dublin 765871
Central Fisheries Board
Balnagowan
Mobhi Boreen, Glasnevin,
Dublin 9
Tel: 379206
Irish Federation of Sea Anglers
Capt G Moorkens
Endsleigh
Templeogue Road
Terenure, Dublin 6
Department of Fisheries and Forestry
Leeson Lane
Leeson Street
Dublin 2
Tel: 600444
International Fly-Fishing Association
R W Newport
"Nairn"
Glenvar Park

Blackrock, Dublin
Tel: Dublin 881712
Irish Specimen Fish Committee
D Brennan
Balnagowan, Mohbi Boreen
Glasnevin, Dublin 9
Tel: 379206
National Coarse Fishing Federation of Ireland
B Coulter
Blaithin
Dublin Road, Cavan
Tel: (049) 31577
National Salmon Anglers' Federation of Ireland
P J Concannon
23 St Assam's Avenue
Raheny, Dublin
Tel: 335888
Trout Anglers' Federation of Ireland
Noel Hales
Bilberry
Midleton, Co Cork.
Tel: (021) 667136

CLUBS

Abbeyfeale Salmon Anglers' Association
J Fitzgibbon
The Square
Abbeyfeale, Co Limerick
Achill Sea Angling Club
Pat Walsh
Curraun
Achill, Co Mayo
Achill Sporting Club
John O'Malley
Island Sports
Keel PO
Achill, Co Mayo
Ardara Anglers' Association
J McGill
Ardara, Co Donegal

Ardfinnan Angling Association
Matthew O'Sullivan
Ardfinnan
Clonmel, Co Tipperary
Argideen Anglers' Association
Mrs Claire O'Reagan
Hill Terrace
Bandon, Co Cork
Askeaton Angling Association
M McCarthy
13 St Francis Avenue
Askeaton, Co Limerick
Athlone Anglers' Association
Jack Brennan
1 Wolfe Tone Terrace
Athlone, Co Westmeath

Atlantic Sea Angling Club
C Gannon
The Bungalow
Glenties, Co Donegal
Athy Angling Association
T McCarthy
36 St Patrick's Avenue
Athy, Co Kildare
Baillieborough Angling Club
Mrs M McCabe
4 Lower Drumbannon
Baillieborough, Co Cavan
Ballaghaderreen Angling Association
J McGoldrick
St Mary's Terrace
Ballaghaderreen, Co Roscommon
Ballina Trout Anglers' Association
Sean O'Connell
5 Humbert Street
Ballina, Co Mayo
Ballinakill Angling Association
D Bergin
The Square
Ballinakill, Co Laois
Ballinasloe Anglers' Association
B Larkin
Sarsfield Road
Ballinasloe, Co Galway
Ballinrobe and District Anglers' Association
Ray Owens
11 Lakelawns
Ballinrobe, Co Mayo
Ballybay and District Angling Association
G Maguire
Ballybay,
Co Monagham
Ballybofey and Stranolar Angling Association
Jas Harkin
Finn View Terrace
Ballybofey, Lifford
Co Donegal
Ballycotton Sea Anglers' Club
Mrs Sheila Egan
Main Street
Ballycotton, Co Cork
Ballyduff Trout Fly Angling Association
J Tobin
Ballyduff, Co Waterford
Ballyhahill Angling Association
Patrick J Walsh
Ballyhahill, Co Limerick
Ballymore Eustace Angling Association
Tom Deegan
928 Briencan
Ballymore Eustace, Co Kildare
Ballymote and District Angling Association
Michael Rogers
O'Connell Street
Ballymote, Co Sligo

**Ballyshannon and District Trout Anglers'
Association**
P McGettigan
Main Street
Condon, Ballyshannon
Co Donegal
Baltimore Deep Sea Angling Club
Mr Heffer
Stone House
Baltimore, Co Cork
Bandon River Angling Association
G P Baines
Riversdale
Bandon, Co Cork
**Bandon River Salmon and Trout Anglers'
Association**
D Cahill
Casement Road
Bandon, Co Cork
Bangor Erris Fishing Club
S Henry
Briska
Bangor Erris
Co Mayo
Bantry Angling Association
D J Ducker
Beach
Bantry, Co Cork
Barrow Angling Club
P Redmond
Brownes Hill Road
Carlow
Belmullet Sea Angling Club
Sean Gannon
American Street
Belmullet, Co Mayo
Belturbet Angling Club
B Galligan
Belturbet, Co Cavan
Birr and District Anglers' Association
Fred Ryan
16 Moorpark Street
Birr, Co Offaly
**Blarney and District Trout Anglers'
Association**
Maurice Kiely
The Bridge, Station Road
Blarney, Co Cork
Boyle and District Angling Club
S Daly
Bridge Street
Boyle, Co Roscommon
Brittas Fishing Club
Desmond Clarke
22 Palmerston Park
Dublin 6
Buncrana Anglers' Association
Major S Spragg
Fahan, Co Donegal

Bundoran and District Anglers' Association
V Battisti
Sligo Road
Bundoran, Co Donegal
Cahirciveen Angling Association
P Donnelly
Valentia Road
Caherciveen, Co Kerry
Cappoquin Angling Club
J Aherne
Cappoquin, Co Waterford
Carlow Angling Association
B Nolan
38 Burrin Street
Carlow
Carlow Salmon Angling Association
N Sheehan
Upper Burrin, Carlow
Carrick-on-Shannon Angling Club
S O'Rourke
Mullaghmore
Carrick-on-Shannon, Co Leitrim
**Carrick-on-Suir and District Anglers'
Association**
P J O'Sullivan
Park View
Carrick-on-Suir, Co Donegal
**Cashel Tipperary and Golden Anglers'
Association**
John Evans
Main Street
Tipperary, Co Tipperary
**Castlebar and District Trout Anglers'
Association**
T Coucill
Humbert Inn
Main Street
Castlebar, Co Mayo
Castlebar Salmon Anglers' Club
Gerard A McCormack
Saleen
Castlebar, Co Mayo
Castleblayney Trout Anglers' Association
Frank Poyntz
Castleblayney, Co Monaghan
Castlebridge Anglers' Association
W Shortle
Castlebridge, Co Wexford
Castletown Trout Anglers' Club
D Twomey
Castletownbere, Co Cork
Castletownbere Trout Anglers' Club
Dr C H Phillips, Mill Cove
Waterfall, Nr Castletownbere
Bantry, Co Cork
Castletownroche Angling Club
J A Batterbury
Main Street
Castletownroche, Co Cork

Cavan Angling Club
Mrs B O'Hanlon
Cavan Tourist Association
St Martins, Creeghan
Cavan, Co Cavan
Clane Angling Association
Anthony Doherty
Raheen
Rathcoffey
Naas, Co Kildare
Clifden Anglers' Association
P Price
Clifden, Co Galway
Clifden Sea Angling Club
F Connolly
Derryclare Guest House
Clifden, Co Galway
Clogheen and District Anglers' Association
M G Gleeson
Cascade View
Clogheen, Co Tipperary
Clonakilty Angling Association
David Spiller
39 Pearse Street
Clonakilty, Co Cork
Clonbur Trout Angling Association
P H O'Malley
Clonbur, Co Mayo
Clones and District Anglers' Association
P F Goodwin
Fermanagh Street
Clones, Co Monaghan
**Clonmel and District Salmon and Trout
Anglers' Association**
Permits:
J Kavanagh
Westgate
Clonmel, Co Tipperary
Cloone Angling Association
Owen Mitchell
Keeldra
Cloone, Co Leitrim
Coachford Trout Anglers' Association
E Hayes
Nadrid
Coachford, Co Cork
Cobh Sea Angling Club
E W Cullinane
1 O'Donovan Place
Cobh, Co Cork
Coleraine Angling Association
Eugene Hayes
Nadrid
Coachford, Co Cork
Collooney and District Angling Association
G B McKenzie
The Rapids
Ballysodare
Co Sligo

Cong and District Angling Association
M L Maye
Cong
Claremorris, Co Mayo
Cootehill Anglers' Club
M McCluskey, NT
Bridge Street
Cootehill, Co Cavan
Cork and District Trout Anglers' Club
Paul Mellamphy
49 Ballyhooly Road
Cork
Cork Salmon Anglers' Association
John Buckley
Raheen House
Carrigrohane   Co Cork
Cork Sea Angling Club
D Looney
37 Mumount Circle
Montenotte, Cork
Cork Trout Anglers' Association
Joe Cahill
87 Patrick Street
Cork
Corofin Salmon Anglers' Association
H F McCullagh
Eyre Square
Galway, Co Galway
Co Longford Angling Association
Peter Malone
121 Sefton Park
Longford
Co Wicklow Anglers' Association
W A Hannon
106 Ardmore Park
Bray, Co Wicklow
Co Wicklow (Salmon) Angling Association
H U Valentine
Shankhill
Ravenscur, Co Dublin
Crosshaven Sea Anglers' Club
Tom Hanlon
1 Waterpark
Carrigaline, Co Cork
Crossmolina Anglers' Club
Frank Corduff
Ballina Street
Co Mayo
Culdaff Angling Association
B Doherty
Donagh Stores
Cardonagh, Co Donegal
Cullane and District Anglers' Association
J O'Brien
Tulla, Co Clare
Dee and Glyde Angling Association
Mrs Manning
Cappocksgreen
Ardee, Co Louth

Deel and Boyne Angling Association
E E Wright
Hyde Park
Killucan, Co Westmeath
Deel Anglers' Association
Philip Dollerey
Ballywilliam
Rathkeale, Co Limerick
Deele Angling Association
P Hoey
Raphoe Road
Convoy, Lifford
Co Donegal
Derravaragh Anglers' Association
Sean Rielly
Rathganny
Multyfarnham, Co Westmeath
Dingle Anglers' Association
M E Burke
Solicitor
Green Street
Dingle, Co Kerry
Dingle Sea Angling Club
Leo Brosnan
13 Marian Park
Dingle, Co Kerry
Dodder Angling Club
R O'Hanlon
82 Braemor Road
Dublin 14
Donegal Anglers' Association
Sean McBrearty
Drumcliffe, Donegal
Drogheda and District Anglers' Club
Gerard Kelly
"Saint Endas"
North Road
Drogheda, Co Louth
Drogheda Sea Angling Club
R Ryan
24 William Street
Drogheda, Co Louth
Drumshanbo AC and Tourist Development Association
Joseph Mooney
Drumshanbo, Co Leitrim
Dublin and District Salmon Anglers' Association
Norman Greene
15 Willington Green
Templeogue, Dublin 12
Dublin City Sea Anglers
P G Cairns
38 Ballyroan Road
Templeogue, Dublin 16
Dublin Trout Anglers' Association
Adrian Keegan
92 St John's Park
Clondalkin, Dublin 22

**Dundalk and District Salmon Anglers'
Association**
G McGuirk
330 Beachmount Drive
Dundalk, Co Louth
Dundalk and District Trout Anglers' Club
J T Quinn
19 St Patrick's Terrace
Dundalk, Co Louth
Dungarvan and District AA
Jas Kiely
1 Shandon Street
Dungarvan, Co Waterford
Dungarvan Sea Angling Club
Tel: 058 41395
Dun Laoghaire Sea Anglers' Association
K Bolster
136 Beaumont Road
Beaumont, Dublin 9
**Dunmanway Salmon and Trout Anglers'
Association**
P McCarthey
Yew Tree
Dunmanway, Co Cork
Dunmore East Sea Angling Club
John Stewart
"Tivoli"
12 Marian Park
Waterford, Co Waterford
East Mayo Anglers' Association
E Kennedy
Bridge Street
Swinford, Co Mayo
Ennis and District Anglers' Association
Joe Guilfoyle
20 Avondale
Newmarket-on-Fergus, Co Clare
Feale Salmon and Trout Anglers' Association
Patrick Mann
Church Street
Abbeyfeale, Co Limerick
Fealebridge and Brosna Angling Association
J O'Connor, NT
Knockbrack NS
Knocknagoshel, Co Kerry
Fermoy Coarse Angling Association
J O'Sullivan
4 Patrick Street
Fermoy
Co Cork
**Fermoy and District Trout Anglers'
Association**
P J O'Reilly
Church Place
Fermoy, Co Cork
Fermoy Salmon Anglers' Association
Patric Phelan
1 Chapel Square
Fermoy, Co Cork

Finn Valley Anglers' Association
P J Coll
Castlefinn, Co Donegal
Foxford Salmon Anglers' Association
Peter Tolan
Church Road
Foxford, Co Mayo
Foyle Sea Angling Club
T Mehan
Malin Road
Moville, Co Donegal
Galway and Corrib Anglers' Association
Cyril Conlon
Eglington Street
Galway, Co Galway
Galway Bay Sea Angling Club
Mrs K Conroy
"Porres"
Dublin Road
Renmore, Co Galway
Galway Deep-Sea Fishing Association
S O'Ciardubain
13 Pearse Avenue
Mervue, Galway, Co Galway
Garda Angling Club
B Prendergast
Garda Club
9–10 Harrington Street
Dublin 8
Glanmire and District Anglers' Association
J O'Sullivan
Lotamore Cottage
Glanmire, Co Cork
Glenbower Trout Anglers' Club
M Lee
Main Street
Killeagh, Co Cork
Glengariff Anglers' Association
A P Tisdall
Firlands
Glengariff, Co Cork
Glengariff Sea Angling Club
John Power
Reemeen
Glengariff, Co Cork
Glenties Anglers' Association
C McDyer
Glenties, Co Donegal
Gort and District Anglers' Association
Colman Keane
Gort, Co Galway
Gweedore Angling Association
William Alcorn
Bunbeg
Letterkenny, Co Donegal
Headford and Corrib AA
Kevin Duffy
Main Street
Headford, Co Galway

Ilen River Anglers' Association
M O'Keefe
Gortnacloy
Skibbereen, Co Cork
Inny Anglers' Association
James Nally
Green View
Multyfarnham
Mullingar, Co Westmeath
Kells Anglers' Association
Tom Murray
Farrell Street
Kells, Co Meath
Kenmare Bay Deep-Sea Anglers' Club
M J O'Connor
12 Main Street
Kenmare, Co Kerry
Kenmare Salmon Anglers' Association
Tony O'Shea
18 Henry Street
Kenmare, Co Kerry
Kilbride Anglers' Club
J D Johnston
54 Avondale Park
Raheny, Dublin 5
Kilgarvan Anglers' Association
M O'Donovan
Killafadda Cottage
Kilgarvan, Co Kerry
Kilkenny Anglers' Association
P A Troy
College Road
Kilkenny, Co Kilkenny
**Killala and District Sea Angling
Association**
Mrs B Maughan
Barrack Street
Killala, Co Mayo
Killybegs Sea Angling Club
Mrs Anne Gallagher
c/o Gallagher Bros
Killybegs, Co Donegal
Kilmallock and District Angling Club
Eamon O'Riordan
6 Gortboy
Kilmallock
Co Limerick
Kilmore Quay Sea Angling Club
E J Doyle
Kilmore Quay
Co Wexford
Kilworth and District Angling Club
Dan Roche
11 McDermot Place
Fermoy, Co Cork
Kinsale Sea Anglers' Club
D Enright
Villa Pio
Monkstown, Co Cork

Laune Anglers' Association
G W Gallagher
"Doirin"
Ballyvelly, Tralee
Co Kerry
Lee Salmon Anglers
Padraig Lucey
5 Perrott Avenue
Cork, Co Cork
Letterkenny and District Anglers' Association
P McLoone
114 Ard O'Donnell
Letterkenny, Co Donegal
Limerick and District Anglers' Association
P J Power
139 Lynwood Park
Limerick, Co Limerick
Longwood Anglers' Association
M F Bird
Riverview
Longwood, Co Meath
**Lough Arrow Fish Preservation
Association**
W Craig
Ballincar
Rosses Point, Co Sligo
Lough Carra Trout Anglers' Association
Sean Murphy
Moorehall, Ballyglass
Claremorris, Co Mayo
Lough Derg Anglers' Association
Honorary Secretary
Portumna, Co Galway
Lough Ennel Preservation Association
Supt John Doddy
Garda Siochana
Mullingar, Co Westmeath
Lough Garman (Sea and River) Angling Club
W J Guilfoyle
12 Casa Rio
Wexford, Co Wexford
Lough Lein Anglers' Association
P Curran
St Anthony's Place
Killarney, Co Kerry
Lough Mask Angling Preservation Society
T Molloy
Tourmakeady, Co Mayo
Lough Owel Trout Preservation Association
L W Murray
Mount Murray
Bunbrosna
Mullingar, Co Westmeath
Loughrea Anglers' Association
John F Quinn
Caheronaun
Loughrea, Co Galway
Lough Sheelin Trout Protection Association
R A Kilroy

Moydristan
Kilnaleck, Co Cavan
Louisburgh and Dist AA
J J Chilbin
Bridge Street
Louisburgh, Co Mayo
Macroom Trout Anglers' Association
B Baker
South Square
Macroom, Co Cork
Maigue Anglers' Association
E P Costello
Ballycarney, Co Limerick
Mallow Game and Coarse Anglers' Club
D Willis
5 Pearse Avenue
Mallow, Co Cork
Manorhamilton and District Anglers' Association
A Flynn
Post Office
Manorhamilton
Co Leitrim
Midland Angling Club
F Killian
Coosan Road
Athlone
Mohill Angling Association
M Cox
Hill Street
Mohill, Co Leitrim
Moy Angling Association
P Tolan
Foxford, Co Mayo
Muckross Fisheries Trust
T Hennebery
The Manor House
Tralee, Co Kerry
Newport Angling Club
Martin Maguire
Castlebar Road
Newport, Co Mayo
Newport Sea Angling Club
Mrs M McGovern
Newport, Co Mayo
North Clare Anglers' Association
Kevin Duffy
Ennestymon, Co Clare
North Kerry Salmon Anglers' Association
J Sheehan
23 Church Street
Listowel, Co Kerry
North Kildare Trout and Salmon Anglers' Association
Patrick Byrne
21 College Park
Newbridge, Co Kildare
Old Head Sea Angling Club
Harry Ormond

5 Fair Hill
Cork, Co Cork
Ormonde Angling Association
Joe O'Donoghue
Gortlandroe
Nenagh, Co Tipperary
Oughterard Angling Association
Tom Tuck
Oughterard, Co Galway
Pontoon and Foxford Angling Association
M P Howley
Gurteen
Foxford, Co Mayo
Prosperous Fishing Club
E O'Farrell
Prosperous
Naas, Co Kildare
Roosky and District Anglers
Mrs B Duffy
Killian Ker House
Roosky, Co Roscommon
Roscommon Gun and Rod Club
John F Neilan
Abbey Street
Roscommon, Co Roscommon
Rosscarbery Sea Angling Club
Kenneth Casey
Tanyard Hill, Rosscarberry, Co Cork
Roscrea and District Angling Association
M O'Connell
Abbey Street
Roscrea, Co Tipperary
Rosses Anglers' Association
Charles Boyle
Cannmere Road
Dungloe, Co Donegal
Rosslare Sea Angling Club
J F O'Brien
Villa Nova
Rosslare Harbour, Co Wexford
Scariff, Mount Shannon and Whitegate Angling Club
P Cahill
Mountshannon, Co Clare
Shannonbridge Anglers Association
D Killeen
Shannonbridge, Co Offaly
Sligo Anglers' Association
J McCarney
Annalen, Cornageeha
Sligo, Co Sligo
Strokestown Angling Club
George Gearty
Bridge Street
Strokestown, Co Roscommon
Swords Angling Club
R Shortt
Church Road
Swords, Co Dublin

Tallow Anglers' Association
John Forde
Main Street
Tallow, Co Waterford
Templemore Anglers' Association
Dick Burke
Loughmore Village
Templemore, Co Tipperary
Thomastown Anglers
John J Dunphy
25 Dangan Terrace
Thomastown, Co Kilkenny
Thurles, Holycross and Ballycamas AA
M L Mockler
Ballcahill
Thurles, Co Tipperary
Tralee Anglers' Association
T Hennebery
The Manor House
Tralee, Co Kerry
Tramore Waterford Sea Angling Club
Margaret Lucas
43 Avondale
Kilcohan
Waterford, Co Waterford
**Trim, Athboy and District Anglers'
Association**
P McManus
Manorland
Trim, Co Meath
**Tulla and District Coarse Angling
Association**
Brian A Culloo
Tulla, Co Clare
**Tullow Salmon and Trout Anglers'
Association**
Mrs Breeda Lennon
c/o Slaney Hotel
Tullow, Co Carlow

Upper Blackwater Angling Association
T Moynihan
Ballydesmond
Mallow, Co Cork
Valentia Harbour Sea Angling Club
Michael Quinlan
Cahirciveen, Co Kerry
Virginia and District Angling Association
M MacNamee
Virginia, Co Cavan
West Clare Angling Association
F Meaney
Francis Street
Kilrush, Co Clare
Westport and District Anglers' Club
John T Gibbons
Fair Green
Wesport, Co Mayo
Westport Sea Angling Club
Francis Clarke
"The Mews"
Rosbeg
Westport, Co Mayo
Westport Boat Club
M Brooker
Westport
**Wexford and District Sea
Angling Club**
J Guerin
Whitewell
Mulgannon, Co Wexford
Youghal Sea Anglers' Club
L Power
17 Dermot Huxley Estate
Youghal, Co Cork

Check before you go

While every effort has been made to ensure that the information given in "Where to Fish" is correct, the position is continually changing and anglers are urged, in their own interests, to make preliminary inquiries before travelling to selected venues. This is especially important with reference to prices quoted. Inevitably, the rate of inflation is affecting stability in this quarter. Anglers' attention is also drawn to the fact that the hotels mentioned under the various fishing stations do not necessarily have water of their own. Any amendments or further data for inclusion in subsequent editions, and any criticism, will be welcome.

ANGLERS ABROAD

14/16 HIGH STREET, WOMBWELL, BARNSLEY, S. YORKSHIRE S73 0AA

For high quality, low cost holidays to Southern Ireland, Northern Ireland, Denmark, Sweden and Spain.

phone Tim Meadows
or
Shaun Brearley

ANGLERS
ABROAD

and talk to fishermen about fishing.

With 17 years travel experience between them

Telephone: (0226) 751704

FISHING ABROAD

THE primary purpose of this section is to give the angler contemplating visiting, or even, in the case of Commonwealth countries, emigrating to, one of the countries listed a brief description of the fishing to be had. It is neither necessary nor practicable to enter into such detail as in the British sections, but the addresses of various authorities from whom further information can be obtained are given, together with that of the appropriate London tourist or Government information office, at the end of each description.

CENTRAL AFRICA

ZAMBIA. Most rivers and lakes carry good stocks of fish, giving very reasonable sport. But the angler must be prepared to travel long distances over rough roads, carrying his own camp equipment and finally making his camp beside the river he intends to fish. There are very few hotels off the main roads, and fewer still in fishing areas, though the Tourist Board is conducting a successful drive for more hotels and rest houses. In spite of this, for parties who appreciate camping holidays in the bush, some delightful trips can be planned, particularly in August and September, when there is little fear of rain and the nights are warm enough to make camping pleasant. Most of the rivers are either heavily wooded right down to the water or are swamp-edged, so the addition of a boat and outboard motor to the camp equipment is a sound policy. On the other hand, canoes and paddlers can be hired, and the latter are usually good guides to the best fishing grounds. Youths are also very helpful as camp attendants, and little trouble is normally experienced in hiring one or two to take care of the heavy work of the camp. The visiting fisherman must remember that the hippopotamus and crocodile are found in nearly all Zambian waters. Wading in rivers can be a dangerous pastime, and hippos, especially with calves, should be given a wide berth.

Indigenous species. These include tiger-fish, which probably provide the best sport, and goliath tiger fish, a separate species running up to 80 lb or more; fish of the Nile perch variety and their close relatives, giant perch (top weight around 200 lb); giant vundu (sampa), large- and small-mouthed bream, catfish, barbels, local pike, yellow belly (cichlid), lake salmon, kupi and labeo.

The great Zambezi and its large tributary, the Kafue, are outstanding among the rivers. A good centre for the Zambezi is Livingstone, though there is a small, comfortable hotel at Mongu, in Western Province. The tiger-fish fishing is splendid and there is excellent sport with bream (cichlids), vundu (common downstream of Victoria Falls) and barbel.

Lake Tanganyika is another anglers' mecca and a good centre is Kasaba Bay, where there are three small lodges. A launch service is operated by the Zambia Travel and Touring Co Ltd. The lake holds giant perch, tiger-fish, yellow belly and vundu among a wide variety of sporting fish.

Apart from Nile perch and sampa, which call for heavy tackle, most of the fish mentioned can be handled with a spinning rod. Steel traces are necessary for tiger-fish, kupi and pike. A light bait-casting rod will usually cover other species. Fishing is free as a rule and can take place all the year round, but most rivers are in spate during the rainy season from December to April.

Exotic species. Zambia is unlikely to prove to be a land in which trout will thrive, owing both to the high temperature range and the lack of suitable highlands, but an exception may be provided by the picturesque Nyika Plateau, north of Chipata on the Malawi border, where an experimental stocking with rainbow trout in the headwaters of the Shire River is being carried out.

Other information can be obtained from the several fishing clubs scattered throughout the territory. For general data inquire of Zambia Veterinary & Tsetse Control Dept, Box RW 60, Ridgeway, Lusaka, or the Zambian National Tourist Board, 2 Palace Gate, Kensington, London W8 5NF.

MALAWI. Excellent sport with rainbow trout may be enjoyed in the bracing climate of the Zomba, Mlanje and Nyika Plateaux as a result of consistent restocking of rivers and streams by the Government. Lake Malawi holds over 200 species, including varieties of catfish, perch and carp. Most of these are found in the Shire River above Livingstone Falls, but below the falls the main species are related to those found in the Zambezi. They include the famous tiger fish. Further information may be obtained from the Angling Society of Malawi, PO Box 744, Blantyre, Malawi.

EAST AFRICA

ETHIOPIA. With large areas of the country only recently opened to tourists, Ethiopia's many rivers and lakes abound with fish, forming a veritable fisherman's paradise.

The best time of the year to visit Ethiopia is during the dry season, which is from late October to the beginning of February. Virtually no rain falls during this period and the sky is usually cloudless. During the period February to mid-April, some rain falls, but not in such quantities as to disrupt sport. Most of the areas which offer good fishing are accessible by road or by air. Cars (with or without chauffeurs) can be hired at Addis Ababa, and Ethiopian Airlines have a good domestic network. Tackle should be brought from one's own country as there are no facilities for hire or purchase.

Indigenous species: Ethiopia has three of Africa's most sought-after fish—the tiger-fish, Nile perch and giant catfish. The tiger-fish is probably the most sporting, giving a good account of itself on reasonably light spinning tackle, like that commonly used for pike. The crushing power of the tiger-fish's jaws is immense, though, and metal spoons are preferable to plastic or wooden lures. Tiger-fish also have extremely sharp teeth, so a wire trace should be used and great care exercised when unhooking the catch. Tiger-fish average 2-6 lbs, although much larger specimens are known to exist and can weigh more than 50 lbs. The Nile perch, which can reach a top weight of nearly 300 lbs, can be caught by live- or dead-baiting (a ledgered tiger-fish is best) or by spinning. A particularly deadly method is to work a medium or large-size plug at mid-water. Tackle should be fairly heavy and line breaking strength should not be less than 18 lbs, in view of the size of the fish and the hazards of underwater snags. Catfish can also be caught by bait-fishing and sometimes will also take a lure. For both of these species a wire trace should also be used, attached to the line by a large swivel. Catfish can make tremendous runs, so make sure that there is plenty of line on the reel.

The best place to try for these species is Lake Chamo in the southern part of the country, and the angler is based at the town of Arba Minch, where there are comfortable hotels. Fishing can be done from boats (although this should be arranged in advance on arrival at Addis Ababa) or from jetties. The Baro River near Gambela is another good source of these fish and the fisherman can stay at the pleasant Ras Hotel. In both areas, the fisherman should remember that he shares the water with hippopotamuses and crocodiles, and wading and swimming is therefore highly inadvisable.

Lake Chamo also contains tilapia, barbus and smaller species of catfish for those who prefer less exerting sport. Light tackle should be used (5 lbs breaking strength is quite suitable) and a strip of meat or worm is a very good bait. These fish are also found at Lake Awassa in the Ethiopian Rift Valley, and at Lake Tana in the north, where they can grow to specimen size—barbus weighing in excess of 20 lbs are not uncommon and even tilapia can reach weights of over 6 lbs.

Imported species: Both brown and rainbow trout have been introduced into the rivers of the Bale Mountains National Park and these have flourished with the high altitude and climate. The trout grow to quite respectable sizes and fish over 8 lbs are caught quite regularly. The Shiya River holds the largest trout but these are more difficult to catch; whereas the Dinka and Ueb have an abundance of smaller fish which almost seem to give themselves up to the angler. Spinning with small blade spinners is the most effective method with the occasional fish falling to the fly. The local children can be recruited as guides and gillies and their willingness to be of service for a small fee holds much to the pleasure of fishing.

There are plans to introduce black bass into some of the lakes but at the time of writing there have been no definite results.

Sea-fishing: Sea fishing in the Red Sea is possible for barracuda, tuna, shark and other tropical species. The centres are Massawa and the Dahlak Islands off the coast. Boats can be hired but one should bring one's own tackle.

KENYA. Kenya is well-developed for the sporting tourist and offers a variety of fishing off the coast, in its rivers and in the lakes of the Great Rift Valley. Licence fees are modest; accommodation of some variety is established at or near virtually all main centres.

The coast. Black, blue and striped marlin; broadbill swordfish, sailfish, yellow fin tuna, wahoo, barracuda, cobia, dorado, mako shark, 36 out of 79 All-Africa records are held at the time of going to press by Kenya anglers. Centres at Mombassa, Shimoni (for the famous Pemba Channel fishing), Kilifi, Watamu, Lamu and Malindi, the latter the largest. Accommodation at club premises or hotels. Charter boats. Good fishing almost all the year round, peaking Oct–April: at its least attractive May–June.

The mountain rivers. Stocked early in the century with brown trout, later with rainbows. Camps with rondavel accommodation at Thiba, Thego, Kimakia, Koiwa. Rest house at Kaibabich; lodges at Ngobit and Kiandorogo. A dozen or more specially recommended hotels and clubs. Camp accommodation may be primitive; nothing should be taken for granted. There are limits on size, method and bags, but wholesale poaching is an ever-present problem despite sincere governmental efforts to curb it.

The lakes. Naivasha is famous for black bass, but the angler in pursuit of them should forget any preconceptions he might have. Smallish coppery-tinted bar-spoons are the most successful lure and the bigger fish are found not so much in the shallows as in pockets of deeper water inshore, where they shelter in the papyrus. In Lake Turkana (formerly Rudolph) the principal quarry are Nile perch and tiger-fish, the former growing to more than 250 lbs. Also in Turkana, the rare and beautiful golden perch, which may weigh 150 lb. Lake Baringo, well off the beaten track, is noted for its tilapia fishing; also for its wildlife-watching potential, but that is a bonus attaching to much of the Kenya fishing. Sport-fishing is now developing in Lake Victoria and the Sasuma Dam. Accommodation at all centres, but the extreme variety of types calls for detailed investigation in advance. Kenya Tourist Office: 13 New Burlington Street, London W1X 1FF. Tel 839 4477/8 and 930 3837.

TANZANIA. Tanzania can provide some of the finest big-game fishing in the world.

Big-game fishing: From October to March there is first-class sport with sailfish, shark, tunny, marlin, wahoo, horse mackerel and dolphin, particularly off Dar es Salaam, around Latham Island and Mafia Island, and also in the Pemba Channel off Tanga. Mafia offers some of the finest sport in the world in quantity, variety and excitement, and here particularly, and in addition to those already mentioned, can be found king fish, barracuda, red snapper and rock cod. There is a lodge on Mafia Island, with 30 air-conditioned rooms. Boats and equipment can be hired from the Seafaris Company. Flights to Mafia Island from the mainland (about 30 minutes run) are operated daily in each direction. Air charter services from Dar es Salaam, also.

Lake fishing: Lake Tanganyika provides the best sport fishing where, from Kigoma, Mwanza and Itungi, it is possible to catch Nile perch, tiger fish and tilapia, which provide excellent sport.

Trout fishing: At the moment, less organised than other branches of the sport, but can be arranged on request.

Further information (licences etc) may be obtained from the Tanzania Tourist Corporation, PO Box 2485, Dar es Salaam, and PO Box 694, Arusha (for Mt Meru fishing), or from Tanzania Tourism Office, Suite 2a, 77 South Audley Street, London W1.

SOUTH AFRICA

CAPE PROVINCE. Since the establishment of large-mouthed and small-mouthed black bass, the inland fisheries of the Cape area have been greatly extended; but this development has not been at the expense of the rainbow trout fisheries, which are as flourishing as ever. A few rivers hold brown trout, and brook trout were also introduced to upland waters some time ago. All the inland waters fall under the laws of the Cape Provincial Administration. In proclaimed trout rivers no fishing may be done at all except with the artificial fly and during the open season for trout, which extends from the beginning of September to the end of May. Trout licences are required, but the charges are extremely moderate. In addition, however, the permission of riparian owners will be needed and sometimes a fee is payable.

Most of the rivers in the Western Cape are within a day's motoring of Cape Town on tarred roads, and some of the best waters are on State Forest Reserves, to which anglers have access on permit. This area has a winter rainfall, and the best months are September, October and November, late April and early May. Steenbras Reservoir holds a rare hybrid known as "tiger trout" which is a cross between brown trout and the Amercian eastern brook trout. The Cape Piscatorial Society (Westminster House, 122 Longmarket Street, 8001 Cape Town) can be approached for general informatiom on inland fishing in the Cape Western Province.

The Olifants River in the Citrusdal and Clanwilliam districts provides excellent fishing for small-mouthed bass and the indigenous yellowfish, *Barbus capensis*. The latter takes artificial lures, is very game and runs as large as 20 lb. Further afield, the mountainous area of East Griqualand, adjoining the Transkei, have rivers which provide boundless opportunities for the trout fisherman.

Sea fishing along the Cape Province's coastline is very good indeed, with hundreds of species to be caught. The big-game potential is only beginning to be realised, and remarkable catches of yellowfin and longfin tuna have been taken. Tuna catches predominate throughout spring, summer and autumn; snoek in the winter months. Skiboat fishing is an interesting and highly successful technique for taking many varieties of off-shore fish. Every type of tackle is available and accommodation is plentiful and comfortable. Among the many sea-angling associations in the Cape Province (some of which are affiliated to the South African Anglers' Union, PO Box 1456, 2000, Johannesburg) are the Rock and Surf Angling Association, 28 Silverlea Avenue, 7800, Wynberg, and the South African Ski-Boat, Light-Tackle Game Fishing Association, PO Box 4191, 8000, Cape Town. The address of the South African Game Fishing Association is PO Box 723, Bedfordview, 2008.

NATAL. The streams originating in the Natal Drakensberg mountains, which rise to 11,000 ft, form several river systems before emptying into the Indian Ocean. Although the sources are in general too steeply graded to support fish life in any quantity, below the torrent source each river enters a series of pools and rapids suitable for trout and other fish. Moreover, the construction of numerous dams in the Natal Midlands has been the means of providing many extra fishable waters.

Only waters at an altitude of about 4,000 ft and more have, in general, been stocked with trout. Below this level most rivers are too warm and silt-laden for the species to thrive. Black bass and carp have been established in a number of these midland dams with tilapia species inhabiting the warmer areas. However, other species to be caught are the indigenous "scaly" (yellowfish), catfish, and eels. The State dams administered by the Natal Parks, Game and Fish Preservation Board (Albert Falls, Midmar, Wagendrift, Spioenkop, Chelmsford, Hazelmere and Craigie Burn) not only provide abundant angling for many types of fish, including those mentioned above, but also provide a wide range of other recreational facilities and comfortable accommodation.

Rainbow and brown trout are the most important sporting fish of the Drakensberg area (midlands) and warmwater angling (carp, black bass, catfish, scaly, eels and tilapia) of the lower inland areas. The open season for trout streams is from September 1 to June 1, but dams are open throughout the year. The best fishing is usually obtained at the beginning and end of the season. From November to February the heavy summer rains and thunderstorms are apt to discolour the lower waters and render fly fishing difficult. It is almost always feasible, however, to obtain fishing on the headwaters or on artificial lakes and dams. The average size of Natal trout runs from about $\frac{1}{2}$ lb to 2 lb, but on the larger waters, especially dams, much heavier fish can be expected and each season a few trout of more than 5 lb are taken. The Natal record for a rainbow trout is 5.54 kg (12 lb 12 oz) caught in the Swartberg district in May 1958.

There are four fly-fishing clubs in Natal: The Underberg-Himeville Trout Fishing Club, PO Box 7, 4590 Underberg; the Natal Fly Fishers' Club, PO Box 1535, 3200 Pietermaritz-burg, the Natal Midlands Fly Fishing Club, c/o M Moor, Avalon, PO Estcourt 3310 and the Flyfishers' Assocation, PO Box 37197, Overpoort 4067. Each of these has control over some private waters (rivers and dams) in different areas, so visiting anglers should refer to all three clubs for information and advice.

Public waters and the Provincial nature reserves (where accommodation is available close to fishing areas) are controlled by the Natal Parks, Game and Fish Preservation Board; all queries regarding licences, accommodation etc should be directed to the Secretary, PO Box 662, 3200 Pietermaritzburg, who will supply full information to visitors and handle reservations. Natal Parks Board rangers are stationed at the more important public fishing areas to assist visitors and enforce regulations for the protection of trout, black bass, carp and indigenous fish.

Sea fishing. The majority of salt water anglers fish in the surf, casting their baits and lures from sandy beaches or from rocky promontories. Estuaries offer sport, while the open sea attracts those who have access to suitable craft. A wide variety of fish may be caught in the surf, ranging from sharks to small members of the bream family. Tackle varies accordingly, but a light fibre-glass rod of about 10–13 ft together with a fixed-spool or multiplying reel gives a chance of catching many of the inshore species. Visitors should acquaint themselves with size restrictions and open seasons which apply to certain species of fish. Full details are obtainable from The Natal Parks Board.

In June and July the annual migration of "sardines" may attract game fish such as king mackerel into the surf and sport is likely to be fast and furious. The best estuarian fishing is Lake St Lucia, a nature reserve controlled by the Natal Parks Board; large numbers of grunter and kob enter the estuary leading to the main lake in spring and autumn. Deep sea angling takes place from ski-boats (small, speedy, flat-bottomed craft) as well as from the larger types of vessel. Advice on the organisation of deep sea trips will be provided by the Natal Parks Board (PO Box 662, 3200, Pietermaritzburg). Tackle for every branch of angling is obtainable. Innumerable hotels, holiday cottages, holiday flats and rest camps provide accommodation for visitors to the Natal or Zululand coastal resorts. Enquiries should be directed to the Durban Publicity Association, PO Box 1044, 4000, Durban.

Other useful addresses: Secretary, Natal Coast Anglers' Union, 77 Waller Crescent, Roseglen, 4091, Durban; Durban Ski-boat Club, PO Box 38210, 4069, Point; Angling Board of Control, PO Box 21099, 4020, Fynnland.

TRANSVAAL. Rainbow trout can be caught in a number of fine mountain streams in the Eastern Transvaal at altitudes varying from 4,000 to 6,000 ft. Magoebaskloof, Sabie, Pilgrim's Rest, Lydenburg, Machadodorp, Belfast, Dullstroom and Waterval Boven are the principal trout fishing centres. Some waters contain only fish over 3 lb in weight. There is no closed season for trout fishing although fishing conditions are at their best in October and April. The rule is fly only, with dry and wet flies being used. Most waters are privately owned and, except where angling clubs have fishing rights, the permission of the riparian owner must be obtained.

Good bass fishing is to be found in a large number of public, club and private waters. Large-mouth bass are widely distributed but some of the best waters are in the White River area of the Eastern Transvaal: dams in that region, such as Longmere, Klipkoppies, Witklip, Stanford and Dagama have produced excellent fishing in recent times. Tiger-fish may be caught in the Komati River at Komatipoort and in the Limpopo. Minimum takeable size, 12 in, daily bag limit, 6. Tiger-fish are best caught in September and October.

Yellowfish abound in the waters of the Transvaal. There are four species, all belonging to the genus *Barbus*. In the Vaal River they grow to 30 lb in weight and can be caught on mealiemeal dough, earthworms, grasshoppers or crabs. The two species of the east-flowing rivers grow to 15 lb and take crab, earthworms, mealiemeal dough and spinners.

Tilapia, commonly known as "kurper", is a very popular fish. There are two species, both being restricted to warmer waters. They can be caught on earthworms, mealiemeal dough (a paste bait) and spinners, with a light trout rod. They average about $1\frac{1}{4}$ lb, but specimens of $4\frac{1}{2}$ lb are commonly caught. The best waters for this species are the Hartebeestpoort, Rust der Winter, Roodeplaat, Loskop and Njelele dams, also those in the White River area—although they may be caught in almost any lowveld water.

Not just the Transvaal, but the whole of the Republic of South Africa is a carp angler's paradise, with the fish attaining exceptional weights in very short periods, due to the nature of South Africa's waters. The record caught on rod and line is 48 lb 10 oz, although much larger specimens have been caught but not recorded, and the heaviest known fish was a monster of $83\frac{1}{4}$ lb which was trapped in an irrigation furrow near Bon Accord Dam north of Pretoria. Carp are found throughout South Africa in many public and private dams. No bag or size limits apply to these fish.

The Transvaal's fisheries are administered by the Transvaal Provincial Administration, Division Nature Conservation, Pretoria. The Provincial Fisheries Institute, Private Bag 1088, 1120 Lydenburg, is the scientific headquarters, and information about fishing in the Transvaal may be obtained from the Senior Fisheries Officer at that address, or from the Rand Piscatorial Assn, PO Box 2813, 2000, Johnannesburg.

General Information: Licences relative to the particular province can be obtained from Receivers of Revenue, magistrates' offices and reputable tackle stores throughout the Republic.

For further information contact the South African Tourism Board, Regency House, 1–4 Warwick Street, London W1R 5WB. Tel: 01-839 9661.

Some time between May and July every year sardines in vast numbers migrate from east to west along the south coast of Natal, followed by large schools of shad, barracuda, shark, and other predatory species of great interest to the angler. In certain conditions of wind and tide, sardines are washed ashore by the shoal to provide pickings for all present, as in the picture.

FISHING IN AUSTRALASIA; INDIA; SRI LANKA AND MALAYSIA

AUSTRALIA

As a result of acclimatisation and planned research in Australia, many of the lakes and rivers in the State of Tasmania, New South Wales, Western Australia and Victoria are well stocked with trout, which sometimes reach a large size. The island State of Tasmania is world-famous as a trout fishing centre, and continues to attract anglers from all parts of the Commonwealth each year.

Many rivers are still subject to flooding despite hydro schemes and this imposes a standstill on angling, so that the tendency is to reduce close seasons. The angler is strongly advised to check on river levels before going to fish. Before water temperatures have warmed up will be found to be the best times—midsummer is generally worst for trout fishing.

Freshwater Murray cod, perch and blackfish are found in good number in Australia. The Murray River, which forms the boundary of the eastern States of Victoria and New South Wales, and its many tributaries provide good sport for thousands of anglers, including trout in the upper reaches, Murray cod may weigh up to 150 lb; another Murray River fish, the callop or golden perch, grows to over 50 lb. Macquairie perch (to 11 lb) and silver perch or grunter (to 6 lb) are also taken. Another perch, or Australian bass, is taken in coastal streams and estuaries.

Australia was said by the late Zane Grey, noted big game authority, to possess the finest big game fishing grounds in the world. Centre of interest for sportsmen is Montague Island, off the coast of New South Wales, where there are marlin, tuna, shark and other big fish. The island is 14m from Bermagui, a safe harbour that can be used in all weathers. The tropical waters of the Great Barrier Reef, which extends for about a thousand miles along the east coast of Queensland, form Australia's most fascinating grounds; there are many unusual varieties of fish. There is good beach and rock fishing almost everywhere.

The principal fishing organisation is the Game Fishing Association of Australia, Birkenhead Point, Drummoyne, NSW 2047.

NEW SOUTH WALES. The streams near Sydney are mostly too small to support a large trout population, but good sport may be had in parts of the Blue Mountains area. Easily best from the fishing point of view, however, is the Snowy Mountains area. Very large reservoirs constructed as part of the hydro-electric scheme in the Southern Alps are now ranked equal to any in the world for brown and rainbow trout. The scenic beauty of the streams and these lakes is outstanding. Lake Eucumbene is the largest of the dams and in recent years has become the mecca of Australian trout anglers, but there are many other fine fisheries. Good accommodation and camping sites are available and many fine fishing waters are reached easily over good roads. Another good area for trout fishing is the New England Tableland, north of Sydney. Centred on the University Town of Armidale, the area's many streams and high altitude provide excellent fishing.

Apart from these new waters, one of the most renowned centres is Cooma, which has produced many of the heavier fish caught in the state. The Murrumbidgee and its tributaries near Kiandra are well worth fishing at the right time.

Atlantic salmon have been introduced into the Burrinjuck Dam, and if they become a self-suporting stock will be tried in other cold water storages.

With the exception of a number of small spawning creeks, which have extended close seasons, and the larger impoundments, which are open all the year round, the trout streams are open to fishing from the beginning of October to the end of May. Other inland waters are open the whole year. The most popular times for trout fishing are in the cooler months of the open season; that is October, November, March, April and May.

It is now necessary for anglers fishing for any species of fish, including trout, to hold an inland angling licence. Licences and information are available from the State Fisheries, 211 Kent Street, Sydney, and from local agents. All fees collected are required to be used for the improvement and protection of the inland fisheries. There are many attractive native species inhabiting the freshwater streams. Murray cod being perhaps the most popular, and the taking of fish up to 50 lb is not uncommon; these fish do, in fact, run much larger.

The State is noted for its attractive coastal lagoons and estuary fisheries. At many excellent resorts bream, flathead, whiting, black fish, etc, give good sport, while big game fish like tuna, marlin and shark abound in waters off the coast. The NSW Game Fishing Association, Birkenhead Point, Drummoyne, NSW 2047, will give further information. Tourist information can be had from the NSW Government Travel Centre, 16 Spring Street, Sydney. The London office of the New South Wales Government is at 66 Strand, London WC2 (01-839 6651).

QUEENSLAND. There are no trout fishing centres, no licence fees and no close season except for Barramundi Angling (Nov 1 to Jan 31). Golden perch or "yellow-belly" are found in the freshwater rivers of the south-west and as far north as the upper river of the Dawson. Murray cod are also caught in the south-western rivers, and freshwater perch or grunters (several species) are found in most inland streams. Barramundi are taken from all inland rivers of eastern Queensland north of and including the Dawson River. Nile perch have been introduced into a number of waters.

Off the coast are the Greater Barrier coral reefs (1,230 miles long), which abound in fish life. Big game fish are plentiful along the whole coastline, and the following species are commonly caught: Marlin, spearfish, tuna, bonito, Spanish mackerel, sharks (white pointer, mako, tiger, whalers, etc), amberjacks, emperor, trevally, etc.

Cairns and Far North Queensland are known world wide as a big game area for the Big Black marlin in the last quarter of the year. Large marlin are regularly landed.

The area off Brisbane provides one of the best light tackle game fish grounds in the world in the first half of the year particularly for tuna and sailfish.

The mainland coast provides excellent estuary beach and rock fishing for bream, whiting, flathead, tailor, trevally, giant perch, grunter, jew fish, and so on.

Further information can be had from the Queensland Tourist and Travel Corporation, 392 Strand, London WC2R 0LZ. Telephone: 01-836 1333.

SOUTH AUSTRALIA. South Australia has very few freshwater streams if the River Murray is excluded. Relatively little trout fishing is available except in some streams near Adelaide and in farm dams. There is no closed season on trout fishing but there is a legal minumum length of 28 cm.

The River Murray, which flows through the State to the sea, supports both commercial and recreational fisheries for native freshwater species, callop, Murray cod, silver perch and catfish and yabbies. Introduced golden carp, common carp, English perch and tench are also caught. Murray cod may not be taken during September, October and November whereas all other fish may be taken through the year.

Very enjoyable and profitable sea fishing can be had along most of the coast of South Australia with rod and line or hand line. Amateur anglers do not require licences; neither do game fishermen who go after the huge white shark. The largest specimen so far caught on game tackle weighed 2,536 lb.

Anglers do not require a licence to fish with a rod or hand line, but must observe legal minimum lengths of fish, bag limits, and closed areas, and must not take protected species. Fishing is not permitted in most Aquatic Reserves.

Tourist information can be had from the South Australian Tourist Bureau, 18 King William Street, Adelaide, and further information on fishery matters from the Director, Department of Fisheries, 135 Pirie Street, Adelaide and the Secretary, South Australian Fly Fishers Association Inc. (Mr C M Shepherd, PO Box 489, North Adelaide 5006.)

TASMANIA. Tasmania, not without justification, describes itself as Australia's "Fishermen's Mecca". A multitude of lakes and rivers are generously stocked with the native blackfish and with introduced brown, rainbow and brook trout, species which have achieved growth-rates on the island second to none. The size-bracket in which the angler expects his captures to fall spans 2–10 lb, with even larger trout an ever-present possibility. Most of the waters are within motoring distance or of air-services from Hobart and Launceston. Mobile campers are widely employed. Guides are available, and can arrange, where necessary, flies, lures, boats and camp services.

Popular waters include Great Lake (situated in the central plateau of the island at an altitude of 3,372 ft, 83 miles from Hobart, the capital, and about the same distance from Launceston, second largest city in the island, situated in the north), Lake King William, Lake St Clair, Lake Echo, Little Pine Lagoon, Brady's, Dee Lagoon, Arthurs Lake, Lake Rowallan and Lake Pedder. Other popular fishing waters are Lake Leake and Tooms Lake on the east coast, Lakes Sorell and Crescent in the central midlands, and Lake Dulverton on the main highway between Hobart and Launceston.

The northern part of the island is more richly endowed with trout streams than the south, having the South Esk, North Esk, Macquarie and Brumby. The north-west has the Mersey, Forth, Leven, Blyth, Duck and Inglis. In the south are the Derwent, and Huon.

Angling licences, full season, 14 days, 3 days, are available from most sports stores, police stations or the Inland Fisheries Commission. The principal angling associations are the Southern Tasmanian Licensed Anglers Association, the Northern Tasmanian Fisheries Association, and the North-Western Fisheries Association. Tourist information can be had from the Tasmanian Government Tourist Bureau, Elisabeth Street, Hobart, and the address of the hon sec, Inland Fisheries Commission, is 127 Davey Street, Hobart 7000.

VICTORIA. The Yarra River, which enters the sea at Melbourne, the capital, is well stocked with brown trout, and rainbow trout are caught at Lake Eildon, 90m from Melbourne. In the Goulburn River at Eildon both browns and rainbows are plentiful and specimens up to 14 lb have been landed. These fish take spinners, and can also be landed on long-tailed flies which imitate the small smelt on which they feed. Other trout fisheries in the Lake Eildon district are the Howqua, Delatite, Jamieson, Big Rivers and Jerusalem Creek, together with a number of tributary streams of this system. These waters all hold both rainbow and brown trout. Good centres in North-Eastern Victoria for waters holding both brown and rainbow trout are Omeo, Swift's Creek, Benambra, Tallangatta, Eskdale, Corryong, Towonga. Lakes Bullen Merri and Purrembete can be fished from Camperdown in the Western District. Both these waters carry very large rainbow trout and Purrumbete also holds quinnat salmon. In the Horsham district, Murray cod, rainbow and brown trout are to be taken in a number of streams and lakes. Good rainbow and brown trout fishing can also be had in a number of streams around Wangaratta and Whitfield, and other trout fisheries are Lakes Konongwootong, at Coleraine, and Wendouree, at Ballarat. Trout fishing in the Murray River is virtually restricted to only a fraction of the river's length above and below Hume Weir, but Murray cod (80–100 lb) and three varieties of perch (to 10 lb) are among other fish to be caught. Little fishing is available in the Snowy River. Good fishing can be had in the Kiewa. In recent years a number of western lakes have been successfuly stocked with rainbow trout. With surveys showing many rivers overstocked with trout, new regulations have been introduced—no close season, no bag limits etc—in an attempt to produce fewer and bigger fish. All anglers must possess an Inland Angling Licence obtainable from the Fisheries and Wildlife Division, 240 Victoria Parade, E Melbourne 3002.

Numerous species and varieties of sea fish can be caught in the bays and estuaries of the State within easy reach of the capital, Melbourne. They include snapper, flathead, whiting, bream, bass and luderick. The snapper appears from September to April and have been taken up to 25 lb. Another bay fish is the pike, which resembles the river pike in some respects. The pike superficially resembles another bay fish, the barracouta, caught in large numbers by both amateur and commercial anglers.

The principal and governing piscatorial body is the Piscatorial Council of Victoria. Tourist information (including a booklet *Fishing in Victoria*) can be had from the Victorian Government Tourist Bureau, 272 Collins Street, Melbourne. The address of the Victorian Government Office in London is Victoria House, Melbourne Place, Strand WC2B 4LG (01-836 2656).

WESTERN AUSTRALIA. Recent years have seen a wide expansion in trout fishing and propagation in Western Australia. Many streams in the south west of the State are now well stocked with brown and rainbow trout, bred at the Pemberton hatcheries, and many excellent catches have been recorded. State record brown and rainbow trout of 9 lb 2 ozs and 7 lb 8 ozs were taken in 1981 and 1982 respectively. Principal trout fishing centres are within easy access of Perth. The trout season runs from September 1 to April 30. Bag limit for trout is 10 per person per day. Legal minimum size for trout is 30 cm; no fish caught may be sold. A native freshwater crayfish, marron, can be taken in the Southwest portion of the State.

Principal centres for ocean fishing are: Exmouth, Shark Bay, Carnarvon, Kalbarri, Geraldton, Fremantle, Perth, Rottnest Island, Rockingham, Mandurah, Bunbury, Busselton, Augusta, Albany and Esperance. Various types of accommodation are available and boats may be hired or chartered at most centres. The fish to be caught include: black and silver bream, kingfish, whiting, tailor, flathead, sea herring, skipjacks, garfish, Australian "salmon", flounder, mullet, mackerel, leather-jackets, snapper, jewfish and groper. Marlin and other gamefish are taken in northern waters and centres for game fishermen are being developed. Prawns and lobsters may be taken in many areas.

A Recreational Fishing Licence must be held for the taking of lobster, maroon or to use a fishing net. The fees for these activities are $9.00, $7.00, $7.00 respectively.

The Fisheries Department located at 108 Adelaide Terrace, Perth and the address of the Western Australian Division of the Australian Anglers' Association is PO Box 375, Subiaco. The address of the Western Australian Government Tourist Bureau is: 772 Hay Street, Perth. The address of the Western Australian Government Office in London is: 115 Strand, London WC2R 0AJ (01-240 2881).

NEW ZEALAND

(Notes compiled by George Aitken)

Fishing in New Zealand can be compared in some ways to Caesar's Gaul, in that it divides into three parts—Trout, Salmon and Big Game angling.

Trout, both brown and rainbow, were introduced about 100 years ago and have long been fully distributed on both islands. Rainbow predominate in the North Island, and Browns in the South, but many waters have a mixture of the two in varying proportions.

The main areas in the North are centred on Lake Taupo and the Rotorua district with its group of important lakes. The rivers flowing into and out of these lakes are also noted fisheries, particularly late in the season when the main runs commence. The Tongariro, Waitahanui, Tauranga-Taupo and others flow into Lake Taupo, while in the Rotorua area there are the Kaituna, Ohau Channel, and Ngongotaha to name a few.

The South Island has thousands of miles of rivers and streams, and numerous lakes of all sizes. It was once calculated, at the turn of the century, that there are 17,000 miles of river fishing in New Zealand, and of course it is all open to the public, subject only to right of access and to reasonable accessibility.

Good trout fishing is widely available, and large trout can still be caught within an hour's drive of the main cities, but obviously many of the best waters are more remote and some are seldom fished, although helicopter or floatplane services are readily available out of the towns of Queenstown, Wanaka and Te Anau to reach places like Lakes Alabaster and McKerrow, or the Pyke and Hollyford rivers for example.

The main, and also the lesser, rivers of Southland and Otago provinces offer excellent dry fly and nymph fishing for brown trout, and fish of from 12 to 15 pounds are caught each season, but a good average would be from 3 to 4 pounds. Guide services are again widely available, although obviously concentrated somewhat in the more popular areas. An Angling Guides Association was formed some time ago, all professional guides are licensed, and are fully supported with 4-wheel drive vehicles and boats as necessary for their local areas.

In general, the open season is from Oct 1 until the end of April but some waters open early to take advantage of the runs of whitebait which provide feed for sea-run trout, while others, principally in the Taupo and Rotorua areas, stay open all the year, particularly the lower reaches of the larger streams feeding Lake Taupo, and Lakes Taupo, Rotorua and Wakatiou themselves.

Salmon, the Pacific Quinnat or King Salmon, introduced to the main Canterbury rivers, are fished for in about eight of them, the main ones being the Waimakariri, Rakaia, Ashburton, Rangitata and Waitaki. The fishing is mainly heavy spinning, with spoons most favoured as lures, in the lower rivers, estuaries and even in the surf at the mouths. A certain amount of fly fishing, using very large lures or flies, is done upriver, notably in the

Rakaia Gorge area. In all the salmon rivers the fish are mostly in the 12 to 20 pound class, but larger are quite frequent. The rivers are often unfishable for many days at a time due to cloudy glacial melt water, and trips undertaken with salmon exclusively in mind are not to be recommended.

Big Game Fishing, made famous by Zane Grey, continues its excellent tradition. The main bases for this are Russell, Paihia and Whangerei in the Bay of Islands, and also out from Tauranga to the Mayor Island area. There are ample charter boats, with professional skippers and hands, based in these places, catering for parties of up to four anglers. The tackle, bait and so on are all provided in the charter. Sailfish, marlin and shark are caught at no great distance from the shore. The southern part of the West Coast of the South Island, known as "Fiordland", is now assuming increased importance for big game fishing. Boats are now based there, at Milford Sound and elsewhere.

Big Game angling is mainly from January to the end of April, with the period from mid-February on offering fine sport.

Licences are needed for trout and salmon fishing. These cover the whole country, with the most minor exceptions, and for a Visitor cost NZ$55 (UK £20) a month, and are available from the New Zealand Tourist Offices in the main cities. It is interesting to note that it is illegal to sell, or offer for sale, either trout or salmon, but your hotel would cook yours for you obviously.

Further Information and advice on any aspects of angling in New Zealand can be obtained by writing to the Tourist Office, New Zealand House, Haymarket, London SW1Y 4TQ. Telephone 01-930 8422.

INDIA

One of the big attractions for the fisherman in India—in more sense than one—is the mighty mahseer. This renowned sporting quarry is found in the upper reaches of the large rivers where the water is cold and the river-bed strewn with boulders and pebbles. It lies in pools above or below the rapids and preys on small fish.

The mahseer can be taken on a spoon, but strong tackle is essential. It not only runs large—the biggest caught on rod and line weighed 119 lb (Cauvery River, South India, 1919)—but is a splendid fighter. The sport has, in fact, been compared most favourably with salmon fishing.

Mahseer abound in the upper reaches of the Brahmaputra and its many tributaries in Assam, and the beautiful Titsa river valley in North Bengal is good just before and after the rainy season (June to September). Large fish may also be taken in the Bombay area—in the Rivers Kalu, Bhima and Mula. One of the best centres in the Punjab is Tajewala, on the River Jamuna. A catch of 80 lb of mahseer a few years ago is recorded in the visitors' book at the Rest House there. The River Jhelum in Kashmir also holds mahseer—fish of more than 90 lb have been taken—but the fishing is not now so good as it was some years ago.

Kashmir is renowned for sport with brown and rainbow trout, which have thrived since they were introduced at the turn of the century. The many streams in the area are regularly stocked from two large hatcheries and are divided into "beats" of about two miles. Great variety is available, the rivers ranging from foaming torrents, when spinning is permitted, to gentle streams suitable for dry fly. There are "fly only" beats. The most suitable flies are those usually included in every angler's selection, but in Kashmir they are usually dressed on hook sizes between No. 9 and No. 5 (old sizes). The season lasts from March 15 to October 15; the permit charge is £2 to £3 per day. The first month of the season is also the rainy season, and fishing is a little uncertain. There is also good trout fishing in the Kulu valley, where the season starts a few days earlier—on March 10.

India's rivers contain numerous other species. The Jamuna at Okhla, in Delhi, for instance, holds no fewer than eight species, including heavy catfish, the silund—a predator running up to 50 lb, which can be taken on a spinner—and a humpbacked fish called the cheetul or moh, which will be seen constantly rising to the surface and turning over broadside. There is also plenty of huge carp in the slow-flowing rivers and the lakes and tanks. The sea fishing can be excellent, too, but is dependent upon seasonal migrations and the weather. A considerable body of angling literature has now been published by the Bombay Natural History Society, 114 Apollo Street.

While the tourist-angler should not expect to find luxurious cabins on his expeditions, numerous camping-sites and comfortable rest-houses have been provided, often in the most beautiful surroundings and at Corbett, the call of the tiger and the trumpeting of wild elephants may sometimes be heard.

So far as tackle is concerned, the trout or mahseer fisherman will be specially well catered for at Srinagar, capital of Kashmir, where he may obtain first-class gear, but rates are rising due to restricted imports, and it is preferable to take one's own equipment.

Further information from the India Government Tourist Office, 7 Cork Street, London W1X 2AB (Tel 01-437 3677).

SRI LANKA (CEYLON)

Nuwara Eliya is the best centre for trout fishing. As it is above the 6,000 ft level, the climate is temperate. Good hotel accommodation is available. The fishing is, with few exceptions, restricted to fly only and most common patterns of wet fly are successful. Dry fly is rarely used, there being little natural fly. There is no statutory close season, though the club imposes one in parts following restocking. Size limits vary from 8 in to 15 in.

The main waters are: Nuwara Eliya stream (flows through the golf course and park); Ambawela stream (8m from Nuwara Eliya; jungle and grassland); Bulu Ella stream ($2\frac{1}{2}$m jungle); Portswood Dam (4m; tea estate); Agra Oya and Gorge Valley rivers (10–15m; tea estates), and the magnificently spectacular Horton Plains stream (30m; jungle and grassland, Nature reserve). Motor transport can be hired. On any of these waters it is possible to maintain an average of 1 lb and several fish over 3 lb are caught.

Trout fishing is now controlled by the Nuwara Eliya District Fishing Club. Stocking has so far been carried out in Portswood Dam, the Horton Plains, Agra Oya and Gorge Valley. For licences application should be made to the Honorary Secretary, Nuwara Eliya District Fishing Club, Court Lodge Estate, Kandapola. Visitors are advised to bring their tackle as fly tackle is scarce in Sri Lanka.

The two main species of indigenous sporting fish in Sri Lanka are the mahseer and the walaya (freshwater shark), found in the jungle rivers of the Low Country, particularly the Mahawehi, the upper reaches of the Kelani and the Amban Ganga. Ceylon mahseer, though small compared with those in some Indian rivers, provide good sport, but fishing for them can be somewhat difficult. Fishing for indigenous sporting fish in Sri Lanka is free. With a shoreline of 1,140 miles and a continental shelf of 10,000 square miles, the seas around Ceylon have an unlimited fishing potential hardly exploited.

The outfalls of 103 major river basins and hundreds of other estuaries, lagoons and coastal lakes all round the island are the most popular spots frequented by local surf casters as well as bait fishermen. Many varieties of game fish of the Carangid family, locally called paraw and know elsewhere as trevally, horse mackerel, etc, are taken. These swift and powerful carnivorous fish attain a length of 5 ft and a weight of 150 lb. The schooling habits of the caranx, their keen eyesight and some built-in sensory mechanism make them congregate in estuaries immediately after monsoons and rains.

Next in popularity among surf-casters come the barracuda and Spanish mackerel. Both these species of voracious predatory fish attain lengths of 6 ft as do other species known locally as "giant perch", "threadfins" and "tassel fish" which frequent the estuaries.

Trolling over the continental shelf yields catches of tuna ranging from the 2–3 ft skipjack to the 6 ft yellowfin and bluefin, the acrobatic dolphin, swordfish and marlin which attain a size to provide a challenge to the best big game fishermen of any country. The broadbill swordfish found in deeper waters reach a length of 15 ft and a weight of well over 1,000 lb. Though reaching only 10 ft and 250 lb, the sailfish compensate for their smaller size by their remarkable agility.

The monsoons regulate the fishing in Sri Lanka Seas. The western and southern coasts are favoured during the North-East monsoon (from October to April) and the east coast during the South-West monsoon (from May to September).

Good hotels and rest-houses (local inns) are available in the fishing areas and information on fishing will gladly be given by the Secretary, Ceylon Sea Anglers Club, 311 Galle Road, Colombo 3. Boats may be hired from professional fishermen.

Further information from Ceylon Tourist Board, 4 Tavistock, London WC1H 9RA (01-278 0639).

MALAYSIA

Some good sport is available in the jungle-covered highlands where fast-flowing, clean streams will delight the eye. These are well stocked with cyprinids or members of the carp family, which include the well-known mahseer of India, known locally as kelah. This group of which the most common species are kelah (up to 20 lb), sebarau (up to 12 lb), and kejor or tengas (up to 8 lb), are sporting fish which fight well when hooked. Kelah and tengas are good to eat. They are best when curried and provide a good change of diet in the jungle when living on operational 24-hour pack rations.

All these fish will take an artificial bait; the most popular being a 1 in or $1\frac{1}{2}$ in silver or silver/copper spoon. A normal salmon spinning outfit is ideal. For those who prefer it, a fixed-spool reel can be used provided it will hold sufficient line. Owing to the crushing power of the jaws of the kelah, extra strong treble or large single hooks should be used and some people recommend the use of a 2 ft wire trace.

Malaysia's National Park, on the borders of Kelantan, Trengganu and Pahang, provides the best fishing, and a visit to the HQ at Kuala Tahan is well worth the journey. It may be reached by rail to Kuala Tembeling and thence by water, in long, narrow, locally-built boats fitted with 40 hp outboard motors which can do the journey up the Sungei Tembeling in three to four hours depending on the condition of the river. At Kuala Tahan there are bungalows and a rest-house providing full board. A number of visitors' lodges and halting bungalows have been built throughout the park so the fishermen can stay near the river they are fishing.

From Kuala Tahan all onward movement is by smaller boats with lower-powered engines to negotiate the shallower rivers, such as the Tahan itself. There are many large pools well stocked with fish in the lower reaches and above the Lata Berkoh barrier many pools and rapids, all excellent fishing water. Malay and Aborigine boatmen are happy to act as guides and are delightful companions.

It is easier and pleasanter to cast from the bank, but this will necessitate some wading where the bank is steep and overhung by the jungle. The water is pleasantly warm and waders would be far too hot to wear. Those with a good sense of balance can try fishing from a slowly paddled perahu, but as this is only a shell at the most 2 ft wide, it is liable to be something of a circus act.

Most reliable times to fish are the months February/March and July/August, because in other months fishing will be spasmodic owing to the heavy rainfall. Spates and floodwater so colour the rivers that fishing is a waste of time.

Apart from the fishing there is always the chance of seeing the wild animals of Malaysia at the many salt licks. There are usually monkeys, iguanas, snakes and flying foxes to be seen, as well as many varieties of birds such as hornbill eagle and kingfishers.

Intending visitors should write well before the date of their visit, giving as much information as possible on their special interests to the Director-General, Dept of Wildlife and National Parks, K19, Govt, Offices Complex, Jalan Duta, Kuala Lumpur, Malaysia, so as to enable the Dept of Wildlife and National Parks to plan their itineraries.

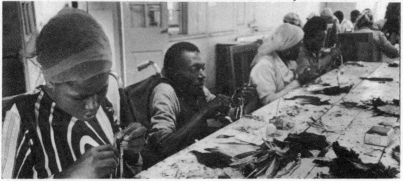

Commercial fly-dressing at a home for the disabled in Kenya.
Photograph: Leonard Cheshire Foundation.

FISHING IN NORTH AMERICA

CANADA

On the Atlantic side of the Dominion there are plenty of salmon rivers in Quebec and New Brunswick, and a good deal of fishing is available to the non-resident who takes out the appropriate provincial licence. There is a great deal of splendid trout fishing in many of the inland lakes and rivers, while in the Great Lakes region there are big muskellunge, and fine black bass fishing in various waters. The land-locked salmon is found in Quebec, both in the tributaries and discharge of Lac St John, and in some lakes in Nova Scotia, such as Grand Lake and Beaver Bank Lake. The "trout" of this side of Canada are char (*Salvelinus fontinalis*), while some of them are migratory and become "sea trout". In the lakes are "grey trout", some of which reach a great size. There are also char (*Salvelinus namaycush*) in the Arctic.

On the other side of Canada, British Columbia offers splendid opportunities of sport with Pacific salmon, steelhead and rainbow trout. Fishing for Pacific salmon has until recently been considered of necessity a matter for tidal waters. The Campbell River, Vancouver Island, has been the most favoured resort, and there quinnat (now known locally as tyee) up to 70 lb have been caught on the troll. At Prince Rupert a 93 lb quinnat was caught on a spoon in 1929 by Mr O P Smith, a professional fisherman. An 82 lb tyee was caught in August, 1951, at Rivers Inlet. The cohoe has been caught on fly, also in tidal waters. Of late years it has become clear that quinnat will take in fresh water in certain conditions. To the far north there are evident possibilities of sport in Yukon and NW Territories.

So far as tackle is concerned, the trend is towards lighter outfits. Brook trout, for instance, are almost universally taken on a nine-foot, five-ounce fly rod, and many anglers use the same rod for steelhead or Kamloops trout, although this is probably foolhardy. Tackle should always be carefully geared to the area and quarry, and on-the-spot advice is desirable.

Much work is done by the Federal and Provincial hatcheries, and waters in various parts of Canada are supplied with fry of species suitable to their needs, chiefly salmonidae.

Note: The Candian Government Office, "Tourism Canada", publishes some useful guides to fishing in Canada, and copies may be obtained from their London Office at Canada House, Trafalgar Square, London SW1Y 5BJ.

ALBERTA. Alberta is fortunate in having more than 4,000 miles of good fishing streams and more than 500 lakes. Fisheries management is the basis of the sportfishery capabilities and as such scientific data collected by the field staff plays the major role in determining fishing seasons and catch limits. Recent changes in regulations include a reduction in the daily catch and possession limits for trout. These and other regulations protect cold water species; however, warm water species are also carefully managed and in this regard seven lakes have been set aside as trophy lakes with specific reduced catch limits.

Closely allied to the management of native fish is the production of fish by hatchery. In 1987, 6.5 million trout were produced and stocked in over 200 lakes and ponds throughout the province. These fish are occasionally stocked in lakes to bolster present breeding populations, however they are usually stocked in lakes which do not contain native fish and which are readily accessible to the public.

There are 15 species of sportfish in Alberta of which there are 9 cold water and 6 warm water sportfish. The cold water sportfish include brook, brown, cutthroat, golden, rainbow, and lake trout, Dolly Varden (bull trout), arctic grayling and Rocky Mountain whitefish. These fish are generally found throughout the lakes and streams in the foothill and mountain areas in the south west of the province.

The warm water sportfish include lake whitefish, walleye, perch, pike, goldeye, and lake sturgeon. These fish are generally found in rivers and lakes throughout the south east and northern areas of the province. The major exception to this distribution is the sturgeon which is restricted to the south east corner of the province.

Further information (including details of new sportfishing regulation) may be obtained by writing to the Fisheries Administrative Assistant, Alberta Fish and Wildlife Division, Main Floor, North Tower, Petroleum Plaza, 9945-108 Street, Edmonton, Alberta, T5K 2C9.

BRITISH COLUMBIA. The game fish of British Columbia comprise three species of salmon, the chinook, or spring (large specimens often referred to as "Tyee"), the pink (tidal waters only) and the cohoe, which may be taken with the fly, but are more easily caught by trolling; all varieties of Pacific Coast trout, particularly the steelhead, the rainbow, and the cut-throat; Arctic grayling; two species of char, of which the commoner is the Dolly Varden; and the Eastern brook trout which has been introduced. The province has a coastline of 7,000 miles and is drained by innumerable rivers and freshwater lakes.

Some of the most important fishing areas are Kootenay District, Okanagan District (including Beaver, Bear, Dee, Ideal, Mabel, Sugar, South and Woods Lakes), Kamloops District (including Adams, East Barriere, Murtle, Shuswarp and Nicola Lakes), Cariboo District (including Quesnel, Horsefly and Canim Lakes, and Fraser and Thompson Rivers), and Princeton District (including Copper-Five-mile, One-mile, Otter Wolf and Sumners Creeks, and Pasayten, Similkameen and Tulameen Rivers). Most of the lakes and rivers are easily accessible, especially by car, and yield excellent fishing. Flying in to the less accessible waters is now a common practice. Lodges, cabins and boats are widely available.

Vancouver Island offers excellent cut-throat and steelhead trout fishing. The important waters are Cowichan, Cameron, Sproat Lakes, Alberni and Qualicum Districts and the Campbell River area. Steelhead trout are in Sproat, Somass, Ash and Stamp Rivers, to name but a few. Quinnat (or spring) salmon and cohoe are found in good quantities in all of the main streams, bays and tributaries of the mainland draining into the Pacific Ocean. On Vancouver Island there is splendid salmon fishing to be had at Brentwood Bay, Saanich Arm, Cowichan Bay, Comox Bay, Port Alberni, Beecher Bay, Victoria, Vancouver and Campbell Bay and river. Campbell River is famous on account of the large Tyee chinook caught there.

Further information (including details of licence charges and open seasons) can be had from the Recreational Fisheries Branch, Ministry of Environment and Parks, Parliament Buildings, Victoria, BC V8V 1X5 and Dept of Fisheries and Oceans, Communications Branch, 1090 W Pender Street, Vancouver BC V6E 2PI. For travel information, write to Ministry of Tourism, Recreation and Culture, Parliament Buildings, Victoria B.C., V8V 1X4.

MANITOBA. Manitoba is at the centre of a country more than 4,500 miles wide, from St John's, Newfoundland on the east to Victoria, British Columbia on the west.

The province is enormous by British standards, covering 250,000 square miles and measuring 735 air miles from north to south. Lake Winnipeg, 40 miles north of the capital city of Winnipeg, is the seventh largest inland body of water in North America. The northern three-fifths of the province is laced with innumerable streams and rivers, and someone claims to have counted more than 90,000 lakes, although many are too small to even appear on a map.

As the trout waters in the wilderness areas of this province become better known, they are acquiring the reputation of providing some of the finest trout fishing in North America. In particular, Gods River in north-eastern Manitoba is famous for trophy-sized brook and lake trout, northern pike and walleye. The Limestone and Weir rivers, tributaries of the Nelson River in the vicinity of Gillam on the Hudson Bay Railway, are other famous brook trout waters. Lake trout (*Cristivomer namaycush*) are widely distributed from the south-eastern area of the province through to the northern boundaries in the deep, cold-water lakes of the Pre-Cambrian shield. Specimens over 40 lb are taken each year.

The Arctic char (*Salvelinus alpinus*) is common along the north-western coast of Hudson Bay and its tributary streams, which include the North Knife, Seal, Little Seal and Caribou rivers. The Arctic grayling (*Thymallus arcticus*), with its spectacular beauty, is the delight of those fly-fishermen who are able to travel to the Churchill area or the fly-in areas in the far North.

Other fish. In the smaller lakes and streams in the southern part of the province, walleye, northern pike and yellow perch are plentiful. In Lake Winnipeg and the tributary Red River, freshwater drum and channel catfish to 30 lbs are taken in large numbers at certain seasons. Winnipeg River is the locale for large walleye, and great northern pike, together with an abundance of small-mouth bass, which provide excellent sport.

Further information (including details of licence charges and open seasons) can be had from Travel Manitoba, Department 8310, 7th Floor, 155 Carlton Street, Winnipeg, Manitoba R3C 3H8.

NEW BRUNSWICK. Atlantic salmon in the Restigouche, Upsalquitch, Kedgwick, Patapedia, Jacquet, Nepisiquit, Tabusintac, North-West Miramichi, South-West Mira-michi, Little South-West Miramichi, Sevogle, Renous, Dungarvon, Cains, Rocky Brook, Clearwater Brook, St John River, Nashwaak, Tobique, Serpentine and Salmon rivers. Parts of some of these streams are leased, some are Crown reserve waters and some are privately owned, but there are open stretches on all except the Kedgwick, Patapedia, Rocky Brook, Clearwater and Serpentine, and non-residents who take out the appropriate provincial licence can fish a good deal of water. Since 1984, salmon larger than 63 cm must be released immediately after capture. Grilse only may be retained by the angler.

In addition to salmon fishing, there is good brook trout fishing in most of the lakes and streams of New Brunswick. Small-mouth bass and landlocked salmon are caught in some waters in the south-west of the province and a few striped bass in the St John River and Bathurst Harbour.

Non-resident licences must be obtained from a Forest Service Office in the province. These must be carried by the holder at all times, but do not convey right of fishing on Crown-reserve waters or any private fishery without the consent of the lessee or owner. Every non-resident when angling on designated Atlantic salmon rivers, requires a licenced guide. One guide is required per angler when fishing from a boat, or one guide for up to three anglers when wading or fishing from shore. There is now a strictly enforced tagging-programme in operation for Atlantic salmon.   Further information, including details of licences and open seasons, can be had from the Department of Natural Resources and Energy, Fish and Wildlife Branch, PO Box 6000, Fredericton E3B 5H1, and New Brunswick Dept of Tourism, PO Box 12345, Fredericton E3B 5C3.

NEWFOUNDLAND and LABRADOR. Newfoundland has probably some of the best game-fishing in North America. Almost a quarter of the island's area is water, and its many fine salmon rivers, some of them practically unfished, flow through unspoiled forest and hill country. During 1986 season a total of 41,698 salmon were angled, of which 41,231 were grilse; 467 large salmon were caught, all in Labrador. Quananiche (land-locked salmon) are common in Newfoundland waters. Several kinds of trout—speckled, brown, rainbow and lake (char). Sea-run brown trout streams in the province are mainly concentrated along a 100-kilometre coastal area immediately south of St. John's; 15- to 20-pound fish are not uncommon. Scheduled (licensed) rainbow trout waters comprise a small group of streams and ponds immediately north of St. John's; rainbows are also frequently caught in unscheduled water throughout the province. All the trout except the brown are at least as plentiful (and on average significantly larger) in Labrador as on the island part of the province; most Labrador angling water are of much more difficult access, however. Tuna fishing was relatively good a decade or more ago, but in recent years only a handful are caught annually (e.g.—four in 1985, five in 1986).

The salmon season varies among groups of rivers and from year to year, ranging from about June 1 to September 15, with most rivers open from mid-June to the first week in September. Scheduled rainbow trout waters are open from late May–early June to mid-September. The province has scheduled salmon rivers on the Island of Newfoundland and in Labrador, and scheduled rainbow trout streams.

Fishing in all inland waters in the province is restricted to rod, hook, and line, with a variety of baits and lures permissable in most waters; angling in scheduled salmon rivers is further restricted to fly fishing only.

Licence-fees for non-residents are as follows. Salmon: $40; trout: $10. A special extra licence is required for fishing in Terra Nova National Park. Licences are obtainable in most tackle and hardware shops and from Department of Development and Tourism, Tourism Branch, PO Box 2016, St John's, Newfoundland, Canada A1C 5R8.

The bag limit for salmon is two retained per day; and four hooked and returned per day: when one or other of these limits has been reached, the angler must cease fishing for the day. There is a season limit of 15 retained, when this has been reached the angler must cease fishing for the season. The bag-limit for lake trout and arctic char is four per day: of other trout and northern pike, 24 per day.

Further details, including licence charges and names and addresses of "operators" and guides can be had from the Department of Development and Tourism *(address above)*.

Further information can be had from the Department of Fisheries & Oceans, Information Bureau, PO Box 5667, St Johns, Newfoundland. Tel: 709 772 4421.

NOVA SCOTIA (including Cape Breton Island). Atlantic salmon in St Mary's, LaHave, Medway, Margaree, Stewiacke, Moser, Musquodoboit, Gold, North, Liscomb and Maccan rivers; some 30 additional rivers have substantial runs of salmon but water levels and conditions are a major factor in the annual take. There are 13 rivers scheduled and posted for fly fishing only, but it should be noted Atlantic salmon may only be taken by fly; brook trout are common in streams and lakes, many of which are accessible from woods roads known as roads to resources; sea trout (brook and brown) in most tidal streams in the Northern and Eastern part of the province; 45 salt water charter boats are available for ground and tuna fishing in all areas except the upper reaches of the Bay of Fundy.

For further information please contact the Department of Tourism, PO Box 456, Halifax, Nova Scotia B3J 2R5. The Department of Tourism publishes several good brochures on outdoor sports activities.

ONTARIO. Brook trout are widely distributed in eastern Canada. In Ontario this excellent game-fish occurs from the Great Lakes northward to streams entering Hudson Bay and James Bay. Included in the eastern part of this area west of the Quebec boundary are Algonquin Park, tributaries of the Upper Ottawa River, North Bay, Timagami-Metachewan, the Porcupine, Matheson-Abitibi and Cochrane areas, the Moosonee and the Goose country.

The western and northern area includes waters draining into Lake Superior west of Sault Ste Marie to Nipigon Bay, Nipigon River (where the world record brook trout $14\frac{1}{2}$ lbs was caught, in 1916), Lake Nipigon Forest Reserve, the Lakehead District and the Lake St Joseph and the Albany wilderness. The numerous tributary waters of the Albany River offer some of the finest trout fishing to be found in Ontario.

In southern Ontario, west of the eastern area, the brook trout waters include the Muskoka lakes, the Haliburton and Hastings highlands and the Magnetawan area. Farther south and west, trout are available in some streams tributary to Lakes Huron, Erie, Ontario, Simcoe and Georgian Bay. Lying between the eastern and western areas of northern Ontario there are numerous brook trout waters, among which are the Sudbury, Manitoulin, Sault, Michipicoten, Mississauga, Gogama, Chapleau, Missinabi-White River-Franz, Elsas, Oba, Hornepayne, Hearst, Kapuskasing, Nakina and Albany River areas.

The range of bass fishing, small-mouth and large-mouth, in Ontario extends from the Ottawa and St Lawrence rivers and Lake Ontario and Lake Erie to Timagami and the north channel of Georgian Bay. Included in this range are the following areas: Long Point Bay (Lake Erie), Rideau lakes, Haliburton Lake District, Kawartha lakes, Muskoka lakes, Lake Nipissing, the French and Pickerel rivers, and the Georgian Bay District areas. In the north-west section of Ontario bass are found in Quitico Park.

The muskellunge range in Ontario includes the Ottawa and St Lawrence rivers, Lake Ontario, Lake Erie, Lake St Clair and Lake Huron, Kaiwartha lake, Lake Nipissing, French and Pickerel rivers and tributary waters. The best fishing is in the mouth of the Moon River and the Lake of the Woods district in the north-western section of the province, an extensive area some 150m wide east to west, and 160m from the international boundary north. This district has hundreds of lakes, and large muskies are taken here every year. Lake trout, lake whitefish, yellow pickerel (walleye) and Gt Northern pike are fairly plentiful throughout the province. Rainbow and brown trout (neither is native to the province) have been stocked in limited areas. Rainbow trout fishing is booming in southern Georgian Bay, especially in the Owen Sound-Collingwood area. The rainbow fishing peaks in the spring and in the fall. In recent years rainbow trout fishing has also become popular in Lake Ontario in the Port Hope area.

Splake, a cross between lake trout and brook trout (speckled trout), have been introduced into some waters for a number of years now and are doing quite well. There exists now some good splake fishing at Owen Sound, Parry Sound and at Providence Bay on Manitoulin Island. Fishing for Pacific salmon, introduced into the Great Lakes, has escalated, especially in Lake Ontario where anglers flock to the Port Credit-Niagara area each year in late summer and early fall to catch large coho and chinook salmon. In the North Channel of Lake Huron and in Lake Superior pink salmon attract many anglers in early fall.

Ontario has revised its non-resident angling licences and instituted special protection for two species, muskellunge and lake trout. Non-resident licences are 4-day, 21-day, seasonal or spousal (for a couple). Non-residents need $5.50 tags (valid for a year) to fish for muskellunge or lake trout; an additional Border Water Tag is required in some areas.

There are nearly 500 fish and game associations in the province, many of which are federated with the Ontario Federation of Anglers and Hunters (Executive Vice President, Box 28, Peterborough, Ontario, K9J 6Y5). Further information (including licence changes) can be had from the Ministry of Natural Resources, Whitney Block, Queen's Park, Toronto, Ontario, M7A 1W3), and the Ministry of Tourism and Trade, 1200 Bay Street, Toronto, Ontario, M5R 2A6.

PRINCE EDWARD ISLAND. This island, which lies in the Gulf of St Lawrence off the north coast of Nova Scotia, has an enviable reputation for its speckled trout fishing. The streams and rivers are spring fed, and the whole province may be considered a natural hatchery for trout and salmon. The salmon fishing, however, is not first class, and the best runs, with the exception of an early run on the Morell River, do not begin until towards the end of the season. Both non-migratory and migratory trout are to be caught. Fishing for rainbow trout can be had in Glenfinnan, and Keefe's lakes. Noted trout streams are the West, Morell and Dunk rivers, and large freshwater dams also afford good sport. Mackerel fishing is becoming popular (late July to September) in coastal waters.

Further information may be obtained from the Prince Edward Island Visitor Services Division, PO Box 940, and Dept of Community Affairs, Fish and Wildlife Unit, PO Box 2000, both Charlottetown, PE1. Post codes C1A 7M5 and C1A 7N8 respectively.

QUÉBEC. Québec is lavishly laced with countless lakes and rivers where a variety of fishing keeps anglers smiling. Over the last few years, the entire Québec population has enjoyed equal access to the wildlife resources. More than 1,200 private clubs have been replaced by a network of some 60 *ZECs, (Zones where Exploitation is Controlled)* which are managed by non-profit organizations authorized by the Government. The present network offers clients some 60 territories, well populated by a rich variety of wildlife species on a land area covering 44,000 km^2 and seven salmon fishing territories spread along a course of 568 km of river.

Fishing and many other activities may be enjoyed in *Québec Parks and Wildlife Reserves*. Fishing may be engaged in by a variety of options: by the day or with stayover; on a lake from a boat or by wading in some streams. The Québec fishing licence is mandatory in all parks and wildlife reserves.

Some private enterprises also offer anglers and hunters a number of accompanying services, including accommodation—these are *outfitter establishments*. Some outfitter establishments hold exclusive fishing, hunting and trapping rights. Those who want to practise any one of these activities within the boundaries of an outfitter's establishment, must engage the services of the establishment concerned.

Québec's Ministère du Loisir, de la Chasse et de la Pêche, (Recreation, Fish and Game department), provides, free of charge, booklets containing a wide range of information on activities within ZECs, Parks and Wildlife Reserves, a list of Outfitter Establishments, opening and closing dates on fishing, hunting and trapping seasons, wildlife species, licences, rates, regulations, among others.

These publications may be obtained by written request or by telephone. The mailing address is: Ministère du Loisir, de la Chasse et de la Pêche 150, Boul. Saint-Cyrille est, Québec, QC, GIR 4YI. Telephone: (418) 643-2464.

SASKATCHEWAN. Pike, perch and walleye are found throughout the province and represent the largest portion of the sport catch. Lake trout and arctic grayling are plentiful in the northern areas. Rainbow, brook, brown and splake trout are stocked in some 120 waters.

A Quebec lake trout that reached double figures before meeting an honourable and pain-free death. Respect for the quarry is at the heart of angling.

Further information (including details of limits, accommodations, outfitters, guides and licence charges) is available from Sask Travel, Department of Tourism and Small Business, 2103 11th Avenue, Regina, Saskatchewan S4P 3V7.

THE UNITED STATES OF AMERICA

The United States of America covers an enormous area of land and water space, offering everything between the near-Arctic conditions met in winter near the 49th parallel and the semi-tropical climate of Florida, Luisiana and Arizona, providing almost every conceivable environmental opportunity for freshwater or saltwater fish-species to exploit to their full advantage. This creates a great swathe of corresponding angling opportunities on such a scale that holidays spent fishing and camping in the backwoods have long been a commonplace of the American way of life as holidays on the coast—and, more recently, on the shores of the Mediterranean—have been of the British.

Such a demand compels a supply: and there is nowhere in the world where so sophisticated a blend of modern comfort and primitive atmosphere can be found at the waterside, made, as it were, to measure. And signs reading "Keep out: fishing private" are not readily to be found in America. Apart from small lakes on private land immediately adjacent to private homes, the water and its inhabitants are the property of the community, managed expertly for the good of all by the community's public agencies. Fishing may not literally be "free", but it is available to all with a few dollars to invest in recreation. The US population is four times Britain's; but the space available for it is ten times greater.

Because of the way in which, traditionally, exchanges-rates and living costs have related, the USA has never in the past figured as a place where the adventurous British angler was likely to take a fishing holiday. All that, though, has now changed and it makes just as much sense, financially and otherwise, for an Englishman to holiday in **Tennessee**, fishing for large-mouth bass, or in **Minnesota** in search of *Esox masquinongy*, as for a Texan to come to Scotland to catch a Spey salmon. Going out from the **Florida Keys** in pursuit of marlin, sailfish or tarpon has for many years been a branch of the sport attracting a trickle of wealthy Britishers, but fishing American freshwaters has been a practice confined to angling writers and such, out to broaden their professional education.

Since it is the state geographically nearest to Britain, let us begin our review of the northern tier of states and their fishing with **Maine**, whose beaches offer the classical opportunity to contact the greatest of all saltwater sporting fish to be angled for feasibly from the shore anywhere, the striped bass. Though scarcer now than in years gone by, unfortunately, there are still fine specimens to be taken by the persistent specialist surf-caster. Offshore, there are cod and pollack, the bluefin tuna, some of these registering on the beam-scale weights of more than 500 lb.

Inland, there is a multitude of wilderness lakes and streams offering sport with small-mouth bass, brown and rainbow trout and the unique native of Eastern North America, the brook trout, actually a fine handsome member of the char family. Atlantic salmon which ran Maine's rivers by the ten thousand a hundred years ago suffered near-extermination, but are now being nursed back by conservation technology.

Moving west to the **Great Lakes**, thoughts turn back to another char, the "lake trout", a fish which grows to great size in deep and cold water throughout this latitude and in Canada. One fishes for them in hopes of a 40-pounder. An attempt to pass over without comment the damage done to some waters, the Great Lakes included, by the consequences of unthinking industrialisation would be dishonest, but remedy is now the order of the day. None has been more spectacular in its success than the stocking of **Lake Michigan** with coho salmon from the Pacific shore. Here, a new and tremendously exciting sport-fishery has been created, as it were, out of nothing, based on a food-supply left uncropped by lake trout no longer present in sufficient numbers to preserve a natural balance. Most see that as a net gain. The coho gives better sport than the "Mackinaw", as it is sometimes named farther north.

On to a state where water-area challenges land-space: Minnesota, as the North American Indian dialect-name implies, and the cream of the fishing for great northern pike (our pike), walleyes (resembling our zander) and the greatest lantern-jaw of them all *Esox masquinongy*, the muskellunge or "muskie". While these predators are distributed throughout the region, Minnesota is the heartland. Muskies there may grow to 80 lb weight and leap like trout when hooked.

Passing through a varied landscape, some of it watered by trout streams, we arrive eventually among the foothills of **the Rockies**, where the brilliantly-coloured dolly varden and cut-throat trout (the former another char, to be pedantic) and representatives of the five sub-species of the so-called "golden" trout join the ranks awaiting the angler's thinning, not to mention the sea-going rainbow trout, the steelhead. It was in the Rocky Mountain watershed that the rainbow, sedentary and sea-going, was first encountered and employed to provide the broodstock for the eventual artificial populating of the entire temperate world with this enormously successful species.

Over the mountains: the ocean: and the feeding grounds of the Pacific salmon, five species, of which two, the king or "Tyee" and the coho, are of sporting significance.

Going back East and starting again farther south, we traverse a band of warmer states, less favourable to the cold-water salmonids, but affording an ideal environment for pickerel (another pike-species) and for the small-mouth and large-mouth bass, the fish on which the romance of North American angling is largely founded. These big athletic cousins of the European perch (called there, incidentally, the "yellow perch") hit surface flies and lures with astonishing ferocity, fight like tigers when hooked and lie habitually in the shade and cover of the water-plant zone where only the most expert of tackle-handlers can present the offering and cope with the ensuing seizure without disaster. As the cooler uplands are again reached, the typical population of the upland waters is met again, and the pattern replicates.

Repeat the journey starting in **Georgia**, and one covers territory with a yet warmer climate, swamplands, and then an area of low rainfall. Traditionally, what fishing there was did not enjoy sporting prestige. The image was one of a poor coloured man employing crude tackle to harvest cheap protein; a typical quarry, the Mississippi catfish. One is south of that section of the lowland region where water-temperature falls low enough to permit salmonids to spawn successfully in natural waters.

But the water-demand for growing population growing also in affluence has necessitated the construction of chains of dams in the drier states; vast new sheets of deep water offering environments novel in their setting, with a variety of temperature regimes encouraging the successful introduction of some of the great sporting species found naturally to the north and west. Even **Arizona**—the "dry county" itself—now provides fine fishing for sport, and offers it in hot sunshine, a combination of pleasures not frequently encountered by the proverbially frozen-fingered angler acquiring lumbago from his water-logged nether end.

We have discussed none but the prime sporting species. They, however, are not the last word. US waters are inhabited also by others; carp, blue-gill sunfish, crappies and what-have-you, fish present in higher population densities and easier to catch, fish whose presence has traditionally ensured that the less expert members of the specialist angler's family on holiday may take their share of the pleasures and the triumphs. The travel business had now started international operations in this field and British anglers can expect a rapid growth in attractive opportunities.

FISHING IN EUROPE

AUSTRIA

Austria is understandably popular with anglers from all over the world, with its abundance of streams and lakes, providing first-class sport with brown and rainbow trout, grayling, char, and coarse fish such as pike and pike-perch, huck, sheat-fish and carp. Some of the main centres tend to be overfished, so a car is immensely valuable; many mountain streams of indescribable beauty are easily reached by road. Much of the sport is on the lower reaches of these mountain rivers, but the more venturesome can often find better fishing on the high alpine streams and lakes. Grayling are highly regarded, often more so than trout, the Traun being one of the best grayling rivers in Europe. Salza, Traisen, Erlauf and Ybbs are other recommended rivers.

To keep the sport at a high level, the authorities maintain strict conservation measures and a specially close watch is kept on pollution and abstraction. Generally speaking the rule is fly only for trout, grayling and char. Spinning is usually only permitted for larger fish such as lake trout, pike, huck, pike-perch, sheatfish and so on, and natural bait only for coarse fisheries. Many waters are controlled by the two principal fishing associations, the Austrian Fishing Association (ÖFG) and the Association of Austrian Workers' Fishing Clubs (VÖAFV). The former issues temporary permits for several trout preserves as well as daily ones costing up to 600 Austrian schillings. Temporary permission and information can be obtained from the association's office. The same applies to the VÖAFV. There is a provincial fishing association in Upper Austria which issues licences (*see below for addresses*).

Wherever he fishes, the visitor usually needs two permits, a general licence issued by the State and costing up to 240 Austrian schillings, according to the province—or a temporary fishing permit from the local owner costing up to 120 schillings for 4 weeks—and a private permit from the local owner which usually costs from 50–150 schillings a day, but may be as much as 600.

More information can be had from the Austrian National Tourist Office, 30 St George Street, London W1R 9FA (01-629 0461). Addresses of the main angling association are Österreichische Fischereigesellschaft, A-1010 Wien 1. Elisabethstrasse 22. Verband der Österreichischen Arbeiter-Fischerei-Vereine, A-1080, Wien VIII, Lenaugasse, 14. Landesfischereiverein (Provincial Fishing Assn), Postfach 185, A-4021, Linz.

BELGIUM

Although Belgium has never made a name for itself as a visiting fisherman's country, it has, in fact, in its many canals and rivers, most of the fish which British fishermen know, with sea fishing along its 40 miles of coast.

In general terms the freshwater fishing water can be divided thus: The Scheldt basin, with the rivers Scheldt, Lys, Rupel, Dyle, Demer, Dendre and Nethe holding bream, roach, perch, pike, burbot, smelt, shad and eels; the Meuse basin, with the rivers Meuse, Semois, Lesse, Sambre, Ourthe, Amblève, Warche and Vesdre holding trout, grayling, chub, barbel, perch, roach, bream, pike, carp, tench and eels; and the streams between the Sambre and the Meuse, holding trout, grayling, chub, perch, pike, roach, bream, carp, tench and eels. Many waters of the lowlands and near industrial centres suffer from pollution and over-fishing.

All Belgian waters fall into one of three categories; closed water, not subject to fishing laws; public, or navigable, water belonging to the State; preserved, or non-navigable water belonging to the landowners. Waters in the last two groups are subject to the fishing laws, and anyone fishing in them must possess a current licence. The cost varies from 30 francs to 500 francs, according to the type of fishing, number of rods used and the number of days' fishing to be done in a week. Trout fishermen should note, for example, that they will need a 500-franc licence to enter the water, in addition to any other permit necessary. Licences may be obtained at post offices. The close seasons are: Coarse fish, from the

Monday following the fourth Sunday of March until the second Sunday of June, with certain exceptions; trout, October 1 to fourth Sunday of March. Fly fishing falls off sharply on the Ardennes streams after June.

For visiting trout fishers the greatest attraction probably lies in the streams of the Ardennes, where many hotels have private fishing and there is a good deal of association water. These are mostly mixed fisheries on the lines of the Hampshire Avon in England, with trout and grayling predominating in the upper reaches and being increasingly joined by coarse fish on moving downstream. The best fishing will usually be found in the least accessible places. Standard British fly patterns will take fish on the Ardennes streams but the local flies should be tried where possible.

Sea fishing along the sandy, shelving coast is largely for dabs and plaice (Oct–June), flounders (all year) and sole (May–Oct), with piers and breakwaters providing sport with conger (all year), cod (Sept–Mar), and whiting (Oct–Jan). Turbot are occasionally taken (May–Sept) and rays, shad and garfish are also caught (Sept–Oct), Zeebrugge, Ostend, Niewpoort, Blakenbergh, and Knokke-Heist are good centres.

Belgian fishing legislation is extremely complex and anglers are strongly advised to consult the local tourist centres. For example, Namur province publishes a special angling brochure in French. Further detailed information (in English) from the Belgian National Tourist Office, 38 Dover Street, London W1X 3RB (01-499 5379) and, in Belgium itself, from the secretary of the Confédération des Sociétés de Pecheurs à la ligne, 1 Place Jean Jacobs, Brussels.

DENMARK

Fishing in Denmark is plentiful, varied and easy to come by. A few of the rivers hold salmon, and many of them sea trout, brown trout and grayling, as well as coarse fish, which are found also in many lakes.

In many places visitors can fish by purchasing tickets from the local fishing association. The association tickets are invariably cheap and available through local tourist bureaux.

The principal rivers are all in Jutland. They are Skjern Aa, Store Aa, Varde Aa, Ribe Aa and Karup Aa. All are game-fish waters, but of them the best salmon fishing is probably to be had on the Skjern and the best sea trout fishing on the Karup. The water is generally good for fly fishing, and the flies used are much the same as those used in this country. Spinning is much practised. Added variety is given by the sea trout fishing which can be had from the rocks and from boats off both the mainland and the various Baltic islands, by ordinary seafishing for cod, coalfish, flatfish, tope, mackerel, garfish, whiting, ling and pollack. Salmon and sea trout fishing in fresh water is best from mid-July to the end of October.

The coarse fishing potential is considerable and relatively unexplored. Many lakes are hardly ever fished and could hold some surprises, notably for the carp fisherman.

Further information about both fishing and accommodation can be had from the Danish Tourist Board, Sceptre House, 169–173 Regent Street, London, W1R 8PY (01-734 2637/8).

FINLAND

Finland can offer the angler no fewer than 62,000 lakes and rivers, and some 3,000 miles of sea-shore and archipelago. In the north and centre of the country he can catch very big fish on very big, remote waters; conditions which, in Europe at any rate, are becoming increasingly harder to find. The long days of midsummer give plenty of fishing time—the best sport in fact is often enjoyed in the brief twilight which elsewhere is called "night". In the South and in the archipelago area the best fishing periods are spring and autumn.

Salmon, sea trout, brown trout and brook trout all run well above the European average, and the size of grayling, too, is often remarkable; four-pounders are not rare. There are also arctic char (*Salvelinus alpinus*) which in the right conditions will take a fly.

The cream of the sport is to be found in Lapland, though there are individual waters farther south which can match them in quality. Some of the best game fishing in Europe is to be found in the region north of Lake Inari, and especially the rivers emptying into the lake. A very good possibility is the lake itself, holding taimen, very big grayling and brown trout to 20 lbs and more. Best fished for during their migratory runs up the tributaries in late summer.

The salmon fishing, however, is not what it was. Hydro-electric schemes have ruined the runs in many famous waterways. Salmon rivers are, however, recovering and several of them can be offered for salmon and sea trout fishing—the Kiiminki, the Simo, the Lesti, and the Torne which Finland shares with Sweden.

There are problems, too, for the fly fisherman. Many rivers are so wide, deep and fast-flowing that comfortable fishing from the bank is out of the question; it is often impossible to reach the salmon and sea trout lies, in fact. Hence on great rivers like the Teno and Näätämö which flow along the frontier with Norway, the fishing is mainly from a boat with an outboard motor from which large flies are cast by short but stout rods over enormous pools and streams—a technique known as "harling". Reels carrying 250 yards of line of up to 1 mm thick and over 40 lb breaking strain are employed.

These rivers, incidentally, are subject to special rules, involving the purchase of a permit from both countries in those parts through which the common national frontier passes. They are heavily poached. The spring fishing is usually best.

Another problem is transport—many of the best waters are "off the beaten track" and although there are excellent air services between the main centres, after that the angler is on his own and must be prepared for a good deal of foot-slogging and camping. A car, with a fibreglass boat strapped to the roof, is a valid alternative where the roads are not too bad.

The Finnish coast with its large archipelago, not to mention the Aland Islands, offers very good prospects for trout, pike, and perch-fishers. Even the immediate surroundings of big cities should not be ignored. As to the catch—the sea area is best.

Some very good coarse fishing is to be found in the south, notably for pike and perch and pike-perch—not, as many believe, a hybrid, but a separate species. Opportunities for the fly fisherman in the south have been extended in recent years by the stocking of ponds with rainbow, brown and brook trout.

Fishing regulations are strict and strictly enforced—there are game wardens even in remote districts. A licence is required. Then a period permit must be bought. They can be bought at state tourist hotels, foresters' offices and camping grounds.

Close seasons: salmon and trout, Sept 10–Nov 16; pike-perch, June; grayling, April and May.

One important accessory for the angler is some form of repellant to ward off mosquito attacks, which can often be unbearable—some Finnish fishermen wear head-nets.

Further information may be had from a useful booklet called *Sports Fishing in Finland* published by the Finnish Tourist Board and "Welcome to Fish", published by the National Board of Forestry and available free from tourist offices. These offices will also help in other ways, or the Finland Travel Bureau, Kaivokatu 10A, 00100 Helsinki can be approached.

FRANCE

Excellent sport with trout and some salmon fishing are available at reasonable cost in this country. French waterways are divided into the navigable public rivers, where fishing rights are owned by the State, and private rivers, where they belong to the riparian owner, fishing association or local authority. Even on the public rivers, however, anglers must belong to an angling and fish-breeding association and pay a tax based on the method of fishing adopted. Most rivers of this type provide coarse fishing only. Trout and salmon rights will nearly always be privately held, but the visitor should have little difficulty in obtaining a permit. Information should be sought from the local club or tackle dealer.

Close seasons vary a great deal according to the locality, especially for salmon, and it is best to make local inquiries. A rough guide, however, would be: salmon, Oct 1 to Jan 10; trout and char, from last Tuesday in Sept to third Friday in Feb; coarse fish, from Tuesday following April 15 to Friday following June 15.

Perhaps the best salmon fishing in France is to be found on a small number of fast-flowing streams in the Western Pyrenees. The noted Gave d'Oloron is in this area. Oloron, Sauveterre and Navarrenx are good centres for this river. The Gave d'Aspe, which joins it at Oloron, and its tributary, the Lourdios, have provided good sport in recent years. They may be fished from Lurbe. At Peyrehorade the Gave d'Oloron is joined by the Gave de Pau, on which sport has also been improving, and Pau itself makes a fine place to stay. Salmon also run up the Gaves d'Ossau and de Nive.

Because of melting snow, the season begins later here than elsewhere in France, but it extends later, too. For the Oloron area the best months are from June to the end of August.

Brittany, too, provides some opportunities for the salmon fisherman, though the fish are on the small side, especially on the River Aulne, which flows into the sea near Brest. Try the Châteaulinn area until April and Chateauneuf-du-Faou later on. Châteaulinn is also a good centre for the Ell'le and from Landerneau and Landivisiau the Ellorn may be fished. Other productive streams are the Blavet, Laita and Odet, which flow into the Atlantic; the Trieux and its tributary the Leff, with Guingamp a suitable venue.

Flowing northwards through picturesque countryside to feed the Loire, the Allier offers the best opportunities for salmon fishermen in Auvergne. This is a region comparatively unknown to British anglers. The place to make for is Brioude, on the upper reaches of the river. The Bajace dam, where salmon congregate before taking the leap, is half a mile away. Vichy, Pont-du-Chateau, Veyre and Issoire are other centres. The upper reaches of the Loire itself can provide good sport. Roanne is a suitable place to stay.

Some of the Normandy rivers have good runs of fish, but the best of the fishing is hard to come by, being largely in the hands of syndicates. The visitor may find opportunities, however, on the Orne and Vire, the Sée, the Sienne and the Sélune, Pontfarcy, Quetteville, Avranches and Ducey are suggested centres.

France is a splendid country for the trout fisherman, with an abundance of well-stocked streams flowing through glorious scenery. He may find solitude and beauty not very far from Paris—in fact, on the upper reaches of the Seine and its tributary, the Ource. A little farther south lies Avallon, from which the Cure and its tributaries may be fished.

But the visitor will find the Pyrenees very hard to beat for trout. The Gave d'Ossau is one of the best of the many first-class streams in this area, offering particularly fine sport at the Fabrège dam. From Lurbe the Gave d'Aspe and its tributary, the Lourdios, may be fished, and excellent sport is available on the Gave d'Oloron above Pont-de-Dognen, the Nive above Itxassou, and the Gave de Pau upstream of Pont-de-Lescar.

In the fascinating and comparatively unexplored regions of Creuse, Haute-Vienne, Corrèze and Lot, are innumerable streams with torrential upper reaches holding fine trout. Downstream they become less tumultuous and wider until, in the Dordogne, they harbour a variety of coarse fish. Figeac is a good centre for the trout. Farther east lies the wild, mountainous region of Lozère, where grand and beautiful rivers like the Lot and its tributary, the Colagne, may be fished. The Bès and Truyère should also be tried.

Wherever one turns in France, it seems, there are trout to be caught. In the Savoy Alps are innumerable streams of quality, like the Isère and Doron, bear Albertville, and the Sierroz, Tillet and Chéron near Chatelard-en-Bauges, the Arvan and Arc, near Saint-Jean-de-Maurienne. Auvergne and the Dauphiny Alps are ideal for the explorer with a fly rod. Grenoble commands a number of valleys through which flow some noted trout streams.

Normandy has some trout fisheries of high repute, like the Risle, Eure, Charenton and Andelles, but they are strictly preserved for the most part. Fishing on the streams of Brittany is more easily obtainable. Quimper is an excellent centre for the large fish of the Odet and its tributaries. Trout abound throughout Finistère, notably in the Aulne tributaries.

The lake fisherman is also well catered for in France, with some splendid opportunities in the Pyrenees, especially near Luz-Saint-Sauveur, and in the Alps. Lakes Leman, Annecy and, farther south, Lauvitel and Besson are good for trout.

One cautionary note for the fly fisherman—many French rivers are so torrential and boulder-strewn that they cannot be fished with fly. It is as well to check with a club or tackle dealer in the area to avoid disappointment. Best months of the fly are generally May, June and Sept in the north and before April and in Sept in the south. British patterns do well in the north, but are not so good in the south.

Further details from the French Tourist Office, 178 Piccadilly, London W1V 0AL, who will supply literature on receipt of 50p in stamps.

FEDERAL REPUBLIC OF GERMANY

Bavaria and the Black Forest offer the best prospects for the trout fisherman. Although pollution and over-fishing are producing a decline in sport, Bavarian waters like the Wiesent, Pegnitz, Loisach, Isar, Ammer, Saalach and Salzach, to name only a few, still offer fishing of high quality amid beautiful surroundings. Brown and rainbow trout, as well as grayling, are widely distributed.

For anglers who like to fly-fish for trout and char from a boat, the Hintersee at Berchtesgaden is highly recommended—the char in particular are good, reaching weights of 6 lb and more.

In the Black Forest, streams like the Kinzig, Murg, Obere Wolf, Nagold and Bernbach provide good sport with trout and grayling. The best waters are usually fly-only.

The Harz mountain area, south-east of Hanover, is also well worth exploring—the Radau, fished from Bad Harzburg, is good. Trout are found, too, in some of the streams and lakes of the Rhineland-Palatinate, especially in the Eifel district, and in some parts of North Rhine-Westphalia and Lower Saxony.

Elswhere there is good coarse fishing. In Baden-Wuerttemberg (apart from the Black Forest) carp, bream, tench, whitebait, roach, barbel, pike, eels and trout can be had in the Neckar Valley, the Hohenloe district, the Swabian Forest area and elsewhere, including trout, pike and barbel fishing in the Danube. Other coarse-fishing areas are the Rhineland-Palatinate (Moselle, Ahr, Lahn), and most of Lower Saxony.

The angler will need a licence from the Landrats or Ordnungsamt (rural district council) or from the local police (Dm 10 to Dm 20) and a permit from the owner or lessee of the fishing. Many Hotels and clubs also have fishing rights. The principal seasons are as follows: river trout, Mar 2–Oct 9; sea trout, March 2–Oct 9; lake trout, Jan 1–Sept 30; river char, Jan 11–Oct 9; lake char, Jan 1–Oct 31; pike, May 1–Dec 31; pike-perch, July 1–Mar 31; huck, May 1 to last day of Feb. (The seasons vary slightly in the different Federal states.)

Intending visitors are advised to obtain a copy of *Deutscher Angelsportfuehrer* (Fishing in Germany) published by Graefe & Unzer-Verlag, Isabellastrasse 32, 8, Muenchen 13 in two volumes covering Southern Germany and Northern and Western Germany. This has English introductions.

Further information about fishing can be had from the German Anglers' Association D2,000 Hamburg 11, Venusberg 36 and the Verband Deutscher Sportfischer, Bahnhofstrasse 37, D6050, Offenbach/Main, and general tourist information (including some on fishing) from the German National Tourist Office, 61 Conduit Street, London WIR OEN (01-734 2600).

ICELAND

Much of the salmon fishing in Iceland is now controlled by the Salmon Fishing Society (Stangaveidifelagid), from whom permits may be obtained through the Iceland Tourist Information Bureau in London (address below). It is as well to inquire about fishing as early as possible, for the best rivers are booked well in advance of the opening of the season. Most of the rivers are well out in the country where hotels are scarce and facilities for the fisherman are limited, but many have adequately furnished fishing huts which are let with the river. Arrangements can be made for accommodation at the nearest farm.

The average weight of the Icelandic salmon is about 10 lb, though fish up to 30 lb are not infrequent and fish up to 40 lb have been landed. There are over fifty rivers frequented by salmon in Iceland, and about half of them are regarded as first-class. The annual catch of salmon fluctuates, but has been as high as 70,000 fish in recent years. In the south the rod-fishing season starts at the beginning of June and in other districts about the middle of June. The season last for about three months. Trout fishing lasts from April to Oct 1.

The great lake at Thingvellir is well stocked with trout, char, and two small fish known by the Icelanders as *murta* and *depla*. The latter two fish have not yet been clearly classified, but some experts think they are char at an early stage of development. The lake, which is called Thingvallavatn, is 30 miles from Reykjavik, and there is a hotel there. Near to the "northern capital" of Iceland, Akureyri, is Lake Myvatn, which is also stocked with trout and char. There are two hotels. Lakes in the interior provide excellent fishing for trout and char, but camping is necessary and transport facilities meagre.

Daily air services are operated by Icelandair. Travel within Iceland is mostly by air and bus services. Further tourist information may be obtained from the Iceland Tourist Information Bureau, 73 Grosvenor Street, London (01-499 9971).

ITALY

Fishing can be had in many parts of Italy, in rivers, mountain torrents and lakes, for trout, pike, perch, carp and several local varieties. Generally speaking, the trout fishing is in waters above the 1,800 ft contour, the close season being Oct 15 to Jan 15. Sport is often good though pollution has caused a sharp decline on many of the lowland lakes. A government rod-fishing license issued by the Provincial Administration is required. It costs about £1.50 and is valid for a year. Ninety per cent of Italian waters are managed by the Italian Sport Fishing Federation (FIPS). Membership costs £2 and is valid for a year. The Bolzano and Trentino districts and the Dolomites are good. Sea fishing is first class. Deep-'sea sport with tuna, albacore and swordfish has become increasingly popular, and so has underwater fishing. Further information can be had from the Italian State Tourist Department in London, 1 Princes Street, London W1 (01-408 1254), from the Federazione Italiana Pesca Sportiva, Viale Tiziano 70, Roma, or from the provincial tourist boards (their addresses may be obtained from the Tourist Dept in London).

LUXEMBOURG

Most of the rivers of Luxembourg are mixed fisheries holding trout and coarse fish, including pike, barbel, chub and tench. Much of the water is private, although visitors can obtain sport on various hotel lengths or on private water with the owner's permission. There is a fine reservoir at the head of the Sûre, heavily stocked with chub and carrying a good head of pike, some of them very large.

A licence is required in order to fish in the Grand Duchy. The legislatioan regulating the practice of fishing is very complex and visitors are advised to contact the "Administration des Eaux et Forêts", PO Box 144, Luxemburg, for up-to-date information.

Tackle can be purchased, and local information gained, from Maison Zeus-Beucher, 62 rue d'Anvers, Luxembourg Ville, GD Luexembourg. Further tourist information, including details of hotels with fishing, can be had from the Luxembourg National Tourist Office, 36/37 Piccadilly, London (01-434 2800).

NORWAY

Norway has acquired a world-wide reputation for its salmon and sea trout, which can be fished for in a superb setting of mountains and fjords, spectacular waterfalls and peaceful valleys. Beats on such renowned waters as the Tana, Alta, Laerdal, Driva and Surna, fetch very high prices and are in the hands of specialised agencies (inquire Hardy's of London and Sporting Services International). Excellent sport at more modest charges may be had from the many hotels with private stretches, especially in the north. The salmon season is from late May to Sept 5 (best in June and July) and the best sea trout fishing is to be had in August, although the season extends into Sept, the actual date varying in different districts.

Floating line fishing is becoming more widely practised, but it is more usual on the big rivers to employ heavy, fast-sinking lines and large flies, from size 3/0 upwards. Streamers and bucktails are popular for salmon, and sea-trout are often fished dry fly or nymph—in the clear waters the fish can often be seen and cast to.

Less well known, and much less expensive, is fishing for brown trout and char, which can be very good indeed. Countless streams and lakes well stocked with trout lie within easy reach of Oslo, while anglers prepared to travel further afield will be amply rewarded. Trout of 25 pounds and over have been caught on the Drammen, near Vikersund, and the Randselven, near Kistefoss, and Lake Mjösa, near Gjövik. Several fish of around this weight have fallen to fly.

Arctic char are mostly found in the deep and cold mountain lakes, where they can provide thrilling sport, though this is a difficult art. There are taxi flights to the lakes from the big towns. The brown trout season varies with altitude, the extremes being late May until mid-Sept. As several rivers have rather swift currents, strong tackle is recommended. Most fishing rights are owned privately, but there are vast areas of Crown land where good fishing may be enjoyed at no great cost. Any fisherman in Norway, in addition to the application fee, is required to take out a licence available from post offices. It covers the entire country for a year and costs Norwegian Kroner 30. Many hotels in the country have their own rivers and lakes for brown trout fishing, making no charge to guests.

Dry-fly fishing is very popular, especially in smaller lakes and tarns or slow rivers. Most suitable gear is a fly-rod of $9\frac{1}{2}$ft to $10\frac{1}{2}$ft, with a No. 7 line, which may be used anywhere at any time. Best flies are those in douce colours, such as March brown and Greenwell's Glory etc. For red char fishing, use stronger colours such as Red Cardinal, Butcher or Coachman, etc. The best all-round spinning lures are those with slow movements and in golden or red colours. For hooking, use Devon or Phantom lures, or artificial minnows. No gaff is required, but a large landing-net is desirable. Rubber boots or waders come in handy, practically everywhere. Foreign visitors bringing in their own tackle are required to have it disinfected due to disease abroad. Boats are available almost everywhere.

Intending visitors are advised to write to the Norwegian Tourist Board, 20 Pall Mall, London, who provide information. "Angling in Norway", £4 from BAS Overseas Publications, 48-50, Sheen Lane, London SW14 8LP, will be found helpful.

PORTUGAL

Salmon and trout are found mostly in the River Minho and its tributaries in the far north, but the lack of controls has diminished sport. Very good sea trout fishing may be enjoyed in the Minho estuary near Moledo and on the Lima near Viana do Castelo. The fish are usually taken on bait or spinner, but fly fishing should prove productive. The coarse fisherman, too, can find sport. All Portuguese rivers hold barbel, while those in the centre and south of the country hold good carp.

The close season for salmon and trout fishing is from Aug 1 to end Feb and for other species from March 15 to end July. Licences for visitors are not as a rule required.

The sea fishing is excellent. This is for many of the fish known to British fishermen in home waters, but in the south it includes game species such as swordfish, blue and white marlin, tunny, bonito and amberjack, as well as blue porbeagle, thresher and mako sharks. School tunny and meagre (the so-called salmon-bass) are also taken.

Many of the fish known to British fishermen reach heavier weights in Portuguese waters. Bass of around 20lb are reported to be taken inshore from boats, for instance, and smaller fish of 10 lb–14 lb from the shore. Large shoals of mackerel up to 6 lb were found by a British team fishing off Peniche in 1956. Good shore fishing for bass can be had more or less everywhere. Other fish regularly caught include: mullet (to 5 lb), conger and dogfish, various types of bream, some running up to 25 lb; pollack, cod, turbot, rock gurnard, wrasse, John Dory, tope and several others. Meagre attain weights up to 90 lb, amberjack to 18 lb, and school tunny to 80 lb. The comparatively recent discovery of this vast potential has led to a rapid development of a number of small fishing ports. Boats and boatmen are available at most of them, and hotel accommodation is reported to be good. Most important of the new-found fishing centres is perhaps Sesimbra, south of Lisbon. Others are Praia da Rocha (for Portimao) and Faro in the south, Cascais (near Estoril), Peniche, Nazaré, and Ericeira (all to the north-west of Lisbon) and Sines (south of Sesimbra). Apart from the fishing, most of these places have good beaches and are good holiday and tourist centres. Boats are available at many places, including Albufeira, Lagos and Monte Gordo.

Visiting anglers will be made welcome at such clubs as the "Clube dos Amadores de Pesca de Portugal", Rua do Salitre 175R/CD, Lisbon Tel: 684805 (for all kinds of angling, especially big game fishing), "Clube Invicta de Pesca Desportiva" at Rua 31 de Janeiro 85-10, Tel: 321557, and the "Amadores de Pesca Reunidos", at Largo des Loios, X79-20, Tel: 324501, both Oporto, where information on local fishing may be obtained and where all visitors will be treated as honorary members. In the Algarve, several hotels provide or can arrange sea fishing parties. They include the Hotels Praia, Algarve and de Baleeira. The best centres in this region are in the Sagres and Cabo Carroeiro areas where large mackerel are frequently taken. Details can be had from Portuguese Airways (TAP-AIR

PORTUGAL), 19 Lower Regent Street, London, who publish an information booklet *Guide to Fishing in Portugal*, or from the Portuguese National Tourist Office, 1/5 New Bond Street, London W1Y 0NP.

SPAIN

Spain is a well-endowed country, offering the most southerly fishing for Atlantic salmon in Europe; brown and rainbow trout, coarse fish including large carp and barbel, both in rivers, and shore fishing for sea bass, mackerel, mullet, conger and other species. Black bass, pike and Danube salmon are among comparatively recent introductions.

Twenty-six rivers draining the Cantabrian range and the Galician Coast are entered by salmon. The Deva-Cares, Navia, Sella, Narcea, and Asón provide the best sport. Arrangements for licences and permits for visitors are not uniform and the British angler contemplating salmon fishing in Spain is advised to contact the Spanish National Tourist Office, 57/58 St James Street, London SW1A 1LD (tel: 01-499 0901). Much the same is to be said of the trout fishing, applying equally to seasons and permitted methods. In some areas, trout grow impressively large. Spain has not yet become as notable for high-grade coarse fishing as it may at some future date, but few who have connected with large carp or barbel in a deep, fast-flowing Spanish river do not cherish ambitions to renew the experience.

The tourist office publishes an interesting full-colour booklet on fishing in the country.

SWEDEN

Sweden cannot be compared with Norway for salmon, but there are splendid opportunities for sea trout, fish of well over 20 lb having been caught on the rod. The country is rich in brown trout waters and well supplied with char and grayling.

The game fisherman will be advised to go north for his sport, where swift and powerful waterways hold some really heavy trout and up which migratory fish run in fair numbers from mid-July onwards; rivers like the Torne älv, Kalix älv and Vindeläven, so far untouched by hydro-electric schemes which have marred sport in so many other Swedish waters.

For the fly fisherman, however, such awe-inspiring torrents present special difficulties. They are too wide, deep and fast-flowing to be fished effectively from the bank, except perhaps for sea trout which swim closer to the shore than salmon but which are not too plentiful in these northern parts. The most productive angling technique is harling— casting large flies into vast pools from a boat equipped with an outboard motor. Quite a few salmon, however, taken on spinning lures, especially where rock ledges can be found to command the pools.

Many once-famous salmon rivers are hardly worth fishing nowadays, notably the Mörrun in Blekinge Province, where the National Board of Crown Forests and Lands (Domänverket) still issues permits for fishing over a 3m stretch. This used to be the best salmon river in the country, but the spring fishing is now chiefly for sea trout kelts and there are relatively few fresh-run fish later on. The Em, Ätran and Örekil are other salmon streams which provide somewhat indifferent sport, though the Em is good for sea trout.

Farther north, in central Sweden, the position on the Dalälven is not much better, but the river still has a fair run of large fish from midsummer to late autumn; harling is again the most effective way of taking them.

If the present situation in regard to salmon fishing is far from favourable, the outlook is somewhat brighter. The Swedes are engaged in a massive restocking programme with smolts which is already bringing results, and a determined drive against pollution has resulted in salmon once again being caught in the centre of Stockholm.

Most of the fishing for sea trout is with the dry fly, as the wet fly will rarely take fish by day. Hackled coch-y-bondhu patterns are commonly employed. Of course in the north "night" fishing is something of a misnomer as it never really gets dark.

There are some very big trout to be caught in the large rivers and lakes of the north—fish of 20 lb and more—and trout also run to a respectable size in the lowland streams. The grayling, too, are not to be despised. It will interest anglers to learn that they can be caught in the sea along the Baltic coast, using small dry flies and keeping well out of sight as grayling in the sea tend to be shy.

Sport with arctic char is confined mainly to the deep cold lakes. It can be exciting at times, but nearly always difficult. Char are best taken on wet fly from the shallows where a stream enters a lake.

Many of the best fishing areas are away from roads and habitation, but the angler who takes a tent with him and is used to mountainous terrain has every chance of success.

There is no stream fishing in the Stockholm region but there is an increasing amount of sport with rainbow, brown and brook trout in artificially stocked lakes.

Pike, perch and carp abound in these lowland lakes and the City of Stockholm issues a card at a modest charge which is valid for several places in Lake Mälaren and in the archipelago.

For salmon and trout fishing, licence charges vary considerably; charges for trout fishing in stocked lakes and ponds are somewhat higher than for natural waters. No charge is made to fish for grayling in the sea.

Close seasons vary widely. For salmon and sea trout it usually runs from Sept 1 to Jan 1, though fishing is prohibited in some waters after Aug 15.

Further and more detailed information can be had from the year book published by Fiskefrämjandet (Association for the Promotion of Sport Fishing), Brunkebergstorg 11, Stockholm, which lists about 1,800 fishing waters. The association cannot, however, answer detailed inquiries from abroad. These should be directed to the Swedish National Tourist Office, 3 Cork Street, London W1X 1HA or to The Fishery Board, Box 2565, S-403 10, Göteborg 1, or DomanTurist AB, Box 521, S-182 15 Danderyd.

SWITZERLAND

There is no shortage of water in Switzerland—20,000 miles of rivers and streams, and 520 square miles of lakes within a small area—and as most of these waters hold trout, the country is a fly-fisherman's dream.

Unfortunately, the dream is often of brief duration, as the streams at appreciable altitudes are in snow spate often until July. But in the lower valleys there is sport to be had from May to the end of the summer. Lake fishing consists mainly in trolling at great depth. Swiss waters may be classed as follows:

The Lakes. Most of the lakes contain trout and char, pike, perch and other coarse fish. The trout and char (*Ombre chevalier*) run to a great size, but they lie at such depths that fly fishing or trolling with a rod is practically useless. Most of the lakes in the central plain are now suffering to some degree from pollution, but they still provide sport. Best results are obtained by spinning with light tackle.

The Great Rivers. Both the Rhine and Rhône hold very big trout. Spinning with a $2\frac{1}{4}$ in silver Devon is the best method, though a small silver-bodied salmon fly will sometimes give good results. The Rhône, above the lake of Geneva, is fishable only till the middle of April. In summer months it is thick with snow water. Many Swiss rivers contain good stocks of coarse fish, including barbel, carp and pike.

Plain and Lower Valley Streams. Trout in these streams run from $\frac{1}{4}$ lb to $2\frac{1}{2}$ lb or more. There is always a good hatch of fly, and the Mayfly is up on most of them from May to July. Wading is not as a rule necessary. Fine tackle is essential. Carry a couple of small silver Devons for thick water.

The Hill Torrents. Trout run four or five to the pound in the best of the hill torrents, rather smaller in the others. As the hatch of fly is usually poor, the upstream worm pays best. The coch-y-bondhu is sometimes useful, while in July and Aug the "daddy-longlegs" is deadly. Wading is usually an advantage. Watch for the spate that often occurs towards midday owing to melting snow.

It should be said that Switzerland, in common with most European countries, is experiencing a growth of angling pressures, but the authorities, concerned to ensure that sport remains at a high level, release at least 100 million fish, mostly trout, from hatcheries every year.

The close season for trout runs most commonly from Oct 1 to Mar 15, and for grayling from Mar 1 to April 30.

Fishing regulations vary. Generally speaking the angler will require a canton licence and may also need a permit for private waters. Further information is obtainable from the local Tourist Offices in the area to be visited. General tourist information can be had from the Swiss National Tourist Office, Swiss Centre, New Coventry Street, London W1V 8EE (01-734 1921).

YUGOSLAVIA

Here is a country well worth exploring by the angler. The rivers are often difficult to reach, but offer sport of the highest quality. Even the more accessible places, sport with trout (brook and rainbow) and grayling is often very good indeed.

Some streams are too torrential for the fly, but many rivers and lakes provide excellent fly fishing. Sport is carefully supervised. Each province, or people's republic, has its own federation of fishing societies which encourages fishing as a sport and protects and restocks the waters.

Mostly the rivers are clear and fast-flowing direct or indirect tributaries of the Danube. There are 25 species of game fish out of a total of 198 all told in Yugoslav waters. Besides brook and rainbow trout there are large river char and marble trout. Among coarse fish, the pike-perch of the Danube basin is a big attraction. In the lakes trout run large and some lakes contain pike, carp and eels. Fishing throughout the country is by district licence, annual, weekly and daily, obtainable from fishery controllers, tourist offices and many of the hotels. There are also restrictions on methods and bags, varying in some instances from district to district.

In Croatia visitors staying in Dubrovnik can easily make one-day fishing expeditions, reaching the river after a drive of only thirty minutes. In Zagreb the Croatian Federation can provide expert guides, linguists as well as fishermen, and tackle. Bosnia and Herzogovina, however, probably form the most interesting fishing region, the best season for brook trout being May and June and from late Sept to the first frosts, while rainbows give best sport then onwards to Feb. The Drina river and tributaries form a splendid and extensive fishery, containing large huck, trout and grayling. Slovenia also affords good sport likely to appeal to British fishermen. There the season is May 1 to Sept 15.

Further detailed information can be had from Sport Fishing Federation of Yugoslavia, Slobodana Penezića Krcuna 35/V, 11000 Belgrade, or through the Yugoslav National Tourist Office, 143 Regent Street, London W1R 8AE (01-734 5243), who issue an excellent English language booklet containing all the necessary detailed information and a directory of suitable hotels.

A memorable $4\frac{1}{2}$ lb brown trout taken on a black wet fly $2\frac{1}{2}$" long, from a tributary of the Danube. Stomach contents included a 6" rainbow trout and a half-digested mole. *Photograph: Cori Gebhart.*

NOTABLE BRITISH AND IRISH FISH, INCLUDING THE OFFICIAL RECORDS

UNTIL the British Record (Rod Caught) Fish Committee was set up in 1957, there was no recognised method of establishing a list of record fish. Such lists as did exist were based largely on data culled from books, the angling press and so on. Clearly, many of the claims were suspect, as the committee found when it examined the lists it had inherited and, as a result, discarded many so-called "records". Four species are still open for initial claims—the sandy ray (*Raja circularis*) the pollan (*Coregonus pollan*), Vendace (*Coregonus vandesius*) and the silver bream (*Blicca bjoerkna*). The qualifying weights are 2 lbs, zero, zero, and 1 lb. As common bream are often slow to acquire the bronze colour characteristic of maturity in this species, anglers should be cautious in entering claims for *Blicca Bjoerkna*.

Fisherman catching fish equal to or greater in weight than the established record should claim recognition of the fish through Peter Tombleson, Secretary, British Record (Rod-caught) Fish Committee, now under the aegis of the National Anglers' Council, 11 Cowgate, Peterborough PE1 1LR (54084) and Peakirk, Peterborough (Glinton 428). A claim should be made as soon as possible after the capture of the fish, preferably by telegram or telephone, and a confirmatory letter should give full details of the catch (date, time, tackle, etc) and the names and addresses of two independent and reliable witnesses capable of identifying the fish, which should be retained for inspection, dead or alive, by the committee or its representative. Fish should not be weighed on spring balances, but on a steel-yard or scales which can be tested if necessary.

The committee is always pleased to receive similar details of any unusual catches. Only fish in the coastal waters of England (including the Channel Islands and the Isle of Man), Scotland, Wales and Northern Ireland are eligible. Fish caught in the Irish Republic should be reported to the Secretary, Irish Specimen Fish Committee, Balnagowan, Mobhi Boreen, Glasnevin, Dublin 9.

Fish marked * in the following lists are those recognised by the BRFC after very careful examination of all the relevant factors, as the official record for the species.

Irish records, that is, those recognised by the Irish Specimen Fish Committee—are indicated thus † in the following lists. **Note:** *The Irish keep separate records for rivers and lakes in respect of pike and brown trout.*

The other notable catches recorded here—ie those apart from the established records— are included for interest only and, because they have not been subjected to such rigorous scrutiny, should not be viewed as beyond question. Further data on any of these fish would be welcome.

Official British Records are as updated at the meeting of the Committee 20/7/87.

FRESHWATER FISH

BARBEL (*Barbus barbus*, Linn)
16 lb 1 oz C H Cassey, while spinning for salmon in the Hampshire Avon at Ibsley on March 6, 1960. Fish was foulhooked and therefore disallowed as a record.
14 lb 6 oz T Wheeler, Thames at Molesey in 1888.
14 lb 6 oz H D Tryon, Hampshire Avon (Royalty Fishery), Sept, 1934.
14 lb 6 oz F W Wallis, Royalty Fishery, Sept 1937. The same angler had another of 14 lb 4 oz from the Royalty in Sept, 1933.
14 lb 4 oz R Jones, Thames at Radcot Bridge in 1909.
14 lb 2 oz P Reading, from a Wessex river, Aug, 1987.
14 lb 1 oz G Buxton, from a Wessex river, Sept, 1984.
14 lb E A Edwards, River Kennet, 1954.
14 lb Mr Simmons, Dorset Stour, Sept, 1930.

13 lb 14 oz C A Taylor, Hampshire Avon, Oct, 1934.
13 lb 14 oz P Mays, Troop Fishery, Dorset Stour, Oct, 1964.
13 lb 12 oz* J Day, Royalty Fishery, Oct, 1962.
13 lb 8 oz J Ginifer, Thames, Sept, 1968.
13 lb 2 oz J Harrigan, Royalty Fishery, Nov, 1965.
13 lb 2 oz E Upton, Royalty Fishery, Oct, 1970.

BLEAK *(Alburnus alburnus*, Linn)
$5\frac{1}{4}$ oz Henry Stubbins, Nottingham, at Radcliffe-on-Trent, about 1890. Recorded by H Coxon in his *Coarse Fish Angling*, 1896.
$4\frac{1}{4}$ oz* B. Derrington, R, Monnow, Oct, 1982.
4 oz 2 dm F Brown on Trent at Long Higgin, 1959.
3 oz 15 dm D Pollard, Staythorpe Pond nr Newark, Aug, 1971.
3 oz 8 dm N D Sizmur, Thames at Walton, Surrey, 1963.

BREAM (COMMON) *(Abramis bramna*, Linn)
16 lb 6 oz* A Bromley, from a Staffordshire mere, Aug, 1986.
15 lb 10 oz J Knowles, Queensford lagoon, July 1985.
(Part of a bag including other bream of 14 lb 14 oz, 13 lb 11 oz and 13 lb 2 oz, caught during two days.)
15 lb 6 oz A Nicholson, Queensford lagoon, Sep, 1984.
13 lb 14 oz C Dean, Oxford gravel pit, 1983.
13 lb 12 oz A Smith, Oxford gravel pit, Aug, 1983.
13 lb 9 oz M C Davison, Beeston Lake, Wroxham, Norfolk, July, 1982.
13 lb 8 oz A R Heslop, private water, Staffs, 1977.
13 lb 8 oz E G Costin, Chiddingstone Castle Lake, in Oct, 1945.
13 lb R Willis, Duchess Lake, Bristol, Sept, 1949.
12 lb 15 oz F T Bench, Tring Reservoirs, Oct, 1945.
12 lb 14 oz G J Harper, Suffolk Stour, July, 1971.
12 lb 14 oz Caught by one of two brothers (Messrs Pugh), Tring Reservoirs, on July 28, 1933. They had two other bream, 12 lb and $10\frac{1}{2}$ lb, on same day.
12 lb $12\frac{1}{2}$ oz A J Fisher, July 30, 1931, Tring Reservoirs (thus beating an Irish fish of $11\frac{3}{4}$ lb, which had held the record for 49 years). Later that year Lord Rothschild reported a fish of 13 lb 10 oz found dying at Tring. Several other fish of 12 lb and over have been taken from Tring.
11 lb 12 oz W Gollins, Ellesmere (Salop), 1970.
11 lb 12 oz† A Pike, River Blackwater (Co Monaghan), 1882.

BREAM (SILVER) *(Blicca bjoernka*, Linn)
4 lb 8 oz C R Rhind from Tortworth Lake, Gloucestershire, in 1923.
4 lb 4 oz K Armstrong, lake at Rugeley, Staffs, Jan, 1970.
4 lb Two fish of this weight were caught by J Bowater from Yorkshire Derwent in July, 1933.
4 lb G Burwash from Thames at Egham in Feb. 1922.
4 lb J Bowater, Yorkshire Derwent, July, 1933.
3 lb $7\frac{1}{2}$ oz A Engers from Plucks Gutter (Stour, Kent), July, 1949.

CARP *(Cyprinus carpio*, Linn)
51 lb 8 oz C Yates, Redmire Pool, Herefordshire, 16/6/80.
45 lb 12 oz R Macdonald, Yateley, summer 1984.
44 lb* Richard Walker on Sept 13, 1952, Redmire Pool, Herefordshire. The best of many huge carp from Redmire. "Dick" Walker himself had another of 31 lb 4 oz in June, 1954.
42 lb R Clay, Billing Aquadrome, Sept, 1966.
40 lb 8 oz E G Price, Redmire Pool, Sept 27, 1959. King carp.
40 lb $0\frac{1}{2}$ oz R Groombridge from a lake at Hemel Hempstead, July, 1956.
38 lb $8\frac{1}{2}$ oz R Bowskill, Redmire Pool, Sept, 1966.
37 lb 8 oz J Sims, Wyver Pool at Belper, Derbys, July, 1968.
37 lb 4 oz D Stanley, W Sedgemoor Drain, Oct, 1986.

36 lb 4 oz W Quinlan, Redmire Pool, Oct, 1970.
35 lb J Hilton, Redmire Pool, Oct, 1967.
34 lb 8 oz J Ward, pond near Wokingham, Berkshire, July 28, 1959.
34 lb 4 oz W Beta, Electricity Cut, River Nene at Peterborough, June, 1965. Thought to be the "record" river carp. The Electricity Cut has produced several big carp—one of 33 lb 12 oz was taken by P Harvey in Jan, 1965.
34 lb P Chillingworth, Billing Aquadrome, June, 1970.
    Fish of over 30 lb (some of them more than 40 lbs) have also come from the Ashlea Pool, Gloucester (two), Waveney Valley Lakes, the Layer Pits, near Colchester and from lakes and ponds in the home counties. Biggest catch of carp is thought to have been taken by Bob Reynolds from Billing Aquadrome. In August, 1957 he took carp of 26 lb 1 oz, 27 lb 9 oz, 27 lb 13 oz, and 28 lb 4 oz, making 109 lb 11 oz in all. The record Irish carp is a fish of 18 lb 12 oz taken by J Roberts from Abbey lake in 1958.

CARP (CRUCIAN) (*Carassius carassius*, Linn)
5 lb $10\frac{1}{2}$ oz* G Halls, King's Lynn lake, June, 1976.
4 lb $15\frac{1}{2}$ oz J Johnstone, Johnson's Lake, New Hythe, Kent, June, 1972.
4 lb 11 oz H C Hinson, Broadwater Lake, Godalming, 1938.
4 lb 10 oz M Benwell, Notts gravel pit, July, 1971.
4 lb $9\frac{1}{2}$ oz, B Cole, Kent lake, Sept, 1971.
4 lb 8 oz F J Axten, Bedfont Lake, July, 1964.
4 lb 8 oz B Burman, Shoebury Park Lake, Sept, 1971.
4 lb $7\frac{1}{2}$ oz A Palfrey, South Ockendon pit, 1962.
4 lb $7\frac{1}{2}$ oz F James, Leighton Buzzard pit, June, 1965.
4 lb $7\frac{1}{2}$ oz A Donison, Guildford lake, Aug, 1968.
4 lb $6\frac{1}{2}$ oz G Bott, Godalming lake, March, 1966.

CHARR (*Salvelinus alpinus*)
4 lb 13 oz* P Savage, Loch Garry, May 1987.
3 lb 5oz A Robertson, Loch Earn, 1985.
3 lb 4 oz S C Rex, Knoydart Dubhlochan, Oct, 1982.
1 lb 12 oz M C Imperiale, Loch Insh, Inverness, May, 1974.
1 lb 11 oz B A Richardson, Lake Windermere, April, 1973.
1 lb 9 oz A Stein, Lake Windermere, March, 1973.

CARP, GRASS (*Ctenopharyngodon idella*)
16 lb* K Crow, from lake near Canterbury, July 1986.
9 lb 12 oz G A Gwilt, Trawsfynydd Lake, June, 1983.

CHUB (*Squalius cephalus*, Linn)
10 lb 8 oz Dr J A Cameron from the Annan in 1955.
8 lb 14 oz Caught out of season on the Wissey by J Roberts in May, 1960, while spinning for trout.
8 lb 12 oz J Lewis, River Mole, Oct, 1964.
8 lb 8 oz D Deeks from Sussex Rother, July, 1951.
8 lb 4 oz G F Smith from Avon at Christchurch, Dec, 1913.
8 lb C Harmell, Royalty Fishery, Aug, 1964.
7 lb 15 oz P Minton, Yorkshire Ouse, Oct, 1964.
7 lb $14\frac{1}{2}$ oz Mrs H M Jones, from Stour at Canford (Dorset) in Sept, 1937.
7 lb 6 oz* W Warren, Hampshire Avon, 1957.

DACE (*Leuciscus leuciscus*, Linn)
1 lb $8\frac{3}{4}$ oz S Horsfield, Derbyshire, Derwent, Jan, 1947.
1 lb 8 oz R W Humphrey, from tributary of Hampshire Avon, Sept, 1932.
1 lb $7\frac{3}{4}$ oz J S Upton, from the Penk, Dec, 1933.
1 lb $7\frac{1}{2}$ oz F W Arnold, River Mole, Jan, 1934.
1 lb $7\frac{1}{2}$ oz S Rolfe, Suffolk Stour, Feb, 1962.
1 lb 7 oz Abe Hibbard, near Sheffield, Feb, 1934.
1 lb 5 oz 2 dm S Wilson, Llynfi, July, 1966.

1 lb 5 oz R Walker, Cam, July, 1938.
1 lb 5 oz J Cartwright, Cynon, 1965.
1 lb $4\frac{1}{2}$ oz* J L Gasson, Little Ouse, Thetford, Feb, 1960.
1 lb 2 oz† J T Henry, River Blackwater, (Cappoquin), 1966.

EEL (*Anguilla anguilla*, Linn)
11 lb 2oz* S Terry, Kingfisher Lake, Hants, 1978.
8 lb 10 oz A Dart, Hunstrete Lake, July, 1969.
8 lb 8 oz C Mitchell, Bitterwell Lake in 1922. An eel of equal weight was taken from a trap on the Warwickshire Avon in Aug, 1960.
8 lb 4 oz J McFarlane, River Tees, 1964.
8 lb 4 oz J Taylor from pond at Arlesey, Bedfordshire, in July, 1958.
8 lb R Jones, Monmouthshire lake, May, 1968. Mr Jones had another from the same lake of 7 lb 8 oz.
8 lb M Bowles, Weirwood Reservoir, June 1986.
7 lb 15 oz P Climo, Monmouthshire lake, May, 1969.
7 lb 13 oz, M Hill, Arlesey Lake, Beds, Aug, 1970.
7 lb $5\frac{1}{4}$ oz B Young, Pluck Pond, Swansea, Aug, 1970.
7 ln 1 oz D Holwill, River Wallington, Fareham, Oct, 1968.
7 lb W F Simmons from Dorset Stour at Christchurch in 1931.
An interesting catch was made by R Smith (13) and W Bush (14) from Hollows Pond, Whipps Cross, London, in Sept, 1958, when an eel weighing 6 lb 8 oz took both boys' baits.

GOLDEN ORFE (*Leusiscus idus*)
5 lb 6 oz M Foot, River Slea, Hants, 1978.
4 lb 12 oz* J Moran, Burton Towers, N Wales, June 1986.
4 lb $3\frac{1}{2}$ oz D R Charles, River Kennet, Aug, 1983.
4 lb 3 oz B T Mills, R Test, Jan, 1976.

GRAYLING (*Thymallus thymallus*, Linn)
7 lb 2 oz From River Melgum by J Stewart, July, 1949. The fish is believed to be somewhat legendary and was eliminated as a record by the British Record Fish Committee in 1968.
4 lb 8 oz Dr T Sanctuary on the Wylye at Bemerton in 1885. A fish of 4 lb 12 oz was netted from the Avon at Longford by G S Marryat and Dr Sanctuary in the same year and returned to the water.
4 lb 4 oz G Bryant on the Itchen.
4 lb Three a fraction over this weight caught by H J Mordaunt and M Headlam on the Test (Oakley Stream) at Mottisfont on Boxing Day, 1905.
4 lb E Chambers, Chess, near Chorley Wood, Jan, 1955. Mr Chambers had another of 3 lb 13 oz on the same outing, making a remarkable brace.
3 lb 14 oz E J Stanton, Driffield Canal, Sept, 1967.
3 lb 12 oz J Wigram on the Test near Stockbridge, in 1873.
3 lb 12 oz J W Gieve from the Test in 1917.
3 lb 10 oz* I White, River Allen, Dorset, Aug, 1983.
2 lb 13 oz P B Goldsmith, R Test, 1981.
2 lb $9\frac{1}{4}$ oz D Hauxvell, R Teviot, Jan 12, 1980.

GUDGEON (*Gobio gobio*, Linn)
$4\frac{1}{4}$ oz* M J Bowen, pond at Ebbw Vale, Gwent, 1977.
$4\frac{1}{4}$ oz Geo Cedric from the Thames at Datchet in Aug, 1933.
$4\frac{1}{4}$ oz W R Bostock from Hogg's Pond, Shipley, near Derby, in Oct, 1935.
$4\frac{1}{4}$ oz J D Lewin from the Soar in 1950.
4 oz 1 dm Caught at Sudbury by O S Hurkett, Mar, 1950.

PERCH (*Perca fluviatilis*, Linn)
5 lb 15 oz 6 dm P Clark, Suffolk Stour, 1949.
5 lb $14\frac{1}{2}$ oz D Florey from Farlows Lake, Dec, 1953.

5 lb 12 oz E V Hodd from Diana Pond, Hampton Court, in Aug, 1957.
5 lb 9 oz* J Shayler from a private lake in Kent, 1985.
5 lb 8 oz† S Drum from Lough Erne, 1946.
5 lb $4\frac{3}{4}$ oz H Green from Stradsett Lake, Norfolk, on Nov 9, 1936.
5 lb 4 oz Caught at Sandford Mill, Woodley, Berks, by Wm Leach in 1873.
5 lb 4 oz K Gardner from a lake in Norfolk, July, 1970. Other fish of over 5 lb were reported from lakes in Worcester and Suffolk, and a pit in Colchester.
4 lb 12 oz S F Baker, Oulton Broad, 1962.

PIKE (*Esox lucius*, Linn)
53 lb Lough Conn in July, 1920, by John Garvin. This fish is entitled to rank as the premier pike landed in Great Britain and Ireland. Mr Garvin caught a 30-pounder on the same day. Bigger pike than this have been reported, including a fish of 72 lb from Loch Ken in 1774 and one of 60 lb found dying at Dowdeswell. One approaching the weight of Mr Garvin's fish 52 lb is said to have been recovered when Whittlesey Mere, Cambs, was drained in 1851.
48 lb Reported from Lough Corrib in 1905.
47 lb 11 oz T Morgan from Loch Lomond in July, 1945.
45 lb 8 oz Reported from Lough Conn, Ballina in 1917. In *The Fishing Gazette* of May 9, 1925, Bernard Brown, the captor, altered these details by giving the weight as 49 lb and the year as 1916.
44 lb 14 oz* M G Linton, Ardleigh Reservoir, Jan, 1987.
42 lb D Amies, River Thurne, Aug, 1985.
42 lb† M Watkins, River Barrow (spoon), 1964, Irish river record.
41 lb 8 oz From Foxborough, Tulsk, Ireland, by P J Mannion in June, 1922.
41 lb Mr Cawley from Lough Conn in Mar, 1918.
40 lb 8 oz From Lough Arrow. The fish was sent to *The Fishing Gazette* in 1900, together with another of 35 lb. These fish were caught on "set lines".
40 lb E Oulton from Lough Ramor in Nov, 1950.
40 lb Lough Erne by John H Thompson in 1922. Hooked while the angler was playing another and smaller pike.
40 lb P Hancock, Horsey Mere, Feb, 1967.
39 lb C Loveland, Knipton Reservoir, 1967.
38 lb 4 oz P Emmings, Cheshunt pit, Dec, 1969.
38 lb H Mumford Smith, Lough Conn, June 8, 1929.
38 lb H A Robinson on Lough Mask in 1905. Various fish from this weight up to 40 lb or more have been reported from Irish lakes, and there is little doubt that most of them have been authentic.
38 lb† P Earl, Lough Ree (minnow), 1967 (Irish lake record).
37 lb 8 oz C Warwick, Avon at Fordingbridge, Oct, 1944.

PIKE PERCH (Walleye) (*Stizostedion Vitreum*)
11 lb 12oz F Adams, The Delph, 1934.

PIKEPERCH (Zander) (*Stizostedion lucioperca*)
17 lb 4 oz* D Litton, Gt Ouse Relief Channel, 1977.
16 lb 6 oz S Smith, Cut-off Channel, Oct, 1976.
15 lb 5 oz W G Chillingworth, Gt Ouse Relief Channel, February 1971. This angler had another of 12 lb 13 oz from the Relief Channel, Feb, 1971.
12 lb 12 oz Neville Fickling, Relief Channel, October, 1979. (This angler had another of 12 lb $6\frac{1}{2}$ oz.) He had another of 12 lb $7\frac{1}{2}$ oz from the same water the previous August.
12 lb 5 oz Dr R B Rickards, Relief Channel, Feb, 1970.

ROACH (*Rutilus rutilus*, Linn)
4 lb 1 oz* R G Jones, Gravel Pits, Notts, 1975.
3 lb 14 oz W Penny, Metropolitan Water Board's Lambeth Reservoir at Molesey, Sept 6, 1938 (1 $18\frac{1}{2}$ in, g $12\frac{5}{8}$ in).
3 lb 14 oz A Brown, Oakham gravel pit near Stamford, Lincs, 1964.

3 lb 14 oz Caught out of season on fly by F I Hodgson while fishing for trout in a spring-fed Lancashire pond in May, 1960.
3 lb 10 oz W Cutting, Hornsea Mere, Yorkshire, in 1917. On the same day he had another 3-pounder.
3 lb 10 oz A Whittock from the Hampshire Avon, Jan, 1953.
3 lb $9\frac{3}{4}$ oz T G Player from the Thames at Sonning in June, 1949.
3 lb 9 oz J Osborn, River Thurne, July, 1962.
Staines Reservoir produced three roach, each weighing 3 lb 6 oz in the autumn of 1962 and 1964.

RUDD (*Scardinius erythrophthalmus*, Linn)
4 lb 1oz* D Webb, Pitsford Reservoir, Sep, 1986.
4 lb 8 oz The Rev E C Alston on a mere near Thetford, July, 1933. He had another of 3 lb 15 oz during the month.
4 lb 4 oz Caught at Blackheath by J F Green, 1888.
3 lb 15 oz W Clews, Moor Lane Fisheries (Staines), 1957.
3 lb 13 oz A Oldfield from a mill pool in Cheshire, 1960.
3 lb 13 oz W Tucker, from the Thames at Chertsey, Jan, 1962.
3 lb 12 oz D A Fisher, pond at Stanmore, July, 1959.
3 lb 12 oz L Lindsay, Landbeach Lake, 1962.
3 lb 12 oz K Palfrey, Bridgwater and Taunton Canal, 1963.
3 lb $10\frac{1}{2}$ oz E G Costin, Home Pond, Swanley, Oct, 1954.
3 lb 10 oz A Brogan, The Delph at Wisbech, July, 1935.
3 lb 10 oz Master D Denham, pit at Shepperton, July, 1954.
3 lb 1 oz† A E Biddlecombe, Kilglass Lake, on worm, 1963.

SALMON (*Salmo salar*, Linn)
69 lb 12 oz By the Earl of Home on Tweed about 1730. The "record" rod-caught salmon for the British Isles. This fish has been described as "somewhat legendary". In 1935, however, the Earl of Home sent a note giving evidence that the fish indeed existed.
67 lb On the Nith at Barjarg by Jock Wallace in 1812. Wallace, a well-known poacher, is said to have played the fish from 8 am to 6 pm.
64 lb* On the Tay (Glendelvine water) by Miss G W Ballantine on Oct 7, 1922. Hooked in the Boat Pool at 6.15 pm and landed half a mile below at 8.5 pm. The fish took a spinning bait, a dace. The biggest salmon caught by a lady. Length 54 in, girth $28\frac{1}{2}$ in. A cast of the fish was made and is at Glendelvine.
61 lb 8 oz On the Tay below Perth by T Stewart on the last day of the season, 1907, with a worm.It took an hour to land.
61 lb J Haggart on the Tay in 1870.
61 lb Mrs Morison on the Deverton on $1\frac{1}{4}$ in fly (the weight probably was more as the fish was not weighed until 24 hours after capture), Oct 21, 1924.
60 lb On the Eden by Lowther Bridger in 1888. Length 54 in, girth 27 in. Exhibited in the British Museum. It appears to be the biggest fish caught on fly in English rivers.
59 lb 8 oz On the Wye at Lower Winforton by Miss Doreen Dovey on Mar 12, 1923. This appears to be not only the record fish for the Wye, but also the biggest spring fish so far caught on a rod in Great Britain.
59 lb On the South Esk by J K Somerville in Oct, 1922. Length 53 in, girth 28 in.
58 lb Reported from the Shannon in 1872.
57 lb 8 oz On the Tweed (Floors water) in 1886 by Mr Pryor. This is usually accounted the biggest Tweed fish.
57 lb† From the Suir by M Maher in 1874. The record fish for Ireland.
57 lb On the Awe by Major A W Huntingdon on July 8, 1921. Length $52\frac{1}{2}$ in, girth $27\frac{1}{2}$ in.
56 lb From the Deveron on Oct 31, 1920, by Col A E Scott. The fish took a 1 in fly. Length 50 in, girth 29 in.
56 lb On the Dee, Ardoe Pool, by J Gordon in 1886.
56 lb From the Eden at Warwick Hall by G Mackenzie in 1892.
56 lb On the Awe (Pol Verie) on June 12, 1923, By H G Thornton. Took a 5/0 fly and fought from 1 pm till 3.30 pm.

SEA TROUT (*Salmo trutta*, Linn)
22 lb 8 oz S R Dwight, Dorset Frome, at 11 am, above the hatches at Bindon Mill, May 18, 1946.
21 lb The Rev A H Upcher, Bothie Pool on the Awe on June 30, 1908. The "record" Scottish sea trout.
21 lb Dorset Frome at Bindon in Mar, 1918, by R C Hardy, Corfe.
20 lb 2 oz* V R Townsend, River Esk, Yorks, Sep, 1986.
20 lb 2 oz T Williams, the Dovey, in June, 1935. The "record" Welsh sea trout.
20 lb G Leavy, River Tweed, Nov, 1983.
16 lb 12 oz T J McManus, Shimna River, Co. Down, N Ireland, Oct, 1983.

TENCH (*Tinca tinca*, Linn)
14 lb 3oz* P A Gooriah, Wraysbury No One, June 1987.
12 lb $8\frac{3}{4}$ oz A Wilson from Wilstone Reservoir, Tring, 1985.
10 lb 2 oz E Edwards, undisclosed private water, 1983.
10 lb $1\frac{1}{4}$ oz A J Chester, Wilstone Reservoir, Herts, 1981.
10 lb 1 oz L W Brown, Peterborough Brick Pit, Aug, 1975.
9 lb 1 oz J Salisbury, gravel pit at Hemingford Grey, Hunts, 1963.
9 lb G Young, Berkshire pond, Oct, 1964.
8 lb 14 oz K Baldock, Staplehurst pit, Aug, 1970.
8 lb 12 oz P Pilley, Middx lake, June, 1970.
8 lb 9 oz F Bailey, Lincolnshire drain, Aug, 1970.
8 lb 8 oz M Foode, Leicester Canal, Aug, 1950.
8 lb 6 oz K Morris, Cheshunt pit, Aug, 1964.
8 lb 6 oz J Brooksbank, Farningham pit, Dec, 1964.
8 lb 4 oz J Marshall, Grantham lake, 1961.
8 lb 4 oz R Hill, Bucks lake, Aug, 1970.
8 lb 2 oz A Lowe, Wraysbury pit (date unknown).
7 lb $13\frac{1}{4}$ oz† Raymond Webb, River Shannon, Lanesboro, 1971 (bread flake).
    Tench of 11 lb and 9 lb 9 oz 12 dm were caught from a pit at Wraysbury, Middlesex, in July, 1959. The larger fish was returned to the water; the smaller was sent to the London Zoo where it subsequently died. An autopsy showed it to be diseased and to contain 1 lb 12 oz of fluid. The larger fish was probably also diseased and neither could be allowed as a new record. Garnafailagh Lough, Westmeath, has produced a remarkable series of big tench in recent years, many over 7 lb.

TROUT (BROWN) (*Salmo trutta*, Linn)
39 lb 8 oz On Loch Awe by W Muir in 1866. It was foul-hooked on a trout fly and took two and a half hours to land. It was set up, but the case was unfortunately lost in a fire.
30 lb 8 oz J W Pepper on spoon bait, Lough Derg, 1861. *The Irish Times* gave credence to this fish in 1903. The same angler claimed to have caught one of 24 lb from Lough Corrib about the same period.
29 lb On Loch Stenness in 1889 on a hand line. A "slob" or estuarine trout. A cast of this fish is in the Flyfishers' Club.
27 lb 8 oz Colonel Dobiggin on the Tay at Murthly in 1842; length $39\frac{1}{2}$ in. Recorded by the late Duke of Rutland in his book on *The Trout*.
27 lb 4 oz Dr H H Almond, of Loretto, on the Inver about 1870. Said to have taken a small salmon fly. Probably a fish from Loch Assynt.
26 lb 2 oz† From Lough Ennel by W Meares on July 28, 1894, on a spoon bait. (Irish lake record.)
22 lb From Loch Rannock by F Twist in 1867.
$21\frac{1}{2}$ lb Lough Derg by James Lucas, keeper at Derry Castle. The fish was preserved. Date of capture uncertain. (There was also a case containing a brace of trout, 16 lb, 13 lb, caught at the same time by trolling.)
21 lb Loch Rannock by Miss Kate Kirby in July, 1904. Probably the biggest trout ever caught by a lady.
20 lb† From the Shannon in February, 1957, by Major H Place on a trolled silver Devon. (Irish river record.)
19 lb $9\frac{1}{4}$ oz* J A F Jackson, Loch Quoich, Invernesshire, 1978.

19 lb $4\frac{1}{2}$ oz From Lower Lough Erne, Co Fermanagh, NI, by T Chartres, April 6, 1974.
19 lb 2 oz F Smith from Lough Corrib on spoon, Aug, 1971.
18 lb 2 oz K J Grant, Loch Garry, Tomdoun, on a Black Pennel fly, in July, 1965.
Note: Lt Col G F McDonald, proprietor of Strathgarve Lodge Hotel, Garve, Ross-shire, has a trout of 26 lb in a glass case reported taken in Loch Garve on September 17, 1892, by Wm Ogilvy Dalgeish. Among notable Thames trout is a fish of 14 lb taken by A Pearson (Shepperton) on fly in August, 1962.

TROUT (RAINBOW) (*Salmo gairdnerii*)
21 lb 4oz* D Graham, Loch Awe, Oct, 1986.
20 lb 7 oz P Cockwill, Avington, Sept, 1986.
19 lb 8 oz* A Pearson, Avington Fisheries, Hants, 1977.
19 lb 2 oz R W Hopkins, Avington Fisheries, Hants, April, 1977.
18 lb+ Richard Walker, Avington Fisheries, Hants, 1976.
18 lb A Pearson, Avington Fisheries, Hants, June, 1976.
14 lb 4 oz J L Farmer, Avington Fisheries, Hants, July, 1975.
13 lb 2 oz Dr W J Drummond, Downton Tannery Stream (tributary of W Avon) Sept 28, 1974.
13 lb M H Lenthall, Exe Valley Fisheries, Dulverton, July 13, 1974.
12 lb 4 oz I L Johnstone (aged 14 yrs) Exe Valley Fisheries, July 5, 1974.
12 lb 4 oz* Miss A P D Berger, Exe Valley Fishery, Dulverton, May, 1974.
10 lb $\frac{1}{4}$ oz M Parker from a private lake in King's Lynn, July, 1970.
8 lb 14 oz Brian Jones, Packington Fisheries, May, 1970 (taken out of Trent RA season).
8 lb 10 oz C F Robinson, River Test at Stockbridge, Aug, 1970.
8 lb 8 oz From Blagdon in Sept, 1924, by Lieut-Colonel J Creagh Scott.
8 lb 7 oz† On Lough Eyes, Co Fermanagh, by Dr J P C Purdon on fly, in March, 1968. Irish record; Fish was just over 4 years of age.

TROUT (AMERICAN BROOK) (*Salvelinus fontinalis*)
5 lb $13\frac{1}{2}$ oz* A Pearson, Avington Fisheries, Hants, 1981.
5 lb 6 oz A Pearson, Avington Fisheries, Hants, 1979.

WELS (Catfish) (*Silurus glanis*)
43 lb 8 oz R J Bray, Tring, 1970.

WHITEFISHES
Group A (*Coregonus clupeoides*)
Local names—schelly (Haweswater, Ullswater), gwyniad (Lake Bala), powan (Loch Lomond, Loch Eck)
2 lb $1\frac{1}{2}$ oz* S M Barrie, Haweswater, 1986.
1 lb 10 oz W Wainwright, Ullswater, 1976.
1 lb 7 oz J M Ryder, Loch Lomond, 1972.
1 lb 4 oz J R Williams, Lake Bala, 1965.

Group B (*Coregonus vandesius*)
Local name—vendace (Derwentwater, Bassenthwaite Lake, Loch Maben).

Group C (*Coregonus pollan*)
Local name—pollan (Loughs Erne, Ree, Derg and Neagh).
Entries in categories B and C awaited since reclassification.

SEA FISH

ANGLER (*Lophius piscatorius*, Linn)
94 lb $12\frac{1}{4}$ oz*S M A Neill .... Belfast Lough .... Nov 1985
82 lb 12 oz K Ponsford .... Mevagissey .... April, 1977
74 lb 8 oz J J McVicar .... Eddystone .... Aug, 1972

71 lb 8 oz†   M Fitzgerald .... Cork (Cobh) .... July, 1964
68 lb 2 oz   H G Legerton .... Canvey Island 1967

BASS (*Morone Labrax*, Linn)
18 lb 6 oz*   R Slater .... off the Eddystone .. Aug, 1975
18 lb 2 oz   F C Borley .... Felixstowe Beach ... Nov, 1943
17 lb 8 oz   W G Byron (caught with a Gig-
                gan bait), 1 $12\frac{1}{4}$ in, g $32\frac{1}{2}$ in .. Castlerock, Derry . Oct 22, 1935
17 lb 4 oz   J Drysdale .... Kinsale .... Aug, 1943
16 lb 6 oz   T Browne .... Bangor .... July, 1935
16 lb†   Major Windham. Reported taken
                with a fly on a trout rod ..... Waterville 1909
        A fish of $18\frac{1}{2}$ lb was reported caught in the Teifi estuary by a salmon fisher in 1956.

BLACK-FISH (*Centrolophus niger*)
3 lb $10\frac{1}{2}$ oz* J Semple .... off Heads of Ayr 1972

BLUEMOUTH (*Helicolenus dactylopterus*)
3 lb $2\frac{1}{2}$ oz* Anne Lyngholm L Shell, S'way 1976

BOGUE (*Boops boops*)
1 lb $15\frac{1}{4}$ oz* S G Torode .... Guernsey CI 1978

BREAM (BLACK) (*Spondyliosoma cantharus*, Gonelin)
6 lb $14\frac{1}{4}$ oz* J A Garlick .... from wreck off Devon
                                                            coast 1977
6 lb $7\frac{3}{4}$ oz   J L D Atkins .... E Blackstone Rocks,
                                                            Devon .... Aug, 1973
6 lb 5 oz   M Brown, jnr .... Menai Straits .... Oct, 1935
6 lb 1 oz   F W Richards .... Skerries Bank ...... Sept, 1969
4 lb 14 oz   A Procter .... Looe .... Aug, 1953
4 lb $12\frac{1}{2}$ oz H Pavey .... Littlehampton 1963

BREAM (GILTHEAD) (*Sparus aurata*)
8 lb 2 oz*   A Marquand .... Guernsey .... Sept, 1983
5 lb 3 oz   P King .... Salcombe .... July, 1983
5 lb   A H Stratton-Knott .... St. Mawes 1978

BREAM, RAY'S (*Brama brama*)
7 lb $15\frac{3}{4}$ oz* G Walker .... Hartlepool 1967

BREAM (RED) (*Pagellus centrodontus*, De La Roche)
9 lb $8\frac{3}{4}$ oz* B H Reynolds .... off Mevagissey ..... July, 1974
9 lb 6 oz†   P Maguire .... Valentia .... Aug, 1963
7 lb 8 oz   A F Bell .... Fowey .... July, 1925
6 lb 3 oz   Brig J A L Caunter .... Nine miles of Looe . June, 1939
5 lb $12\frac{1}{2}$ oz Brig J A L Caunter .... Looe 1954

BRILL (*Scopthalmus rhombus*, Linn)
16 lb*   A H Fisher .... Derby Haven, Isle of Man 1950
13 lb 10 oz   J L Williams .... Brighton 1933

BULL HUSS (*Scyliorhinus stellaris*)
22 lb 4 oz*   M L Hall .... Minehead 1986
21 lb 3 oz   J Holmes .... Hat Rock, Looe 1955
21 lb   F C Hales .... Poole, Dorset ...... Aug, 1936
21 lb   H Jupp .... Brighton .... Oct, 1953
20 lb   F Matthews .... Newhaven .... Sept, 1954
19 lb 12 oz†   M Courage .... Bray 1969

CATFISH (*Anarhichas lupus*)
24 lb 3 oz*   N Trevelyan .... Whitby 1980
15 lb 12 oz   E Fisher .... off Filey, Yorkshire 1973
12 lb 12½ oz G M Taylor .... Stonehaven, Scotland 1978

COALFISH, or Saithe (*Gadus virens*, Linn)
37 lb 5 oz*   D Brown .... S of Eddystone 1986
35 lb 4 oz   T Neatby .... 50m off Whitby .... July, 1983
33 lb 10 oz   W H Saunders .... off Dartmouth, Devon Jan, 1983
33 lb 7 oz   L M Saunders .... Start Point, Devon 1980
30 lb 12 oz   A F Harris .... S of Eddystone ..... Feb, 1973
29 lb 2½ oz   R Phillips .... SE of Eddystone .... Jan, 1973
27 lb 12½ oz J J McVicar .... Eddystone .... Jan, 1972
26 lb 2 oz   T J Trust .... Start Point, Devon, ... 1971
24 lb 7 oz†   J E Hornibrook .... Kinsale 1967
23 lb 8 oz   Capt Hugo Millais .... Land's End (Carnbase) ... 1921

COD (*Gadus callarias*, Linn)
53 lb*   G Martin .... Start Point, Devon . June, 1972
46 lb 0½ oz   R Baird .... Firth of Clyde ..... Feb, 1970
45 lb 14 oz   D D Dinnie .... Gourock .... Jan, 1970
44 lb 8 oz   Brandon Jones .... Barry (Glam) .... Mar, 1966
42 lb†   Ian L Stewart .... Ballycotton 1921
34 lb   The late R Blair .... Ballycotton 1916
33 lb 8 oz   John E Timmins .... Kinsale .... Sept, 1962
      A cod of 140 lb landed at Hull Fish Dock in July, 1927, is worth adding to the record as
a remarkable specimen, though it was not, of course, an angling trophy.

COMBER (*Serrana cabrilla*)
1 lb 13 oz*   Master B Phillips .... off Mounts Bay 1977

CONGER (*Conger conger*, Linn)
109 lb 6 oz* R W Potter .... SE of Eddystone ... Sept, 1976
102 lb 8 oz   R B Thomson .... off Mevagissey ..... June, 1974
95 lb 11 oz   W K Oaten .... Berry Head, S Devon July, 1973
92 lb 13 oz   P H Ascott .... Torquay .... June, 1970
85 lb   C E Chapman .... Hythe (Hants) ...... June, 1970
84 lb   H A Kelly .... Dungeness .... July, 1933
      On the same day this angler had four more congers, 70 lb, 33½ lb, 21 ½ lb, 15½ lb.
80 lb 8 oz   H J West .... Brixham .... July, 1966
74 lb   Mrs H Eathorne .... Looe 1954
72 lb†   James Green .... Valentia .... June, 1914
66 lb   W H Pryce .... Coverack .... June, 1941
63 lb 3 oz   Miss B Klean .... Hastings 1922

DAB (*Limanda limanda*, Linn)
2 lb 12¼ oz* R Islip .... Gairloch .... Aug, 1975
2 lb 10¾ oz   A B Hare .... Skerries Bank ..... April, 1968
2 lb 9½ oz   M L Watts .... Morfa Beach, Port
                                              Talbot .... July, 1936
2 lb 8½ oz   L White .... Netley Pier,
                                              Southampton ..... Nov, 1937
2 lb 5½ oz   C Stone .... Ryde, I o W .... Dec, 1934
2 lb 4¼ oz   N Coleman .... Hastings .... Jan, 1951
2 lb 4 oz   P A Heale .... Southsea .... Dec, 1933
1 lb 12½ oz† I V Kerr .... Kinsale 1963

DOGFISH, BLACK-MOUTHED (*Galeus melastomus*)
2 lb 13½ oz* J H Anderson .... L Fyne 1977

DOGFISH (LESSER SPOTTED), or Rough Head (*Scyliorhinus caniculus*, Linn)
4 lb 8 oz*   J Beattie .... Ayr Pier 1969
4 lb 2 oz   B J Solomon .... Newquay .... Oct, 1976
3 lb 15 oz†   unknown .... S Ireland 1980
3 lb 12½ oz   A Gibson .... Firth of Clyde ..... July, 1967

FLOUNDER (*Platichthys flesus*, Linn)
5 lb 11½ oz*   A G L Cobbledick .... Fowey 1956
5 lb 5½ oz   D Clark .... Littlesea .... Mar, 1957
4 lb 13 oz   R Hitchman .... Exmouth 1949
4 lb 5 oz   E F J Plumridge .... Fowey Estuary .... April, 1938
4 lb 3 oz†   J L McMonagle .... Killala Bay 1963

FORKBEARD, GREATER (*Phycis blennoides*)
4 lb 11¼ oz*   Miss M Woodgate .... Falmouth 1969

GARFISH (*Belone belone*, Linn)
3 lb 10¼ oz†   E G Bazzard .... Kinsale .... Sept, 1967
3 lb 8 oz   Hanson Horsey .... Kinsale .... Oct, 1969
3 lb*   J Nardini .... Penzance 1981
2 lb 14 oz   K C Ettle .... Kinsale .... Aug, 1968
2 lb 14 oz   D O'Donovan .... Kinsale .... Aug, 1968
2 lb 13 oz
14 dm   Stephen Claeskens .... Newton Ferrers ..... Aug, 1971
2 lb 12 oz   K C Ettle .... Kinsale .... Aug, 1968
2 lb 12 oz   M L Walsh .... Ballycotton .... June, 1967
2 lb 11¾ oz   Dennis Collins .... Kinsale 1966
2 lb 10½ oz   J O'Sullivan .... Courtmacsherry,
                                    Co Cork .... Aug, 1971
2 lb 10 oz   Mrs Sandra Parker .... Kinsale .... Sept, 1969
2 lb 9 oz 2 dm   A W Bodfield .... Dartmouth 1963
2 lb 9 oz   F T Goffin .... Coverack .... July, 1935

GREATER WEEVER (*Trachinus draco*)
2 lb 4 oz*   P Ainslie .... Brighton 1927

GURNARD, Yellow, or Tub Fish, (*Trigela lucerna*, Linn)
12 lb 3 oz*   G J Reynolds .... Langland Bay, Wales 1976
11 lb 7¼ oz   C W King .... Wallasey 1952
10 lb 8 oz†   C Gammon .... Belmullet 1970
10 lb 2¼ oz   E Sederholm .... Belmullet .... May, 1969
9½ lb   W Adams .... Isle of Man 1907

GURNARD (GREY) (*Eutrigla gurnardus*)
3 lb 1 oz†   B Walsh .... Rosslare Bay 1967
2 lb 7 oz*   D Swinbanks .... Caliach Point
                                    Isle of Mull ...... July, 1976
2 lb 2 oz   D H Taylor .... Off Portrush, NI ... July, 1973
1 lb 10 oz   D Cameron-McIntosh .... Isle of Arran 1971
1 lb 6 oz   K R Manson .... Bressay, Shetland 1971

GURNARD (RED) (*Aspitrigla cuculus*)
5 lb*   D B Critchley (captor nine years
              of age) .... off Rhyl .... July, 1973
4 lb 9½ oz   C Butler .... off Anglesey .... June, 1973
4 lb 4¾ oz   W R Shaw .... Conway .... June, 1973

GURNARD, STREAKED (*Trigloporus lastoviza*)
1 lb 6½ oz*   H Livingstone Smith .... L Goil, Firth of Clyde 1971

HADDOCK (*Gadus aegifinus*, Linn)
13 lb 11¼ oz*G Bones .... off Falmouth 1978
12 lb 10 oz   Sub-Lieut K P White .... Manacles,
                                          Falmouth Bay ..... Jan, 1975
10 lb 13½ oz†F A E Bull .... Kinsale, Co Cork ... July, 1964
10 lb 12 oz   A H Hill .... Looe .... July, 1972
10 lb 0½ oz   David Hare .... Valentia 1971
9 lb 14½ oz   J O'Gilvie .... Valentia .... Aug, 1969
9 lb 8¾ oz   L A Derby .... Kinsale .... June, 1965
9 lb 4½ oz   Mrs M Morley .... Mevagissey 1969
9 lb 2¼ oz   Eric Smith .... Kinsale .... July, 1963

HADDOCK, NORWAY (*Sebastes viviparus*)
1 lb 13½ oz* T Barrett .... off Southend-on-Sea 1975

HAKE (*Merluccius merluccius*, Linn)
25 lb 5½ oz*†H W Steele .... Belfast Lough 1962
20 lb   Frank Vinnicombe .... Falmouth .... Aug, 1960
17½ lb   Mrs J T Ashby .... Penzance 1911

HALIBUT (*Hippoglossus hippoglossus*)
234 lb*   C Booth .... off Dunnet Head,
                                          Scotland 1979
212 lb 4 oz   J A Hewitt .... off Dunnet Head ... Aug, 1975
196 lb   J T Newman .... off Dunnet Head,
                                          Caithness .... April, 1974
161 lb 12 oz   W E Knight .... Orkney .... Aug, 1968
152¾ lb†   E C Henning .... Valentia 1926
     He also had two, 128¾ lb, 120½ lb on another day in 1926.
135 lb   J N Hearn .... Ballycotton 1912
     A Halibut weighing 500 lb was landed by a commercial fishing boat at Grimsby in
October, 1957.

HERRING (*Clupea haringus*)
1 lb 1 1oz*   B Barden .... off Bexhill-on-Sea 1973

JOHN DORY (*Zeus Faber*, Linn)
11 lb 14 oz*   J Johnson .... off Newhaven 1977
10 lb 12 oz   B L Perry .... Porthallow, Cornwall 1963
8 lb 8 oz   J F Vallin .... Mevagissey 1922
8 lb 4 oz   R Brown, Dreadnought SAS ..... Fowey .... July, 1932

LING (*Molva molva*, Linn)
57 lb 8 oz*   I Duncan .... off Stonehaven ..... May, 1982
57 lb 2½ oz   H Solomons .... off Mevagissey 1975
50 lb 8 oz   B M Coppen .... off Eddystone ...... Mar, 1974
46 lb 8 oz†   A J C Bull .... Kinsale .... July, 1965
46 lb   T D Walker .... off Plymouth .... Mar, 1974
45 lb   H C Nicholl .... Penzance 1912

LUMPSUCKER (*Cyclopterus lumpus*)
14 lb 3 oz*   W J Burgess .... Felixstowe Beach 1970

MACKEREL (*Scomber scombrus*, Linn)
6 lb 2½ oz*   W J Chapple .... 1½ miles off Penberth
                                          Cove, Cornwall 1984
5 lb 6½ oz   S Beasley .... Eddystone Lighthouse 1969
4 lb 11 oz   L A Seward .... Flamborough Head 1963
4 lb 0½ oz   F/Lt P Porter .... Peel, Isle of Man . June 9, 1952

3 lb 10 oz   A Cave .... Peel, Isle of Man ... Aug, 1953
3 lb 8 oz   W Adams 1906
3 lb 6 oz†   J O'Connell .... Valentia 1969
A fish of $4\frac{1}{2}$ lb was caught at Looe in June, 1935, by W C Butters on a handline.

MEGRIM (*Lepidohumbus wiffiagonis*)
3 lb $12\frac{1}{2}$ oz* Master P Christie .... Gairloch .... Aug, 1973

MONKFISH (*Squatina squatina*, Linn)
69 lb†   Monsieur Fuchs .... Westport .... July, 1958
66 lb*   C G Chalk .... Shoreham 1965
62 lb   S Morris .... Littlehampton 1919
62 lb   A E Beckett .... Porthcawl 1960
A fish of 68 lb was reported from Beaulieu in August, 1953.

MULLET (GREY, THICKED-LIPPED) (*Chelon Labrosus*)
14 lb $2\frac{3}{4}$ oz* R S Gifford .... Aberthaw, S Wales 1979
10 lb 1oz   P/O P C Libby .... Portland 1952
8 lb 12 oz   W E Wallis .... Portland 1921
8 lb 7 oz   F V Daunou .... Margate .... About 1903

MULLET (GREY, THIN-LIPPED) (*Liza ramada*)
6 lb 4 oz*   H E Mephan .... Kentish Rother 1981
3 lb 7 oz   D Davenport .... Christchurch Estuary   Aug, 1983
3 lb 2 oz   J Corner   Christchurch Harbour   July, 1983

MULLET (GOLDEN GREY) (*Liza aurata*)
2 lb $11\frac{1}{2}$ oz* D M Bohan .... Fort Doyle
                                           Alderney C O 1984
2 lb $10\frac{1}{4}$ oz F Odoire .... Alderney .... Nov, 1983
2 lb 10 oz   R J Hopkins .... Burry Port 1976

MULLET (RED) (*Mullus surmuletus*)
3 lb 10 oz*   J E Martel .... Guernsey .... Oct, 1967
2 lb 1 oz 3 dmT F Cleal .... Guernsey .... Oct, 1967

OPAH (*Lampris guttatus*)
128 lb*   A R Blewitt .... Mounts Bay, Penzance ... 1973

PELAMID (BONITO) (*Sarda sarda*)
8 lb $13\frac{1}{4}$ oz* J Parnell .... Torbay 1969

PERCH, DUSKY (*Epinephelus guaza*)
28 lb*   D Cope .... off Durlston Head
                                           Dorset 1973

PLAICE (*Pleuronectes platessa*, Linn)
10 lb $3\frac{1}{2}$ oz* Master H Gardiner .... Longa Sound .... Oct, 1974
7 lb 15 oz   Ian Brodie .... Salcombe .... Oct, 1964
7 lb 13 oz 1 dmW F Parker .... Teignmouth 1961
7 lb 6 oz   D Brown .... Dartmouth (Skerries) June, 1963
7 lb 6 oz   J P Wright .... Dartmouth .... May, 1960
7 lb 5 oz 6 dmC Riggs .... Teign Estuary 1949
7 lb†   E Yemen .... Portrush 1964

POLLACK, or Lythe (*Gadus pollachius*, Linn)
27 lb 6 oz*   R S Milkins .... Salcombe 1986
26 lb 7 oz   R C Perry .... 31 miles S of
                                           Salcombe 1984

25 lb	R J Hosking	Eddystone	1972
23 lb 8 oz	G Bartholomew	Newquay	1957
22 lb 8 oz	W Digby	Looe	1955
21 lb	Capt Hugo Millais	Land's End (Carnbase)	1921

Capt Millais had others of 17 lb and 18 lb at the same place.

20 lb 8 oz	Mrs Hugo Millais	Land's End (Carnbase)	1921

Mrs Millais also had a specimen of $19\frac{1}{2}$ lb.

20 lb 8 oz	J H Layton	Lochinver	1920

POUTING (*Gadus luscus*, Linn)

5 lb 8 oz*	R S Armstrong	Berry Head	1969
4 lb 10 oz	H B Dare	Coverack	Sept, 1935
4 lb 10 oz†	W G Pales	Ballycotton	1937
4 lb 9 oz	E Burton	Belfast Lough	April, 1968

PUFFER FISH (*Lagocephalus Lagocephalus*)

6 lb $9\frac{1}{4}$ oz*	S Atkinson	Chesil Beach	Oct, 1975

RAY (BLOND) (*Raia brachyura*, Lafont)

37 lb 12 oz*	H T Pout	Salcombe	Oct, 1973
36 lb 8 oz†	D Minchin	Cork (Cobh)	Sept, 1964
35 lb 9 oz	A J Pearce	Portland	May, 1970
34 lb 8 oz	T Hutchinson	Cobh	Sept, 1967

RAY (BOTTLE-NOSED) (*Raja alba*)

76 lb*	R Bulpitt	off The Needles, I o W	1970

RAY (CUCKOO) (*Raia naevus*)

5 lb 11 oz*	V Morrison	off Causeway Coast, NI	1975
5 lb 6 oz†	K Derbyshire	Causeway Coast, Co Antrim	Aug, 1971
5 lb 3 oz	P J Rankin	off Causeway Coast, NI	1974
5 lb	N C McLean	Lamlash Bay, Isle of Arran	June, 1968

RAY (EAGLE) (*Myliobatis aquila*)

52 lb 8 oz*	R J Smith	off Nab Tower, I o W	1972

RAY (ELECTRIC) (*Torpedo nobiliana*)

96 lb 1 oz*	N J Cowley	off Dodman Point, Cornwall	July, 1975
47 lb 8 oz	R J F Pearce	Long Quarry, Torquay	Aug, 1971

RAY (MARBLED ELECTRIC) (*Torpedo marinurata*)

2 lb $8\frac{1}{2}$ øz*	B T Maguire	St. Aubin, Jersey	July, 1983

RAY (SMALL-EYED) (*Raia microcellata*)

16 lb $6\frac{1}{2}$ oz*	J B Lush	off Minehead	April, 1982
16 lb 4 oz	H T Pout	Salcombe	Sept, 1973
13 lb $11\frac{1}{2}$ oz	H T Pout	Bolt Tail, Devon	1971
13 lb 8 oz	Mrs T Whippy	Pevensey Bay	Aug, 1969
12 lb $1\frac{1}{2}$ oz	A T Scoones	Littlehampton	July, 1969

RAY (SPOTTED) (*Raia montagui*)

16 lb 3 oz	E Lockwood	Lerwick, Shetland	1970
14 lb 3 oz	W C Furnish	St Anne's Head, Pembroke	1970
7 lb 12 oz*	J Cochrane	off Causeway Coast, NI	Aug, 1982
6 lb 14 oz	H A Jamieson	Causeway Coast, NI	1978

RAY (STING) (*Trigon pastinaca*, Linn)
61 lb 8 oz*   V W Roberts .... off Pwllheli 1979
59 lb   J M Buckley .... Clacton-on-Sea 1952
52 lb 8 oz   T E Stone .... Lymington River mouth .. 1938
52 lb   J Manser .... Brighton .... June, 1954
51 lb 8 oz   P J Hill .... Hastings .... Oct, 1956

RAY (THORNBACK) (*Raia clavata*, Linn)
57 lb   S G Lugger .... Exmouth .... July, 1951
38 lb*   J Patterson, Jnr .... Rustington Beach ... May, 1935
37 lb†   M J Fitzgerald .... Kinsale .... May, 1961

RAY (UNDULATE) (*Raja undulata*)
21 lb 4 oz*   K Skinner .... St. Catherine's Lighthouse,
                                              Jersey, CI .... Sept, 1983
20 lb 12¼ oz F J Casado .... Off Corbierre,
                                              Jersey, CI .... May, 1982
19 lb 7 oz   L R LePage .... Herm, CI 1970

ROCKLING (THREE-BEARDED) (*Onos tricirratus*, Block)
3 lb 2 oz*   N Docksey .... Portland .... Oct, 1976
2 lb 14¼ oz   S F Bealing .... Poole Bay .... Oct, 1972
2 lb 13 oz 2 dmK Westaway .... Portland Harbour ... June, 1966

SCAD, or Horse Mackerel (*Trachurus trachurus*, Linn)
3 lb 5¼ oz*   M A Atkins .... Torbay 1978
3 lb 4½ oz   D O Cooke .... Mewstone, Plymouth 1971
3 lb 3 oz   J B Thorton .... Deal .... July, 1934

SHAD (ALLIS) (*Alosa alosa*)
4 lb 12½ oz* P B Gerrard .... Chesil Beach, Dorset 1977
3 lb 4½ oz   B H Sloane .... Princess Pier, Torquay ... 1964

SHAD (TWAITE) (*Alosa finta*, Cuvier)
3 lb 2 oz*   T Hayward .... Deal .... Nov, 1949
3 lb 2 oz*   S Jenkins .... Torbay 1954

SHARK, SIX-GILLED (*Hexanchus priseus*)
9 lb 8 oz*   F E Beeston .... off Plymouth 1976

SHARK (BLUE) (*Carcharinus glaucus*, Linn)
218 lb*   N Sutcliffe .... Looe .... July, 1959
206 lb†   J L McGonagle .... Achill .... Oct, 1959
184 lb   T Robinson .... Looe 1960
180 lb   H Widdett .... Looe 1955
180 lb   F A Mitton .... Looe 1960

SHARK (MAKO) (*Isurus oxyrhinchus*, Raf)
500 lb*   Mrs J M Yallop .... Eddystone Light 1971
498 lb 8 oz   K Burgess .... Looe .... July, 1966
476 lb   W J Rogers .... Falmouth .... July, 1964
435 lb   S G Miller .... Looe .... June, 1964
428 lb 8 oz   J E Sefton .... Looe 1961
     It was not until 1956 that the mako shark was positively identified as a British species, and it is probable that some of the fish listed earlier as porbeagles were, in fact, makos.

SHARK (PORBEAGLE) (*Lamna cornubica*, Gonetin)
465 lb*   J Potier .... off Padstow,
                                              Cornwall .... July, 1976

430 lb	D Bougourd	South of Jersey	1969
367 lb	B D Phillipps	Jersey, CI	June, 1960
365 lb†	Dr O'Donnel Browne	Keem Bay, Co Mayo	1932
324 lb	T Paince	Nab Tower	Aug, 1968
311 lb	K C Wilson	Looe	1961
300 lb††	J Eathorne	Looe	1951

The identification of the mako shark in British waters has thrown some doubt on the authenticity of this list. Dr O'Donnel Browne's fish was certainly a porbeagle, but the one marked †† is now thought probably to have been a mako. Fish caught since 1956 are definitely porbeagles.

SHARK, SIX-GILLED (*Hexanchus priseus*)

9 lb 8 oz*	F E Beeston	off Plymouth	1976

SHARK (THRESHER) (*Alopias vulpes*, Gonetin)

323 lb*	S Mills	Nab Tower, off Portsmouth	July, 1982
295 lb	H J Aris	Dunose Head, I o W	1978
280 lb	H A Kelly	Dungeness	1933
149 lb	R Romilly Lunge	Christchurch	July, 1937

SKATE (COMMON) (*Raia batis*, Linn)

336 lb	Captor unknown	Beer	1934
227 lb*	P Banks	off Tobermory	1986
226 lb 8 oz	R S Macpherson	Shetland	Aug, 1970
221 lb†	T Tucker	Ballycotton	1913
218 lb 8 oz	E C Henning	Valentia	1927
214 lb	J A E Olsson	Scapa Flow	July, 1968
211 lb	Dr C Ayton Marrett	Ballycotton	1912
208 lb	Leonard F Hopkins	Clare Island, Co Mayo	Aug, 1971
205 lb	A W Bowie	Kinsale	Aug, 1956

SMOOTHHOUND (*Mustelus mustelus*)

28 lb*	A T Chilvers	Heacham	1969

SMOOTHHOUND (STARRY) (*Mustelus asterias*)

28 lb*	R Grady	Maplin Sands, Essex	1980
23 lb 2 oz	D Carpenter	Bradwell on Sea	1972

SOLE (*Solea solea*, Linn)

6 lb 2 oz*	J Bartram	Nr Braye, Alderney, CI	1984
5 lb 7 oz	L Dixon	Alderney, CI	1980
4 lb 8 oz	H C L Pike	Alderney, CI	1978
4 lb 3½ oz	R Wells	Redcliffe Beach	Mar, 1974
4 lb 1 oz 14 dm	R A Austin	Guernsey	Dec, 1967
4 lb	M Stinton	Clevedon Pier	Sept, 1943
3 lb 4 oz	S Hayman	Weymouth	Nov, 1956

SOLE (LEMON) (*Microstumus Kitt*)

2 lb 7¾ oz*	W N Callister	Douglas, Isle of Man	1980
2 lb 3 oz	D R Duke	Douglas, Isle of Man	1971

SPANISH MACKEREL (*Scomber japonicus*)

1 lb ½ oz*	P Jones	off Guernsey CI	1972

SPURDOG (*Squalus acanthias*, Linn)

21 lb 3½ oz*	P R Barnett	off Porthleven	1977

20 lb 3 oz   J Newman .... Needles .... May, 1972
17 lb 1 oz   S Bates .... Deal 1971
16 lb 12½ oz R Legg .... Chesil Beach 1964
16 lb 4 oz†   C McIvor .... Strangford Lough ..... June, 1969
15 lb 12 oz   John Rowe .... Killala Bay, Sligo ..... Aug, 1967
15 lb 5 oz   J S W Fisher .... Strangford Lough ...... Oct, 1971
15 lb   W Hamilton .... Strangford Lough ..... July, 1969
14 lb 6 oz   J C Nott .... Clare Island .... June, 1969
14 lb 1 oz   D R Angiolini .... Valentia .... Sept, 1968
14 lb   R Wickens .... Kinsale .... Oct, 1962

SUNFISH (*Mola mola*)
108 lb*   T F Sisson .... Saundersfoot .... Aug, 1976
49 lb 4 oz   M G H Merry .... Cornwall .... Aug, 1976

TADPOLE FISH (*Raniceps raninus*)
1 lb 13¾ oz* D A Higgins .... Whitley Bay 1977

TOPE (*Eugaleus galeus*, Linn)
79 lb 12 oz* P J Richards .... Bradwell-on-Sea 1986
74 lb 11 oz   A B Harries .... Caldy Island .... July, 1964
73 lb 3 oz
(female)   L Andrews .... Hayling Island 1949
65 lb   Lt-Col R I P Earle .... Studland 1956
64 lb 8 oz   J H Swan .... Camel Estuary, Padstow July, 1963
62 lb 11 oz   A J Drew .... Herne Bay 1911
62 lb 8 oz
(female)   R J Weston .... Eastbourne .... June, 1955
62 lb 2 oz
(female)   A B Fitt .... Herne Bay .... June, 1951
62 lb (male) D S Southcombe .... Weymouth 1946
61 lb 8 oz
(female)   G T Northover .... Herne Bay .... June, 1936
60 lb 12 oz† C McIver .... Strangford Lough 1968

TORSK (*Brosme brosme*)
15 lb 7 oz*   D J MacKay .... Pentland Firth .... July, 1982
12 lb 1 oz   D Pottinger .... Shetland 1968

TRIGGER FISH (*Balistes carolinensis*)
4 lb 9¼ oz*   E Montacute .... Weymouth Bay 1975

TUNA, BIG-EYE* (*Thunnus obesus*)
66 lb 12 oz* S Atkinson .... Newlyn Harbour ....Oct 1985

TUNA BLUE-FIN (Tunny) (*Thunnus thynnus*)
   The fish given in the following list were all caught in the North Sea tunny fishing
grounds off Scarborough and Whitby:

851 lb*	L. Mitchell-Henry, 1933	764 lb	H W Holgate, 1934
812 lb	Colonel E T Peel, 1934	763 lb	G Baker, 1933
798 lb	H G Smith, 1934	762 lb	M W Holgate, 1935
798 lb	Colonel E T Peel, 1932	749 lb	S Cohen, 1949
785 lb	Major R T Laughton, 1947	747 lb	H E Weatherley, 1952
		660 lb	H E Weatherley, 1954

TURBOT (*Scopthalmus maximus*, Linn)
33 lb 12 oz* R Simcox .... Salcombe, Devon 1980
32 lb 8 oz†   Unknown .... S Ireland 1980
32 lb 3 oz   D Dyer .... off Plymouth .... May, 1976

31 lb 4 oz	Paul Hutchings (11)	Eddystone Light	July, 1972
29 lb	G M W Garnsey	The Manacles	Aug, 1964
28 lb $0\frac{1}{2}$ oz	T Tolchard	Dartmouth	1961
27 lb 14 oz	F S Stenning	Salcombe	1907
26 lb 8 oz	J F Eldridge	Valentia	1915
25 lb 8 oz	Mat Kearney	Cork Harbour	Aug, 1971
25 lb 4 oz	R Tolchard (age 12)	off Dartmouth	June, 1958

WHITING (*Gadus merlangus*, Linn)

6 lb 12 oz*	N R Croft	Falmouth	1981
6 lb 4 oz	S Dearman	Bridport	April, 1977
6 lb 3 oz 3 dm	Mrs R Barrett	Rame Head, Cornwall	1971
6 lb	E H Tame	Shieldaig	Mar, 1940
5 lb 2 oz	H C Nicoll	Penzance	1912
5 lb 1 oz	H W Antenbring	Shieldaig	June, 1938

WITCH (*Glyptocaphalus cynoglossus*)

1 lb $2\frac{3}{4}$ oz*	T J Barathey	Colwyn Bay	1967

WRASSE (BALLAN) (*Labrus bergylta*, Ascanius)

12 lb 1 oz	F A Mitchell-Hedges	Looe	1912
12 lb	F A Mitchell-Hedges	Looe	1912
11 lb 8 oz	F A Mitchell-Hedges	Looe	1912
10 lb 12 oz	F A Mitchell-Hedges	Looe	1912
9 lb 6 oz*	M Goodacre	Eddystone gully	1981
7 lb $13\frac{1}{2}$ oz	D R Gabe	off Start Point, Devon	1978
7 lb 10 oz 15 dm	B K Lawrence	Trevose Head, Cornwall	1970
7 lb 6 oz†	A J King	Killybegs	1964

WRASSE (CUCKOO) (*Labrus mixtus*)

2 lb $0\frac{1}{2}$ oz*	A M Foley	Plymouth	Nov, 1973
1 lb $14\frac{3}{4}$ oz	R G Berry	Sennen, Cornwall	Sept, 1973
1 lb $12\frac{1}{2}$ oz	L C Le Cras	Guernsey	Aug, 1972
1 lb 10 oz 8 dm	B Perry	Torquay	Sept, 1971

WRECKFISH (*Polyprion americanus*)

10 lb 10 oz*	B McNamara	off Eddystone	1980
7 lb 10 oz	Cdr E St J Holt	Looe, Cornwall	1974

Black bream 4 lbs 14 ozs 12 drms. Caught Alderney C.I. 25/9/84. *Photograph by courtesy of National Anglers's Council.*

THE SALMON AND TROUT ASSOCIATION

This association is the only body which exists solely to protect the interests of game fish, fisheries and fishermen in the United Kingdom.

Director: James Ferguson, Fishmongers' Hall, London EC4R 9EL. 01-283 5838.

Field Secretary–England and Wales:
Bill Davies, 29 Neales Close, Harbury, Warwicks CV33 9JQ. 0926 612661.

ENGLAND
North West Water Authority Region
T A F Barnes, (Regional Representative), Woodplumpton House, Woodplumpton, Nr Preston, Lancs. Tel No Catforth 690392.

1. **North & West Cumbria:**
   E P Ecroyd, (Branch Chairman), Low House, Armathwaite, By Carlisle, Cumbria. Tel No Armathwaite 242.
   Major R O G Wood, (Branch Organiser), Sycamore House, Glassonby, Penrith, Cumbria. Tel No Lazonby 448.
2. **South Cumbria & North Lancashire:**
   G B Lawson, (Branch Chairman and Secretary), 37 Birkett Drive, Ulverston, Cumbria, LA12 9LS. Tel No (0229) 54736.
   J K Sharp, (Branch Treasurer), 2 Birchwood Close, Kendal, Cumbria.
4. **Lancashire:**
   T A F Barnes, (Branch Chairman), Woodplumpton House, Woodplumpton, Nr Preston, Lancs. Tel No Catforth 690392.
   J M Croft (Branch Organiser & Secretary), Moss Side Farm, Chipping, Preston PR3 2ND. Tel No Longridge 2223.
5. **Cheshire & Manchester:**
   W F Williams (temp Branch Organiser), 1 Westwood Drive, Brooklands, Sale, Cheshire. Tel No 061 962 1233.
6. **Merseyside:**
   S Newton, (Branch Chairman), 13 Mount Pleasant, Oxton, Birkenhead, Merseyside. Tel No 051-652 6242

Northumbrian Water Authority Region
C H Noble, (Regional Chairman), 30 The Green, Hurworth-on-Tees, Darlington, Co Durham. Tel No Darlington 720450. (Work) 0325 462845.

Dr P A Lintern, (Regional Vice-Chairman), The Knoll, Stokesley Road, Guisborough, Cleveland, TS14 8DL.
J B Woodham, CBE, (Regional Organiser), "Lea Rig", 10 Manor Drive, Hilton-in-Cleveland, Yarm, Cleveland, TS15 9LE. Tel No 0642 590 889.
S Currie (Regional Stillwater Fisheries Officer), 62 Newcastle Road, Chester-le-Street, Co Durham.
Dr D J Alcock (Regional Pollution Officer), 17 High Barm Road, School Aycliffe, Darlington, Co Durham.
J G Ellison, (Regional Water Abstraction Officer), 3 Burnside Court, Hartburn Avenue, Stockton-on-Tees, Cleveland.
P S Jackson, (Regional Abstraction Officer), 14 Sudburn Avenue, Staindrop, Darlington, Co Durham, DL2 3JY.
J E D Brown, (Regional Migratory Fish Officer), Baydale Farm, Coniscliffe Road, Darlington, Co. Durham.
7. **Northumbria:**
   E S J Standen, (Branch Chairman), 6 Friar's Pardon, Hurworth-on-Tees, Darlington, Co Durham, DL2 2DZ. Tel No Darlington 720450.
   C H Noble, (Branch Organiser), 25 The Green, Hurworth-on-Tees, Darlington, Co Durham DL2 2AA. Tel No Darlington 720450 (Work 0325 462845).
57. **Cleveland:**
   Dr P A Lintern (Branch Chairman), The Knoll, Stokesley Road, Guisborough, Cleveland TS14 8DI.
   J B Woodham, CBE, (Branch Organiser), "Lea Rig", 10 Manor Drive, Hilton-in-Cleveland, Yarm, Cleveland, TS15 9LE. Tel No 0642 590 889.
   J J W Spooner (Branch Secretary/Treasurer), 9 Gipsy Lane, Middlesborough, Cleveland TS7 0DX.

Severn-Trent Water Authority Region
P Buckland-Large, Regional Representative.

8. **Shropshire:**
    Major H M Milnes (Branch President), Marnwood, Buildwas, Shopshire TF8 7BJ. Tel No (095 245) 2211.
    P C Unsworth (Branch Chairman), The Rope Walk, Lyth Hill, Shrewsbury SY3 0BS. (074372) 2553, Office (0743 253671).
    R T Williams, (Branch Organiser), The Old Vicarage, Leaton, Bomere Heath, Shrewsbury, Shropshire, S74 3AP. Tel No 0743 253671.

11. **North Powys & Lake Vyrnwy:**
    Lt Colonel Sir John Baynes, Bt, (Branch Chairman), Talwrn Bach, Llanfyllin, Powys SY22 5LQ. (069 184) 576.

12. **Nottinghamshire & Derbyshire:**
    J B R Fryer, (Branch Chairman), The Old Beeches, Church Lane, Muggington, Weston-under-Wood, Derby. Tel No Ashbourne 60495.
    P D Prince, (Branch Secretary), The Garage, Youlgreave, Nr Bakewell, Derbys, DE4 1WN. Tel No Youlgreave 427. (Office 206.)
    R Rondle, (Branch Treasurer), 136 Killisick Road, Arnold, Nottingham.
    R F Lombard, (Branch Events Organiser), Yeardsley Hall Farm, Yeardsley Lane, Furness Vale, Stockport, Cheshire, SK12 7PS.
    J Grosvenor (Branch Recruitment Officer), Woodthorpe Hall Farm, Ashover Road, Old Tupton, Derbys S42 6HJ.

13. **Staffordshire:**
    F J Hull (Branch Chairman), Copperkins, Shay Lane, Furton, Newport, Salop TF10 8DA.
    J M Bevan, BA, (Branch Organiser), 66 Sneyd Avenue, Westlands, Newcastle-under-Lyme, Staffs. Tel No (Home) 0782 616848. (Office) 0782 613918.
    R Hawley (Branch Treasurer), Wellington House, Stone, Staffs.

14. **West Midlands & Warwickshire:**
    Lord Guernsey, (Branch Chairman), Packington Hall, Meriden, Nr Coventry, West Midlands, CV7 7HF. Tel No Meriden 22754.
    D C Devereux (Branch Secretary/Treasurer), 5 Beaudesert Park, Birmingham Road, Henley-in-Arden, Warwicks. Tel No Henley-in-Arden 3866.

15. **Leicestershire:**
    P Buckland-Large, (Branch Chairman), Crudwell House, Holmfield Avenue, Stoneygate, Leicester. Tel No Leicester 707607.
    I Kilgour, (Branch Organiser), 24 All Saints Road, Thurcaston, Leicester. Tel No (0533) 350025.
    N Everson (Branch Treasurer), 65 Knighton Road, Leicester.

56. **Worcestershire:**
    T Beale (Branch Chairman), 17 Avon Green, Wyre Piddle, Pershore, Worcs.
    D Malpass (Branch Organiser), 82 Oak Crescent, Malvern, Worcs.

Yorkshire Water Authority Region

Yorkshire Region (including North Humberside):
C T Waite, (Regional President), Estate Office, Wensley, Leyburn, North Yorkshire, DL8 4HW. Tel No Leyburn 2314.
D P H Hield, (Regional Chairman), "Personal", Hield Brothers Ltd, Brigella House, Bradford, W Yorks, BD5 0AQ. Tel No Bradford 571181.
Colonel J D Ellerbeck, MC, TD, (Regional Deputy Chairman), Manor House, Scruton, Northallerton, N Yorks, DL7 0RD. Tel No Kirkby Fleetham 270.
Colonel J D Ellerbeck, MC, TD, (Regional Treasurer), Manor House, Scruton, Northallerton, N Yorks, DL7 0RD. Tel No Kirkby Fleetham 270.
W N Bygate, M B E, TD, (Regional Deputy Treasurer) 6 Park Mews, Pool-in-Wharfedale, Otley, W Yorks. LS1 1LE. Tel No 0532 843650.
G R Stocks, (Regional Abstraction Officer), 6 School Walk, Old Edlington, Nr Doncaster, South Yorkshire, DN12 1PU. Tel No Rotherham 862497.
N Ayling, (Regional Water Resources Officer), 35 Turker Lane, Northallerton, N Yorks, DL6 1QL. Tel No 0609 774261.

16. **North & East Yorkshire:**
    S Madden, (Branch Chairman), "Brimley", Molescroft, Beverley, Yorkshire. Tel No 0482 882392.
    D Sutton, (Branch Vice-Chairman), PO Box 10, 4/5 Silver St, Hull, HU1 1NZ.
    M Martin, (Branch Organiser) 1 Astral Road, Hessle, Hull, HU13 9DD. Tel No 0482 641472.
    J Storrs-Fox, (Branch Treasurer), 22 Station Road, South Cave, Brough, NU15 2AA.

17. **Leeds & District:**
R B Roberts, JP, (Branch Chairman), Cedar Green, 84 The Fairway, Leeds, LS17 7PD.
P Guest, (Branch Organiser), "Tanwood", Margaret Avenue, Bardsey, Leeds, W Yorks LS17 9AU. Tel No (0937) 72326.

18. **Nidderdale:**
Major P J Furse, (Branch Chairman), 56 York Place, Harrogate, N Yorks. Tel No Harrogate 58324.
D C G Walker (Branch Organiser), Weir House, Nidd Bank, Knaresborough, N Yorks HG5 9BX.

20. **South Yorkshire:**
Mrs S Murray (Branch Chairman), 3 Belgrave Drive, Sheffield S10. (0742) 302123.
G R Stocks (Regional Abstraction Officer), 6 School Walk, Old Edlington, Nr Doncaster, S Yorks. DN12 1PU. Tel No 0709 862497.
D Chapman (Branch Abstraction & Pollution Officer) 27 Mortain Road, Moorgate, Rotherham, Yorkshire. Tel No 0709 70463.

21. **Swaledale & Wensleydale:**
Colonel J D Ellerbeck, MC, TD, (Branch President), Manor House, Scruton, Northallerton, N Yorks, DL7 ORD. Tel No Kirkby Fleetham 270.
Lt Co HS Le Messurier, (Branch Chairman) Thornton Grange, Thornton Steward, Ripon, Yorks. Tel No Bedale 50351.
J Gormley (Branch Organiser), Treske Ltd., Station Works, Thirsk, N Yorks YO7 4NY.
Mrs D E Porter (Branch Secretary), Tyrella, Woodside, Leyburn, North Yorkshire DL8 5DS.

23. **Western Yorkshire:**
D P H Hield, (Branch Chairman), "Personal", Hield Brothers Ltd, Brigella House, Bradford, W Yorks, BD5 0AQ. Tel No Bradford 571181.
P A Ormonroyd, (Branch Organiser), 8 Nidderdale Walk, Baildon, Shipley, W Yorks, BD17 6TW.

Anglian Water Authority Region
A J Cony (Regional Representative), Lavendon Mill, Olney, Bucks. Tel No (0234) 711228.

24. **Northamptonshire, North Buckinghamshire, Cambridgeshire & Bedfordshire:**
A J Cony, (Branch Chairman), Lavendon Mill, Olney, Bucks. Tel No (0234) 711228.

L Beecroft, (Branch Secretary), 207 Cherry Hinton Road, Cambridge. Tel No (0223) 49270.
G M Vickers, (Liaison Officer), 6a Kings Parade, Cambridge. Tel No Cambridge 63728.
D G Valentine, (Branch Treasurer), 5 Church Street, St Ives, Huntingdon, Cambs. Tel No St Ives 63728. Office: St Ives 63150.

25. **Norfolk:**
F A Seaman, (Branch Chairman), Milfield, Dereham, Norfolk. Tel No Dereham 4334.
Lt Commander L D Temple-Richards, (Branch Organiser), Vale Farm, Stibbard, Fakenham, Norfolk. Tel No Great Ryburgh 217.

26. **Lincolnshire & South Humberside:**
K Raynor, (Branch Chairman), Hill View Trout Fishery, Skegness Road, Hogsthorpe, Skegness, Lincs.
Sqn Leader G G Bevan (Branch Organiser), The Old Rectory, West Ashby, Horncastle, Lincs. Tel No (06582) 3503.
Mrs G P D Hall, (Assistant Branch Organiser), Manby House, Manby, Louth, Lincolnshire, LN11 8UF. Tel No South Cockerington (050782) 777.

27. **Hertfordshire:**
R C Tottle (Branch Organiser), 4 Caversham Avenue, Palmers Green, London.

59. **Essex:**
B C Furzer (Branch Organiser), 10 Bonningtons, Thriftwood Hutton, Brentwood, Essex.

58. **Suffolk:**
D M B Barnes, (Branch Chairman), High House, High Rougham, Bury St Edmunds, Suffolk.
C H Peacock, (Branch Organiser), Stable House, Water Lane, Bures, Suffolk. Tel No Bures 227153.

Thames Water Authority Region
J A G Coates, CBE (Regional Representative), 3 The Forge, Bridge Street, Hungerford, Berkshire RG17 0EG. Tel No (0488) 833694.

28. **Chilterns:**
W J Deem, (Branch Chairman), 50 Orchard Lane, Amersham, Bucks. Tel No Amersham 5952. (Work) Amersham 5782345 Ext 520.
J Paxton, (Branch Organiser), Denton Cottage, Denton, Cuddesdon, Oxford. Tel No Wheatley 4400

29. **Berkshire:**
M Metcalfe, (Branch Chairman), Walnut Tree Cottage, Sulham, Pangbourne, Berks. Tel No Pangbourne 2494.
J A G Coates, CBE, (Branch Organiser), 3 The Forge, Bridge Street, Hungerford, Berks RG17 0EG.
I M Hunter (Treasurer), Sapele, Flowers Hill, Pangbourne, Berks.
D A Rees (Secretary), Rathgar Cottage, Courtlands Hill, Pangbourne, Berks RG8 7DE.

30. **London:**
D G E Crole (Branch Organiser), 29A Dunraven Road, London W12 7QZ. Tel No (01) 743 8293.

31. **Surrey:**
R Morgan (Branch Chairman), Mayflower Cottage, Winterford, Cranleigh, Surrey.
A W Bird (Vice-Chairman), Wild Dene, 83 Raglan Road, Reigate, Surrey RH2 0ES.
P J Stabbins, (Branch Secretary), 4 Durfold Drive, Reigate, Surrey, RH2 0HA. Tel No Reigate 47777.
C L T Jenkins (Branch Treasurer), Little Lodge, Fairmile Lane, Cobham, Surrey K11 2DG.

Southern Water Authority Region
Dr E B Worthington, CBE, MA, PhD (Regional Representative), Colin Godmans, Furner's Green, Nr Uckfield, E Sussex TN22 3RR.

33. **Hampshire:**
H A Pawson, (Branch Chairman), The Manor House, Chilcomb, Nr Winchester, Hants. Tel No (0962) 61482.
G M Clarkson, (Branch Organiser), Troutbourne, Wotton, Abinger Hammer, Dorking, Surrey.

34. **East Sussex:**
G Perring (Branch Chairman), Brackenside, Ashdown Road, Forest Row, Sussex RH18 5BW.
P L McArthur, MC, TD (Branch Secretary), Pear Tree Cottage, Buckham Hill, Isfield, E Sussex TN22 5XZ. Tel No Uckfield 2552.
G Pink (Branch Treasurer), Wallenside, Tompsetts Bank, Forest Row, E Sussex. Tel No Forest Row 2063.

9. **West Sussex:**
G G Ferguson, (Branch Chairman), Malthouse, Chithurst, Rogate, Nr Petersfield, Hants.
D Swabey, (Branch Organiser), 'Two Trees", 30 Shepherds Way, Liphook, Hants, GU30 7HF. Tel No 0428 723452.

35. **Kent:**
M W Cutler, (Branch Chairman), c/o Argles & Court, 12 Mill St, Maidstone, Kent. Tel No 0622 57461.
C W B Jardine, (Branch Organiser), Mayfly Cottage, 7 Uplees Cottages, Oare, Faversham, Kent. Tel No 0795 538078.

Wessex Water Authority Region
D Gifford (Regional Representative), 239 Badminton Road, Downend, Bristol, Avon. Tel No Bristol 562974.

32. **Wiltshire:**
Dr H M Darlow, (Branch Chairman), "Cuckoo Pen", Porton, Salisbury, Wilts.
H M Lancaster (Branch Organiser/Secretary), The Coach House, Biddertone, Chippenham, Wilts. Tel No (0249) 713112.

36. **Gloucestershire, Avon & Somerset:**
The Lord Darling, (Branch President), Puckpits, Limpley Stoke, Bath, Avon.
D Gifford, (Branch Chairman), 239 Badminton Road, Downend, Bristol, Avon. Tel No Bristol 562974.
A W Lamport, (Branch Secretary), 14 Woodland Grove, Claverton Down, Bath, Avon.
E Coots (Branch Treasurer), 112 Church Lane, Backwell, Avon BS19 3QF. Tel No Flaxburton 2341.
T Whish (Branch Stillwater Representative), 27 Arbutus Drive, Coombe, Bristol BS9 2PW.

37. **Dorset:**
Major A E Hill, (Branch Chairman), The Mill House, Hooke Springs Trout Farm, Hooke, Beaminster, Dorset. Tel No Beaminster 862553.
R Slocock (Branch Organiser), Wessex Flyfishing, Lawrence's Farm, Southover, Nr Dorchester, Dorset.

South West Water Authority Region

Devon & Cornwall:
Group Captain P Norton-Smith, CBE, DFC, AFC, (Regional Representative), Little Warham House, Beaford, Winkleigh, N Devon. EX19 8AB. Tel No Beaford 317.

38. **North Devon:**
Group Captain P Norton-Smith, CBE, DFC, AFC, (Branch Chairman), Little Warham House, Beaford, Winkleigh, N Devon. EX19 8AB. Tel No Beaford 317.

R F C Parrington, (Branch Organiser/ Secretary), "Bakers Elstone", Elstone, Chulmleigh, North Devon.

39. **South & East Devon & Tamar:**
M Charleston, (Branch Chairman), The Gifthouse, Buckland Monachorum, Yelverton, Devon.
A D Everett, (Branch Organiser/ Secretary), Melrose Cottage, Blackawton, Totnes, Devon. Tel No Blackawton 456.

41. **Cornwall:**
T E F Mutton, (Branch Chairman), Lamorran, Old Falmouth Road, Truro, Cornwall. Tel No Truro 73858.
S Gardiner, (Branch Secretary/ Treasurer), 68 Trefusis Road, Flushing, Falmouth, Cornwall TR11 5TY.
G White (Abstraction Officer), 11 Falmouth Road, Truro, Cornwall. Tel No (0872) 77012.

WALES
Welsh Water Authority Region (which includes the Wye catchment area):
Professor O G Williams, CBE, (Regional Representative), Meini Gwynion, Brynsiencyn, Anglesey, Gwynedd, LL61 6HJ. Tel No (024873) 505.

10. **Herefordshire:**
M Speight (Branch Chairman), c/o T A Matthews & Co, 6/7 King Street, Hereford HR4 9BS.
T Jessop (Branch Secretary), c/o Russell, Baldwin & Bright, South Street, Leominster, Herefordshire.
R W Darlington, (Branch Treasurer), 1, Havelock Road, Leominster, Herefordshire.
P B Cocks, (Branch Public Relations Officer), "Sunny Croft", 36 Penn Grove Road, Hereford.

42. **Clwyd:**
Col. The Lord Langford, OBE, DL, (Branch President), Bodrhyddan, Rhuddlan, Clwyd, N Wales, LL18 5SB.
Professor R L Hartles, (Branch Chairman) Efail Wen, Prion, Denbigh, Clwyd, LL16 4SF. Tel No (074578) 395.
M G Dempsey, (Branch Organiser), Plas Aney Nursing Home, Hendy Road, Mold, Clwyd.

43. **Gwynedd:**
Professor O G Williams, CBE, (Branch Chairman), Meini Gwynion, Brynsiencyn, Anglesey, Gwynedd, LL61 6HJ. Tel No (024873) 505.

R Harding Roberts, (Branch Secretary), Crafnant, 38 Ffriddoedd Road, Bangor, Gwynedd, LL57 2TW.

44. **Glamorgan:**
Dr W O Williams, (Branch Chairman), "Lonisa", 208 Derwen Fawr Road, Sketty, Swansea, West Glamorgan, SA2 8EA. Tel No (0792) 203074.
D Nehemiah, (Branch Secretary), 13 East Cliff, Pennard, Swansea, SA3 2AS.
R Denner, (Assistant Branch Secretary), Broadmead, 24 Oldway, Bishopston, Swansea, West Glamorgan, SA3 3DE.

45. **Dyfed:**
G Roberts, (Branch Organiser), "Talrhyn", Tresaith Road, Aberporth, Cardigan, Dyfed, SA43 2EB. Tel No (0239) 810515.
M E Jones (Branch Stillwater Representative), 30 Llwyn Hudol, Tan-y-Brim, Bangor, Gwynedd.

46. **Powys (South) & Gwent:**
N S Brabner, (Branch Chairman), Gliffaes Hotel Ltd, Crickhowell, Powys, NP8 1RH. Tel No Bwlch 730371.
R P Pomfret, (Branch Organiser), 15 High Street, Abergavenny, Gwent. Tel No Abergavenny 3640.

47. **SCOTLAND:**
A Tennant (Regional Representative), Muiresk House, Turriff, Aberdeenshire AB5 7HD. Tel No 08886 2417.
Lt Col R A Campbell (Regional Representative), Altries, Maryculter, Aberneen AB1 0BD. Tel No 0224 733258.
Guy Bentinck(Organiser), 2 Queen's Road, Aberdeen AB9 8BD.

48. **NORTHERN IRELAND**
W Ross MP (Regional Representative), Turmel, Dungiven, Co Londonderry, NI.
G E J Simpson, (Regional Organiser), 26 Donegall Park Avenue, Belfast, BJ15 4EU. Tel No Belfast 773844.
T Morrison (Chairman), Mayola Park Cottage, Castledawson, Co Londonderry.
Sir Patrick MacNaughton (Vice-Chairman), Dundarave, Bushmills, Co Antrim.
K E McCracken (Secretary), 67 Carricknakielt Road, Maghera, Co Londonderry.
S Donaghy (Treasurer), 34/6 Maghera Street, Kilrea, Co Londonderry.

INDEX TO RIVERS AND FISHING STATIONS (Great Britain and Ireland)

Entries appearing as for example "Annan (River)" with "river" or "lake", etc., in parentheses, indicate that the reference is to a town or village and a water of the same name

ADVERTISERS INDEX